Billy Budd

Sailor

BILLY BUDD

SAILOR

(An Inside Narrative)

BY HERMAN MELVILLE

*Reading Text and Genetic Text, Edited from the Manuscript
with Introduction and Notes*

by

HARRISON HAYFORD

and

MERTON M. SEALTS, JR.

THE UNIVERSITY OF CHICAGO PRESS
CHICAGO & LONDON

Library of Congress Catalog Card Number: 62-17135

THE UNIVERSITY OF CHICAGO PRESS, CHICAGO & LONDON
The University of Toronto Press, Toronto 5, Canada

Preface

In *Moby Dick* Melville's Ishmael says, "If, at my death, my executors, or more properly my creditors, find any precious MSS. in my desk, then here I prospectively ascribe all the honor and the glory to whaling; for a whale-ship was my Yale College and my Harvard." As it happened, manuscripts were found in Melville's own desk at the time of his death in 1891, manuscripts which have since been judged precious. The desk itself now stands in a Melville memorial room at Pittsfield; Yale and Harvard have ascribed honor and glory to the author; and Harvard treasures the manuscripts. The chief work among them, *Billy Budd*, has become a classic of American literature, and the world acknowledges itself Melville's debtor.

Yet Melville's executors—if literary scholars and critics may claim that title—have still not rendered an adequate accounting of those manuscripts, few of which have been well edited and some of which have not been edited at all. Even the manuscript of *Billy Budd* has not heretofore been exhaustively studied, and no definitive text has been established by previous editors. Although much thought has been devoted to its interpretation, critics have by no means reached agreement: what after the first quarter century of criticism (1921–46) had seemed to be virtually a consensus, that the work constituted Melville's "testament of acceptance," has been flatly contradicted during the decade of the 1950's by those reading the novel as an ironic reiteration of all his lifelong quarrels and denials. Perhaps this inability of critics to agree upon the "meaning" of *Billy Budd* should not be a matter for wonder or regret; perhaps the capacity of the work to elicit continued interest from critics of various schools and to suggest various "significances" (Melville's own term) should be taken for a sign that it is indeed a literary masterpiece. Perhaps, moreover, no final "agreement" among critics is either possible or even desirable. In any case, it is our hope that a comprehensive scholarly edition of the work will narrow the ground of disagreement and widen that of understanding.

For such an edition the manuscript of *Billy Budd* must be thoroughly studied and properly set forth so as to establish a fully reliable text annotated in a useful way, thus opening new perspectives for scholarship and criticism. The present volume aims at these objectives by offering two separate texts, each with related commentary. In one, the Genetic Text, we give an exact transcription of what appeared in the *Billy Budd* manuscript as it stood at the time of Melville's death. An analysis, table, and discussion accompanying the Genetic Text explain what our study of the manuscript has revealed concerning the genesis and development of the story through its successive stages of growth. Since the manuscript itself, which Mrs. Melville characterized as "unfinished," was never prepared for the printer, we give in the Reading Text the wording that in our judgment most closely approximates Melville's final intention had a new fair copy been made without his engaging in further expansion or revision. Notes to the Reading Text gloss words, identify allusions, point out affiliations with possible sources and analogues in Melville's reading and in his own writing, and offer explication of key passages with reference to the findings of scholarship and criticism, including our own investigations. The Introduction summarizes the development of the manuscript, reviews the history of the text, and indicates ways in which our work clarifies central problems of interpretation.

This edition has grown out of studies of Melville's late writings conducted by the present editors over a period of some fifteen years. Analysis of the *Billy Budd* manuscript in particular was first undertaken in 1953, when Mr. Hayford's preliminary examination confirmed a suggestion advanced by Leon Howard: that further study could lead to the establishment of a much more accurate text and to a sounder understanding of Melville's process of composing *Billy Budd* than scholarship had yet provided. Active collaboration of the two editors began in 1955 with their decision to join in preparing a new edition to be based on an entirely independent transcription of the manuscript. The work of transcription occupied the full attention of both editors during extended periods of study at the Houghton Library of Harvard University, where the manuscript is now located; it is a joint and equal effort. Mr. Hayford took the initial responsibility for setting forth this transcription in the Genetic Text and for preparing the associated textual analysis. Mr. Sealts, following principles mutually agreed upon, prepared the Reading Text and the accompanying notes and commentary, drawing upon materials assembled by both editors. Each of us has contributed to the Preface and Introduction as well as to all other parts of the volume. The division of labor has thus been anything but absolute, with the editors remaining in close consultation with one another during every stage of an undertaking for which we assume undivided responsibility.

For reference by other students of Melville we shall deposit in the Houghton Library a full collation, prepared by Mr. and Mrs. Sealts, of the present Reading Text with the Genetic Text and with the previous texts of Raymond Weaver and F. Barron Freeman.

It is our pleasure to record the indebtedness we share with all students of Melville to Eleanor Melville Metcalf, who inherited the manuscript of *Billy Budd*, made it available to its pioneering editor, Raymond Weaver, and subsequently presented it to the Harvard College Library. Her generosity and interest have encouraged all scholars while favoring none. For authorization to edit the manuscript, and to make use of other Melville materials at Harvard, we thank Professor William A. Jackson, librarian of the Houghton Library, where Miss Carolyn Jakeman and Mr. William H. Bond have also been unfailingly kind and helpful during our extended investigations there.

We acknowledge with appreciation the further assistance of library staffs at Northwestern University and Lawrence College, at the Universities of Chicago, Minnesota, Washington, and Wisconsin, at the Widener and Newberry libraries, and at the United States Information Service and British Institute libraries in Florence, Italy. Mrs. L. J. Kewer and Mr. Thomas J. Wilson of the Harvard University Press have supplied us with valuable information concerning the publishing history of *Billy Budd*. For leave of absence to work on this project and for grants in aid toward research expenses Mr. Hayford makes acknowledgment to the College of Liberal Arts and the Graduate School of Northwestern University.

Among individual scholars who have offered encouragement, helpful information, and constructive criticism at various stages of our work we owe particular debts to Professors Leon Howard and Fredson Bowers, who have been of great help in the determination of editorial procedures, and to C. Merton Babcock, Ben C. Bowman, the late Merrell R. Davis, Philip Durham, Alfred R. Ferguson, French Fogle, William H. Gilman, Ralph H. Hayford, Wilson Heflin, Lewis Leary, Jay Leyda, Perry Miller, C. Northcote Parkinson, Leland R. Phelps, Walter B. Scott, Jr., James Sledd, and Eleanor M. Tilton.

HARRISON HAYFORD
MERTON M. SEALTS, JR.

Contents

Editors' Introduction

GROWTH OF THE MANUSCRIPT

The manuscript of *Billy Budd* as Melville left it at his death in 1891 may be most accurately described as a semi-final draft, not a final fair copy ready for publication. After his death Mrs. Melville, indeed, called the story "unfinished." She had used exactly the same word in December of 1885 when reporting Melville's retirement from his nineteen years of employment as a customs inspector: "He has a great deal [of] unfinished work at his desk which will give him occupation." The "unfinished work" of 1885 may have included the short poem of three or four leaves on which he was working early in 1886, the poem that ultimately became the ballad "Billy in the Darbies" with which the novel concludes. The novel itself developed out of a brief prose headnote setting the scene and introducing the speaker of this poem. An understanding of just how the story took form during the last five years of its author's life has been a major objective of our genetic study of the *Billy Budd* manuscript.

As *Billy Budd* grew under Melville's hand, along with other works both in prose and in verse with which he was engaged, it passed through several distinct stages and substages of development that comprised three major phases, in each of which its original focus was radically altered. Our genetic analysis has followed the course of its growth from the surviving leaves of the ballad and its headnote to Melville's late pencil revisions of his semi-final draft. It has established the fact that more than once, believing his work to be essentially complete, he undertook to put his manuscript into fair-copy form, but each time he was led into further revision and elaboration; what still further changes he might have made had he lived to continue work on the manuscript are of course conjectural. The following section outlines the main phases of the story's development, as established by our analysis of the manuscript. The degree to which *Billy Budd* remained an "unfinished" work is a matter for critical evaluation in the light of detailed evidence assembled in the table and discussion accompanying our Genetic Text.

Early in 1886, when Melville took up, or perhaps began, the work that became *Billy Budd*, he had in mind neither the plot of a novel nor any one of the characters as they later emerged in the course of his writing. What he did have, in the initial phase of development now represented by four extant draft leaves (Plates I–IV), was a short composition in both prose and verse that in its complete form ran to perhaps five or six leaves. The focal character was Billy (Billy Budd in the prose headnote), a sailor on the eve of his execution—but a different Billy from the young sailor of the novel who is hanged for striking and killing his superior officer. This Billy was an older man, condemned for fomenting mutiny and apparently guilty as charged, though in his brief initial presentation Melville emphasized the sailor's reverie as he faces death, rather than the events leading up to his condemnation. The prose sketch and ballad thus placed a character in a situation but stopped short of telling a story.

During the first two years of Melville's retirement, 1886–87, a narrative about Billy Budd emerged out of this material. By November of 1888 Melville had incorporated the ballad and expanded the headnote sketch through several stages into a story that ran to something over 150 manuscript leaves. In constructing its plot he had entered a second phase of development with his introduction of John Claggart, whose presence resulted in a major shift of focus. Billy, no mutineer in this phase, reacts to a false charge of mutiny by striking and killing his accuser, Claggart; this is the act that leads to his condemnation here and in all subsequent stages of the story's growth.

A third and final phase of development, during which the manuscript grew to its ultimate length of 351 leaves, began after November, 1888, when Melville set out (not for the first time) to put his story into fair-copy form. During the ensuing winter months or perhaps in the following spring he made another major shift of focus, which involved the full-scale delineation of a third principal character, Captain the Honorable Edward Fairfax Vere, who had previously figured only as the commander in whose presence Billy struck Claggart and by whom the summary sentence of hanging was imposed upon the young sailor. So minor was this commander's part in the second phase of the story's growth that only a few leaves stood between the killing of Claggart and the beginning of the ballad; in the third phase, by contrast, Billy's trial, Vere's long speech to the court, and the dramatized execution and related episodes intervene, and an analysis of Vere's character is now provided in new antecedent chapters. The several stages and substages within this final phase of development occupied Melville until the end of his life, revision being still in progress when he died.

Thus, in the period of over five years between his retirement from the Custom House and his death, Melville had carried the work through a series of developments intricate in detail but clear in their general lines of growth. In three main phases he had introduced in turn the three main characters: first Billy, then Claggart, and finally Vere. As the focus of his attention shifted from one to another of these three principals, the plot and thematic emphasis of the expanding novel underwent consequent modifications within each main phase. Just where the emphasis finally lay in the not altogether finished story as he left it is, in essence, the issue that has engaged and divided the critics of *Billy Budd*.

Within these three broad phases of development, certain of the various stages and substages deserve further attention because of particularly important elements with which they deal and problems which they raise. To the initial phase, in which Billy was the only major character, belong the surviving draft leaves of the ballad and headnote; they are from the first substage of what we designate Stage *A*. (See Plates I–IV.) Although the situation then presented in the ballad was basically the same as that in its final version, with a sailor speaker already named Billy confronting his execution, there are conspicuous differences. The earlier Billy, as we have said, was an older Billy, for his musings included a dreamy reminiscence of days and ships "no more" and of a larger "general muster" of former shipmates "from every shore" ("Christian Pagan Cannibal breed") than the later and younger Billy could have assembled. This Billy was more like the reminiscing sailors of Melville's *John Marr* volume— John Marr himself, Bridegroom Dick, Tom Deadlight—where the ballad might well have appeared in 1888 had not the story that sprouted from its headnote already overshadowed it. That this early Billy was indeed guilty of mutiny seems clear from his expression "the game is up" and its subsequent revisions: first "The little game," then "My little game," and finally "Our little game"; all these phrases point to his actual implication in some sort of plot. (Even in the final version of the ballad the innocent phrase "Ay, ay, all is up" derives from the incriminating expression of the earlier versions.)

The single draft leaf (Plate I) surviving from the headnote, though a part of this same substage, is of later composition than the material in the ballad leaves which it was designed to introduce in the manner of similar headnotes: those to "John Marr" and "Tom Deadlight" in *John Marr* and also those to other poems Melville never completed or published. It was originally a single long sentence—like some of the headnotes, in the present tense. Much of its language has been carried over into the novel itself and is embedded in the physical description of Billy in Ch. 2, which similarly tells of his beauty, his genial temper, and his evidently noble lineage. In the headnote as in the ballad leaves themselves Melville presented a sailor older than the Billy of the novel. Initially he was not a foretopman—the foretop being a station for the younger men, as the novel was to explain—but "Captain of a gun's crew," a post for a more mature man. In this substage the historical and national setting remained unspecified, but according to the headnote it is wartime, the warship is already a seventy-four, and Billy has been "summarily condemned at sea to be hung as the ringleader of an incipient mutiny the spread of which was apprehended." Whether he was in fact guilty, as seems clear in the ballad draft, the surviving leaf of the headnote does not actually state; in any case, his capital offense is different from what it later became following Melville's introduction of Claggart.

From these four draft fragments antedating the novel itself it is impossible to be sure what main theme and dominant effect Melville had in mind for his ballad as it first stood. Presumably its general form was that of a rambling reverie, as in the other sailor poems on which he was at work. The general situation in all of them is the same: a sailor, usually an old sailor, is musing over bygone days and his own approaching end. Ships and shipmates of the past, the barbaric good nature and genial fellowship of sailors, and some sort of contrast between their simplicity and the way of "the world" are common thematic elements. The opening lines of the original ballad of Billy Budd are a characteristic variation of this last theme. As in the final version, the verse begins abruptly with Billy's comment on the visit and prayer of the chaplain, who, since he is referred to only by pronouns, must have been introduced as a secondary character in the missing portion of the prose headnote.

> Very good of him, Ay, so long to stay
> And down on his marrow bone here to pray
> For the likes of me. Nor bad his story,
> The Good Being hung and gone to glory.—
>   (Plate II)

PLATE I

From Stage *A* (now Leaf 3v of "Daniel Orme")

This leaf, which at Stage *A* began Melville's draft headnote to the ballad, is all that survives of the prose of that stage. Compare its matter and phrasing with those of Leaves 38–39 of the final manuscript.

PLATE II

From Stage *A:* Leaf [347a] ("Daniel Orme," 17v)

The earliest of three surviving draft leaves of the ballad, Leaf [347a], bearing a version of the opening lines, is a clear working copy of a still earlier draft. One or more clips once occupied the lower half of this leaf.

PLATE III

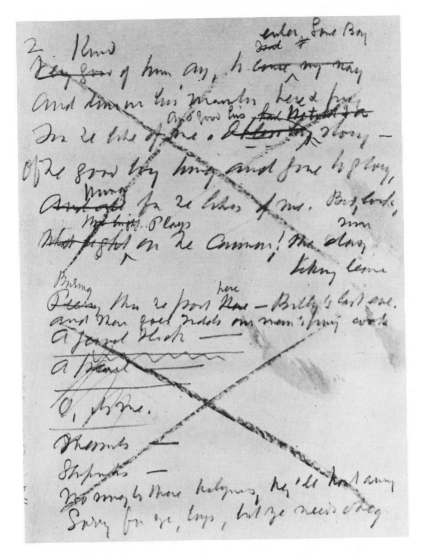

From Stage *A:* Leaf [347b] ("Daniel Orme," 4v)

Leaf [347b] carries a version of the opening lines of the ballad later than that on [347a].
A patch once covered the canceled segment following the sixth line.

PLATE IV

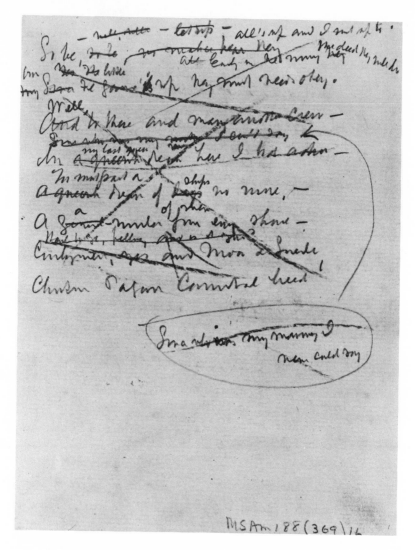

From Stage *A:* Leaf [347c] ("Daniel Orme," 16v)

Leaf [347c] opens with a later version of the last two lines of [347b]. A clip or patch was once pinned to the lower segment of the leaf.

PLATE V

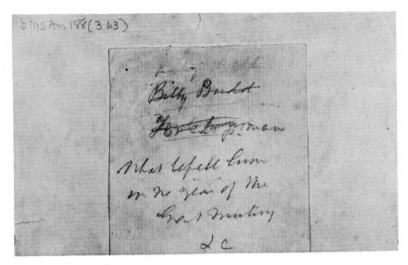

Leaf [1a] 352, top segment

Leaf [229d] 358, top segment

Leaf [135a] 353, top segment

These segments show the intervention of Mrs. Melville's hand in the manuscript after Melville's death, (*a*) retracing words of the canceled and superseded early pencil-draft title slip mounted on Leaf [1a]; (*b*) recording her misconjecture that Leaves [229d, e, f] 358–360 might be a preface; and (*c*) calling for "insertion" of Leaves [135a and b] 353–354—the superseded chapter "Lawyers, Experts, Clergy."

PLATE VI

Leaf 2

The opening leaf of the story carries Melville's pencil notations of (*a*) the date when he began inscription of the Stage *D* fair copy sequence, to which the leaf belongs; (*b*) the date when he began a revision, at Stage *X* or *E;* and (*c*) the latest title.

PLATE VII

Leaf [80a] 363, top segment

Leaf 81, top segment

Leaf [80a] shows Melville's notation on the cover of a folder for Ch. 7; Leaf 81 shows Mrs. Melville's copy of the notation, on the first leaf of the chapter. Also in Mrs. Melville's hand on [80a] is the notation "Van Tromp," and on 81, in the last line, her alteration of "a" to "the."

PLATE VIII

Leaf [334a] 361

Leaf 344, lower segment

Leaf [334a] 361 carries Melville's rough notes, at Stage *X*, for what became Ch. 28 and 30. Leaf 344 ended the story at Stage *B*, when the ballad was followed by the news account; to 344 Melville later added the pencil-draft coda reproduced here, but during Stage *X*, when he reversed the order of ballad and news account, he canceled the coda. We have found no satisfactory reading of the last word in its second line.

The major effect here is one of irony, arising from Billy's naïvely thinking it "good" of the chaplain to visit such a lowly prisoner and humbly "to pray / For the likes of me." In his final version of the ballad Melville dropped his direct reference to the gospel story, perhaps after his prose elaboration (in what is now Ch. 24 of *Billy Budd*) of the encounter between Billy and the chaplain, though in the novel he retained and exploited in other ways his suggestive juxtaposition of the condemned sailor with the figure of Christ "hung and gone to glory." Billy's "sailor-way of taking clerical discourse" is compared in the novel to the reception of the Christian gospel "long ago on tropic isles by any superior *savage*, so-called"; as for the chaplain, drawn as a "worthy" man "possessing the good sense of a good heart," he is termed "incongruous" as "the minister of the Prince of Peace serving in the host of the God of War," where he "lends the sanction of the religion of the meek to that which practically is the abrogation of everything but brute Force." This same incongruity between religion and war, repeatedly stressed in Melville's writings from *White-Jacket* through *Clarel* to "Bridegroom Dick" and *Billy Budd*, was evidently a major element in his original conception of Billy's situation.

Nothing in the surviving leaves of the ballad or headnote suggests the presence of Claggart in Melville's first delineation of Billy and his circumstances. When Claggart was either introduced or brought to the fore as the cause of Billy's predicament, the second phase in Melville's development of the work was inaugurated. This phase must have begun as a substage of what we designate Stage *A*; Claggart's emergence at some point within Stage *A* can be inferred from the earliest surviving leaves of the final manuscript, those of Stage *B*, substage *Ba*, which were copied forward from Stage *A*. In the new phase, which established the story's setting as the Revolutionary era, just after the mutinies of 1797 in the British navy at Spithead and the Nore occasioned by naval abuses, Melville presented Claggart—mostly from the outside—as a master-at-arms of the period. His original Billy, a mature "Captain of a gun's crew" aboard an unnamed seventy-four, he modified into a young merchant sailor impressed into a British warship, called the *Indomitable*. Opposite Billy, Melville now set an antagonist, Claggart, who, conceiving a mortal dislike for him, begins to scheme actively against him. Billy, described as a model sailor, is brought face to face with the master-at-arms in their commander's presence, where he responds to a false accusation of mutiny by striking and killing Claggart. Melville's juxtaposition of the two characters as protagonist and antagonist evidently led him to heighten Billy's youth, naïveté, heart, goodness, and brightness and to deepen Claggart's antipathetic experience, sophistication, intellect, evil, and darkness. The characterization of Billy was probably carried nearly as far at this phase as Melville was ever to take it, but Claggart's inner nature remained to be studied further in the final phase of the novel's development.

Just how fully Stage *A* explored the relations between Billy and Claggart is uncertain, since no leaves later than the draft headnote and ballad actually survive from that stage. Probably in the early months of 1888, when Melville was selecting and engrossing the poems he would include in *John Marr and Other Sailors*, he inscribed a fair copy of the story that ran to something over 70 leaves. The surviving leaves of this fair copy, which we designate Stage *B*, are the earliest still standing in the final manuscript, having been retained and carried forward through the various subsequent copy stages. From the very earliest leaves among them, those of substage *Ba*, it is clear that by the end of Stage *A* the story and characters as just outlined were in fact present, and that Melville was then beginning his dramatization of actual scenes. In *Ba*, Billy's impressment and farewell to the *Rights-of-Man* were described, Claggart's understrappers were said to be stirring up trouble for Billy aboard the *Indomitable*, the interview on deck between the master-at-arms and the captain was related though not dramatized, and Claggart's accusation of Billy and the latter's fatal blow were given their location within the captain's cabin. As the active antagonist, Claggart in the second phase had come to occupy the foreground of the work, as Iago occupies the foreground of *Othello*. Billy, less active, was now somewhat overshadowed; Vere appeared only as the commander who witnessed the false accusation and the retaliatory blow and who thereupon, without ado, imposed the summary sentence of death by hanging. No issue was made of the execution. After relating Billy's death, the story ended not with the ballad, as in Stage *A*, but with the garbled news account now standing in Ch. 29 (the penultimate chapter of the final version).

At this time, early in 1888, it would seem that Melville thought he had completed his story, for he began to make a fair copy, at *Ba;* but even as he inscribed it he was drawn into further elaborations and major expansions which he incorporated on the inserted leaves we designate as substages *Bb* and *Bc* and the closely related Stage *C*. His elaborations at *Bb*, for the most part, sketched the historical background of the story and emphasized the immediate consequences for the British navy of the Nore and Spithead mutinies. Searching for

material about these events, he discovered, as he remarks in what is
now Ch. 3, that details were not "readily to be found in the libraries."
It was evidently at this substage that he came upon the *Naval History
of Great Britain* by the historian James, who is named and quoted in
that same chapter. At this point too, stimulated by Southey's *Life of
Nelson*, he was led into the digression on Nelson and Trafalgar that
now constitutes Ch. 4.

The leaves that stood in the manuscript at Stage *Bb* carry many
slight secretarial corrections in the hand of Mrs. Melville, which suggest that at this time (perhaps only a little later in 1888 than *Ba*) she
was preparing to copy the manuscript, as she later copied that of the
Timoleon volume of 1891 after making similar corrections. If so, she
was forestalled by her husband's launching into still a further series
of expansions at *Bc* and *C*. One class of these new additions amounted
to a program of dramatizing Claggart's campaign against Billy and
included such other dramatized material as the dialogue between
Billy and the mustering officer about Billy's paternity, development
of the Dansker as observer and confidant, the soup-spilling episode
witnessed by Claggart, and—slightly later—the encounters between
Billy and the Dansker. Following closely upon these dramatized additions came a series of elaborations of another class, also at substage
Bc and Stage *C*, in which Melville for the first time ventured into the
"murky labyrinth" of Claggart's inner nature and greatly expanded
his analysis in what became—after tortuous revisions at later stages
—Ch. 11, 12, 13, and 17. Extensive and significant as were these
amplifications at *Bb*, *Bc*, and *C*, they are to be seen in perspective as
only a continuation of the second, or Claggart, phase of development,
in which one class of additions dramatized the outward manifestations
of his hostility to Billy Budd and another class began to analyze its
inward motivation.

After drafting the elaborations just mentioned, Melville once again
sought to put his manuscript into fair-copy form, by the tidying-up
copy stage which we designate Stage *D*. At the top of a new first leaf
—which still stands as the opening leaf of the story—he penciled "Friday Nov. 16. 1888. / Began." (Plate VI); and on later leaves he
noted the dates "Nov 17" and "Nov 18" at intervals that probably
marked a day's copy work. The fair-copy sequence of this stage extended only from the opening leaf to the point where the fair-copy
sequence of Stage *C* began—covering, that is, the present Ch. 1–10.
Within it, Melville made only a few slight additions: in Ch. 1 he
added the Negro sailor and characterizations of Captain Graveling

and Lieutenant Ratcliffe; in Ch. 9 he made some revisions in his sketch of the Dansker. At this same time, deciding to exclude from the story his digression on Nelson added at *Bb*, he removed from the manuscript to a separate folder the leaves of what is now Ch. 4. These various changes, it will be noted, affected only the first ten chapters; the remainder of the story when Melville finished Stage *D* stood essentially as it did at Stage *C*, and still ended not with the ballad but with the garbled news account. On the last leaf of that final chapter Melville had by Stage *D* appended, in pencil, a one-sentence coda to the entire narrative: "Here ends a story not unwarranted by what sometimes happens in this [one undeciphered word] world of ours—Innocence and infamy, spiritual depravity and fair repute". (See Plate VIII and note to Leaf 344.) The coda, it seems apparent, was meant to bring out the main point of the story as it then stood: that the judgment and memory of "the world" may attribute to human beings the direct opposite of their true natures; innocence may be consigned to infamy, spiritual depravity may be awarded fair repute.

In the third and final phase of development, another radical shift of focus occurred when Captain Vere was for the first time brought into the foreground. This phase embraced the stages subsequent to *D* which we designate *X, E, F, G*, and the late pencil revisions. Though in it Melville made very little change in his treatment of Billy he continued to restate and rework the details of his already extensive analysis of Claggart, especially in Stage *E*. He also made other revisions, including a tentative restoration of the chapter on Nelson (Ch. 4), the change of the name of Vere's ship from *Indomitable* to *Bellipotent*, and a reversal of the order of his two final chapters so as to end the story not with the news account but with the ballad, as in the initial Stage *A*. (With regard to this last change, incidentally, he neglected to revise the news account to reflect his recent elaboration of the captain's role: specifically to mention the fact of Vere's death in addition to the deaths of Claggart and Budd.) Throughout this phase, the chief effect of his revisions was to transform Vere into a character whose importance equals—and according to some critics even surpasses—that of Billy and Claggart.

In the early part of this third phase, Melville developed Captain Vere in a major role from the point at which Claggart first accuses Billy (Ch. 18 in the final version) through the confrontation scene and the newly created trial and execution scenes (Ch. 19–25), to the now added chapter on Vere's death (Ch. 28; Plate VIII). This transformation of the captain's role was made during the extensive pencil-draft substages that constituted Stage *X*. In the middle of the phase, during Stage *E*, Melville also elaborated his original brief and external introduction of the captain (Ch. 6) and filled out the "sketch of him outlined in a previous chapter" with an altogether new inward analysis of Vere as "an exceptional character," in a chapter "To be inserted after first account of him" (Ch. 7; Plate VII). Finally, in the last part of the third phase, after putting the pencil drafts of Stage *X* into fair copy at Stages *F* and *G*, he made late pencil revisions of his treatment of the surgeon's role which affect the whole interpretation of Captain Vere and his course of action. These late revisions bear so directly on central critical problems, both of interpretation and of evaluation, that they must be described in some detail here. In the final section of the Introduction (pp. 34–39) their implications for criticism are explored.

The crucial revision of the surgeon's role occurred at that point in the story where Billy has struck and killed Claggart and the surgeon has pronounced Claggart dead. At Stage *Ga* the surgeon's part in the scene was purely routine; Vere briefly explained the circumstances to him and instructed him to withdraw, commenting that "before taking action I must have a few moments to mature the line of conduct I shall adopt." When Claggart fell under Billy's blow Vere had said "Fated boy," but he had not decided at once how to act. The case, he remarks to the surgeon, is without precedent and "could not have happened at a worse time either for me or the striker of the blow" (Leaves [229b]356, [229c]357). The surgeon's thoughts—the only ones assigned him at this stage—were reported in narrative summary that shaded into authorial commentary:

> Too well the thoughtful officer knew what his superior meant. As the former withdrew he could not help thinking how worse than futile the utmost discretion sometimes proves in a world subject to unfor[e]seeable fatalities; the prudent method adopted by Captain Vere to obviate publicity and trouble having resulted in an event that necessitated the former, and, under existing circumstances in the navy indefinit[e]ly magnified the latter. (Leaf [229c]357, at *Ga*)

Then followed a chapter that began with the three manuscript leaves erroneously printed in all previous editions of *Billy Budd* as the "Preface" (Leaves [229d–f]358–60; Plate V). Taking up the point about "existing circumstances in the navy," the expository chapter pointed out that in 1797

it was something caught from the Revolutionary Spirit that at Spithead emboldened the man-of-war's men to rise against real abuses, and afterwards at the Nore to make inordinate aggressive demands, successful resistance to which was confirmed only when the ringleaders were hung for an admonitory spectacle to the anchored fleet. (Stage *Ga*)

It was on the basis of these reflections that the narrator then in effect underwrote Vere's view of the case, doing so in the course of an extended passage still standing in the final manuscript (Leaves 238–45), which concluded as follows:

Feeling that unless quick action was taken on it[,] the deed of the foretopman so soon as it should be known on the gun-decks would tend to awaken any slumbering embers of disaffection among the crew, a sense of the urgency of the case overruled every other consideration. But tho' a conscientious dis-[c]iplinarian he was no lover of authority for mere authority's sake. Very far was he from embracing opportunities for monopolising to himself the perils of moral responsibility[,] none at least that could properly be referred to an official superior or shared with him by his official equals or even subordinates. So thinking[,] he was glad it would not be at variance with usage to turn the matter over to a summary court of his own officers, reserving to himself as the one on whom the ultimate accountability would rest, the right of maintaining a supervision of it, or informally interposing at need. Accordingly a drum-head court was summarily convened, he electing the individuals composing it. . . . (Leaves 244–245, at *Fa*)

As the entire sequence stood at Stage *Ga*, the tenor of Melville's attitude toward Vere was relatively straightforward. Only on the matter of the captain's "circumspectness" in guarding "as much as possible against publicity" did he bring in doubts. Even on this point his narrative voice is noncommittal: Vere "may or may not have erred"; some other officers later criticized him (from jealousy, his friends said); and there was "some imaginative ground for invidious comment" on the temporary secrecy that resembled policy in the palace of Peter the Barbarian. But Melville's subsequent changes have the effect—whatever their intention—of bringing Vere's behavior very much into question.

First, beginning where the surgeon infers that Claggart is already dead, Melville removed six leaves from the manuscript (Leaves [229a–f]355–60, including those later mislabeled "Preface"). In their place he substituted eight other leaves drafted in pencil (Leaves 230–37) which emphasize Vere's "excited manner" and "passionate interjections," and the fact that the surgeon ("as yet wholly ignorant of the affair" and "unapprised of the antecedents") is "profoundly discomposed" by them. The surgeon is also now said to be "disturbed" by the captain's apparent "desire for secrecy." Before the surgeon's withdrawal from the cabin, Vere now directs him to apprise the other officers of his intended drumhead court and to enjoin them to secrecy meanwhile. Instead of following this scene with a consideration of "the Revolutionary Spirit," as at *Ga*, Melville reports the surgeon's "disquietude," his reflections on what he has seen and heard, and his ensuing question whether "Captain Vere was suddenly affected in his mind." The surgeon is said to think that instead of convening a drumhead court Vere should "place Billy Budd in confinement and in a way dictated by usage, and postpone further action in so extraordinary a case, to such time as they should rejoin the squadron, and then refer it to the Admiral"; and the officers are said to agree (Leaves 234–36). Finally, in two paragraphs that serve as a new introduction to the next chapter (Ch. 21), Melville pushed even further the question of Vere's state of mind, asking as narrator: "Who in the rainbow can draw the line" between sanity and insanity? And he concludes, noncommittally: "Whether Captain Vere, as the Surgeon professionally & privately surmised, was really the sudden victim of any degree of aberration, every one must determine for himself by such light as this narrative may afford."

Which way—if either—Melville expected the reader to determine the question he had thus raised concerning Vere's possible "aberration" is by no means clear. Equally unclear is the larger question of what attitude the story as a whole conveys toward the captain. The lighting afforded by the narrative is not, so to speak, from a single source; it is of the sort characterized in *Moby Dick* (Ch. 3) as from "unequal cross-lights." As Claggart, during the second phase of the story's development, had tended to overshadow its original protagonist, so now in the third and final phase the emerging and ambiguous figure of Vere had moved toward the central position he has since been awarded by many interpreters of the novel. To these complex questions of tone and focus we suggest one avenue of approach in our section below on critical perspectives.

The foregoing alteration in the surgeon's role was the most significant of the numerous local changes Melville made in the course of the final revisions which we term the "late pencil stage." In this stage he appears to have gone through his whole manuscript, now of some 350 leaves, making a series of pencil revisions. He replaced some words and phrases on almost every leaf; he canceled, transposed, and elaborated passages; he added patches and inserted or substituted a few leaves, notably the eight concerning the surgeon. Perhaps Melville made these revisions inconsecutively and sporadically, perhaps in order from beginning to end of the narrative. At some point in the course of them he wrote on the last leaf, below the ballad, "End of

Book / April 19th 1891". The notation may have been his last addition to the manuscript. More likely he went back again after the "End," as he had repeatedly done during its five-year growth, to make further pencil revisions during the last summer of his life. The changes affecting the surgeon were likely made then; relevant leaves were not left in good order. Both the second Vere chapter (Ch. 7) and the Nelson digression were still in folders, not yet inserted into the narrative. In short, the manuscript was in a heavily revised, still "unfinished" state when he died, on September 28, 1891.

HISTORY OF THE TEXT

Although Melville never published *Billy Budd*, internal evidence clearly shows that he certainly meant to do so. For its posthumous publication he left no directives, however, at least none that survive, and in fact there are no specific external references to the novel by Melville himself.

Billy Budd remained unpublished until 1924, when it was edited by Raymond Weaver in Volume XIII of the Standard Edition of Melville's *Complete Works* (London: Constable and Company). In 1928 a different version of this text, by the same editor, appeared in *Shorter Novels of Herman Melville* (New York: Horace Liveright, Black and Gold Library). Despite numerous variations these may be considered essentially the same text. A second text, edited on quite different principles by F. Barron Freeman, was published in 1948, in *Melville's Billy Budd* (Cambridge: Harvard University Press). All the many reprintings of *Billy Budd* are, strictly speaking, versions of one or the other of these two basic texts: Weaver's 1924 text with his own 1928 modification; or Freeman's 1948 text. Since Freeman's text itself in fact depends on Weaver's 1928 text in an unfortunate way, Weaver's is the only text up to the present one to have been drawn from an entirely independent transcription of the manuscript. All the versions mentioned were of course ultimately derived from the single manuscript, for there is no other source.

A basic fact about the textual situation was recognized by Weaver in 1928: "Such is the state of the *Billy Budd* manuscript that there can never appear a reprint that will be adequate to every ideal." The most obvious editorial ideal, of course, would be to put before the reader precisely what the author would have published. But, as Weaver perceived, no "reprint" (i.e., text) can hope to do that, for the simple reason that in many details Melville's intention cannot be ascertained because of "the state of the manuscript." Therefore two general courses are open to an editor. He may "edit" the manuscript in the sense of preparing a text as near as he can make it to what he judges Melville would have (and this shades into *should have*) wanted a publisher to put before the reader, then or now; in this case he will have a "reading text," an edition for the general reader, but he will not be able to follow in every detail what is in the manuscript. This is the course Weaver chose. On the other hand, an editor may "edit" the manuscript in the sense of reporting in every detail exactly what Melville put on the paper, including the revisions, and doing so in a way that accounts for all the writing of any sort that appears in the manuscript. In this case the editor will have a "literal" text, showing, ideally, all earlier readings, an edition for the scholar; but he will not have a coherent, consistent, and mechanically uniform narrative for the general reader, a text such as Melville would have wanted his publisher to issue. This is the sort of course Freeman attempted to follow. Each text, Weaver's and Freeman's, gained advantages and suffered limitations of its chosen method. In addition, each had its individual shortcomings and errors. Weaver himself, in his 1928 version, undertook to improve his earlier text of 1924; anthologists have offered various improved versions of Freeman's text of 1948. Several of these versions are based on collation with the manuscript but none of them is based on a thorough study of it, and all of them involve— as in fact does Freeman's own text—inconsistent compromises with his principle of giving literally what is on the paper. The fundamental fact to be recognized, again, is that no single text can possibly encompass both Weaver's and Freeman's objectives. For that reason the present editors have prepared two separate texts: one a genetic text, the other a reading text based on it.

As stated, Weaver's purpose in both his versions was to prepare a text for the general reader, rather than any sort of literal transcription. Concerning his 1924 version, he wrote: "The text . . . has, so far as possible, been printed verbatim from Melville's manuscript. Here and there, however, owing to the heavily corrected condition of many of the papers, slight adjustments in the interests of grammar or of style have been made in Melville's wording." This statement minimized the large number of his actual departures from the manuscript. These departures are easy enough to understand: Weaver at the time thought of *Billy Budd* as a story of no great importance, and he was editing it for a volume of gleanings, simply to fill out Constable's edition of Melville's complete works. He had no idea it would soon come to be considered a masterpiece.

Describing his 1928 Liveright version, Weaver stated that it differed only occasionally from that of 1924. Actually there were many variations, more than forty being corrections of erroneous readings in the earlier volume. But these corrections are scattered, however, and the persistence of other errors in the 1928 version seems to indicate that Weaver had undertaken no systematic collation of his printer's copy with the original manuscript. In "editing for intelligibility with the least possible departure from accuracy," as he described his own procedure in 1928, he obviously did not interpret "accuracy" as requiring faithful transcription of the final manuscript readings.

Weaver saw evident signs that the manuscript is "in a more or less tentative state as to details," and therefore in both of his versions he took it rather as duty than as license to correct and improve what he found there, in the way he supposed Melville himself would, or should, have done, had he prepared a final copy for the printer. One might say that Weaver's way of editing was pretty much that of a publisher's copy editor styling an inconsistently prepared and not very important manuscript by a contributor for whose words he felt no awe. Though his valuation of *Billy Budd* went up after the favorable notices by the English reviewers of the Constable edition of 1924, he prepared his second version of 1928 too with none of the tools or tone or respect for the literal marks on the paper with which an academic textual editor would now approach such a work. Melville's wording, on the whole, he followed, as well as he could, but in an independent way. Where he found an interlined revision not easily legible, he sometimes adopted the canceled earlier reading rather than strain after the author's latest wording; or if such an "illegible" revision was an addition, he simply ignored it. Sometimes he discarded a revision Melville had made, and restored an earlier wording he himself preferred; and occasionally he restored canceled words or phrases he could not willingly let die. Twenty-odd times he altered word forms—singular to plural or the reverse, tenses, and moods. Elsewhere he modified both grammar and idiom, often by adding new words of his own. He dropped initial "But" from six sentences while letting it stand in numerous others. Going beyond alterations of word and phrase, he freely broke up or combined sentences, shifted some forty paragraph divisions, and changed clearly indicated chapter divisions as well. He made little attempt to adhere to the punctuation or capitalization of the manuscript. He kept the anglicized spelling imposed by Constable in 1924.

It must be insisted, all the same, that these *intentional* changes which Weaver made in the accidentals of punctuation and other mechanical details, and even those he made in matters of substance— of words, sentences, paragraphs, and chapters—were, in theory, justifiable in the light of his editorial assumptions, when given "the state of the manuscript." He believed he must exercise taste as well as discretion, and he did so.

But other, *unintentional* departures that Weaver made from the manuscript were less excusable. He committed many plain errors. Through oversight, it appears, he added or dropped words by the dozen, and he misread perfectly legible ones by the score. Most of these mistakes even a cursory collation of his transcription with the original manuscript should have revealed and corrected. The signs are plain enough that his text was prepared hurriedly.

The major crippling weakness from which Weaver's text suffered, however, was a prior editorial lapse: he had not studied the manuscript sufficiently. Such a "reading text" as he was preparing should have been based upon a thorough analysis of the manuscript, for without such analysis an editor cannot understand the significance of what appears in it, or be sure of the final readings. Apparently Weaver did not attempt to find out what might be learned from "its heavily corrected condition." Both the undertaking of such an analysis and the presentation of a literal text remained to be done by later editors.

Up to 1948, while *Billy Budd* grew steadily in critical esteem, Weaver's two versions of his text remained the only published transcription. His text was reprinted in the Liveright edition itself and in several anthologies. It was translated into French (1935), German (1938), and Italian (1942). Meanwhile no one seems, at least publicly, to have questioned its adequacy. One editor, however, was emboldened by Weaver's remarks on the state of the manuscript, and by the discrepancies between his two versions, to make some changes. This was William Plomer, who prepared the *Billy Budd* published by John Lehmann (London, 1946). Plomer described his text as "the same as that of the Constable edition, but for a few small emendations, some of them Mr. Raymond Weaver's, and some mine." Incidentally, this charming little book was the first publication of *Billy Budd* as a separate volume—the first, that is, in English, for a bibliographical curiosity is that its first separate publication was in the French translation by Pierre Leyris (Paris: Attinger, 1935), and that the German and Italian translations also antedated its first separate publication in

English. It has never been published separately in the United States, as it has abroad, simply as a reading text.

In 1948 the second text of *Billy Budd* appeared, edited by F. Barron Freeman, in his *Melville's Billy Budd*. Derived from Freeman's unpublished thesis, "The Manuscripts of Herman Melville's *Billy Budd*" (Harvard, 1942), this book was the first effort to establish a "definitive text" based upon a study of the manuscript. In Freeman's words, his book was "an attempt to present the first accurate transcription, with all variant readings, of the manuscripts of *Billy Budd;* the first publication of Melville's previously undiscovered short story, 'Baby Budd, Sailor,' out of which he wrote his last novel; the first extended analysis of the novel and short story, together with a biographical account of the neglected last years of his life . . ." (p. vii).

Although not all the claims in this statement were satisfactorily realized, Freeman did more than anyone else had yet done to advance understanding of the manuscript. First, from his study of it, he discovered the major fact about the process of its composition: that Melville gradually built up the novel by a process of expansion. Second, Freeman made available a text far closer than either of Weaver's versions to what Melville wrote, and he printed many (though by no means all) of the earlier ("variant") readings. And third, Freeman offered in his introduction a still valuable treatment of the later Melville and of the structure, characters, themes, and language of *Billy Budd*.

Making our ensuing statement of the shortcomings and errors of Freeman's edition is an unwelcome task, for we are well aware of our debt to his work. But we must nevertheless point them out in order to clear the ground not only for our own textual analysis but also for subsequent interpretation.

In the first place, Freeman's study of the manuscript was inadequate, and it thereby entailed certain mistakes and limitations in genetic matters as well as certain textual errors. Though his study revealed the *general* process of composition by expansion, it was fallacious in its reasoning and quite mistaken in its specific conclusions about the growth of the story (pp. vii–xii, 69–73). In his book Freeman gave no account of how he had arrived at these conclusions, but referred the interested reader to the typescript of his thesis in the Harvard College Library (p. xii). The thesis, however, falls far short of providing the announced documented presentation of "a complete description of the state of the manuscripts [*sic*] and their pagination," and it does not in fact present a satisfactory analysis of the manuscript. (There is, let us say here, only *one* manuscript, though Freeman all along misleadingly refers to "the manuscripts" without making clear his reason for doing so.)

To begin with a major genetic matter, Freeman was quite mistaken in his "excision of the short story" he titles "Baby Budd, Sailor," and his analysis fails to account in detail for the grounds on which he made it. From our own analysis we must declare, simply, that in the manuscript "Baby Budd, Sailor" does not exist. At no stage of the composition of *Billy Budd* did Melville have a version constituting, corresponding to, or even approximating the text Freeman mistakenly presented under the title "Baby Budd, Sailor." Freeman "excised" that altogether supposititious short story from the single manuscript, and did so by processes of reasoning which he did not completely explain but whose results are demonstrably faulty. His text of "Baby Budd, Sailor" consists, actually, of segments from various copy stages, some early and some late. It is a composite "story" made up of the earliest *surviving* versions of various segments that he could not show to have been added at any given time. But the result, "Baby Budd, Sailor," is not a story that existed as such at any one stage. It is altogether factitious. And indeed most of its materials can be shown to be of later composition than much that Freeman's reasoning obliged him to discard. His conclusion, for example, that the "original short story" consisted largely of the dramatized scenes, and that the analytical "interpretive ramifications" were later additions, is just about the reverse of the actual case. Finally, as to the title itself, he does not explain its provenience, and we can find no warrant at all that such a title as "Baby Budd, Sailor" ever existed.

In another genetic particular, Freeman's study of the manuscript led him to a mistaken conclusion. He supposed that the sketch titled "Daniel Orme," which he transcribed and included in his book as a "related fragment," "was once intended to be part of the novel." This " fragment," he wrote, "must have first been written with the idea of inserting it in the novel and then was finally discarded" (p. xi). But his evidence for this supposition was a faulty reading of Melville's notations on the folder which holds the sketch. Freeman transcribed the relevant portion of the notations thus: "Daniel Orme / omitted of/Billy Budd". But what Melville actually wrote was "Daniel Orme / & / Omitted of Billy Budd". Freeman (following Weaver) ignored the large ampersand, thus making "Omitted of Billy Budd" a descriptive comment on "Daniel Orme" rather than simply a notation of materials stored in the folder in addition to "Daniel Orme." There is, therefore, no evidence that Melville ever meant this sketch to be a part of *Billy Budd*. However, Freeman's discussion (p. 52) of the similarities between the two old sailors, Daniel Orme and the Dansker, does not depend on this error and is not vitiated by it. (See also Freeman's article, "The Enigma of Melville's 'Daniel Orme,' " 1944.)

A serious limitation of the usefulness of Freeman's edition came from his quite mistaken inferences about the stages of composition and revision (pp. ix–xi) and his incorrect supposition that it is impossible to tell, or not feasible to show, when the various revisions were made. On this basis he decided to lump all the additions and changes as parts of one long revision and thus to report no distinctions between changes made at various stages of composition and revision. Presenting the final manuscript readings as his running text he placed superseded materials in footnotes simply as "variant readings from earlier versions." The consequent serious limitation is that Freeman's presentation denies the reader an opportunity to follow the growth of particular passages and to see what was present at successive stages, to the illuminating degree actually possible. Furthermore, his method of presenting these footnoted earlier readings is often quite misleading in the terminology and symbols employed.

Aside from these genetic matters lying outside the final text of the story, Freeman's text itself has three major errors likewise stemming from his inadequate analysis of the manuscript. It also incorporates what we believe to be a mistaken judgment in a major textual matter. And finally it has numerous minor errors deriving from faulty transcription.

All three of the major errors arose primarily because Freeman failed to recognize the handwriting of Mrs. Melville, which appears at various points in *Billy Budd* and other late manuscripts of her husband; like Weaver, Freeman mistook all the handwriting for Melville's own (see Freeman, pp. 66–67). This led him—following Weaver in the first major error—to accept three discarded leaves (358–60) as the "Preface." For doing so the only authority either Weaver or Freeman had is a penciled query on the first of these leaves: "Preface for / Billy Budd?" (See Plate V.) But in fact the handwriting of this query is not Melville's; it is his wife's. Mrs. Melville's query is one of many silent witnesses that after her husband's death she sorted his papers; in doing so she evidently found these leaves and recognized them as belonging to *Billy Budd*, but not realizing that they were superseded leaves, penciled on them her conjecture that they might be a "preface." Her question mark is fatal to any authority her notation might be supposed to have. And in fact nothing whatever indicates that Melville himself ever intended these superseded leaves to serve as a preface. Freeman (pp. 132, 234) realized that the leaves had originally belonged at the point in the narrative, just after the killing of Claggart, where Vere remarks to the surgeon that the event could not have happened at a worse time. But mistaking the notation for Melville's own, and failing to see that it was Mrs. Melville who had altered the last lines of Leaf 360 in order to complete a sentence that Melville originally continued but canceled on what is now Leaf 238, Freeman followed Weaver in accepting and printing the discarded leaves as the "Preface."

A second major error in Freeman's (as in Weaver's) text was the inclusion of two more superseded leaves, headed "Lawyers, Experts, Clergy." This error arose in the same way, from another of Mrs. Melville's notations. On the first of the two superseded leaves (353, 354) she penciled "For Billy Budd / Find proper place for insertion". (See Plate V.) Again Freeman followed Weaver in mistaking her notation for Melville's own. Weaver placed the two leaves about where they had originally stood, though this meant interrupting Melville's later leaf-number sequence and ignoring another, and correct, notation by Mrs. Melville. Freeman adhered to Weaver's placing but, honoring the chapter division and title which Weaver had ignored, printed the leaves as Ch. 12 in his edition.

The third major error concerns the title of the work. No version has been given just the final title which its author gave it. Here again the failure of its editors to recognize Mrs. Melville's hand in the manuscript is in large part to blame. For the title of the story two versions survive. One occurs in pencil draft on a slip attached to a separate leaf: "*Billy Budd / Foretopman* / What befell him / in the year of the / Great Mutiny / &c". The other occurs as a penciled addition at the top of the first leaf of the story proper: "Billy Budd / Sailor / (An inside narrative.)". (See Plates V, VI.) That the second of these was in fact Melville's final intention for the title is made clear by all genetic evidence. It was inscribed later than the other; and it stands, as stated, on the first leaf of the story, inscribed without revision. As to the other title, that it was superseded is clear: it was inscribed at an earlier stage as a draft, and was left incomplete by cancellation of its main title. It belongs, evidently, among the class of leaves restored by Mrs. Melville in her sorting of the manuscripts after her husband's death; for hers is the hand in which the canceled main title was reinstated, first by her writing "Billy Budd" above Melville's cancellation, and then later by her retracing, in pencil, the canceled *"Billy Budd / Foretopman"*. (See Plate V.) That it was she also who mounted on a separate leaf the slip with the superseded title draft seems likely. Similar variant draft-titles exist for many of Melville's late prose pieces and projected collections of verse, in some of which Mrs. Melville's hand appears as here.

Although there is thus, on genetic grounds, no question that Melville intended "Billy Budd / Sailor / (An inside narrative.)" as his final title, neither Weaver nor Freeman perceived the fact, and both used the earlier form. Later versions of Freeman's text reprinted in anthologies have been assigned almost all the possible combinations of the two forms but never the author's own final title. None of those who have subsequently "corrected" Freeman's text by reference to the manuscript have recognized these three major textual errors initiated by Weaver, for none have recognized Mrs. Melville's hand in the manuscript. The present edition is the first to reject the supposed "Preface," to exclude the "Lawyers, Experts, Clergy" episode from the final text, and to use the author's own final title.

In one further textual matter of another class—that of editorial judgment—we believe that Freeman erred in following Weaver. This concerns the name of Captain Vere's ship. Some twenty-five times throughout the manuscript the name *Indomitable* occurs, but in six instances, found in two widely separated chapters well along in the story, the name given is *Bellipotent*. Our analysis of the manuscript has revealed that Melville, at the late stage when he was composing his chapter (28 in this edition) on the engagement between Vere's seventy-four and the French line-of-battle ship, decided to change *Indomitable* to *Bellipotent*. Creation of this episode involved him in consideration of the appropriate naming of warships—long a favorite topic of his. At first he called the French ship the *Directory*, but finally he assigned it "the aptest name ever given a warship": in English, the *Atheist*. (See note to Leaf 336.) At the same time and evidently for the similar reason of aptness he introduced the change from *Indomitable* to *Bellipotent*, using the new name twice in the chapter under his hand. The other four occurrences of *Bellipotent* are in Ch. 18, which begins with Vere's chase of an unnamed French frigate. Although this passage stands some 150 leaves back in the manuscript, the evidence of the ink shows that Melville inscribed the two passages at the same late copy stage, going directly from Ch. 28 back to Ch. 18.

Melville did not live, however, to substitute *Bellipotent* for *Indomitable* in other chapters of the narrative, and indeed by what we conclude was a lapse of memory rather than a deliberate change of mind he used the name *Indomitable* in two other possibly later pencil-draft passages. (By a similar lapse of memory he inadvertently retained at two points in his final fair-copy version of the trial scene a "lieutenant of minor grade" as a ghostly fourth member of the three-man court after he had eliminated him at an earlier stage, and even in his later pencil revision he removed the lieutenant at only one of the two points. We have finally exorcised this ghost-lieutenant who has haunted all previous editions.) To secure consistency, Freeman, like Weaver before him, substituted *Indomitable* wherever *Bellipotent* occurs, not on genetic grounds but merely because that name occurs first and more frequently. This choice, we are convinced by the preponderant genetic evidence, is a mistaken one. (Weaver, by a curious scribal lapse in his 1928 version, preserved part of the word *Bellipotent* while substituting *Indomitable* in the last sentence of the passage on the death of Vere, where he gives for "the *Bellipotent*'s senior officer of marines" the reading "the *Indomitable*'s potent senior officer of marines"!) The present Reading Text is the first to employ *Bellipotent* throughout the narrative.

What we have referred to as Freeman's minor textual errors, as contrasted to the major ones discussed above, were inaccurate transcriptions of single words and punctuation marks. Some account of these numerous errors is called for because they have led to much comment and "correction" while the major errors have hitherto gone unrecognized. Freeman, as we have stated, did not seek to present a "normalized" reading text like Weaver's but to give exactly what Melville had written. In principle, except for one stated class of corrections, he intended to add, omit, or alter nothing from the manuscript reading. In adopting this policy he took on an obligation not assumed by Weaver: the obligation of literal transcription. Freeman's was thus a more exacting standard than Weaver's; but unfortunately the execution was not satisfactory.

Freeman was involved in contradictions from the beginning. Although aiming to transcribe a literal text, he spoke of his transcription as "an effort to establish a definitive text" (p. ix), meaning, evidently, one which would become the standard text for all readers; and led by the needs of the general reader, as distinguished from the scholar, he departed at once from literal transcription in his avowed policy of silently correcting Melville's misspellings and of inserting a few required words, letters, and punctuation marks in diamond brackets (pp. xi–xii). He also silently supplied chapter numbers, unbracketed. On the other hand, he allowed various anomalous literal readings to stand. For example, he printed the titles Melville had drafted for four chapters, even though the other chapters have none—an obvious mechanical inconsistency in the manuscript, betokening its unfinished state. The draft title of the chapter about Nelson was "Concerning 'the greatest sailor since the world began.'" After this title Mrs. Melville wrote her conjectural (though correct) ascription: "Tennyson?" Not recognizing her hand, Freeman printed "Tennyson?" even though to the general reader the question mark in any case would be meaningless—as indeed it is when Freeman's text is reprinted *literatim* in anthologies. Such procedures indicated Freeman's supposition that his text could serve both as a literal, scholar's text and as a "definitive," reader's text; it is in fact a kind of compromise between the two, which ends up by being not quite either one. Hence anthologists reprinting it for general or class use have almost all felt the necessity to make further silent, bracketed, or footnote corrections on behalf of their readers. (For example, many omit the question mark from "Tennyson?" or offer a footnote asserting that it represented Melville's intention to check the quotation.) Hence, too, uncertainties about the text arose not long after its publication in November, 1948.

In June, 1951, following the discovery of a number of errors in transcription, the Harvard University Press temporarily withdrew the book from sale. In 1951–52, Miss Elizabeth Treeman, one of the press's editors, compared the Freeman printed text with the manuscript in the Houghton Library, noting corrections in a copy of the book. In September, 1952, she transcribed these corrections into another copy which was used as the basis for the text in the college anthology edited by Bradley, Beatty, and Long (*The American Tradition in Literature*, 1956), though these editors introduced a few bracketed insertions. Subsequently, she prepared a pamphlet of *Corrigenda*, which the Harvard Press issued in June, 1953, when it again offered the book for sale. (The foregoing paragraph is based upon information supplied by the Harvard University Press.)

This *Corrigenda* pamphlet, correcting the main text only, not the footnoted "variants," listed over five hundred departures from the literal manuscript readings, including "only those changes about which there can be little or no doubt" but excluding certain minor departures as well as the corrections Freeman himself had avowed. About four hundred errata were in matters of accidentals: punctuation, spelling, hyphenation, italics, and so on. Only about one hundred involved changes of words. Despite their number we have called these errors "minor" because almost all are trivial in themselves and because even taken together they are of far less consequence than the unnoticed errors we have discussed above as major.

One is bound to ask: How did so many errors occur in an edition to which so much care had obviously been devoted? A simple explanation emerges from a comparison of Freeman's errors with Weaver's 1928 readings. The comparison reveals that in 65 per cent of the 500-odd total errors listed in the *Corrigenda* pamphlet, Freeman's readings coincide with those of Weaver; and of Freeman's one-hundred-odd verbal errors, over eighty agree with Weaver's readings. The inference from this coincidence in errors is obvious: that in preparing his text Freeman did not make an independent transcription from the manuscript alone; that instead he used a copy of Weaver's 1928 version as the basis of his text, collating it with the manuscript and correcting on its pages the rich harvest of errors he saw, but overlooking many other errors—those in which, therefore, his text agrees with Weaver's. This editorial procedure unquestionably induced the bulk of the errors in transcription later recorded in the *Corrigenda* pamphlet. In another one-fifth of his errors, however, Freeman erred where Weaver had been correct. (To confuse matters still further, the *Corrigenda* pamphlet is itself in error in a dozen instances where Freeman was actually correct; often its extreme literalism defeats Melville's obvious intention.)

The foregoing extended discussion of errors should not be allowed to obscure the fact that Freeman's text was far more faithful to the manuscript than was Weaver's. Freeman corrected misreadings of Weaver more numerous, gross, and damaging than those he overlooked or introduced. He deciphered many obscure words and contributed greatly to the definitive text at which he aimed. To him, as to Weaver, all subsequent editors must owe a debt. But this is not to imply that the proper procedure is simply to "improve" the readings of Weaver and Freeman. The present edition, to repeat, is based on a new and independent transcription of the manuscript, not on a corrected version of an earlier text.

The history of the text of *Billy Budd* after 1948 may be indicated briefly. Until the present edition, no study of the manuscript or new text has been attempted. All of the texts printed in various anthologies are simply more or less "corrected" versions of Freeman's—unless they revert, as some do, to Weaver's. With the issuance of the *Corrigenda* pamphlet Freeman's book was restored to sale but allowed to go out of print in March, 1958. By this time *Billy Budd* had become a standard piece for college classes, but most anthologists who have reprinted Freeman's text, incorporating the corrigenda, have felt constrained to tinker with a few of its readings here and there in the interest of the general reader. Three, at least, have taken the trouble to collate it with the manuscript and have made various minor changes, some of them misguided. The most thorough of these collations was that of Jay Leyda, for *The Portable Melville* (New York: Viking, 1952). Leyda prepared his text before the *Corrigenda* pamphlet appeared. He corrected many errors and gave the first accurate readings of a few difficult words. He dropped the chapter numbers supplied by earlier editors and made other changes in accidentals, largely to emphasize the tentative character of the work. No editor's name appears with the text of *Billy Budd* printed in *Selected Writings of Herman Melville* (New York: Modern Library, 1952); it was "based on existing editions, with corrections made by a comparison with the manuscript." Likewise, Milton R. Stern, in preparing the text for the Dutton Everyman volume including *Typee* and *Billy Budd* (1958), collated the so-called Freeman-Treeman text with the manuscript and introduced some minor (and some mistaken) corrections and emendations. None of these versions, however, as stated, represents anything more than a cursorily corrected version of Freeman's text. All still have minor misreadings some of which stem from Weaver, via Freeman, and all perpetuate the major errors discussed above. Unlike the present edition, not one of them is an independent transcription based upon a detailed analysis of the manuscript.

PERSPECTIVES FOR CRITICISM

That *Billy Budd* was not given to the public until 1924, during the initial enthusiasm of the "Melville revival," has had important consequences for its interpretation and evaluation. So too has the form of its editorial presentation, as should now be apparent from the foregoing discussion of the growth of its manuscript and the publication history of its text. It is axiomatic that sound criticism demands a sound text, one that reflects as accurately as possible an author's final intention concerning his work; until a reliable text is established, criticism of that work must be regarded as tentative.

"Whenever a dead author is 'revived,' " wrote Matthew Josephson in 1928, surveying the rising interest in Melville during the 1920's, "we must bear in mind that nothing of him has been changed. It is we, his readers, who are changed, and for whom he has gained other values." Applied to *Billy Budd* in particular, Josephson's statement has an unintended irony. Melville has indeed "gained other values" for his readers since the waning years of his life and contemporary fame, as a proliferating body of scholarship and criticism clearly attests. But between the 1920's and the 1960's there have been still further shifts in literary taste and judgment, bringing sharp divisions and even complete reversals of opinion concerning the focus, the tone, and the artistic worth of his final novel. In important respects, moreover, that novel as set before its readers by all previous editors is not the novel as Melville left it—which is to say that something of its author, contrary to Josephson, *has* in fact been changed. The mislabeled "Preface" that opens every published text of *Billy Budd* before the present edition is a conspicuous example of such change, and an important one. A number of recent critical essays are grounded squarely on the assumption that in this "Preface" Melville intended to establish a basic tone and point of reference for the entire novel; as we have shown, however, *Billy Budd* under its author's hand never began with a preface, and the passage so labeled is actually a discarded fragment of what is now Ch. 19. A reader who in good faith interprets the novel in terms of the "Preface" will scarcely be honoring Melville's intention, nor will he be in a position to write definitive criticism.

It is in recent years, since the close of World War II, that outright controversy has divided the readers of *Billy Budd*. During the first twenty-five years of criticism (1921–46) there was some disagreement over its literary merit but little of the now-familiar debate concerning its intention and tone. Beginning with Raymond Weaver in his pioneering life of Melville (1921), the earliest commentators generally saw the novel as embodying a sharply drawn conflict between good and evil, personified in Billy and Claggart and finally resolved in tragic terms. When Weaver first published the work in 1924, in a British edition of Melville, the British reviewers who immediately hailed its quality also set the long-prevailing pattern of its interpretation. J. Middleton Murry, emphasizing its autobiographical implications and religious overtones, at once called it Melville's "last will and spiritual testament"; E. L. Grant Watson, following Murry and others, subsequently coined the most celebrated epithet so far applied to *Billy Budd:* "Melville's testament of acceptance." Through the early forties *Billy Budd* continued to be read in this way, primarily as a work of "spiritual autobiography," tragic in tone, in which Billy, Claggart, and Vere played parts corresponding respectively to Christ, Satan, and God. Not all critics saw Billy as a Christ-figure, however, nor did everyone award him the hero's role. As we have shown, Melville himself had begun his story with the title character, then gradually shifted his attention to Claggart and ultimately to Vere; now Lewis Mumford, Yvor Winters, and Charles Weir, Jr., were paying increasing attention to the captain, and in 1946 Raymond Short identified Vere as indeed "the true hero of the novel."

Meanwhile, as early as 1943, a query in the *Explicator*, signed "T. T. E.," had raised a portentous question. Might not *Billy Budd* be regarded "as rather more concerned with social repercussions and less concerned with personal ethics" than its earlier critics had realized? ("In this respect the 'Preface,' " according to T. T. E., "deserves special note.") Charles Anderson (1940) had already addressed himself to the possibility that in Melville's "inside" knowledge of an execution at sea, the *Somers* case of 1842 in the American navy, might be found the "genesis" of *Billy Budd*. Following Anderson's lead, Newton Arvin and other scholars were to take the novel as an oblique commentary on the *Somers* affair, which was said to have wrecked the naval career of Melville's cousin Guert Gansevoort, first lieutenant of the *Somers*. By 1948, when F. Barron Freeman had demonstrated Melville's further dependence on other historical and literary source material, it was clear that *Billy Budd* could no longer be read simply for autobiographical commentary or religious allegory. Though Freeman continued to dwell upon religious implications of a work whose tragic hero is not Christ but a "Christlike" figure, Herbert Schneider and Richard Chase had already challenged the classification of *Billy Budd* and its hero as "tragic," and both Chase and Charles Olson had specified the Christlike attributes of Billy as inhibiting his fulfilment of the protagonist's role in secular tragedy.

Though few critics of the day were willing to entertain the strictures of Chase and Olson upon the esthetic qualities of *Billy Budd* (some of which Simon had anticipated in 1939), it became clear from articles and reviews appearing in the immediate wake of Freeman's edition that the novel was due for vigorous reassessment. With Joseph Schiffman's assertion in 1950 that *Billy Budd* is neither a "testament of acceptance" nor a tragedy but "a tale of irony," there began a series of "ironist" readings of the novel that dominated criticism in the 1950's. To critics of the ironist persuasion—Schiffman, Campbell,

Sale, Casper, Zink, Thompson, Wagner, Withim—Billy is a passive victim of injustice, social or divine; Captain Vere is no hero but a reactionary authoritarian; and the novel as a whole is Melville's final ironic protest against the repressive structure of society (Vere's "forms, measured forms"), or of the cosmos itself. Instead of attesting Melville's "acceptance" (in Grant Watson's phrase), or what Freeman had called his "recognition of necessity," the work is for Withim "Melville's testament of resistance."

Since the ironist critics not only take vigorous issue with other readings of *Billy Budd* but also disagree among themselves, a possible effect of their work has been to undermine confidence in the artistic integrity of a novel that apparently admits such various interpretations. Even if irony is present in one or more passages, does it necessarily follow that Melville's own views are always diametrically opposite those expressed by the "I" who tells the story, as Thompson would have it? Or that *Billy Budd* should be read in the manner of Vern Wagner, as "a parody of tragedy," with an Ahab-like Claggart displacing both Billy and Vere as its real protagonist? Certainly not all recent critics have been ironists. The moral-religious-metaphysical approach continues in the work of Arvin, Stone, Pearson, and Mason, and more recently in that of Stewart and Miller. B. R. McElderry, Jr., and Richard and Rita Gollin, through investigation of sources and analogues of the *Billy Budd* theme, and Eleanor Tilton and Richard H. Fogle, studying the novel in the context of Melville's other late writings, have broadened the discussion beyond the black-and-white antithesis of tragedy versus comedy, acceptance versus resistance, and cases for or against Captain Vere. As Fogle has shown, moreover, "tragedy" and "irony" are not mutually exclusive terms with respect to *Billy Budd*.

Now that a reliable text of the novel has been provided, we believe the way is cleared for definitive criticism. Avenues are opened as well to further scholarly investigation. We wish, in the following paragraphs, to indicate a number of the new perspectives, for criticism as well as scholarship, afforded by the complete transcription of the manuscript and our detailed analysis of its genesis and development.

Those who have looked at *Billy Budd* in the perspective of its genesis have done so hitherto mostly in terms of its supposed source, the *Somers* mutiny case of 1842. Apart from Freeman's suggestive introduction to his edition, Leon Howard's biography of Melville was the most notable attempt to place the work in the context of his last years. Howard related it not only to the *Somers* case but to Melville's other late writings. He examined the *Billy Budd* manuscript and was the first to recognize from it that the novel had developed out of a headnote for the ballad, following the pattern of composition by unforeseen expansion which (as Howard had shown) shaped many of Melville's earlier works and which was going on in other prose headnotes to poems with which he was concurrently engaged. Our detailed analysis confirms Howard's original insight and general placing of the work. At the same time, however, it necessitates a reassessment of his hypotheses concerning the details of the story's development. Particularly it requires re-examination of his, and all other, assumptions about the relation between *Billy Budd* and the *Somers* case.

The commonly accepted view that the *Somers* mutiny case was in effect the "source" of *Billy Budd* must be modified. The assumption has been, in general, that when Melville set out to write the story he adapted his central characters and situation from those involved in the events aboard the American brig-of-war. Certain facts encouraged such a view. Melville had referred to the case twice in *White-Jacket*. His cousin, Guert Gansevoort, first lieutenant of the brig, was as deeply involved in the affair as any man but the commander, Alexander Slidell Mackenzie, and the three men hanged—Acting Midshipman Philip Spencer, Boatswain's Mate Samuel Cromwell, and Seaman Elisha Small. Possibly Melville had heard or read his cousin's inside story, and in one of the *John Marr* poems there is a vignette of Guert Gansevoort as "Tom Tight," who will not babble about just such a case. Moreover, Melville mentions the *Somers* case directly in *Billy Budd* itself, at the climax of the trial scene. (See Leaf 281 and note, *the U.S. brig-of-war* Somers.)

There are obvious similarities in the two cases: a suspected mutiny, a "drumhead court" or officers' council clearly dominated by the commander, a central question of military expediency versus justice, execution by hanging, and an unresolved outcome that leaves many observers feeling that the commander has done an injustice and perhaps as many others feeling that he is the hero of a moral crisis. Further similarities in detail appear. Aboard the *Somers*, for example, there was also a "temptation scene" in which Spencer sought a recruit much as Claggart's emissary solicited Billy. And one of the men to be hanged (Small, not Spencer) said "God bless that flag!"

But there are also obvious differences between the two cases—indeed Melville calls attention to them in *Billy Budd* (Leaf 282). The *Somers* affair occurred in the American, not the British, navy; on a small training brig, not on a ship of the line; within living memory in 1842, not in the revolutionary era of 1797; in time of peace, not in time of war; three men were hanged, not one; Philip Spencer was a green acting-midshipman, the ne'er-do-well son of the Secretary of War, not an obscure and fatherless able seaman of phenomenal natural innocence. Spencer had confessedly plotted a mutiny; the question was not whether he had plotted it but whether he would have carried it into action and whether his plot so endangered the ship that it was *necessary*, as the commander and his officers decided, to hang him and the two others. As to the "drumhead court," none was in fact held aboard the *Somers:* Commander Mackenzie requested his officers to give him their "united council [*sic*]"—not to hold a *court*, which he recognized he had no right to convene. The officers, in *council*, headed by Lieutenant Gansevoort, questioned various men and concluded that the safety of the ship required that the prisoners be put to death. The prisoners were not arraigned, not formally tried, not allowed to confront witnesses or offer a defense. Whatever the status of Captain Vere's "drumhead court," it was at least a court in form: Billy was charged and tried, the sole witness was heard, Billy was asked to speak for himself, and a formal sentence was passed. (See note to Leaf 233, *a drumhead court.*)

Because of the striking similarities, and Melville's own relation to the case, the above differences have been regarded as deliberate alterations he made, perhaps to veil the actual source of his story, perhaps to serve his artistic purposes. The central situation and issue seemed fundamentally the same. But in perspective of the story's genesis, as revealed by our analysis, the theory that Melville *began* with the *Somers* case becomes untenable. Not only do the differences appear more significant; the similarities appear less so. The situation defined both in the original headnote and in the first phase of the story's development resembles the *Somers* case only in that a man is to be hanged for "mutiny the spread of which was apprehended"; the central character, Billy the handsome sailor, and the setting on a British seventy-four in the revolutionary era right after the Nore and Spithead mutinies are quite different. The second phase of development, which brought in Claggart and his plot against Billy, likewise has no convincing parallel with the *Somers* case, despite efforts that have been made to equate Claggart, rather arbitrarily, with either Captain Mackenzie or Lieutenant Gansevoort. What remains strongest among the similarities between the two cases is precisely that part of the story which was not present at all through the first two phases of its development—the part which was not the earliest but the latest to evolve: that including Captain Vere, the trial scene, and the issues raised by Vere's argument to the court. In the story as it began and as it developed in the three years between early 1886 through 1888 none of that part existed. Nevertheless, it seems likely that the *Somers* case was in some way related to the emergence of Captain Vere and creation of the trial scene. That case, we conclude, was not the primary and motivating source of *Billy Budd* but in the story's last phase was certainly a cogent analogue, even as Melville's comment in the novel suggests.

Freed from what has seemed a sufficient "source" in the *Somers* mutiny case, scholars may now reassess the importance of the case relative to that of such literary parallels as those pointed out by McElderry and by Richard and Rita Gollin in Douglas Jerrold's *Black-Ey'd Susan* and *The Mutiny at the Nore* and Marryat's *The King's Own*—parallels far closer to Billy himself as a character and to his original situation than anything in the *Somers* case. Scholars may also be encouraged to look for new parallels and sources. In literature, for example, the naval novels of Cooper offer a surprising number of affinities, in characters, situations, and themes, as well as in particulars of style and phrasing. His *The Two Admirals* and *Wing-and-Wing* are especially suggestive, the former having a naval officer not unlike Captain Vere, the latter having a setting in Nelson's fleet in the Mediterranean waters and containing naval trial scenes and a hanging at the yardarm. Only a few of the many similarities are pointed out in our Notes and Commentary. In British naval history of the Napoleonic era there may be some actual case which suggested the situation presented in the original ballad and headnote. (Anderson, who examined historical sources, sought parallels to the fully developed story rather than the ballad.) "Tom Deadlight," in the *John Marr* volume, is similar in form as well as setting; it seems likely that Melville may have been moved to write both poems by his reading about the era in fiction or history.

American naval history, too, may offer unsuspected analogues to some aspects of *Billy Budd*. There was, for example, a hanging in the United States fleet blockading the coast of Mexico in 1846. A young seaman called Samuel Jackson, on the ship *St. Mary's*, struck a lieutenant who had ordered the man's shoes thrown overboard because he left them between the guns in neglect of the lieutenant's orders. Jackson was tried by a court martial convened on the authority of Commodore Conner; he was convicted of striking an officer, was sentenced to death, and was hanged at the yardarm, on September 17, 1846. In the long eyewitness account by the Rev. Fitch W. Taylor (the chaplain who visited and prayed for Jackson as he lay in confinement), some note is made of the peculiar fact that there was no movement in Jackson's body when he was hanged—the explanation offered is that he was killed by the concussion of the signal gun, over which he stood before being run up. (See Taylor, *The Broad Pennant; or a Cruise in the United States Flag Ship of the Gulf Squadron during the Mexican Difficulties* [New York, 1848], pp. 262–83.) Readers who find Captain Vere's action intolerable in a far more aggravated case under more trying circumstances in the old British navy may be moved by this and other possible examples to give more weight to Melville's carefully prepared historical context in "a narration essentially having less to do with fable than with fact." (See also Cameron, "*Billy Budd* and 'An Execution at Sea,'" 1956.)

Another insufficiently explored area of sources and parallels involves both naval history, minor "literature," and Melville's own experiences in the navy on the frigate *United States*. Parallels sufficient to make *White-Jacket* a major source for naval matters in *Billy Budd* have been pointed out by various scholars, and we have recorded many in our Notes and Commentary. But there are unexplored contiguous fields. Here might be uncovered the backgrounds of the second, or Claggart, phase of *Billy Budd*. Whence did Melville derive the evil master-at-arms who took an immediate irrational dislike to the handsome sailor, tormented him through understrappers, and finally enmeshed him in a false accusation? This "phenomenal nature" was not a creation of Melville's old age. The resemblance of Claggart to Bland, the gentlemanly master-at-arms of the *Neversink* in *White-Jacket,* has often been remarked; their identity in a "depravity according to nature" is unmistakable. But Melville derived Bland, it would appear, not from the actual master-at-arms of the frigate *United States* but from another master-at-arms in the U.S. navy, of whom he had read and perhaps had heard tales. This man is briefly described by William McNally, a one-time shipmate, as master-at-arms on the *Fairfield* in 1828–31:

There was an individual on board of that ship whose name was Sterritt; but he was better known in the navy, by the cognomen of "Jimmey Leggs." He had been on board the frigate Constitution, as a master at arms, and had there incurred such hatred for his tyranny and villainy, that his life was unsafe. . . . This man was destitute of every moral or honorable principle—destitute alike of every good feeling that reigns in the human breast; and the punishment which he had at different times received from seamen, for his cruelty towards them, only increased his malignity and hatred. He had been several times so badly bruised and injured by them, that his life was despaired of—and on one occasion, they had committed an act upon his person which left him of the neuter gender, or of "no sex, at all," as Byron expresses it. But he recovered; and the seamen, who are ever ready to ascribe to supernatural agency the most common occurrences, believed him to be in league with his great proto-type, the devil. . . . This notorious character was the brother of the O'Hare who was hung at Baltimore, many years ago, for robbing the mail. After the death of his brother he assumed another name. He fell, the first victim of cholera morbus, in 1834, on board the receiving ship Hudson at New York—dying, despised and hated by all who knew him. . . . (*Evils and Abuses in the Naval and Merchant Service* [Boston, 1839], pp. 89–91; see note to Leaf 88, *the master-at-arms.*)

Melville incorporated many of these and other details from McNally in his account of Bland in *White-Jacket* (Ch. 44), and it seems likely from the parallel of the consonants that he remembered the name Sterritt in assigning the name Claggart. But his analysis of the moral psychology of both Bland and Claggart went far beyond anything in McNally's indignant little book. Furthermore, Bland had not been represented in *White-Jacket* as tormenting any chosen victim. Two other evil figures Melville had portrayed earlier had done so, however. The first was Jackson, in *Redburn*, who seemed specially to hate a young sailor—Redburn himself—on account of his youth, fair cheeks, and good health, but who worked no plot against him. The second was the ugly mate, Radney, of "The Town-Ho's Story" in *Moby Dick* (Ch. 54), who also envied a handsome and popular sailor, Steelkilt, whom he hounded into a retaliatory blow and into mutiny.

Outside Melville's own earlier writings, but in the orbit of old ship-mates and sailing days in which his thoughts were revolving as he worked over the *John Marr* poems, was another tale of the sea that has elements in common with *Billy Budd*. This is a short pamphlet tale, *Orlando Melville or the Victims of the Press-Gang* (Boston, 1848), by E. Curtiss Hine, a shipmate of Melville on the *United States* in 1843–44 who was probably the original of "Lemsford the poet" in *White-Jacket*. (See Hayford, 1951.) If so, Hine was one of the group of literary tars who along with Melville gathered about the handsome sailor captain-of-the-maintop, Jack Chase. Though external record has as yet revealed no acquaintance between Hine and Melville, the brief tale whose hero bears the name Melville is perhaps evidence enough upon which to rest the fulcrum of a surmise. The plot of the tale concerns a handsome young Englishman who is impressed into the British navy, where he serves on the frigate *Macedonian*, at the time of the War of 1812. In what might be termed "an inside story," the master-at-arms—called Jimmy Leggs—falsifies charges against Orlando's Irish companion and also brings Orlando's sweetheart (disguised as a sailor) to the gratings to be stripped and flogged. The villain is foiled and the sweetheart is spared exposure, however, by the encounter in which the *Macedonian* was defeated by the *United States*. Jack Chase, Englishman, had served aboard the *Macedonian*, though of course not in 1812. An able-seaman of mature years, more like the older Billy of the original headnote, "Jack must have been a by-blow of some British Admiral" (*White-Jacket*, Ch. 4). He was "spokesman of the crew, on every suitable occasion always foremost," in accord with the prescription for the Handsome Sailor in Ch. 1 of *Billy Budd*, which the later Billy fitted only "with important variations." May we not venture to surmise, from all the foregoing matters, the existence in Melville's reminiscences of some cluster of personal experiences, associations, and naval folklore—matters that had entered the maintop discussions of Jack Chase and his disciples? May not such matters, too, have entered and merged in the shaping of *Billy Budd?*

In his last years, "thrown more and more upon retrospective musings," like his John Marr, Melville had become increasingly preoccupied with memories of his own earlier years and with reflections upon that historic Past, "in the time before steamships," that had come to seem infinitely grander and nobler than the prosaic Present. As a product of his old age *Billy Budd* shares many of the materials, attitudes, and themes that entered his other writings of this final period. Like the external materials suggested above, the themes in these writings have been insufficiently explored as a context for the themes of the novel, which is too often viewed in unmediated juxtaposition with the work of his young manhood in the 1840's and 1850's, nearly half a century earlier. Such exploration would lead back from external sources and materials—in history, literature, and experience—to consideration of internal relations and critical problems.

Our Genetic Text opens various possibilities for such internal study of *Billy Budd* both in the process of creation and in its end state. Beyond the broad phases of development outlined in the first section of this Introduction, what was the retired customs inspector, who had long ago written *Moby Dick*, accomplishing in the leisurely process of proliferating revision that occupied his "quiet, grass-growing" last years, a process terminated by the death of the author rather than the completion of his manuscript? In many of the late pieces, it would appear, he accomplished little—he was puttering. In *Billy Budd*, however, he achieved a work that has entered the canon of major American fiction and is usually listed second to *Moby Dick* among his novels. Wherein lay the difference between *Billy Budd* and the other late pieces? Did its quality of greatness emerge with one transforming major stroke somewhere in the gradual process of growth by accretion? Were all the instances of his minute verbal revision necessary to its greatness, or were many of them merely nervous or fussy gestures? To what extent do the revisions show a sure intuition of what was vital in the work as it stood at the end in semi-final manuscript? To what extent are many of the revisions purely random strokes that overlie and obscure the emerging conception? Into what categories do the stylistic revisions fall? Similar questions about the process of revision will occur to every reader. Many problems relevant to interpretation and evaluation will likewise suggest themselves—interrelated problems about form, theme, and language, to which study of the Genetic Text may suggest answers.

In conclusion, by way of example, we wish to open one suggestive line of analysis in order to show the bearing of our genetic study upon the problem of tone and focus occasioned by the crucial late revisions.

It seems fair to say that were it not for the effect of Melville's late pencil revisions (as summarized above, pp. 9–11) the critical controversy of the last dozen years over the story's tone in relation to Vere and his actions would scarcely have arisen. Even those interpreters who disapprove Vere's course could not well question the author's evident design as revealed at Stage *Ga*, to establish that course in terms of "existing conditions in the navy." The cumulative effect—whatever the intention—of his subsequent deletions and insertions, however, was to throw into doubt not only the rightness of Vere's decision and the soundness of his mind but also the narrator's own position concerning him. As the revised sequence now stands, it is no longer as narrator but in terms of the surgeon's reflections that Melville introduces the reaction to Vere and his plan to place Billy on trial. He leaves the narrator pointedly noncommittal, telling the reader in so many words that he must decide for himself concerning the captain's state of mind. Yet in the unmodified paragraphs that Melville allowed to stand immediately after the surgeon's reflections, the narrator presents Vere's position in a sympathetic tone (Leaves 238–45). Also, following the narrator's allusion to the *Somers* case as "History, and here cited without comment," Melville retained a quotation from "a writer whom few know" (obviously Melville himself), the tenor of which is exculpatory, or at worst extenuative. The next chapter (Ch. 22), also retained after the revision, reports Vere's closeted interview with Billy in a tone unmistakably favorable to the captain. In sum, it is the late revisions—those involving the surgeon—which raise doubts; those passages composed earlier which are still retained tend to represent Vere favorably.

What, then, did Melville suppose was the effect of his late revisions? What attitude was he himself taking when he made them? Had he in fact completed them? And what may a reader make of them?

If only in view of the narrator's reservations (at both stages) concerning Vere's "maintenance of secrecy" in the case (Leaf 242), it would seem unwise to infer, as some readers have done, that Melville's final attitude toward Vere was one of unequivocal endorsement. Conversely, if the "prudent surgeon" was intended to replace the narrator as a spokesman for the author himself, the reader would of course conclude that Melville too condemned Vere's position. But it is not justifiable to take the revisions simply in that light.

For one thing, there are the retained passages, pointed out above, in which the narrator's tone and comments are sympathetic to Vere. For another thing, given the near-caricature of the surgeon embodied in Ch. 26 (inscribed earlier at Stage F/G), which emphasizes his unimaginative obtuseness—in line with Melville's usual treatment of doctors and other "men of science"—it is hardly justifiable to take his views of Vere as embodying Melville's own. And for a third thing, one obvious point of the revisions was to re-emphasize the important theme, already otherwise developed in various ways, that to such ordinary minds as the surgeon's, or those of the officers of the court, such truly "exceptional natures" as any of the three principals—Billy and Claggart as well as Vere—are in effect closed books. Thus the surgeon's attitude toward Vere's behavior parallels his obtuse attitude toward the "phenomenal" lack of motion in Billy's suspended body.

A final and major point is that in making the revision Melville was doing what he had consistently done in the whole course of composition: he was *dramatizing* the situation (and its implications) which he had previously *reported*. The point may be served by a quotation from Charles Olson (1949), who preferred Freeman's composite "Baby Budd" to the supposedly later *Billy Budd*, as more dramatic. In expanding the story, Olson declared, Melville "worked over and over as though the hand that wrote was Hawthorne's, with his essayism, his hints, the veil of his syntax, until the celerity of the short story was run out, the force of the juxtapositions interrupted, and the secret of Melville as artist, the presentation of ambiguity by the event direct, was lost in the Salem manner." Actually, as we have shown, *Billy Budd* developed in almost the opposite way, from exposition into dramatization. Yet the terms of Olson's criticism, if not the conclusions, are highly relevant.

Both of the conspicuous developments in the third and final phase —the prominent role now given to Vere and the revised role given to the surgeon—arose when Melville transformed what had been statements and implications into dramatic terms. The first development, that of Vere's new role, was entailed in Melville's creation of the trial scene. This scene dramatized the same considerations that had dictated Billy's execution from the Stage *A* headnote onward—not only his naval crime but the officers' apprehensions of the spread of mutiny. (Thus, in a sense, Vere's position was predetermined by the nature of the situation addressed from the start, though the quality of Vere's awareness of that position was not.) The scene also dramatized the conflict of military duty with human feeling, which from the beginning was a generating source of the story's pathos. This conflict had already been shaped through the series of more or less congruent dichotomies that inform the story (nature versus society, feeling versus reason, rights-of-man versus ordered forms, Christian morality versus war, and so on). By means of the trial scene the hitherto diffused conflict was brought into dramatic focus, in the breasts of the court of officers, and most of all in Captain Vere's intense realization of the claims of both sides. The peculiar fervor of his argument to the reluctant officers is generated by the conflict working within himself.

The preservation of two superseded leaves enables us to observe in some detail the way in which Melville dramatized one passage in the trial scene. The leaves (from Stage *C*) are those of the superseded digressive chapter "Lawyers, Experts, Clergy" (Leaves [135a]353, [135b]354). There Melville had speculated, "by the way," upon the problem offered courts by such evil natures as he had attributed to Claggart and associated with the biblical "mystery of iniquity" (Leaf 135). "Can it be the phenomenon," he asked, "that in some criminal cases puzzles the courts? For this cause have our juries at times not only to endure the prolonged contentions of lawyers with their fees but also the yet more perplexing strife of the medical experts with theirs?" And he went on, "But why leave it to them? why not subpoena as well the clerical proficients?" Later, dramatizing this speculation at Stage *X*, Melville created a court scene that gave an immediacy to precisely these questions. The thoughtful marine officer, in effect a juror in a criminal case, is presented as puzzled just so by Claggart's motivation: "Why should he have so lied, so maliciously lied," he asks Billy, "since you declare there was no malice between you?" The question touches on "a spiritual sphere wholly obscure to Billy's thoughts," as indeed to those of the marine captain and his colleagues. But Vere, who is presented as a character capable of divining that sphere, answers in terms taken over directly from Melville's own earlier speculations quoted above: "Ay, there is a mystery," he says, "but, to use a scriptural phrase, it is a 'mystery of iniquity,' a matter for psychologic theologians to discuss" (Leaves 258–59). Vere's next speech is also drawn from the earlier passage on "clerical proficients" who "know something about those intricacies involved in the question of moral responsibility"; in this next speech he admits Billy's case is an exceptional one which "well might be referred to a jury of casuists." A civil court, it was said in the earlier phrase already quoted, must "endure the prolonged contentions" of such experts; now Vere, to whose speech Melville adapted the phrase, objects that "strangely we prolong proceedings" (Leaf 257) and insists that the military court must act summarily. One further motif of the "Lawyers, Experts, Clergy" chapter remained to be salvaged—Melville's slurs on "the medical experts" who for fees directly contradict each other. This motif, in effect, he partly dramatized in the obtuse surgeon who, not understanding the cause of his captain's unwonted behavior, "professionally and privately surmised" that he was the sudden victim of mental aberration. Partly, also, Melville repeated the slur in the same passage with the surgeon's surmise: "to draw the exact line of demarcation few will undertake, though for a fee . . . some professional experts will."

Thus the late pencil revision involving the surgeon followed a process Melville had repeatedly engaged in from the beginning. The process was very likely that by which (during Stage *A*) he had converted his original headnote summary and character sketch of Billy Budd into a plotted story, though of that transformation we have no direct evidence. Certainly it was the process by which he had turned into scenes his narrative statements of such events as Billy's impressment, his ignorance of his paternity, and Claggart's use of understrappers to harass Billy.

All along, Melville's dramatization had the effect, among others, of dissociating the narrator from commitments he had earlier made or positions that Melville might wish to insinuate without endorsing. Although this effect of noncommittal "alienation" was sometimes incidental to his dramatizations, it was often—perhaps usually—deliberately sought. A transparent example is the attribution of the commentary on Vere's course at the end of Ch. 21 to "a writer whom few know" (earlier to "a writer whom nobody knows, and who being dead recks not of the oblivion")—the writer obviously being Melville himself. The "honest scholar, my senior" (Leaves 127–30) falls in the same class. Similarly, but more effectively, Melville created the Dansker as a shrewd and experienced old man to whom to assign speculations concerning "what might eventually befall a nature" such as Billy's when "dropped into a world" as oddly incongruous with it as the warship's environment (Leaves 110–11). A telling example may be cited in the scene between the captain and the surgeon: in the earlier version the narrator himself equates Billy's fatal blow with "the divine judgment on Ananias"; in the revised version Melville gives the phrase to Captain Vere as a sudden dramatic exclamation—one of those which arouse the surgeon's disquietude. The effect, analogously, of many of Melville's stylistic revisions is to achieve the same "pithy, guarded" tone as the Dansker's comments, if not their "cynicism." "The secret of Melville as artist" Charles Olson defined as "the presentation of ambiguity by the event direct." The whole episode involving the surgeon is a complex example of Melville's working toward direct presentation, and the effect was certainly, in the end, one of ambiguity. Other means than direct presentation, however, contribute to that effect, among them the guarded, noncommittal statements by the narrator.

Also contributing to the effect of ambiguity, it may be suggested, are what must be described genetically as inconsistencies.* That these inconsistencies merge, in their effect, with the ambiguities is not altogether fortuitous. In raising, through the surgeon's reactions and his "private and professional" surmises, some question about Vere's course and even his sanity, Melville was deliberately dissociating the narrator from commitment and throwing "cross-lights" upon Vere. The disagreements and prolonged contentions among what Melville might have called "the critical experts" are but the proper issue of his

* In making his late revisions Melville had also introduced certain inconsistencies and uncertainties (if not outright contradictions) as to what, according to "usage," was the captain's proper course under the circumstances. See note to Leaf 233, *a drumhead court,* which also adduces statutes of the period applicable to such a case.

requiring every reader to "determine for himself." But the rhetorical question "Who in the rainbow can draw the line . . . ?" should be a warning to critics who find the lines of demarcation in the story easy to determine and who suppose Melville's own attitude was altogether clear cut. To Melville's mind, after all, the question was not simply the rightness or wrongness, sanity or insanity, of the captain's action, but also the very existence of a problematical world in which such a story as he had been so long developing and brooding upon was (in his guarded phrase) "not unwarranted." His story was an epitome, in art, of such a world.

Would Melville himself, in a "finished" version of *Billy Budd*, perhaps have removed the inconsistencies, if not have resolved the ambiguities, concerning the captain? And more fundamentally, would he have undertaken further adjustments of emphasis among his three principals? Only conjectural answers are possible, of course. In our judgment, however, these questions, posed by our analysis of the manuscript and study of its development, bring critical debate about the work into a new perspective: Was the story as it stood when Melville died (and as we have now presented it in our edited Reading Text) complete in all significant respects though "unfinished" in details? Or, on the other hand, was it, because still under revision at a passage crucially affecting its tone and focus (and perhaps for other reasons as well), radically "unfinished"? In short, is *Billy Budd* a unified work of art?

A possible—and appropriately ambiguous—answer is suggested by Melville's own words in *Moby Dick:*

. . . I now leave my cetological System standing thus unfinished, even as the great Cathedral of Cologne was left, with the crane still standing upon the top of the uncompleted tower. . . . God keep me from ever completing anything. This whole book is but a draught—nay, but the draught of a draught. Oh, Time, Strength, Cash, and Patience! (Ch. 32)

Perhaps the "unfinished" *Billy Budd* should be regarded in this light. Melville's often declared conception of the relation between reality and literature, between "truth" and the writer's attempt to see and state it, involved both incompletion and formal imperfection as a necessity: a work that is faithful to reality *must* in the end be both incomplete and unshapely, since truth is both elusive and intractable and the writer is limited in "Time, Strength, Cash, and Patience." "Truth uncompromisingly told," he wrote near the end of *Billy Budd*, "will always have its ragged edges; hence the conclusion of such a narration is apt to be less finished than an architectural finial."

BILLY BUDD

SAILOR

(An inside narrative)

1

In the time before steamships, or then more frequently than
now, a stroller along the docks of any considerable seaport would
occasionally have his attention arrested by a group of bronzed
mariners, man-of-war's men or merchant sailors in holiday attire, ashore on liberty. In certain instances they would flank, or
like a bodyguard quite surround, some superior figure of their
own class, moving along with them like Aldebaran among the
lesser lights of his constellation. That signal object was the
"Handsome Sailor" of the less prosaic time alike of the military
and merchant navies. With no perceptible trace of the vainglorious about him, rather with the offhand unaffectedness of
natural regality, he seemed to accept the spontaneous homage
of his shipmates.

A somewhat remarkable instance recurs to me. In Liverpool,
now half a century ago, I saw under the shadow of the great
dingy street-wall of Prince's Dock (an obstruction long since
removed) a common sailor so intensely black that he must needs
have been a native African of the unadulterate blood of Ham—
a symmetric figure much above the average height. The two
ends of a gay silk handkerchief thrown loose about the neck
danced upon the displayed ebony of his chest, in his ears were big
hoops of gold, and a Highland bonnet with a tartan band set off
his shapely head. It was a hot noon in July; and his face, lus-
trous with perspiration, beamed with barbaric good humor.
In jovial sallies right and left, his white teeth flashing into view,
he rollicked along, the center of a company of his shipmates.
These were made up of such an assortment of tribes and complexions as would have well fitted them to be marched up by
Anacharsis Cloots before the bar of the first French Assembly
as Representatives of the Human Race. At each spontaneous
tribute rendered by the wayfarers to this black pagod of a fellow—the tribute of a pause and stare, and less frequently an

6 exclamation—the motley retinue showed that they took that sort of pride in the evoker of it which the Assyrian priests doubtless showed for their grand sculptured Bull when the faithful prostrated themselves.

7 To return. If in some cases a bit of a nautical Murat in setting forth his person ashore, the Handsome Sailor of the period in question evinced nothing of the dandified Billy-be-Dam, an amusing character all but extinct now, but occasionally to be encountered, and in a form yet more amusing than the original, at the tiller of the boats on the tempestuous Erie Canal or, more *8* likely, vaporing in the groggeries along the towpath. Invariably a proficient in his perilous calling, he was also more or less of a mighty boxer or wrestler. It was strength and beauty. Tales of his prowess were recited. Ashore he was the champion; afloat the spokesman; on every suitable occasion always foremost. Close-reefing topsails in a gale, there he was, astride the weather yardarm-end, foot in the Flemish horse as stirrup, both hands tugging at the earing as at a bridle, in very much the attitude of young Alexander curbing the fiery Bucephalus. A superb figure, tossed up as by the horns of Taurus against the thunder-*9* ous sky, cheerily hallooing to the strenuous file along the spar.

The moral nature was seldom out of keeping with the physical make. Indeed, except as toned by the former, the comeliness and power, always attractive in masculine conjunction, hardly could have drawn the sort of honest homage the Handsome Sailor in some examples received from his less gifted associates.

10 Such a cynosure, at least in aspect, and something such too in nature, though with important variations made apparent as the story proceeds, was welkin-eyed Billy Budd—or Baby Budd, as more familiarly, under circumstances hereafter to be given, he at last came to be called—aged twenty-one, a foretopman of the British fleet toward the close of the last decade of the eighteenth century. It was not very long prior to the time of the narration that follows that he had entered the King's serv-*11* ice, having been impressed on the Narrow Seas from a home-

ward-bound English merchantman into a seventy-four outward
bound, H.M.S. *Bellipotent;* which ship, as was not unusual in
those hurried days, having been obliged to put to sea short of
her proper complement of men. Plump upon Billy at first sight
in the gangway the boarding officer, Lieutenant Ratcliffe,
pounced, even before the merchantman's crew was formally
mustered on the quarter-deck for his deliberate inspection. And
him only he elected. For whether it was because the other men
when ranged before him showed to ill advantage after Billy, or
whether he had some scruples in view of the merchantman's
being rather short-handed, however it might be, the officer contented himself with his first spontaneous choice. To the surprise
of the ship's company, though much to the lieutenant's satisfaction, Billy made no demur. But, indeed, any demur would
have been as idle as the protest of a goldfinch popped into
a cage.

Noting this uncomplaining acquiescence, all but cheerful, one
might say, the shipmaster turned a surprised glance of silent
reproach at the sailor. The shipmaster was one of those worthy
mortals found in every vocation, even the humbler ones—the
sort of person whom everybody agrees in calling "a respectable
man." And—nor so strange to report as it may appear to be—
though a ploughman of the troubled waters, lifelong contend-
ing with the intractable elements, there was nothing this honest
soul at heart loved better than simple peace and quiet. For the
rest, he was fifty or thereabouts, a little inclined to corpulence,
a prepossessing face, unwhiskered, and of an agreeable color—a
rather full face, humanely intelligent in expression. On a fair
day with a fair wind and all going well, a certain musical chime
in his voice seemed to be the veritable unobstructed outcome
of the innermost man. He had much prudence, much conscientiousness, and there were occasions when these virtues were the
cause of overmuch disquietude in him. On a passage, so long as
his craft was in any proximity to land, no sleep for Captain

Graveling. He took to heart those serious responsibilities not so heavily borne by some shipmasters.

Now while Billy Budd was down in the forecastle getting his kit together, the *Bellipotent*'s lieutenant, burly and bluff, nowise disconcerted by Captain Graveling's omitting to proffer the customary hospitalities on an occasion so unwelcome to him, an omission simply caused by preoccupation of thought, unceremoniously invited himself into the cabin, and also to a flask from the spirit locker, a receptacle which his experienced eye instantly discovered. In fact he was one of those sea dogs in whom all the hardship and peril of naval life in the great prolonged wars of his time never impaired the natural instinct for sensuous enjoyment. His duty he always faithfully did; but duty is sometimes a dry obligation, and he was for irrigating its aridity, whensoever possible, with a fertilizing decoction of strong waters. For the cabin's proprietor there was nothing left but to play the part of the enforced host with whatever grace and alacrity were practicable. As necessary adjuncts to the flask, he silently placed tumbler and water jug before the irrepressible guest. But excusing himself from partaking just then, he dismally watched the unembarrassed officer deliberately diluting his grog a little, then tossing it off in three swallows, pushing the empty tumbler away, yet not so far as to be beyond easy reach, at the same time settling himself in his seat and smacking his lips with high satisfaction, looking straight at the host.

These proceedings over, the master broke the silence; and there lurked a rueful reproach in the tone of his voice: "Lieutenant, you are going to take my best man from me, the jewel of 'em."

"Yes, I know," rejoined the other, immediately drawing back the tumbler preliminary to a replenishing. "Yes, I know. Sorry."

"Beg pardon, but you don't understand, Lieutenant. See here, now. Before I shipped that young fellow, my forecastle was a rat-pit of quarrels. It was black times, I tell you, aboard the

Rights here. I was worried to that degree my pipe had no comfort for me. But Billy came; and it was like a Catholic priest striking peace in an Irish shindy. Not that he preached to them or said or did anything in particular; but a virtue went out of him, sugaring the sour ones. They took to him like hornets to treacle; all but the buffer of the gang, the big shaggy chap with the fire-red whiskers. He indeed, out of envy, perhaps, of the newcomer, and thinking such a "sweet and pleasant fellow," as he mockingly designated him to the others, could hardly have the spirit of a gamecock, must needs bestir himself in trying to get up an ugly row with him. Billy forebore with him and reasoned with him in a pleasant way—he is something like myself, Lieutenant, to whom aught like a quarrel is hateful—but nothing served. So, in the second dogwatch one day, the Red Whiskers in presence of the others, under pretense of showing Billy just whence a sirloin steak was cut—for the fellow had once been a butcher—insultingly gave him a dig under the ribs. Quick as lightning Billy let fly his arm. I dare say he never meant to do quite as much as he did, but anyhow he gave the burly fool a terrible drubbing. It took about half a minute, I should think. And, lord bless you, the lubber was astonished at the celerity. And will you believe it, Lieutenant, the Red Whiskers now really loves Billy—loves him, or is the biggest hypocrite that ever I heard of. But they all love him. Some of 'em do his washing, darn his old trousers for him; the carpenter is at odd times making a pretty little chest of drawers for him. Anybody will do anything for Billy Budd; and it's the happy family here. But now, Lieutenant, if that young fellow goes—I know how it will be aboard the *Rights*. Not again very soon shall I, coming up from dinner, lean over the capstan smoking a quiet pipe— no, not very soon again, I think. Ay, Lieutenant, you are going to take away the jewel of 'em; you are going to take away my peacemaker!" And with that the good soul had really some ado in checking a rising sob.

"Well," said the lieutenant, who had listened with amused

interest to all this and now was waxing merry with his tipple; "well, blessed are the peacemakers, especially the fighting peacemakers. And such are the seventy-four beauties some of which you see poking their noses out of the portholes of yonder warship lying to for me," pointing through the cabin window at the *Bellipotent.* "But courage! Don't look so downhearted, man. Why, I pledge you in advance the royal approbation. Rest assured that His Majesty will be delighted to know that in a time when his hardtack is not sought for by sailors with such avidity as should be, a time also when some shipmasters privily resent the borrowing from them a tar or two for the service; His Majesty, I say, will be delighted to learn that *one* shipmaster at least cheerfully surrenders to the King the flower of his flock, a sailor who with equal loyalty makes no dissent.—But where's my beauty? Ah," looking through the cabin's open door, "here he comes; and, by Jove, lugging along his chest—Apollo with his portmanteau!—My man," stepping out to him, "you can't take that big box aboard a warship. The boxes there are mostly shot boxes. Put your duds in a bag, lad. Boot and saddle for the cavalryman, bag and hammock for the man-of-war's man."

The transfer from chest to bag was made. And, after seeing his man into the cutter and then following him down, the lieutenant pushed off from the *Rights-of-Man.* That was the merchant ship's name, though by her master and crew abbreviated in sailor fashion into the *Rights.* The hardheaded Dundee owner was a staunch admirer of Thomas Paine, whose book in rejoinder to Burke's arraignment of the French Revolution had then been published for some time and had gone everywhere. In christening his vessel after the title of Paine's volume the man of Dundee was something like his contemporary shipowner, Stephen Girard of Philadelphia, whose sympathies, alike with his native land and its liberal philosophers, he evinced by naming his ships after Voltaire, Diderot, and so forth.

But now, when the boat swept under the merchantman's stern, and officer and oarsmen were noting—some bitterly and

others with a grin—the name emblazoned there; just then it was
that the new recruit jumped up from the bow where the cox-   *29*
swain had directed him to sit, and waving hat to his silent shipmates sorrowfully looking over at him from the taffrail, bade
the lads a genial good-bye. Then, making a salutation as to the
ship herself, "And good-bye to you too, old *Rights-of-Man*."

"Down, sir!" roared the lieutenant, instantly assuming all
the rigor of his rank, though with difficulty repressing a smile.

To be sure, Billy's action was a terrible breach of naval de-   *30*
corum. But in that decorum he had never been instructed; in
consideration of which the lieutenant would hardly have been
so energetic in reproof but for the concluding farewell to the
ship. This he rather took as meant to convey a covert sally on
the new recruit's part, a sly slur at impressment in general, and
that of himself in especial. And yet, more likely, if satire it was
in effect, it was hardly so by intention, for Billy, though happily
endowed with the gaiety of high health, youth, and a free
heart, was yet by no means of a satirical turn. The will to it
and the sinister dexterity were alike wanting. To deal in double
meanings and insinuations of any sort was quite foreign to his
nature.

As to his enforced enlistment, that he seemed to take pretty   *31*
much as he was wont to take any vicissitude of weather. Like
the animals, though no philosopher, he was, without knowing
it, practically a fatalist. And it may be that he rather liked this
adventurous turn in his affairs, which promised an opening
into novel scenes and martial excitements.

Aboard the *Bellipotent* our merchant sailor was forthwith
rated as an able seaman and assigned to the starboard watch
of the foretop. He was soon at home in the service, not at all dis-   *32*
liked for his unpretentious good looks and a sort of genial happy-
go-lucky air. No merrier man in his mess: in marked contrast
to certain other individuals included like himself among the impressed portion of the ship's company; for these when not actively employed were sometimes, and more particularly in the

last dogwatch when the drawing near of twilight induced revery, apt to fall into a saddish mood which in some partook of sullenness. But they were not so young as our foretopman, and no *33* few of them must have known a hearth of some sort, others may have had wives and children left, too probably, in uncertain circumstances, and hardly any but must have had acknowledged kith and kin, while for Billy, as will shortly be seen, his entire family was practically invested in himself.

34 Though our new-made foretopman was well received in the top and on the gun decks, hardly here was he that cynosure he had previously been among those minor ship's companies of the merchant marine, with which companies only had he hitherto consorted.

He was young; and despite his all but fully developed frame, in aspect looked even younger than he really was, owing to a lingering adolescent expression in the as yet smooth face all but *35* feminine in purity of natural complexion but where, thanks to his seagoing, the lily was quite suppressed and the rose had some ado visibly to flush through the tan.

To one essentially such a novice in the complexities of factitious life, the abrupt transition from his former and simpler sphere to the ampler and more knowing world of a great warship; this might well have abashed him had there been any conceit or vanity in his· composition. Among her miscellaneous *36* multitude, the *Bellipotent* mustered several individuals who however inferior in grade were of no common natural stamp, sailors more signally susceptive of that air which continuous martial discipline and repeated presence in battle can in some degree impart even to the average man. As the Handsome Sailor, Billy Budd's position aboard the seventy-four was something analogous to that of a rustic beauty transplanted from the provinces and brought into competition with the highborn dames of the court. But this change of circumstances he scarce noted. As little did he observe that something about him provoked an ambiguous smile in one or two harder faces among the bluejackets. Nor less unaware was he of the peculiar favorable effect his person and demeanor had upon the more intelligent gentlemen of the quarter-deck. Nor could this well have been otherwise. Cast in a mold peculiar to the finest physical examples of those Englishmen in whom the Saxon strain would seem not at all to partake of any Norman or other admixture, he showed in face that humane look of reposeful good nature which the Greek sculptor in some instances gave to his heroic strong man, Hercules. But this again was subtly modified by another and pervasive quality. The ear, small and shapely, the arch of the foot, the curve in mouth and nostril, even the indurated hand dyed to the orange-tawny of the toucan's bill, a hand telling alike of the halyards and tar bucket; but, above all, something in the mobile expression, and every chance attitude and movement, something suggestive of a mother eminently favored by Love and the Graces; all this strangely indicated a lineage in direct contradiction to his lot. The mysteriousness here became less mysterious through a matter of fact elicited when Billy at the capstan was being formally mustered into the service. Asked by the officer, a small, brisk little gentleman as it chanced, among other questions, his place of birth, he replied, "Please, sir, I don't know."

"Don't know where you were born? Who was your father?"

"God knows, sir."

Struck by the straightforward simplicity of these replies, the officer next asked, "Do you know anything about your beginning?"

"No, sir. But I have heard that I was found in a pretty silk-lined basket hanging one morning from the knocker of a good man's door in Bristol."

41   "*Found*, say you? Well," throwing back his head and looking up and down the new recruit; "well, it turns out to have been a pretty good find. Hope they'll find some more like you, my man; the fleet sadly needs them."

   Yes, Billy Budd was a foundling, a presumable by-blow, and, evidently, no ignoble one. Noble descent was as evident in him as in a blood horse.

42   For the rest, with little or no sharpness of faculty or any trace of the wisdom of the serpent, nor yet quite a dove, he possessed that kind and degree of intelligence going along with the unconventional rectitude of a sound human creature, one to whom not yet has been proffered the questionable apple of knowledge. He was illiterate; he could not read, but he could sing, and like the illiterate nightingale was sometimes the composer of his own song.

   Of self-consciousness he seemed to have little or none, or about as much as we may reasonably impute to a dog of Saint Bernard's breed.

43   Habitually living with the elements and knowing little more of the land than as a beach, or, rather, that portion of the terraqueous globe providentially set apart for dance-houses, doxies, and tapsters, in short what sailors call a "fiddler's green," his simple nature remained unsophisticated by those moral obliquities which are not in every case incompatible with that manufacturable thing known as respectability. But are sailors, frequenters of fiddlers' greens, without vices? No; but less often than with landsmen do their vices, so called, partake of crooked-

44 ness of heart, seeming less to proceed from viciousness than exuberance of vitality after long constraint: frank manifestations in accordance with natural law. By his original constitution aided by the co-operating influences of his lot, Billy in many respects was little more than a sort of upright barbarian, much such perhaps as Adam presumably might have been ere the urbane Serpent wriggled himself into his company.

   And here be it submitted that apparently going to corroborate the doctrine of man's Fall, a doctrine now popularly ignored, it is observable that where certain virtues pristine and unadulterate peculiarly characterize anybody in the external uniform of civilization, they will upon scrutiny seem not to be derived from custom or convention, but rather to be out of keeping with these, as if indeed exceptionally transmitted from a period prior to Cain's city and citified man. The character marked by such qualities has to an unvitiated taste an untampered-with flavor like that of berries, while the man thoroughly civilized, even in a fair specimen of the breed, has to the same moral palate a questionable smack as of a compounded wine. To any stray inheritor of these primitive qualities found, like Caspar Hauser, wandering dazed in any Christian capital of our time, the good-natured poet's famous invocation, near two thousand years ago, of the good rustic out of his latitude in the Rome of the Caesars, still appropriately holds:

> Honest and poor, faithful in word and thought,
> What hath thee, Fabian, to the city brought?

Though our Handsome Sailor had as much of masculine beauty as one can expect anywhere to see; nevertheless, like the beautiful woman in one of Hawthorne's minor tales, there was just one thing amiss in him. No visible blemish indeed, as with the lady; no, but an occasional liability to a vocal defect. Though in the hour of elemental uproar or peril he was everything that a sailor should be, yet under sudden provocation of strong heart-feeling his voice, otherwise singularly musical, as if expressive of the harmony within, was apt to develop an organic hesitancy, in fact more or less of a stutter or even worse. In this particular Billy was a striking instance that the arch interferer, the envious marplot of Eden, still has more or less to do with every human consignment to this planet of Earth. In every case, one way or another he is sure to slip in his little card, as much as to remind us—I too have a hand here.

The avowal of such an imperfection in the Handsome Sailor should be evidence not alone that he is not presented as a conventional hero, but also that the story in which he is the main figure is no romance.

[[53]]

3

49   At the time of Billy Budd's arbitrary enlistment into the *Bellipotent* that ship was on her way to join the Mediterranean fleet. No long time elapsed before the junction was effected. As one of that fleet the seventy-four participated in its movements, though at times on account of her superior sailing qualities, in the absence of frigates, dispatched on separate duty as a scout and at times on less temporary service. But with all this the story has little concernment, restricted as it is to the inner life of one particular ship and the career of an individual sailor.

50   It was the summer of 1797. In the April of that year had occurred the commotion at Spithead followed in May by a second and yet more serious outbreak in the fleet at the Nore. The latter is known, and without exaggeration in the epithet, as

51 "the Great Mutiny." It was indeed a demonstration more menacing to England than the contemporary manifestoes and conquering and proselyting armies of the French Directory. To the British Empire the Nore Mutiny was what a strike in the fire brigade would be to London threatened by general arson. In a crisis when the kingdom might well have anticipated the famous signal that some years later published along the naval line of battle what it was that upon occasion England expected

52 of Englishmen; *that* was the time when at the mastheads of the three-deckers and seventy-fours moored in her own roadstead— a fleet the right arm of a Power then all but the sole free conservative one of the Old World—the bluejackets, to be numbered by thousands, ran up with huzzas the British colors with the union and cross wiped out; by that cancellation transmuting the flag of founded law and freedom defined, into the enemy's red meteor of unbridled and unbounded revolt. Reasonable discontent growing out of practical grievances in the

53 fleet had been ignited into irrational combustion as by live cinders blown across the Channel from France in flames.

The event converted into irony for a time those spirited strains of Dibdin—as a song-writer no mean auxiliary to the English government at that European conjuncture—strains celebrating, among other things, the patriotic devotion of the British tar: "And as for my life, 'tis the King's!"

Such an episode in the Island's grand naval story her naval historians naturally abridge, one of them (William James) candidly acknowledging that fain would he pass it over did not "impartiality forbid fastidiousness." And yet his mention is less 54 a narration than a reference, having to do hardly at all with details. Nor are these readily to be found in the libraries. Like some other events in every age befalling states everywhere, including America, the Great Mutiny was of such character that national pride along with views of policy would fain shade it off into the historical background. Such events cannot be ignored, but there is a considerate way of historically treating them. If a well-constituted individual refrains from blazoning aught amiss or calamitous in his family, a nation in the like circumstance may without reproach be equally discreet.

Though after parleyings between government and the ring- 55 leaders, and concessions by the former as to some glaring abuses, the first uprising—that at Spithead—with difficulty was put down, or matters for the time pacified; yet at the Nore the unforeseen renewal of insurrection on a yet larger scale, and em- 56 phasized in the conferences that ensued by demands deemed by the authorities not only inadmissible but aggressively insolent, indicated—if the Red Flag did not sufficiently do so—what was the spirit animating the men. Final suppression, however, there was; but only made possible perhaps by the unswerving loyalty of the marine corps and a voluntary resumption of loyalty among influential sections of the crews.

To some extent the Nore Mutiny may be regarded as analogous to the distempering irruption of contagious fever in a frame 57 constitutionally sound, and which anon throws it off.

At all events, of these thousands of mutineers were some of

the tars who not so very long afterwards—whether wholly prompted thereto by patriotism, or pugnacious instinct, or by both—helped to win a coronet for Nelson at the Nile, and the naval crown of crowns for him at Trafalgar. To the mutineers, those battles and especially Trafalgar were a plenary absolution and a grand one. For all that goes to make up scenic naval display and heroic magnificence in arms, those battles, especially Trafalgar, stand unmatched in human annals.

4

58   In this matter of writing, resolve as one may to keep to the main road, some bypaths have an enticement not readily to be withstood. I am going to err into such a bypath. If the reader will keep me company I shall be glad. At the least, we can promise ourselves that pleasure which is wickedly said to be in sinning, for a literary sin the divergence will be.

Very likely it is no new remark that the inventions of our
59   time have at last brought about a change in sea warfare in degree corresponding to the revolution in all warfare effected by the original introduction from China into Europe of gunpowder. The first European firearm, a clumsy contrivance, was, as is well known, scouted by no few of the knights as a base implement, good enough peradventure for weavers too craven to stand up crossing steel with steel in frank fight. But as ashore knightly valor, though shorn of its blazonry, did not cease with
60   the knights, neither on the seas—though nowadays in encounters there a certain kind of displayed gallantry be fallen out of date as hardly applicable under changed circumstances—did the nobler qualities of such naval magnates as Don John of Austria, Doria, Van Tromp, Jean Bart, the long line of British admirals, and the American Decaturs of 1812 become obsolete with their wooden walls.

Nevertheless, to anybody who can hold the Present at its *61*
worth without being inappreciative of the Past, it may be forgiven, if to such an one the solitary old hulk at Portsmouth,
Nelson's *Victory*, seems to float there, not alone as the decaying
monument of a fame incorruptible, but also as a poetic reproach,
softened by its picturesqueness, to the *Monitors* and yet
mightier hulls of the European ironclads. And this not altogether because such craft are unsightly, unavoidably lacking
the symmetry and grand lines of the old battleships, but equally for other reasons.

There are some, perhaps, who while not altogether inacces- *62*
sible to that poetic reproach just alluded to, may yet on behalf
of the new order be disposed to parry it; and this to the extent
of iconoclasm, if need be. For example, prompted by the sight
of the star inserted in the *Victory*'s quarter-deck designating
the spot where the Great Sailor fell, these martial utilitarians
may suggest considerations implying that Nelson's ornate publication of his person in battle was not only unnecessary, but
not military, nay, savored of foolhardiness and vanity. They *63*
may add, too, that at Trafalgar it was in effect nothing less
than a challenge to death; and death came; and that but for
his bravado the victorious admiral might possibly have survived the battle, and so, instead of having his sagacious dying *64*
injunctions overruled by his immediate successor in command,
he himself when the contest was decided might have brought
his shattered fleet to anchor, a proceeding which might have
averted the deplorable loss of life by shipwreck in the elemental
tempest that followed the martial one.

Well, should we set aside the more than disputable point
whether for various reasons it was possible to anchor the fleet,
then plausibly enough the Benthamites of war may urge the
above. But the *might-have-been* is but boggy ground to build on. *65*
And, certainly, in foresight as to the larger issue of an encounter, and anxious preparations for it—buoying the deadly way
and mapping it out, as at Copenhagen—few commanders have

been so painstakingly circumspect as this same reckless declarer of his person in fight.

Personal prudence, even when dictated by quite other than selfish considerations, surely is no special virtue in a military man; while an excessive love of glory, impassioning a less burning impulse, the honest sense of duty, is the first. If the name *Wellington* is not so much of a trumpet to the blood as the simpler name *Nelson*, the reason for this may perhaps be inferred from the above. Alfred in his funeral ode on the victor of Waterloo ventures not to call him the greatest soldier of all time, though in the same ode he invokes Nelson as "the greatest sailor since our world began."

At Trafalgar Nelson on the brink of opening the fight sat down and wrote his last brief will and testament. If under the presentiment of the most magnificent of all victories to be crowned by his own glorious death, a sort of priestly motive led him to dress his person in the jewelled vouchers of his own shining deeds; if thus to have adorned himself for the altar and the sacrifice were indeed vainglory, then affectation and fustian is each more heroic line in the great epics and dramas, since in such lines the poet but embodies in verse those exaltations of sentiment that a nature like Nelson, the opportunity being given, vitalizes into acts.

Yes, the outbreak at the Nore was put down. But not every grievance was redressed. If the contractors, for example, were no longer permitted to ply some practices peculiar to their tribe everywhere, such as providing shoddy cloth, rations not sound, or false in the measure; not the less impressment, for one thing, went on. By custom sanctioned for centuries, and judicially maintained by a Lord Chancellor as late as Mansfield, that mode of manning the fleet, a mode now fallen into a sort of

abeyance but never formally renounced, it was not practicable
to give up in those years. Its abrogation would have crippled   69
the indispensable fleet, one wholly under canvas, no steam
power, its innumerable sails and thousands of cannon, everything in short, worked by muscle alone; a fleet the more insatiate in demand for men, because then multiplying its ships
of all grades against contingencies present and to come of the
convulsed Continent.

Discontent foreran the Two Mutinies, and more or less it   70
lurkingly survived them. Hence it was not unreasonable to apprehend some return of trouble sporadic or general. One instance of such apprehensions: In the same year with this story,
Nelson, then Rear Admiral Sir Horatio, being with the fleet
off the Spanish coast, was directed by the admiral in command
to shift his pennant from the *Captain* to the *Theseus;* and for
this reason: that the latter ship having newly arrived on the   71
station from home, where it had taken part in the Great Mutiny, danger was apprehended from the temper of the men;   72
and it was thought that an officer like Nelson was the one, not
indeed to terrorize the crew into base subjection, but to win
them, by force of his mere presence and heroic personality,
back to an allegiance if not as enthusiastic as his own yet as true.

So it was that for a time, on more than one quarter-deck,
anxiety did exist. At sea, precautionary vigilance was strained
against relapse. At short notice an engagement might come on.
When it did, the lieutenants assigned to batteries felt it incumbent on them, in some instances, to stand with drawn swords
behind the men working the guns.

But on board the seventy-four in which Billy now swung his   73
hammock, very little in the manner of the men and nothing
obvious in the demeanor of the officers would have suggested

to an ordinary observer that the Great Mutiny was a recent event. In their general bearing and conduct the commissioned officers of a warship naturally take their tone from the commander, that is if he have that ascendancy of character that ought to be his.

74   Captain the Honorable Edward Fairfax Vere, to give his full title, was a bachelor of forty or thereabouts, a sailor of distinction even in a time prolific of renowned seamen. Though allied to the higher nobility, his advancement had not been altogether owing to influences connected with that circumstance. He had seen much service, been in various engagements, always acquitting himself as an officer mindful of the welfare of his men, but never tolerating an infraction of discipline; thoroughly versed in the science of his profession, and intrepid to the verge of

75 temerity, though never injudiciously so. For his gallantry in the West Indian waters as flag lieutenant under Rodney in that admiral's crowning victory over De Grasse, he was made a post captain.

Ashore, in the garb of a civilian, scarce anyone would have taken him for a sailor, more especially that he never garnished unprofessional talk with nautical terms, and grave in his bearing, evinced little appreciation of mere humor. It was not out

76 of keeping with these traits that on a passage when nothing demanded his paramount action, he was the most undemonstrative of men. Any landsman observing this gentleman not conspicuous by his stature and wearing no pronounced insignia, emerging from his cabin to the open deck, and noting the silent deference of the officers retiring to leeward, might have taken

77 him for the King's guest, a civilian aboard the King's ship, some highly honorable discreet envoy on his way to an important post. But in fact this unobtrusiveness of demeanor may have proceeded from a certain unaffected modesty of manhood sometimes accompanying a resolute nature, a modesty evinced at all times not calling for pronounced action, which shown in

78 any rank of life suggests a virtue aristocratic in kind. As with

some others engaged in various departments of the world's more heroic activities, Captain Vere though practical enough upon occasion would at times betray a certain dreaminess of mood. Standing alone on the weather side of the quarter-deck, one hand holding by the rigging, he would absently gaze off at the blank sea. At the presentation to him then of some minor matter interrupting the current of his thoughts, he would show more or less irascibility; but instantly he would control it.   79

In the navy he was popularly known by the appellation "Starry Vere." How such a designation happened to fall upon one who whatever his sterling qualities was without any brilliant ones, was in this wise: A favorite kinsman, Lord Denton, a freehearted fellow, had been the first to meet and congratulate him upon his return to England from his West Indian cruise; and but the day previous turning over a copy of Andrew Marvell's poems had lighted, not for the first time, however, upon the lines entitled "Appleton House," the name of one of the seats of their common ancestor, a hero in the German wars of   80
the seventeenth century, in which poem occur the lines:

> This 'tis to have been from the first
> In a domestic heaven nursed,
> Under the discipline severe
> Of Fairfax and the starry Vere.

And so, upon embracing his cousin fresh from Rodney's great victory wherein he had played so gallant a part, brimming over with just family pride in the sailor of their house, he exuberantly exclaimed, "Give ye joy, Ed; give ye joy, my starry Vere!" This got currency, and the novel prefix serving in familiar parlance readily to distinguish the *Bellipotent*'s captain from another Vere his senior, a distant relative, an officer of like rank in the navy, it remained permanently attached to the surname.

81   In view of the part that the commander of the *Bellipotent* plays in scenes shortly to follow, it may be well to fill out that sketch of him outlined in the previous chapter.

Aside from his qualities as a sea officer Captain Vere was an exceptional character. Unlike no few of England's renowned sailors, long and arduous service with signal devotion to it had not resulted in absorbing and *salting* the entire man. He had a *82* marked leaning toward everything intellectual. He loved books, never going to sea without a newly replenished library, compact but of the best. The isolated leisure, in some cases so wearisome, falling at intervals to commanders even during a war cruise, never was tedious to Captain Vere. With nothing of that literary taste which less heeds the thing conveyed than the vehicle, his bias was toward those books to which every serious mind of superior order occupying any active post of authority in the world naturally inclines: books treating of actual men and *83* events no matter of what era—history, biography, and unconventional writers like Montaigne, who, free from cant and convention, honestly and in the spirit of common sense philosophize upon realities. In this line of reading he found confirmation of his own more reserved thoughts—confirmation which he had vainly sought in social converse, so that as touching most fundamental topics, there had got to be established in him some positive convictions which he forefelt would abide in him essentially unmodified so long as his intelligent part remained unimpaired. In view of the troubled period in which his lot was cast, this was well for him. His settled convictions were as a *84* dike against those invading waters of novel opinion social, political, and otherwise, which carried away as in a torrent no few minds in those days, minds by nature not inferior to his own. While other members of that aristocracy to which by birth he belonged were incensed at the innovators mainly because their theories were inimical to the privileged classes, Captain Vere disinterestedly opposed them not alone because they seemed to him insusceptible of embodiment in lasting institutions, but at war with the peace of the world and the true welfare of mankind.

With minds less stored than his and less earnest, some officers of his rank, with whom at times he would necessarily consort, found him lacking in the companionable quality, a dry and bookish gentleman, as they deemed. Upon any chance withdrawal from their company one would be apt to say to another something like this: "Vere is a noble fellow, Starry Vere. 'Spite the gazettes, Sir Horatio" (meaning him who became Lord Nelson) "is at bottom scarce a better seaman or fighter. But between you and me now, don't you think there is a queer streak of the pedantic running through him? Yes, like the King's yarn in a coil of navy rope?"

Some apparent ground there was for this sort of confidential criticism; since not only did the captain's discourse never fall into the jocosely familiar, but in illustrating of any point touching the stirring personages and events of the time he would be as apt to cite some historic character or incident of antiquity as he would be to cite from the moderns. He seemed unmindful of the circumstance that to his bluff company such remote allusions, however pertinent they might really be, were altogether alien to men whose reading was mainly confined to the journals. But considerateness in such matters is not easy to natures constituted like Captain Vere's. Their honesty prescribes to them directness, sometimes far-reaching like that of a migratory fowl that in its flight never heeds when it crosses a frontier.

The lieutenants and other commissioned gentlemen forming Captain Vere's staff it is not necessary here to particularize, nor needs it to make any mention of any of the warrant officers.

85

86

87

88

But among the petty officers was one who, having much to do with the story, may as well be forthwith introduced. His portrait I essay, but shall never hit it. This was John Claggart, the master-at-arms. But that sea title may to landsmen seem

89 somewhat equivocal. Originally, doubtless, that petty officer's function was the instruction of the men in the use of arms, sword or cutlass. But very long ago, owing to the advance in gunnery making hand-to-hand encounters less frequent and giving to niter and sulphur the pre-eminence over steel, that function ceased; the master-at-arms of a great warship becoming a sort of chief of police charged among other matters with the duty of preserving order on the populous lower gun decks.

90 Claggart was a man about five-and-thirty, somewhat spare and tall, yet of no ill figure upon the whole. His hand was too small and shapely to have been accustomed to hard toil. The face was a notable one, the features all except the chin cleanly cut as those on a Greek medallion; yet the chin, beardless as Tecumseh's, had something of strange protuberant broadness in its make that recalled the prints of the Reverend Dr. Titus Oates, the historic deponent with the clerical drawl in the time of Charles II and the fraud of the alleged Popish Plot. It served Claggart in his office that his eye could cast a tutoring glance. His brow was of the sort phrenologically associated with more

91 than average intellect; silken jet curls partly clustering over it, making a foil to the pallor below, a pallor tinged with a faint shade of amber akin to the hue of time-tinted marbles of old. This complexion, singularly contrasting with the red or deeply bronzed visages of the sailors, and in part the result of his official seclusion from the sunlight, though it was not exactly displeasing, nevertheless seemed to hint of something defective or abnormal in the constitution and blood. But his general aspect and manner were so suggestive of an education and

92 career incongruous with his naval function that when not actively engaged in it he looked like a man of high quality, social and moral, who for reasons of his own was keeping incog. Noth-

ing was known of his former life. It might be that he was an
Englishman; and yet there lurked a bit of accent in his speech
suggesting that possibly he was not such by birth, but through
naturalization in early childhood. Among certain grizzled sea   *93*
gossips of the gun decks and forecastle went a rumor perdue
that the master-at-arms was a *chevalier* who had volunteered
into the King's navy by way of compounding for some mysterious swindle whereof he had been arraigned at the King's
Bench. The fact that nobody could substantiate this report   *94*
was, of course, nothing against its secret currency. Such a rumor
once started on the gun decks in reference to almost anyone
below the rank of a commissioned officer would, during the
period assigned to this narrative, have seemed not altogether
wanting in credibility to the tarry old wiseacres of a man-of-war
crew. And indeed a man of Claggart's accomplishments, without prior nautical experience entering the navy at mature life,
as he did, and necessarily allotted at the start to the lowest
grade in it; a man too who never made allusion to his previous
life ashore; these were circumstances which in the dearth of
exact knowledge as to his true antecedents opened to the invidious a vague field for unfavorable surmise.

But the sailors' dogwatch gossip concerning him derived a   *95*
vague plausibility from the fact that now for some period the
British navy could so little afford to be squeamish in the matter
of keeping up the muster rolls, that not only were press gangs
notoriously abroad both afloat and ashore, but there was little
or no secret about another matter, namely, that the London
police were at liberty to capture any able-bodied suspect, any   *96*
questionable fellow at large, and summarily ship him to the
dockyard or fleet. Furthermore, even among voluntary enlistments there were instances where the motive thereto partook
neither of patriotic impulse nor yet of a random desire to experience a bit of sea life and martial adventure. Insolvent debtors of minor grade, together with the promiscuous lame ducks
of morality, found in the navy a convenient and secure refuge,

secure because, once enlisted aboard a King's ship, they were as much in sanctuary as the transgressor of the Middle Ages harboring himself under the shadow of the altar. Such sanctioned irregularities, which for obvious reasons the government would hardly think to parade at the time and which consequently, and as affecting the least influential class of mankind, have all but dropped into oblivion, lend color to something for the truth whereof I do not vouch, and hence have some scruple in stating; something I remember having seen in print though the book I cannot recall; but the same thing was personally communicated to me now more than forty years ago by an old pensioner in a cocked hat with whom I had a most interesting talk on the terrace at Greenwich, a Baltimore Negro, a Trafalgar man. It was to this effect: In the case of a warship short of hands whose speedy sailing was imperative, the deficient quota, in lack of any other way of making it good, would be eked out by drafts culled direct from the jails. For reasons previously suggested it would not perhaps be easy at the present day directly to prove or disprove the allegation. But allowed as a verity, how significant would it be of England's straits at the time confronted by those wars which like a flight of harpies rose shrieking from the din and dust of the fallen Bastille. That era appears measurably clear to us who look back at it, and but read of it. But to the grandfathers of us graybeards, the more thoughtful of them, the genius of it presented an aspect like that of Camoëns' Spirit of the Cape, an eclipsing menace mysterious and prodigious. Not America was exempt from apprehension. At the height of Napoleon's unexampled conquests, there were Americans who had fought at Bunker Hill who looked forward to the possibility that the Atlantic might prove no barrier against the ultimate schemes of this French portentous upstart from the revolutionary chaos who seemed in act of fulfilling judgment prefigured in the Apocalypse.

But the less credence was to be given to the gun-deck talk touching Claggart, seeing that no man holding his office in a man-of-war can ever hope to be popular with the crew. Besides, in derogatory comments upon anyone against whom they have a grudge, or for any reason or no reason mislike, sailors are much like landsmen: they are apt to exaggerate or romance it.

About as much was really known to the *Bellipotent*'s tars of the master-at-arms' career before entering the service as an astronomer knows about a comet's travels prior to its first ob- *101* servable appearance in the sky. The verdict of the sea quidnuncs has been cited only by way of showing what sort of moral impression the man made upon rude uncultivated natures whose conceptions of human wickedness were necessarily of the narrowest, limited to ideas of vulgar rascality—a thief among the swinging hammocks during a night watch, or the man-brokers and land-sharks of the seaports.

It was no gossip, however, but fact that though, as before *102* hinted, Claggart upon his entrance into the navy was, as a novice, assigned to the least honorable section of a man-of-war's crew, embracing the drudgery, he did not long remain there. The superior capacity he immediately evinced, his constitutional sobriety, an ingratiating deference to superiors, together with a peculiar ferreting genius manifested on a singular occasion; all this, capped by a certain austere patriotism, abruptly advanced him to the position of master-at-arms.

Of this maritime chief of police the ship's corporals, so called, *103* were the immediate subordinates, and compliant ones; and this, as is to be noted in some business departments ashore, almost to a degree inconsistent with entire moral volition. His place put various converging wires of underground influence under the chief's control, capable when astutely worked through his understrappers of operating to the mysterious discomfort, if nothing worse, of any of the sea commonalty.

104   Life in the foretop well agreed with Billy Budd. There, when not actually engaged on the yards yet higher aloft, the topmen, who as such had been picked out for youth and activity, constituted an aerial club lounging at ease against the smaller stun'sails rolled up into cushions, spinning yarns like the lazy gods, and frequently amused with what was going on in the busy world of the decks below. No wonder then that a young fellow of Billy's disposition was well content in such society. Giving no cause of offense to anybody, he was always alert at

105   a call. So in the merchant service it had been with him. But now such a punctiliousness in duty was shown that his topmates would sometimes good-naturedly laugh at him for it. This heightened alacrity had its cause, namely, the impression made upon him by the first formal gangway-punishment he had ever witnessed, which befell the day following his impressment. It had been incurred by a little fellow, young, a novice afterguardsman absent from his assigned post when the ship was being put about; a dereliction resulting in a rather serious hitch to that maneuver, one demanding instantaneous promptitude

106   in letting go and making fast. When Billy saw the culprit's naked back under the scourge, gridironed with red welts and worse, when he marked the dire expression in the liberated man's face as with his woolen shirt flung over him by the executioner he rushed forward from the spot to bury himself in the crowd, Billy was horrified. He resolved that never through remissness would he make himself liable to such a visitation or do or omit aught that might merit even verbal reproof. What then was his surprise and concern when ultimately he found himself getting into petty trouble occasionally about such matters as the stowage of his bag or something amiss in his hammock, matters un-

107   der the police oversight of the ship's corporals of the lower

decks, and which brought down on him a vague threat from one of them.

So heedful in all things as he was, how could this be? He could not understand it, and it more than vexed him. When he spoke to his young topmates about it they were either lightly incredulous or found something comical in his unconcealed anxiety. "Is it your bag, Billy?" said one. "Well, sew yourself up in it, bully boy, and then you'll be sure to know if anybody meddles with it."

Now there was a veteran aboard who because his years began to disqualify him for more active work had been recently assigned duty as mainmastman in his watch, looking to the gear belayed at the rail roundabout that great spar near the deck. At off-times the foretopman had picked up some acquaintance with him, and now in his trouble it occurred to him that he might be the sort of person to go to for wise counsel. He was an old Dansker long anglicized in the service, of few words, many wrinkles, and some honorable scars. His wizened face, time-tinted and weather-stained to the complexion of an antique parchment, was here and there peppered blue by the chance explosion of a gun cartridge in action. 108

He was an *Agamemnon* man, some two years prior to the time of this story having served under Nelson when still captain in that ship immortal in naval memory, which dismantled and in part broken up to her bare ribs is seen a grand skeleton in Haden's etching. As one of a boarding party from the *Agamemnon* he had received a cut slantwise along one temple and cheek leaving a long pale scar like a streak of dawn's light falling athwart the dark visage. It was on account of that scar and the affair in which it was known that he had received it, as well as from his blue-peppered complexion, that the Dansker went among the *Bellipotent*'s crew by the name of "Board-Her-in-the-Smoke." 109

Now the first time that his small weasel eyes happened to 110 light on Billy Budd, a certain grim internal merriment set all his ancient wrinkles into antic play. Was it that his eccentric unsentimental old sapience, primitive in its kind, saw or thought it saw something which in contrast with the warship's environment looked oddly incongruous in the Handsome Sailor? But after slyly studying him at intervals, the old Merlin's equivocal merriment was modified; for now when the twain would meet, it would start in his face a quizzing sort of look, but it would be but momentary and sometimes replaced by an expression of speculative query as to what might eventually befall a nature like that, dropped into a world not without some mantraps and against whose subtleties simple courage lacking experience and address, and without any touch of defensive ugliness, is of little avail; and where such innocence as man is capable of does yet in a moral emergency not always sharpen the faculties or enlighten the will.

However it was, the Dansker in his ascetic way rather took to Billy. Nor was this only because of a certain philosophic interest in such a character. There was another cause. While the old man's eccentricities, sometimes bordering on the ursine, repelled the juniors, Billy, undeterred thereby, revering him as a salt hero, would make advances, never passing the old *Agamemnon* man without a salutation marked by that respect which is seldom lost on the aged, however crabbed at times or whatever their station in life.

There was a vein of dry humor, or what not, in the mastman; and, whether in freak of patriarchal irony touching Billy's youth and athletic frame, or for some other and more recondite reason, from the first in addressing him he always substituted *Baby* for Billy, the Dansker in fact being the originator of the name by which the foretopman eventually became known aboard ship.

Well then, in his mysterious little difficulty going in quest of the wrinkled one, Billy found him off duty in a dogwatch ruminating by himself, seated on a shot box of the upper gun deck, now and then surveying with a somewhat cynical regard certain of the more swaggering promenaders there. Billy recounted his trouble, again wondering how it all happened. The salt seer attentively listened, accompanying the foretopman's recital with queer twitchings of his wrinkles and problematical little sparkles of his small ferret eyes. Making an end of his story, the foretopman asked, "And now, Dansker, do tell me what you think of it."

The old man, shoving up the front of his tarpaulin and deliberately rubbing the long slant scar at the point where it entered the thin hair, laconically said, "Baby Budd, *Jemmy Legs*" (meaning the master-at-arms) "is down on you." *114*

"*Jemmy Legs!*" ejaculated Billy, his welkin eyes expanding. "What for? Why, he calls me 'the sweet and pleasant young fellow,' they tell me."

"Does he so?" grinned the grizzled one; then said, "Ay, Baby lad, a sweet voice has Jemmy Legs."

"No, not always. But to me he has. I seldom pass him but there comes a pleasant word." *115*

"And that's because he's down upon you, Baby Budd."

Such reiteration, along with the manner of it, incomprehensible to a novice, disturbed Billy almost as much as the mystery for which he had sought explanation. Something less unpleasingly oracular he tried to extract; but the old sea Chiron, thinking perhaps that for the nonce he had sufficiently instructed his *116* young Achilles, pursed his lips, gathered all his wrinkles together, and would commit himself to nothing further.

Years, and those experiences which befall certain shrewder men subordinated lifelong to the will of superiors, all this had developed in the Dansker the pithy guarded cynicism that was his leading characteristic.

1❶

The next day an incident served to confirm Billy Budd in his incredulity as to the Dansker's strange summing up of the case submitted. The ship at noon, going large before the wind, was rolling on her course, and he below at dinner and engaged in some sportful talk with the members of his mess, chanced in a sudden lurch to spill the entire contents of his soup pan upon the new-scrubbed deck. Claggart, the master-at-arms, official rattan in hand, happened to be passing along the battery in a bay of which the mess was lodged, and the greasy liquid streamed just across his path. Stepping over it, he was proceeding on his way without comment, since the matter was nothing to take notice of under the circumstances, when he happened to observe who it was that had done the spilling. His countenance changed. Pausing, he was about to ejaculate something hasty at the sailor, but checked himself, and pointing down to the streaming soup, playfully tapped him from behind with his rattan, saying in a low musical voice peculiar to him at times, "Handsomely done, my lad! And handsome is as handsome did it, too!" And with that passed on. Not noted by Billy as not coming within his view was the involuntary smile, or rather grimace, that accompanied Claggart's equivocal words. Aridly it drew down the thin corners of his shapely mouth. But everybody taking his remark as meant for humorous, and at which therefore as coming from a superior they were bound to laugh "with counterfeited glee," acted accordingly; and Billy, tickled, it may be, by the allusion to his being the Handsome Sailor, merrily joined in; then addressing his messmates exclaimed, "There now, who says that Jemmy Legs is down on me!"

"And who said he was, Beauty?" demanded one Donald with some surprise. Whereat the foretopman looked a little foolish, recalling that it was only one person, Board-Her-in-the-Smoke,

who had suggested what to him was the smoky idea that this
master-at-arms was in any peculiar way hostile to him. Meantime that functionary, resuming his path, must have momentarily worn some expression less guarded than that of the bitter
smile, usurping the face from the heart—some distorting expression perhaps, for a drummer-boy heedlessly frolicking along
from the opposite direction and chancing to come into light
collision with his person was strangely disconcerted by his
aspect. Nor was the impression lessened when the official, im-
petuously giving him a sharp cut with the rattan, vehemently
exclaimed, "Look where you go!"

11

What was the matter with the master-at-arms? And, be the
matter what it might, how could it have direct relation to Billy
Budd, with whom prior to the affair of the spilled soup he had
never come into any special contact official or otherwise? What
indeed could the trouble have to do with one so little inclined
to give offense as the merchant-ship's "peacemaker," even him
who in Claggart's own phrase was "the sweet and pleasant
young fellow"? Yes, why should Jemmy Legs, to borrow the
Dansker's expression, be "down" on the Handsome Sailor? But,
at heart and not for nothing, as the late chance encounter may
indicate to the discerning, down on him, secretly down on him,
he assuredly was.

Now to invent something touching the more private career
of Claggart, something involving Billy Budd, of which something the latter should be wholly ignorant, some romantic incident implying that Claggart's knowledge of the young blue-
jacket began at some period anterior to catching sight of him
on board the seventy-four—all this, not so difficult to do,
might avail in a way more or less interesting to account for

whatever of enigma may appear to lurk in the case. But in fact there was nothing of the sort. And yet the cause necessarily to be assumed as the sole one assignable is in its very realism as much charged with that prime element of Radcliffian romance, the mysterious, as any that the ingenuity of the author of *The Mysteries of Udolpho* could devise. For what can more partake of the mysterious than an antipathy spontaneous and profound such as is evoked in certain exceptional mortals by the mere aspect of some other mortal, however harmless he may be, if not called forth by this very harmlessness itself?

Now there can exist no irritating juxtaposition of dissimilar personalities comparable to that which is possible aboard a great warship fully manned and at sea. There, every day among all ranks, almost every man comes into more or less of contact with almost every other man. Wholly there to avoid even the sight of an aggravating object one must needs give it Jonah's toss or jump overboard himself. Imagine how all this might eventually operate on some peculiar human creature the direct reverse of a saint!

But for the adequate comprehending of Claggart by a normal nature these hints are insufficient. To pass from a normal nature to him one must cross "the deadly space between." And this is best done by indirection.

Long ago an honest scholar, my senior, said to me in reference to one who like himself is now no more, a man so unimpeachably respectable that against him nothing was ever openly said though among the few something was whispered, "Yes, X—— is a nut not to be cracked by the tap of a lady's fan. You are aware that I am the adherent of no organized religion, much less of any philosophy built into a system. Well, for all that, I think that to try and get into X——, enter his labyrinth and get out again, without a clue derived from some source other than what is known as 'knowledge of the world'—that were hardly possible, at least for me."

"Why," said I, "X——, however singular a study to some,

is yet human, and knowledge of the world assuredly implies the knowledge of human nature, and in most of its varieties."

"Yes, but a superficial knowledge of it, serving ordinary purposes. But for anything deeper, I am not certain whether to know the world and to know human nature be not two distinct branches of knowledge, which while they may coexist in the same heart, yet either may exist with little or nothing of the other. Nay, in an average man of the world, his constant rubbing with it blunts that finer spiritual insight indispensable to *129* the understanding of the essential in certain exceptional characters, whether evil ones or good. In a matter of some importance I have seen a girl wind an old lawyer about her little finger. Nor was it the dotage of senile love. Nothing of the sort. But he knew law better than he knew the girl's heart. Coke and Blackstone hardly shed so much light into obscure spiritual places as the Hebrew prophets. And who were they? Mostly recluses."

At the time, my inexperience was such that I did not quite see the drift of all this. It may be that I see it now. And, indeed, if that lexicon which is based on Holy Writ were any longer *130* popular, one might with less difficulty define and denominate certain phenomenal men. As it is, one must turn to some authority not liable to the charge of being tinctured with the biblical element.

In a list of definitions included in the authentic translation of Plato, a list attributed to him, occurs this: "Natural Depravity: a depravity according to nature," a definition which, though savoring of Calvinism, by no means involves Calvin's dogma *131* as to total mankind. Evidently its intent makes it applicable but to individuals. Not many are the examples of this depravity which the gallows and jail supply. At any rate, for notable instances, since these have no vulgar alloy of the brute in them, but invariably are dominated by intellectuality, one must go elsewhere. Civilization, especially if of the austerer sort, is auspicious to it. It folds itself in the mantle of respectability.

It has its certain negative virtues serving as silent auxiliaries.
132 It never allows wine to get within its guard. It is not going too
far to say that it is without vices or small sins. There is a phenomenal pride in it that excludes them. It is never mercenary
or avaricious. In short, the depravity here meant partakes nothing of the sordid or sensual. It is serious, but free from acerbity.
Though no flatterer of mankind it never speaks ill of it.

But the thing which in eminent instances signalizes so exceptional a nature is this: Though the man's even temper and discreet bearing would seem to intimate a mind peculiarly subject
133 to the law of reason, not the less in heart he would seem to riot
in complete exemption from that law, having apparently little
to do with reason further than to employ it as an ambidexter
implement for effecting the irrational. That is to say: Toward
the accomplishment of an aim which in wantonness of atrocity
would seem to partake of the insane, he will direct a cool judg-
134 ment sagacious and sound. These men are madmen, and of the
most dangerous sort, for their lunacy is not continuous, but occasional, evoked by some special object; it is protectively secretive, which is as much as to say it is self-contained, so that when,
moreover, most active it is to the average mind not distinguishable from sanity, and for the reason above suggested: that
whatever its aims may be—and the aim is never declared—the
method and the outward proceeding are always perfectly rational.

Now something such an one was Claggart, in whom was the
mania of an evil nature, not engendered by vicious training or
corrupting books or licentious living, but born with him and
innate, in short "a depravity according to nature."

135 Dark sayings are these, some will say. But why? Is it because
they somewhat savor of Holy Writ in its phrase "mystery of
iniquity"? If they do, such savor was far enough from being
intended, for little will it commend these pages to many a
reader of today.

The point of the present story turning on the hidden nature

of the master-at-arms has necessitated this chapter. With an added hint or two in connection with the incident at the mess, the resumed narrative must be left to vindicate, as it may, its own credibility.

12

That Claggart's figure was not amiss, and his face, save the chin, well molded, has already been said. Of these favorable points he seemed not insensible, for he was not only neat but careful in his dress. But the form of Billy Budd was heroic; and if his face was without the intellectual look of the pallid Claggart's, not the less was it lit, like his, from within, though from a different source. The bonfire in his heart made luminous the rose-tan in his cheek. *136*

In view of the marked contrast between the persons of the twain, it is more than probable that when the master-at-arms in the scene last given applied to the sailor the proverb "Handsome is as handsome does," he there let escape an ironic inkling, not caught by the young sailors who heard it, as to what it was that had first moved him against Billy, namely, his significant personal beauty. *137*

Now envy and antipathy, passions irreconcilable in reason, nevertheless in fact may spring conjoined like Chang and Eng in one birth. Is Envy then such a monster? Well, though many an arraigned mortal has in hopes of mitigated penalty pleaded guilty to horrible actions, did ever anybody seriously confess to envy? Something there is in it universally felt to be more shameful than even felonious crime. And not only does everybody disown it, but the better sort are inclined to incredulity when it is in earnest imputed to an intelligent man. But since its lodgment is in the heart not the brain, no degree of intellect supplies a guarantee against it. But Claggart's was no vulgar form of the passion. Nor, as directed toward Billy Budd, did it *138* *139* *140* partake of that streak of apprehensive jealousy that marred Saul's visage perturbedly brooding on the comely young David. Claggart's envy struck deeper. If askance he eyed the good looks, cheery health, and frank enjoyment of young life in Billy Budd, it was because these went along with a nature that, as Claggart magnetically felt, had in its simplicity never willed malice or experienced the reactionary bite of that serpent. To him, the spirit lodged within Billy, and looking out from his welkin eyes as from windows, that ineffability it was which

141 made the dimple in his dyed cheek, suppled his joints, and dancing in his yellow curls made him pre-eminently the Handsome Sailor. One person excepted, the master-at-arms was perhaps the only man in the ship intellectually capable of adequately appreciating the moral phenomenon presented in Billy Budd. And the insight but intensified his passion, which assuming various secret forms within him, at times assumed that of cynic disdain, disdain of innocence—to be nothing more than innocent! Yet in an aesthetic way he saw the charm of it, the courageous free-and-easy temper of it, and fain would have shared it, but he despaired of it.

142 With no power to annul the elemental evil in him, though readily enough he could hide it; apprehending the good, but powerless to be it; a nature like Claggart's, surcharged with energy as such natures almost invariably are, what recourse is left to it but to recoil upon itself and, like the scorpion for which the Creator alone is responsible, act out to the end the part allotted it.

13

143 Passion, and passion in its profoundest, is not a thing demanding a palatial stage whereon to play its part. Down among the groundlings, among the beggars and rakers of the garbage, profound passion is enacted. And the circumstances that provoke

it, however trivial or mean, are no measure of its power. In the
present instance the stage is a scrubbed gun deck, and one of
the external provocations a man-of-war's man's spilled soup.

Now when the master-at-arms noticed whence came that
greasy fluid streaming before his feet, he must have taken it—
to some extent wilfully, perhaps—not for the mere accident it
assuredly was, but for the sly escape of a spontaneous feeling
on Billy's part more or less answering to the antipathy on his
own. In effect a foolish demonstration, he must have thought,
and very harmless, like the futile kick of a heifer, which yet
were the heifer a shod stallion would not be so harmless. Even
so was it that into the gall of Claggart's envy he infused the
vitriol of his contempt. But the incident confirmed to him certain telltale reports purveyed to his ear by "Squeak," one of
his more cunning corporals, a grizzled little man, so nicknamed
by the sailors on account of his squeaky voice and sharp visage
ferreting about the dark corners of the lower decks after interlopers, satirically suggesting to them the idea of a rat in a cellar.

From his chief's employing him as an implicit tool in laying
little traps for the worriment of the foretopman—for it was
from the master-at-arms that the petty persecutions heretofore
adverted to had proceeded—the corporal, having naturally
enough concluded that his master could have no love for the
sailor, made it his business, faithful understrapper that he was,
to foment the ill blood by perverting to his chief certain innocent frolics of the good-natured foretopman, besides inventing
for his mouth sundry contumelious epithets he claimed to have
overheard him let fall. The master-at-arms never suspected
the veracity of these reports, more especially as to the epithets,
for he well knew how secretly unpopular may become a master-
at-arms, at least a master-at-arms of those days, zealous in his
function, and how the bluejackets shoot at him in private their
raillery and wit; the nickname by which he goes among them
(Jemmy Legs) implying under the form of merriment their
cherished disrespect and dislike. But in view of the greediness

144

145

146

147

148

of hate for pabulum it hardly needed a purveyor to feed Claggart's passion.

An uncommon prudence is habitual with the subtler depravity, for it has everything to hide. And in case of an injury but suspected, its secretiveness voluntarily cuts it off from enlightenment or disillusion; and, not unreluctantly, action is taken upon surmise as upon certainty. And the retaliation is apt to be in monstrous disproportion to the supposed offense; for when in anybody was revenge in its exactions aught else but an inordinate usurer? But how with Claggart's conscience? For though consciences are unlike as foreheads, every intelligence, not excluding the scriptural devils who "believe and tremble," has one. But Claggart's conscience being but the lawyer to his will, made ogres of trifles, probably arguing that the motive imputed to Billy in spilling the soup just when he did, together with the epithets alleged, these, if nothing more, made a strong case against him; nay, justified animosity into a sort of retributive righteousness. The Pharisee is the Guy Fawkes prowling in the hid chambers underlying some natures like Claggart's. And they can really form no conception of an unreciprocated malice. Probably the master-at-arms' clandestine persecution of Billy was started to try the temper of the man; but it had not developed any quality in him that enmity could make official use of or even pervert into plausible self-justification; so that the occurrence at the mess, petty if it were, was a welcome one to that peculiar conscience assigned to be the private mentor of Claggart; and, for the rest, not improbably it put him upon new experiments.

14

Not many days after the last incident narrated, something befell Billy Budd that more graveled him than aught that had previously occurred.

It was a warm night for the latitude; and the foretopman, whose watch at the time was properly below, was dozing on the uppermost deck whither he had ascended from his hot hammock, one of hundreds suspended so closely wedged together over a lower gun deck that there was little or no swing to them. He lay as in the shadow of a hillside, stretched under the lee of the booms, a piled ridge of spare spars amidships between foremast and mainmast among which the ship's largest boat, the launch, was stowed. Alongside of three other slumberers from below, he lay near that end of the booms which approaches the foremast; his station aloft on duty as a foretopman being just over the deck-station of the forecastlemen, entitling him according to usage to make himself more or less at home in that neighborhood.

153

Presently he was stirred into semiconsciousness by somebody, who must have previously sounded the sleep of the others, touching his shoulder, and then, as the foretopman raised his head, breathing into his ear in a quick whisper, "Slip into the lee forechains, Billy; there is something in the wind. Don't speak. Quick, I will meet you there," and disappearing.

154

Now Billy, like sundry other essentially good-natured ones, had some of the weaknesses inseparable from essential good nature; and among these was a reluctance, almost an incapacity of plumply saying *no* to an abrupt proposition not obviously absurd on the face of it, nor obviously unfriendly, nor iniquitous. And being of warm blood, he had not the phlegm tacitly to negative any proposition by unresponsive inaction. Like his sense of fear, his apprehension as to aught outside of the honest and natural was seldom very quick. Besides, upon the present occasion, the drowse from his sleep still hung upon him.

155

However it was, he mechanically rose and, sleepily wondering what could be in the wind, betook himself to the designated place, a narrow platform, one of six, outside of the high bulwarks and screened by the great deadeyes and multiple columned lanyards of the shrouds and backstays; and, in a great warship of that time, of dimensions commensurate to the hull's magnitude; a tarry balcony in short, overhanging the sea, and so secluded that one mariner of the *Bellipotent*, a Nonconformist old tar of a serious turn, made it even in daytime his private oratory.

In this retired nook the stranger soon joined Billy Budd. There was no moon as yet; a haze obscured the starlight. He could not distinctly see the stranger's face. Yet from something in the outline and carriage, Billy took him, and correctly, for one of the afterguard.

"Hist! Billy," said the man, in the same quick cautionary whisper as before. "You were impressed, weren't you? Well, so was I"; and he paused, as to mark the effect. But Billy, not knowing exactly what to make of this, said nothing. Then the other: "We are not the only impressed ones, Billy. There's a gang of us.—Couldn't you—help—at a pinch?"

"What do you mean?" demanded Billy, here thoroughly shaking off his drowse.

"Hist, hist!" the hurried whisper now growing husky. "See here," and the man held up two small objects faintly twinkling in the night-light; "see, they are yours, Billy, if you'll only——"

But Billy broke in, and in his resentful eagerness to deliver himself his vocal infirmity somewhat intruded. "D—d—damme, I don't know what you are d—d—driving at, or what you mean, but you had better g—g—go where you belong!" For the moment the fellow, as confounded, did not stir; and Billy, springing to his feet, said, "If you d—don't start, I'll t—t—toss you back over the r—rail!" There was no mistaking this, and the mysterious emissary decamped, disappearing in the direction of the mainmast in the shadow of the booms.

"Hallo, what's the matter?" here came growling from a forecastleman awakened from his deck-doze by Billy's raised voice. And as the foretopman reappeared and was recognized by him:

"Ah, Beauty, is it you? Well, something must have been the   *159*
matter, for you st—st—stuttered."

"Oh," rejoined Billy, now mastering the impediment, "I
found an afterguardsman in our part of the ship here, and I bid
him be off where he belongs."

"And is that all you did about it, Foretopman?" gruffly demanded another, an irascible old fellow of brick-colored visage
and hair who was known to his associate forecastlemen as "Red
Pepper." "Such sneaks I should like to marry to the gunner's
daughter!"—by that expression meaning that he would like to
subject them to disciplinary castigation over a gun.

However, Billy's rendering of the matter satisfactorily ac-   *160*
counted to these inquirers for the brief commotion, since of all
the sections of a ship's company the forecastlemen, veterans
for the most part and bigoted in their sea prejudices, are the
most jealous in resenting territorial encroachments, especially
on the part of any of the afterguard, of whom they have but a
sorry opinion—chiefly landsmen, never going aloft except to
reef or furl the mainsail, and in no wise competent to handle a
marlinspike or turn in a deadeye, say.

15

This incident sorely puzzled Billy Budd. It was an entirely new   *161*
experience, the first time in his life that he had ever been personally approached in underhand intriguing fashion. Prior to
this encounter he had known nothing of the afterguardsman,
the two men being stationed wide apart, one forward and aloft
during his watch, the other on deck and aft.

What could it mean? And could they really be guineas, those
two glittering objects the interloper had held up to his (Billy's)
eyes? Where could the fellow get guineas? Why, even spare but-   *162*
tons are not so plentiful at sea. The more he turned the matter

over, the more he was nonplussed, and made uneasy and discomfited. In his disgustful recoil from an overture which, though he but ill comprehended, he instinctively knew must involve evil of some sort, Billy Budd was like a young horse fresh from the pasture suddenly inhaling a vile whiff from some chemical factory, and by repeated snortings trying to get it out of his nostrils and lungs. This frame of mind barred all desire of holding further parley with the fellow, even were it but for the purpose of gaining some enlightenment as to his design in approaching him. And yet he was not without natural curiosity to see how such a visitor in the dark would look in broad day.

163

He espied him the following afternoon in his first dogwatch below, one of the smokers on that forward part of the upper gun deck allotted to the pipe. He recognized him by his general cut and build more than by his round freckled face and glassy eyes of pale blue, veiled with lashes all but white. And yet Billy was a bit uncertain whether indeed it were he—yonder chap about his own age chatting and laughing in freehearted way, leaning against a gun; a genial young fellow enough to look at, and something of a rattlebrain, to all appearance. Rather chubby too for a sailor, even an afterguardsman. In short, the last man in the world, one would think, to be overburdened with thoughts, especially those perilous thoughts that must needs belong to a conspirator in any serious project, or even to the underling of such a conspirator.

164

165

Although Billy was not aware of it, the fellow, with a sidelong watchful glance, had perceived Billy first, and then noting that Billy was looking at him, thereupon nodded a familiar sort of friendly recognition as to an old acquaintance, without interrupting the talk he was engaged in with the group of smokers. A day or two afterwards, chancing in the evening promenade on a gun deck to pass Billy, he offered a flying word of good-fellowship, as it were, which by its unexpectedness, and equivocalness under the circumstances, so embarrassed Billy that he knew not how to respond to it, and let it go unnoticed.

166

Billy was now left more at a loss than before. The ineffectual speculations into which he was led were so disturbingly alien to him that he did his best to smother them. It never entered his mind that here was a matter which, from its extreme questionableness, it was his duty as a loyal bluejacket to report in the proper quarter. And, probably, had such a step been suggested to him, he would have been deterred from taking it by the thought, one of novice magnanimity, that it would savor overmuch of the dirty work of a telltale. He kept the thing to himself. Yet upon one occasion he could not forbear a little disburdening himself to the old Dansker, tempted thereto perhaps by the influence of a balmy night when the ship lay becalmed; the twain, silent for the most part, sitting together on deck, their heads propped against the bulwarks. But it was only a partial and anonymous account that Billy gave, the unfounded scruples above referred to preventing full disclosure to anybody. Upon hearing Billy's version, the sage Dansker seemed to divine more than he was told; and after a little meditation, during which his wrinkles were pursed as into a point, quite effacing for the time that quizzing expression his face sometimes wore: "Didn't I say so, Baby Budd?"

"Say what?" demanded Billy.

"Why, *Jemmy Legs* is *down* on you."

"And what," rejoined Billy in amazement, "has *Jemmy Legs* to do with that cracked afterguardsman?"

"Ho, it was an afterguardsman, then. A cat's-paw, a cat's-paw!" And with that exclamation, whether it had reference to a light puff of air just then coming over the calm sea, or a subtler relation to the afterguardsman, there is no telling, the old Merlin gave a twisting wrench with his black teeth at his plug of tobacco, vouchsafing no reply to Billy's impetuous question, though now repeated, for it was his wont to relapse into grim silence when interrogated in skeptical sort as to any of his sententious oracles, not always very clear ones, rather partak-

167

168

169

ing of that obscurity which invests most Delphic deliverances from any quarter.

Long experience had very likely brought this old man to that bitter prudence which never interferes in aught and never gives advice.

16

170 Yes, despite the Dansker's pithy insistence as to the master-at-arms being at the bottom of these strange experiences of Billy on board the *Bellipotent*, the young sailor was ready to ascribe them to almost anybody but the man who, to use Billy's own expression, "always had a pleasant word for him." This is to be wondered at. Yet not so much to be wondered at. In certain matters, some sailors even in mature life remain unsophisticated enough. But a young seafarer of the disposition of our athletic foretopman is much of a child-man. And yet a child's utter innocence is but its blank ignorance, and the innocence more or
171 less wanes as intelligence waxes. But in Billy Budd intelligence, such as it was, had advanced while yet his simple-mindedness remained for the most part unaffected. Experience is a teacher indeed; yet did Billy's years make his experience small. Besides, he had none of that intuitive knowledge of the bad which in natures not good or incompletely so foreruns experience, and therefore may pertain, as in some instances it too clearly does pertain, even to youth.

172 And what could Billy know of man except of man as a mere sailor? And the old-fashioned sailor, the veritable man before the mast, the sailor from boyhood up, he, though indeed of the same species as a landsman, is in some respects singularly distinct from him. The sailor is frankness, the landsman is finesse. Life is not a game with the sailor, demanding the long head— no intricate game of chess where few moves are made in straight-

forwardness and ends are attained by indirection, an oblique, tedious, barren game hardly worth that poor candle burnt out in playing it.

Yes, as a class, sailors are in character a juvenile race. Even *173* their deviations are marked by juvenility, this more especially holding true with the sailors of Billy's time. Then too, certain things which apply to all sailors do more pointedly operate here and there upon the junior one. Every sailor, too, is accustomed *174* to obey orders without debating them; his life afloat is externally ruled for him; he is not brought into that promiscuous commerce with mankind where unobstructed free agency on equal terms—equal superficially, at least—soon teaches one that unless upon occasion he exercise a distrust keen in proportion to the fairness of the appearance, some foul turn may be served him. A ruled undemonstrative distrustfulness is so habitual, not with businessmen so much as with men who know their kind in less shallow relations than business, namely, certain men of the world, that they come at last to employ it all *175* but unconsciously; and some of them would very likely feel real surprise at being charged with it as one of their general characteristics.

17

But after the little matter at the mess Billy Budd no more *176* found himself in strange trouble at times about his hammock or his clothes bag or what not. As to that smile that occasionally sunned him, and the pleasant passing word, these were, if not more frequent, yet if anything more pronounced than before.

But for all that, there were certain other demonstrations now. When Claggart's unobserved glance happened to light on belted *177* Billy rolling along the upper gun deck in the leisure of the second dogwatch, exchanging passing broadsides of fun with other young promenaders in the crowd, that glance would follow the

178   cheerful sea Hyperion with a settled meditative and melancholy expression, his eyes strangely suffused with incipient feverish tears. Then would Claggart look like the man of sorrows. Yes, and sometimes the melancholy expression would have in it a touch of soft yearning, as if Claggart could even have loved Billy but for fate and ban. But this was an evanescence, and quickly repented of, as it were, by an immitigable look, pinching and shriveling the visage into the momentary semblance

179   of a wrinkled walnut. But sometimes catching sight in advance of the foretopman coming in his direction, he would, upon their nearing, step aside a little to let him pass, dwelling upon Billy for the moment with the glittering dental satire of a Guise. But upon any abrupt unforeseen encounter a red light would flash forth from his eye like a spark from an anvil in a dusk smithy.

180   That quick, fierce light was a strange one, darted from orbs which in repose were of a color nearest approaching a deeper violet, the softest of shades.

Though some of these caprices of the pit could not but be observed by their object, yet were they beyond the construing of

181   such a nature. And the thews of Billy were hardly compatible with that sort of sensitive spiritual organization which in some cases instinctively conveys to ignorant innocence an admonition of the proximity of the malign. He thought the master-at-arms acted in a manner rather queer at times. That was all. But the occasional frank air and pleasant word went for what they purported to be, the young sailor never having heard as yet of the "too fair-spoken man."

182   Had the foretopman been conscious of having done or said anything to provoke the ill will of the official, it would have been different with him, and his sight might have been purged if not sharpened. As it was, innocence was his blinder.

So was it with him in yet another matter. Two minor officers, the armorer and captain of the hold, with whom he had never exchanged a word, his position in the ship not bringing him into contact with them, these men now for the first began to cast upon Billy, when they chanced to encounter him, that peculiar glance which evidences that the man from whom it comes has been some way tampered with, and to the prejudice of him upon whom the glance lights. Never did it occur to Billy as a thing to be noted or a thing suspicious, though he well knew the fact, that the armorer and captain of the hold, with the ship's yeoman, apothecary, and others of that grade, were by naval usage messmates of the master-at-arms, men with ears convenient to his confidential tongue.   *183*

But the general popularity that came from our Handsome Sailor's manly forwardness upon occasion and irresistible good nature, indicating no mental superiority tending to excite an invidious feeling, this good will on the part of most of his shipmates made him the less to concern himself about such mute aspects toward him as those whereto allusion has just been made, aspects he could not so fathom as to infer their whole import.   *184*

As to the afterguardsman, though Billy for reasons already given necessarily saw little of him, yet when the two did happen to meet, invariably came the fellow's offhand cheerful recognition, sometimes accompanied by a passing pleasant word or two. Whatever that equivocal young person's original design may really have been, or the design of which he might have been the deputy, certain it was from his manner upon these occasions that he had wholly dropped it.   *185*

It was as if his precocity of crookedness (and every vulgar villain is precocious) had for once deceived him, and the man he had sought to entrap as a simpleton had through his very simplicity ignominiously baffled him.   *186*

But shrewd ones may opine that it was hardly possible for Billy to refrain from going up to the afterguardsman and bluntly demanding to know his purpose in the initial interview so abruptly closed in the forechains. Shrewd ones may also think it but natural in Billy to set about sounding some of the other impressed men of the ship in order to discover what basis, if   *187* any, there was for the emissary's obscure suggestions as to plotting disaffection aboard. Yes, shrewd ones may so think. But something more, or rather something else than mere shrewdness is perhaps needful for the due understanding of such a character as Billy Budd's.

188   As to Claggart, the monomania in the man—if that indeed it were—as involuntarily disclosed by starts in the manifestations detailed, yet in general covered over by his self-contained and rational demeanor; this, like a subterranean fire, was eating its way deeper and deeper in him. Something decisive must come of it.

18

189   After the mysterious interview in the forechains, the one so abruptly ended there by Billy, nothing especially germane to the story occurred until the events now about to be narrated.

Elsewhere it has been said that in the lack of frigates (of course better sailers than line-of-battle ships) in the English *190*   squadron up the Straits at that period, the *Bellipotent 74* was occasionally employed not only as an available substitute for a scout, but at times on detached service of more important kind. This was not alone because of her sailing qualities, not common in a ship of her rate, but quite as much, probably, that the character of her commander, it was thought, specially adapted him for any duty where under unforeseen difficulties a prompt initiative might have to be taken in some matter demanding knowledge and ability in addition to those qualities implied in *191*   good seamanship. It was on an expedition of the latter sort, a somewhat distant one, and when the *Bellipotent* was almost at her furthest remove from the fleet, that in the latter part of an afternoon watch she unexpectedly came in sight of a ship of the enemy. It proved to be a frigate. The latter, perceiving through the glass that the weight of men and metal would be heavily against her, invoking her light heels crowded sail to get away. After a chase urged almost against hope and lasting until about the middle of the first dogwatch, she signally succeeded in *192* effecting her escape.

Not long after the pursuit had been given up, and ere the excitement incident thereto had altogether waned away, the master-at-arms, ascending from his cavernous sphere, made his appearance cap in hand by the mainmast respectfully waiting the notice of Captain Vere, then solitary walking the weather side of the quarter-deck, doubtless somewhat chafed at the failure of the pursuit. The spot where Claggart stood was the place allotted to men of lesser grades seeking some more particular interview either with the officer of the deck or the *193* captain himself. But from the latter it was not often that a sailor or petty officer of those days would seek a hearing; only some exceptional cause would, according to established custom, have warranted that.

Presently, just as the commander, absorbed in his reflections, was on the point of turning aft in his promenade, he became sensible of Claggart's presence, and saw the doffed cap held in deferential expectancy. Here be it said that Captain Vere's *194* personal knowledge of this petty officer had only begun at the time of the ship's last sailing from home, Claggart then for the first, in transfer from a ship detained for repairs, supplying on board the *Bellipotent* the place of a previous master-at-arms disabled and ashore.

No sooner did the commander observe who it was that now deferentially stood awaiting his notice than a peculiar expression came over him. It was not unlike that which uncontrollably will flit across the countenance of one at unawares encountering *195* a person who, though known to him indeed, has hardly been long enough known for thorough knowledge, but something in whose aspect nevertheless now for the first provokes a vaguely repellent distaste. But coming to a stand and resuming much of his wonted official manner, save that a sort of impatience lurked in the intonation of the opening word, he said "Well? What is it, Master-at-arms?"

With the air of a subordinate grieved at the necessity of being a messenger of ill tidings, and while conscientiously determined to be frank yet equally resolved upon shunning overstatement, Claggart at this invitation, or rather summons to disburden, spoke up. What he said, conveyed in the language of no uneducated man, was to the effect following, if not altogether in these words, namely, that during the chase and preparations for the possible encounter he had seen enough to convince him that at least one sailor aboard was a dangerous character in a ship mustering some who not only had taken a guilty part in the late serious troubles, but others also who, like the man in question, had entered His Majesty's service under another form than enlistment.

At this point Captain Vere with some impatience interrupted him: "Be direct, man; say *impressed men*."

Claggart made a gesture of subservience, and proceeded. Quite lately he (Claggart) had begun to suspect that on the gun decks some sort of movement prompted by the sailor in question was covertly going on, but he had not thought himself warranted in reporting the suspicion so long as it remained indistinct. But from what he had that afternoon observed in the man referred to, the suspicion of something clandestine going on had advanced to a point less removed from certainty. He deeply felt, he added, the serious responsibility assumed in making a report involving such possible consequences to the individual mainly concerned, besides tending to augment those natural anxieties which every naval commander must feel in view of extraordinary outbreaks so recent as those which, he sorrowfully said it, it needed not to name.

Now at the first broaching of the matter Captain Vere, taken by surprise, could not wholly dissemble his disquietude. But as Claggart went on, the former's aspect changed into restiveness under something in the testifier's manner in giving his testi-

mony. However, he refrained from interrupting him. And
Claggart, continuing, concluded with this: "God forbid, your   *200*
honor, that the *Bellipotent*'s should be the experience of the
_____"

"Never mind that!" here peremptorily broke in the superior,
his face altering with anger, instinctively divining the ship that
the other was about to name, one in which the Nore Mutiny
had assumed a singularly tragical character that for a time jeopardized the life of its commander. Under the circumstances he
was indignant at the purposed allusion. When the commissioned
officers themselves were on all occasions very heedful how they   *201*
referred to the recent events in the fleet, for a petty officer unnecessarily to allude to them in the presence of his captain, this
struck him as a most immodest presumption. Besides, to his
quick sense of self-respect it even looked under the circumstances something like an attempt to alarm him. Nor at first
was he without some surprise that one who so far as he had
hitherto come under his notice had shown considerable tact in
his function should in this particular evince such lack of it.

But these thoughts and kindred dubious ones flitting across   *202*
his mind were suddenly replaced by an intuitional surmise
which, though as yet obscure in form, served practically to
affect his reception of the ill tidings. Certain it is that, long
versed in everything pertaining to the complicated gun-deck   *203*
life, which like every other form of life has its secret mines and
dubious side, the side popularly disclaimed, Captain Vere did
not permit himself to be unduly disturbed by the general tenor
of his subordinate's report.

Furthermore, if in view of recent events prompt action should
be taken at the first palpable sign of recurring insubordination,
for all that, not judicious would it be, he thought, to keep the
idea of lingering disaffection alive by undue forwardness in
crediting an informer, even if his own subordinate and charged   *204*
among other things with police surveillance of the crew. This   *205*
feeling would not perhaps have so prevailed with him were it

[[*93*]]

not that upon a prior occasion the patriotic zeal officially evinced by Claggart had somewhat irritated him as appearing rather supersensible and strained. Furthermore, something even in the official's self-possessed and somewhat ostentatious manner in making his specifications strangely reminded him of a bandsman, a perjurous witness in a capital case before a court-martial ashore of which when a lieutenant he (Captain Vere) had been a member.

206   Now the peremptory check given to Claggart in the matter of the arrested allusion was quickly followed up by this: "You say that there is at least one dangerous man aboard. Name him."

"William Budd, a foretopman, your honor."

"William Budd!" repeated Captain Vere with unfeigned astonishment. "And mean you the man that Lieutenant Ratcliffe took from the merchantman not very long ago, the young fellow who seems to be so popular with the men—Billy, the Handsome Sailor, as they call him?"

207   "The same, your honor; but for all his youth and good looks, a deep one. Not for nothing does he insinuate himself into the good will of his shipmates, since at the least they will at a pinch say—all hands will—a good word for him, and at all hazards. Did Lieutenant Ratcliffe happen to tell your honor of that adroit fling of Budd's, jumping up in the cutter's bow under the merchantman's stern when he was being taken off? It is even masked by that sort of good-humored air that at heart he resents his impressment. You have but noted his fair cheek. A mantrap may be under the ruddy-tipped daisies."

208   Now the Handsome Sailor as a signal figure among the crew had naturally enough attracted the captain's attention from the first. Though in general not very demonstrative to his officers, he had congratulated Lieutenant Ratcliffe upon his good fortune in lighting on such a fine specimen of the *genus homo*, who in the nude might have posed for a statue of young Adam before the Fall. As to Billy's adieu to the ship *Rights-of-Man*,

which the boarding lieutenant had indeed reported to him, but, in a deferential way, more as a good story than aught else, Captain Vere, though mistakenly understanding it as a satiric sally, had but thought so much the better of the impressed man for it; as a military sailor, admiring the spirit that could take an arbitrary enlistment so merrily and sensibly. The foretopman's 209 conduct, too, so far as it had fallen under the captain's notice, had confirmed the first happy augury, while the new recruit's qualities as a "sailor-man" seemed to be such that he had thought of recommending him to the executive officer for promotion to a place that would more frequently bring him under his own observation, namely, the captaincy of the mizzentop, replacing there in the starboard watch a man not so young whom partly for that reason he deemed less fitted for the post. 210 Be it parenthesized here that since the mizzentopmen have not to handle such breadths of heavy canvas as the lower sails on the mainmast and foremast, a young man if of the right stuff not only seems best adapted to duty there, but in fact is generally selected for the captaincy of that top, and the company under him are light hands and often but striplings. In sum, Captain Vere had from the beginning deemed Billy Budd to be what in the naval parlance of the time was called a "King's bargain": that is to say, for His Britannic Majesty's navy a capital invest- 211 ment at small outlay or none at all.

After a brief pause, during which the reminiscences above mentioned passed vividly through his mind and he weighed the import of Claggart's last suggestion conveyed in the phrase "mantrap under the daisies," and the more he weighed it the less reliance he felt in the informer's good faith, suddenly he turned upon him and in a low voice demanded: "Do you come to me, Master-at-arms, with so foggy a tale? As to Budd, cite me an act or spoken word of his confirmatory of what you in general charge against him. Stay," drawing nearer to him; "heed what you speak. Just now, and in a case like this, there is a 212 yardarm-end for the false witness."

"Ah, your honor!" sighed Claggart, mildly shaking his shapely head as in sad deprecation of such unmerited severity of tone. Then, bridling—erecting himself as in virtuous self-assertion— he circumstantially alleged certain words and acts which collectively, if credited, led to presumptions mortally inculpating Budd. And for some of these averments, he added, substantiating proof was not far.

213   With gray eyes impatient and distrustful essaying to fathom to the bottom Claggart's calm violet ones, Captain Vere again heard him out; then for the moment stood ruminating. The mood he evinced, Claggart—himself for the time liberated from the other's scrutiny—steadily regarded with a look difficult to render: a look curious of the operation of his tactics, a look such as might have been that of the spokesman of the envious children of Jacob deceptively imposing upon the troubled patriarch the blood-dyed coat of young Joseph.

214   Though something exceptional in the moral quality of Captain Vere made him, in earnest encounter with a fellow man, a veritable touchstone of that man's essential nature, yet now as to Claggart and what was really going on in him his feeling partook less of intuitional conviction than of strong suspicion clogged by strange dubieties. The perplexity he evinced proceeded less from aught touching the man informed against—as Claggart doubtless opined—than from considerations how best to act in regard to the informer. At first, indeed, he was natu-
215   rally for summoning that substantiation of his allegations which Claggart said was at hand. But such a proceeding would result in the matter at once getting abroad, which in the present stage of it, he thought, might undesirably affect the ship's company. If Claggart was a false witness—that closed the affair. And therefore, before trying the accusation, he would first practically test the accuser; and he thought this could be done in a quiet, undemonstrative way.

       The measure he determined upon involved a shifting of the
216   scene, a transfer to a place less exposed to observation than the

broad quarter-deck. For although the few gun-room officers there at the time had, in due observance of naval etiquette, withdrawn to leeward the moment Captain Vere had begun his promenade on the deck's weather side; and though during the colloquy with Claggart they of course ventured not to diminish the distance; and though throughout the interview Captain Vere's voice was far from high, and Claggart's silvery and low; and the wind in the cordage and the wash of the sea helped the more to put them beyond earshot; nevertheless, the interview's *217* continuance already had attracted observation from some topmen aloft and other sailors in the waist or further forward.

Having determined upon his measures, Captain Vere forthwith took action. Abruptly turning to Claggart, he asked, "Master-at-arms, is it now Budd's watch aloft?"

"No, your honor."

Whereupon, "Mr. Wilkes!" summoning the nearest midshipman. "Tell Albert to come to me." Albert was the captain's hammock-boy, a sort of sea valet in whose discretion and fidelity his master had much confidence. The lad appeared. *218*

"You know Budd, the foretopman?"

"I do, sir."

"Go find him. It is his watch off. Manage to tell him out of earshot that he is wanted aft. Contrive it that he speaks to no- *219* body. Keep him in talk yourself. And not till you get well aft here, not till then let him know that the place where he is wanted is my cabin. You understand. Go.—Master-at-arms, show yourself on the decks below, and when you think it time for Albert to be coming with his man, stand by quietly to follow the sailor in."

19

Now when the foretopman found himself in the cabin, closeted there, as it were, with the captain and Claggart, he was surprised enough. But it was a surprise unaccompanied by appre- *220* hension or distrust. To an immature nature essentially honest and humane, forewarning intimations of subtler danger from one's kind come tardily if at all. The only thing that took shape in the young sailor's mind was this: Yes, the captain, I have always thought, looks kindly upon me. Wonder if he's going to make me his coxswain. I should like that. And may be now he is going to ask the master-at-arms about me.

221   "Shut the door there, sentry," said the commander; "stand without, and let nobody come in.—Now, Master-at-arms, tell this man to his face what you told of him to me," and stood prepared to scrutinize the mutually confronting visages.

With the measured step and calm collected air of an asylum physician approaching in the public hall some patient beginning to show indications of a coming paroxysm, Claggart deliberately advanced within short range of Billy and, mesmerically looking him in the eye, briefly recapitulated the accusation.

222   Not at first did Billy take it in. When he did, the rose-tan of his cheek looked struck as by white leprosy. He stood like one impaled and gagged. Meanwhile the accuser's eyes, removing not as yet from the blue dilated ones, underwent a phenomenal change, their wonted rich violet color blurring into a muddy purple. Those lights of human intelligence, losing human expression, were gelidly protruding like the alien eyes of certain uncatalogued creatures of the deep. The first mesmeristic glance was one of serpent fascination; the last was as the paralyzing lurch of the torpedo fish.

223   "Speak, man!" said Captain Vere to the transfixed one, struck by his aspect even more than by Claggart's. "Speak! Defend yourself!" Which appeal caused but a strange dumb gesturing and gurgling in Billy; amazement at such an accusation so suddenly sprung on inexperienced nonage; this, and, it may be, horror of the accuser's eyes, serving to bring out his lurking defect and in this instance for the time intensifying it

224   into a convulsed tongue-tie; while the intent head and entire form straining forward in an agony of ineffectual eagerness to

obey the injunction to speak and defend himself, gave an expression to the face like that of a condemned vestal priestess in the moment of being buried alive, and in the first struggle against suffocation.

Though at the time Captain Vere was quite ignorant of Billy's liability to vocal impediment, he now immediately divined it, since vividly Billy's aspect recalled to him that of a bright young schoolmate of his whom he had once seen struck by much the same startling impotence in the act of eagerly rising in the class *225* to be foremost in response to a testing question put to it by the master. Going close up to the young sailor, and laying a soothing hand on his shoulder, he said, "There is no hurry, my boy. Take your time, take your time." Contrary to the effect intended, these words so fatherly in tone, doubtless touching Billy's heart to the quick, prompted yet more violent efforts at utterance—efforts soon ending for the time in confirming the paralysis, and bringing to his face an expression which was as a crucifixion to behold. The next instant, quick as the flame from *226* a discharged cannon at night, his right arm shot out, and Claggart dropped to the deck. Whether intentionally or but owing to the young athlete's superior height, the blow had taken effect full upon the forehead, so shapely and intellectual-looking a feature in the master-at-arms; so that the body fell over lengthwise, like a heavy plank tilted from erectness. A gasp or two, and he lay motionless.

"Fated boy," breathed Captain Vere in tone so low as to be almost a whisper, "what have you done! But here, help me."

The twain raised the felled one from the loins up into a sitting *227* position. The spare form flexibly acquiesced, but inertly. It was like handling a dead snake. They lowered it back. Regaining erectness, Captain Vere with one hand covering his face stood to all appearance as impassive as the object at his feet. Was he absorbed in taking in all the bearings of the event and what was best not only now at once to be done, but also in the sequel? Slowly he uncovered his face; and the effect was as if the moon

228   emerging from eclipse should reappear with quite another aspect than that which had gone into hiding. The father in him, manifested towards Billy thus far in the scene, was replaced by the military disciplinarian. In his official tone he bade the foretopman retire to a stateroom aft (pointing it out), and there remain till thence summoned. This order Billy in silence mechanically obeyed. Then going to the cabin door where it opened on the quarter-deck, Captain Vere said to the sentry without, "Tell somebody to send Albert here." When the lad appeared, his master so contrived it that he should not catch sight of the

229   prone one. "Albert," he said to him, "tell the surgeon I wish to see him. You need not come back till called."

When the surgeon entered—a self-poised character of that grave sense and experience that hardly anything could take him aback—Captain Vere advanced to meet him, thus unconsciously intercepting his view of Claggart, and, interrupting the other's wonted ceremonious salutation, said, "Nay. Tell me how it is with yonder man," directing his attention to the prostrate one.

230   The surgeon looked, and for all his self-command somewhat started at the abrupt revelation. On Claggart's always pallid complexion, thick black blood was now oozing from nostril and ear. To the gazer's professional eye it was unmistakably no living man that he saw.

"Is it so, then?" said Captain Vere, intently watching him. "I thought it. But verify it." Whereupon the customary tests confirmed the surgeon's first glance, who now, looking up in unfeigned concern, cast a look of intense inquisitiveness upon

231   his superior. But Captain Vere, with one hand to his brow, was standing motionless. Suddenly, catching the surgeon's arm convulsively, he exclaimed, pointing down to the body, "It is the divine judgment on Ananias! Look!"

Disturbed by the excited manner he had never before observed in the *Bellipotent*'s captain, and as yet wholly ignorant of the affair, the prudent surgeon nevertheless held his peace, only again looking an earnest interrogatory as to what it was that had resulted in such a tragedy.

But Captain Vere was now again motionless, standing absorbed in thought. Again starting, he vehemently exclaimed, "Struck dead by an angel of God! Yet the angel must hang!" *232*

At these passionate interjections, mere incoherences to the listener as yet unapprised of the antecedents, the surgeon was profoundly discomposed. But now, as recollecting himself, Captain Vere in less passionate tone briefly related the circumstances leading up to the event. "But come; we must dispatch," *233* he added. "Help me to remove him" (meaning the body) "to yonder compartment," designating one opposite that where the foretopman remained immured. Anew disturbed by a request that, as implying a desire for secrecy, seemed unaccountably strange to him, there was nothing for the subordinate to do but comply.

"Go now," said Captain Vere with something of his wonted manner. "Go now. I presently shall call a drumhead court. Tell the lieutenants what has happened, and tell Mr. Mordant" (meaning the captain of marines), "and charge them to keep *234* the matter to themselves."

20

Full of disquietude and misgiving, the surgeon left the cabin. Was Captain Vere suddenly affected in his mind, or was it but a transient excitement, brought about by so strange and extraordinary a tragedy? As to the drumhead court, it struck the surgeon as impolitic, if nothing more. The thing to do, he thought, was to place Billy Budd in confinement, and in a way dictated by usage, and postpone further action in so extraordinary a case to such time as they should rejoin the squadron, and then refer it to the admiral. He recalled the unwonted agi-

235   tation of Captain Vere and his excited exclamations, so at variance with his normal manner. Was he unhinged?

But assuming that he is, it is not so susceptible of proof. What then can the surgeon do? No more trying situation is conceivable than that of an officer subordinate under a captain whom he suspects to be not mad, indeed, but yet not quite unaffected in his intellects. To argue his order to him would be insolence. To resist him would be mutiny.

In obedience to Captain Vere, he communicated what had happened to the lieutenants and captain of marines, saying nothing as to the captain's state. They fully shared his own surprise

236   and concern. Like him too, they seemed to think that such a matter should be referred to the admiral.

21

Who in the rainbow can draw the line where the violet tint ends and the orange tint begins? Distinctly we see the difference of the colors, but where exactly does the one first blendingly enter into the other? So with sanity and insanity. In pronounced cases there is no question about them. But in some supposed cases, in various degrees supposedly less pronounced, to draw the exact line of demarcation few will undertake, though for a fee becoming considerate some professional experts will. There is nothing namable but that some men will, or undertake to, do it for pay.

237   Whether Captain Vere, as the surgeon professionally and privately surmised, was really the sudden victim of any degree of aberration, every one must determine for himself by such light as this narrative may afford.

238   That the unhappy event which has been narrated could not have happened at a worse juncture was but too true. For it was close on the heel of the suppressed insurrections, an aftertime

very critical to naval authority, demanding from every English sea commander two qualities not readily interfusable—prudence and rigor. Moreover, there was something crucial in the case.

In the jugglery of circumstances preceding and attending the event on board the *Bellipotent*, and in the light of that martial code whereby it was formally to be judged, innocence and guilt personified in Claggart and Budd in effect changed places. In a legal view the apparent victim of the tragedy was he who had sought to victimize a man blameless; and the indisputable deed of the latter, navally regarded, constituted the most heinous of military crimes. Yet more. The essential right and wrong involved in the matter, the clearer that might be, so much the worse for the responsibility of a loyal sea commander, inasmuch as he was not authorized to determine the matter on that primitive basis.

Small wonder then that the *Bellipotent*'s captain, though in general a man of rapid decision, felt that circumspectness not less than promptitude was necessary. Until he could decide upon his course, and in each detail; and not only so, but until the concluding measure was upon the point of being enacted, he deemed it advisable, in view of all the circumstances, to guard as much as possible against publicity. Here he may or may not have erred. Certain it is, however, that subsequently in the confidential talk of more than one or two gun rooms and cabins he was not a little criticized by some officers, a fact imputed by his friends and vehemently by his cousin Jack Denton to professional jealousy of Starry Vere. Some imaginative ground for invidious comment there was. The maintenance of secrecy in the matter, the confining all knowledge of it for a time to the place where the homicide occurred, the quarter-deck cabin; in these particulars lurked some resemblance to the policy adopted in those tragedies of the palace which have occurred more than once in the capital founded by Peter the Barbarian.

239

240

241

242

〚 *103* 〛

243   The case indeed was such that fain would the *Bellipotent*'s captain have deferred taking any action whatever respecting it further than to keep the foretopman a close prisoner till the ship rejoined the squadron and then submitting the matter to the judgment of his admiral.

But a true military officer is in one particular like a true monk. Not with more of self-abnegation will the latter keep his vows of monastic obedience than the former his vows of allegiance to martial duty.

244   Feeling that unless quick action was taken on it, the deed of the foretopman, so soon as it should be known on the gun decks, would tend to awaken any slumbering embers of the Nore among the crew, a sense of the urgency of the case overruled in Captain Vere every other consideration. But though a conscientious disciplinarian, he was no lover of authority for mere authority's sake. Very far was he from embracing opportunities for monopolizing to himself the perils of moral responsibility, none at least that could properly be referred to an official su-

245   perior or shared with him by his official equals or even subordinates. So thinking, he was glad it would not be at variance with usage to turn the matter over to a summary court of his own officers, reserving to himself, as the one on whom the ultimate accountability would rest, the right of maintaining a supervision of it, or formally or informally interposing at need. Accordingly a drumhead court was summarily convened, he electing the individuals composing it: the first lieutenant, the captain of marines, and the sailing master.

246   In associating an officer of marines with the sea lieutenant and the sailing master in a case having to do with a sailor, the commander perhaps deviated from general custom. He was prompted thereto by the circumstance that he took that soldier to be a judicious person, thoughtful, and not altogether incapable of grappling with a difficult case unprecedented in his prior experience. Yet even as to him he was not without some latent misgiving, for withal he was an extremely good-natured

man, an enjoyer of his dinner, a sound sleeper, and inclined   *247*
to obesity—a man who though he would always maintain
his manhood in battle might not prove altogether reliable in a
moral dilemma involving aught of the tragic. As to the first
lieutenant and the sailing master, Captain Vere could not but be
aware that though honest natures, of approved gallantry upon
occasion, their intelligence was mostly confined to the matter
of active seamanship and the fighting demands of their profession.

The court was held in the same cabin where the unfortunate
affair had taken place. This cabin, the commander's, embraced
the entire area under the poop deck. Aft, and on either side,
was a small stateroom, the one now temporarily a jail and the   *248*
other a dead-house, and a yet smaller compartment, leaving a
space between expanding forward into a goodly oblong of
length coinciding with the ship's beam. A skylight of moderate
dimension was overhead, and at each end of the oblong space
were two sashed porthole windows easily convertible back into
embrasures for short carronades.

All being quickly in readiness, Billy Budd was arraigned,
Captain Vere necessarily appearing as the sole witness in the
case, and as such temporarily sinking his rank, though singularly maintaining it in a matter apparently trivial, namely, that   *249*
he testified from the ship's weather side, with that object having caused the court to sit on the lee side. Concisely he narrated
all that had led up to the catastrophe, omitting nothing in
Claggart's accusation and deposing as to the manner in which
the prisoner had received it. At this testimony the three officers
glanced with no little surprise at Billy Budd, the last man they
would have suspected either of the mutinous design alleged by
Claggart or the undeniable deed he himself had done. The first   *250*
lieutenant, taking judicial primacy and turning toward the
prisoner, said, "Captain Vere has spoken. Is it or is it not as
Captain Vere says?"

In response came syllables not so much impeded in the utterance as might have been anticipated. They were these: "Captain Vere tells the truth. It is just as Captain Vere says, but it is not as the master-at-arms said. I have eaten the King's bread and I am true to the King."

"I believe you, my man," said the witness, his voice indicating a suppressed emotion not otherwise betrayed.

251 "God will bless you for that, your honor!" not without stammering said Billy, and all but broke down. But immediately he was recalled to self-control by another question, to which with the same emotional difficulty of utterance he said, "No, there was no malice between us. I never bore malice against the master-at-arms. I am sorry that he is dead. I did not mean to kill him. Could I have used my tongue I would not have struck him. But he foully lied to my face and in presence of my 252 captain, and I had to say something, and I could only say it with a blow, God help me!"

In the impulsive aboveboard manner of the frank one the court saw confirmed all that was implied in words that just previously had perplexed them, coming as they did from the testifier to the tragedy and promptly following Billy's impassioned disclaimer of mutinous intent—Captain Vere's words, "I believe you, my man."

Next it was asked of him whether he knew of or suspected aught savoring of incipient trouble (meaning mutiny, though the explicit term was avoided) going on in any section of the ship's company.

253 The reply lingered. This was naturally imputed by the court to the same vocal embarrassment which had retarded or obstructed previous answers. But in main it was otherwise here, the question immediately recalling to Billy's mind the interview with the afterguardsman in the forechains. But an innate repugnance to playing a part at all approaching that of an informer against one's own shipmates—the same erring sense of uninstructed honor which had stood in the way of his reporting the matter at the time, though as a loyal man-of-war's man it

was incumbent on him, and failure so to do, if charged against him and proven, would have subjected him to the heaviest of penalties; this, with the blind feeling now his that nothing really was being hatched, prevailed with him. When the answer came it was a negative.

"One question more," said the officer of marines, now first speaking and with a troubled earnestness. "You tell us that what the master-at-arms said against you was a lie. Now why should he have so lied, so maliciously lied, since you declare there was no malice between you?"

At that question, unintentionally touching on a spiritual sphere wholly obscure to Billy's thoughts, he was nonplussed, evincing a confusion indeed that some observers, such as can readily be imagined, would have construed into involuntary evidence of hidden guilt. Nevertheless, he strove some way to answer, but all at once relinquished the vain endeavor, at the same time turning an appealing glance towards Captain Vere as deeming him his best helper and friend. Captain Vere, who had been seated for a time, rose to his feet, addressing the interrogator. "The question you put to him comes naturally enough. But how can he rightly answer it?—or anybody else, unless indeed it be he who lies within there," designating the compartment where lay the corpse. "But the prone one there will not rise to our summons. In effect, though, as it seems to me, the point you make is hardly material. Quite aside from any conceivable motive actuating the master-at-arms, and irrespective of the provocation to the blow, a martial court must needs in the present case confine its attention to the blow's consequence, which consequence justly is to be deemed not otherwise than as the striker's deed."

This utterance, the full significance of which it was not at all likely that Billy took in, nevertheless caused him to turn a wistful interrogative look toward the speaker, a look in its dumb expressiveness not unlike that which a dog of generous breed might turn upon his master, seeking in his face some elucidation

254

255

256

257

of a previous gesture ambiguous to the canine intelligence. Nor was the same utterance without marked effect upon the three officers, more especially the soldier. Couched in it seemed to them a meaning unanticipated, involving a prejudgment on the speaker's part. It served to augment a mental disturbance previously evident enough.

The soldier once more spoke, in a tone of suggestive dubiety addressing at once his associates and Captain Vere: "Nobody is present—none of the ship's company, I mean—who might shed lateral light, if any is to be had, upon what remains mysterious in this matter."

"That is thoughtfully put," said Captain Vere; "I see your drift. Ay, there is a mystery; but, to use a scriptural phrase, it is a 'mystery of iniquity,' a matter for psychologic theologians to discuss. But what has a military court to do with it? Not to add that for us any possible investigation of it is cut off by the lasting tongue-tie of—him—in yonder," again designating the mortuary stateroom. "The prisoner's deed—with that alone we have to do."

To this, and particularly the closing reiteration, the marine soldier, knowing not how aptly to reply, sadly abstained from saying aught. The first lieutenant, who at the outset had not unnaturally assumed primacy in the court, now overrulingly instructed by a glance from Captain Vere, a glance more effective than words, resumed that primacy. Turning to the prisoner, "Budd," he said, and scarce in equable tones, "Budd, if you have aught further to say for yourself, say it now."

Upon this the young sailor turned another quick glance toward Captain Vere; then, as taking a hint from that aspect, a hint confirming his own instinct that silence was now best, replied to the lieutenant, "I have said all, sir."

The marine—the same who had been the sentinel without the cabin door at the time that the foretopman, followed by the master-at-arms, entered it—he, standing by the sailor throughout these judicial proceedings, was now directed to take him back to the after compartment originally assigned to the prisoner and his custodian. As the twain disappeared from view, the three officers, as partially liberated from some inward constraint associated with Billy's mere presence, simultaneously stirred in their seats. They exchanged looks of troubled indecision, yet feeling that decide they must and without long delay. For Captain Vere, he for the time stood—unconsciously with his back toward them, apparently in one of his absent fits— gazing out from a sashed porthole to windward upon the monotonous blank of the twilight sea. But the court's silence continuing, broken only at moments by brief consultations, in low earnest tones, this served to arouse him and energize him. Turning, he to-and-fro paced the cabin athwart; in the returning ascent to windward climbing the slant deck in the ship's lee roll, without knowing it symbolizing thus in his action a mind resolute to surmount difficulties even if against primitive instincts strong as the wind and the sea. Presently he came to a stand before the three. After scanning their faces he stood less as mustering his thoughts for expression than as one inly deliberating how best to put them to well-meaning men not intellectually mature, men with whom it was necessary to demonstrate certain principles that were axioms to himself. Similar impatience as to talking is perhaps one reason that deters some minds from addressing any popular assemblies.

When speak he did, something, both in the substance of what he said and his manner of saying it, showed the influence of unshared studies modifying and tempering the practical training of an active career. This, along with his phraseology, now and then was suggestive of the grounds whereon rested that imputation of a certain pedantry socially alleged against him by certain naval men of wholly practical cast, captains who nevertheless would frankly concede that His Majesty's navy mustered no more efficient officer of their grade than Starry Vere.

What he said was to this effect: "Hitherto I have been but the witness, little more; and I should hardly think now to take an-

262

263

264

265

other tone, that of your coadjutor for the time, did I not perceive in you—at the crisis too—a troubled hesitancy, proceeding, I doubt not, from the clash of military duty with moral scruple—scruple vitalized by compassion. For the compassion, how can I otherwise than share it? But, mindful of paramount obligations, I strive against scruples that may tend to enervate decision. Not, gentlemen, that I hide from myself that the case is an exceptional one. Speculatively regarded, it well might be referred to a jury of casuists. But for us here, acting not as casuists or moralists, it is a case practical, and under martial law practically to be dealt with.

"But your scruples: do they move as in a dusk? Challenge them. Make them advance and declare themselves. Come now; do they import something like this: If, mindless of palliating circumstances, we are bound to regard the death of the master-at-arms as the prisoner's deed, then does that deed constitute a capital crime whereof the penalty is a mortal one. But in natural justice is nothing but the prisoner's overt act to be considered? How can we adjudge to summary and shameful death a fellow creature innocent before God, and whom we feel to be so?—Does that state it aright? You sign sad assent. Well, I too feel that, the full force of that. It is Nature. But do these buttons that we wear attest that our allegiance is to Nature? No, to the King. Though the ocean, which is inviolate Nature primeval, though this be the element where we move and have our being as sailors, yet as the King's officers lies our duty in a sphere correspondingly natural? So little is that true, that in receiving our commissions we in the most important regards ceased to be natural free agents. When war is declared are we the commissioned fighters previously consulted? We fight at command. If our judgments approve the war, that is but coincidence. So in other particulars. So now. For suppose condemnation to follow these present proceedings. Would it be so much we ourselves that would condemn as it would be martial law operating through us? For that law and the rigor of it, we are not responsible. Our vowed responsibility is in this: That however pitilessly that law may operate in any instances, we nevertheless adhere to it and administer it. *270*

"But the exceptional in the matter moves the hearts within you. Even so too is mine moved. But let not warm hearts betray heads that should be cool. Ashore in a criminal case, will an upright judge allow himself off the bench to be waylaid by some tender kinswoman of the accused seeking to touch him with her tearful plea? Well, the heart here, sometimes the feminine in man, is as that piteous woman, and hard though it be, she must here be ruled out."

He paused, earnestly studying them for a moment; then resumed. *271*

"But something in your aspect seems to urge that it is not solely the heart that moves in you, but also the conscience, the private conscience. But tell me whether or not, occupying the position we do, private conscience should not yield to that imperial one formulated in the code under which alone we officially proceed?"

Here the three men moved in their seats, less convinced than agitated by the course of an argument troubling but the more the spontaneous conflict within.

Perceiving which, the speaker paused for a moment; then abruptly changing his tone, went on. *272*

"To steady us a bit, let us recur to the facts.—In wartime at sea a man-of-war's man strikes his superior in grade, and the blow kills. Apart from its effect the blow itself is, according to the Articles of War, a capital crime. Furthermore ——"

"Ay, sir," emotionally broke in the officer of marines, "in one sense it was. But surely Budd purposed neither mutiny nor homicide."

"Surely not, my good man. And before a court less arbitrary and more merciful than a martial one, that plea would largely extenuate. At the Last Assizes it shall acquit. But how here? We proceed under the law of the Mutiny Act. In feature no *273* child can resemble his father more than that Act resembles in spirit the thing from which it derives—War. In His Majesty's service—in this ship, indeed—there are Englishmen forced to fight for the King against their will. Against their conscience,

274 for aught we know. Though as their fellow creatures some of us may appreciate their position, yet as navy officers what reck we of it? Still less recks the enemy. Our impressed men he would fain cut down in the same swath with our volunteers. As regards the enemy's naval conscripts, some of whom may even share our own abhorrence of the regicidal French Directory, it is the same on our side. War looks but to the frontage, the appearance. And the Mutiny Act, War's child, takes after the father. Budd's intent or non-intent is nothing to the purpose.

275 "But while, put to it by those anxieties in you which I cannot but respect, I only repeat myself—while thus strangely we prolong proceedings that should be summary—the enemy may be sighted and an engagement result. We must do; and one of two things must we do—condemn or let go."

"Can we not convict and yet mitigate the penalty?" asked the sailing master, here speaking, and falteringly, for the first.

"Gentlemen, were that clearly lawful for us under the cir-

276 cumstances, consider the consequences of such clemency. The people" (meaning the ship's company) "have native sense; most of them are familiar with our naval usage and tradition; and how would they take it? Even could you explain to them— which our official position forbids—they, long molded by arbitrary discipline, have not that kind of intelligent responsiveness that might qualify them to comprehend and discriminate. No, to the people the foretopman's deed, however it be worded in the announcement, will be plain homicide committed in a fla-

277 grant act of mutiny. What penalty for that should follow, they know. But it does not follow. *Why?* they will ruminate. You know what sailors are. Will they not revert to the recent outbreak at the Nore? Ay. They know the well-founded alarm—

the panic it struck throughout England. Your clement sentence they would account pusillanimous. They would think that we flinch, that we are afraid of them—afraid of practicing a lawful rigor singularly demanded at this juncture, lest it should provoke new troubles. What shame to us such a conjecture on their   278 part, and how deadly to discipline. You see then, whither, prompted by duty and the law, I steadfastly drive. But I beseech you, my friends, do not take me amiss. I feel as you do for this unfortunate boy. But did he know our hearts, I take him to be of that generous nature that he would feel even for us on whom in this military necessity so heavy a compulsion is laid."

With that, crossing the deck he resumed his place by the   279 sashed porthole, tacitly leaving the three to come to a decision. On the cabin's opposite side the troubled court sat silent. Loyal lieges, plain and practical, though at bottom they dissented from some points Captain Vere had put to them, they were without the faculty, hardly had the inclination, to gainsay one whom they felt to be an earnest man, one too not less their superior in mind than in naval rank. But it is not improbable that   280 even such of his words as were not without influence over them, less came home to them than his closing appeal to their instinct as sea officers: in the forethought he threw out as to the practical consequences to discipline, considering the unconfirmed tone of the fleet at the time, should a man-of-war's man's violent killing at sea of a superior in grade be allowed to pass for aught else than a capital crime demanding prompt infliction of the penalty.

Not unlikely they were brought to something more or less akin to that harassed frame of mind which in the year 1842 actuated the commander of the U.S. brig-of-war *Somers* to re-   281 solve, under the so-called Articles of War, Articles modeled upon the English Mutiny Act, to resolve upon the execution at sea of a midshipman and two sailors as mutineers designing the seizure of the brig. Which resolution was carried out though in

282 a time of peace and within not many days' sail of home. An act vindicated by a naval court of inquiry subsequently convened ashore. History, and here cited without comment. True, the circumstances on board the *Somers* were different from those on board the *Bellipotent*. But the urgency felt, well-warranted or otherwise, was much the same.

283 Says a writer whom few know, "Forty years after a battle it is easy for a noncombatant to reason about how it ought to have been fought. It is another thing personally and under fire to have to direct the fighting while involved in the obscuring smoke of it. Much so with respect to other emergencies involving considerations both practical and moral, and when it is imperative promptly to act. The greater the fog the more it imperils the steamer, and speed is put on though at the hazard of running somebody down. Little ween the snug card players in the cabin of the responsibilities of the sleepless man on the bridge."

284 In brief, Billy Budd was formally convicted and sentenced to be hung at the yardarm in the early morning watch, it being now night. Otherwise, as is customary in such cases, the sentence would forthwith have been carried out. In wartime on the field or in the fleet, a mortal punishment decreed by a drumhead court—on the field sometimes decreed by but a nod from the general—follows without delay on the heel of conviction, without appeal.

22

285 It was Captain Vere himself who of his own motion communicated the finding of the court to the prisoner, for that purpose going to the compartment where he was in custody and bidding the marine there to withdraw for the time.

Beyond the communication of the sentence, what took place at this interview was never known. But in view of the character of the twain briefly closeted in that stateroom, each radically

sharing in the rarer qualities of our nature—so rare indeed as   *286*
to be all but incredible to average minds however much cultivated—some conjectures may be ventured.

It would have been in consonance with the spirit of Captain
Vere should he on this occasion have concealed nothing from
the condemned one—should he indeed have frankly disclosed
to him the part he himself had played in bringing about the
decision, at the same time revealing his actuating motives. On
Billy's side it is not improbable that such a confession would   *287*
have been received in much the same spirit that prompted it.
Not without a sort of joy, indeed, he might have appreciated
the brave opinion of him implied in his captain's making such
a confidant of him. Nor, as to the sentence itself, could he have
been insensible that it was imparted to him as to one not afraid
to die. Even more may have been. Captain Vere in end may
have developed the passion sometimes latent under an exterior
stoical or indifferent. He was old enough to have been Billy's
father. The austere devotee of military duty, letting himself
melt back into what remains primeval in our formalized hu-   *288*
manity, may in end have caught Billy to his heart, even as
Abraham may have caught young Isaac on the brink of reso-
lutely offering him up in obedience to the exacting behest. But
there is no telling the sacrament, seldom if in any case revealed
to the gadding world, wherever under circumstances at all akin
to those here attempted to be set forth two of great Nature's
nobler order embrace. There is privacy at the time, inviolable
to the survivor; and holy oblivion, the sequel to each diviner   *289*
magnanimity, providentially covers all at last.

The first to encounter Captain Vere in act of leaving the compartment was the senior lieutenant. The face he beheld, for the
moment one expressive of the agony of the strong, was to that
officer, though a man of fifty, a startling revelation. That the
condemned one suffered less than he who mainly had effected
the condemnation was apparently indicated by the former's
exclamation in the scene soon perforce to be touched upon.

23

290 Of a series of incidents within a brief term rapidly following each other, the adequate narration may take up a term less brief, especially if explanation or comment here and there seem requisite to the better understanding of such incidents. Between the entrance into the cabin of him who never left it alive, and him who when he did leave it left it as one condemned to die; between 291 this and the closeted interview just given, less than an hour and a half had elapsed. It was an interval long enough, however, to awaken speculations among no few of the ship's company as to what it was that could be detaining in the cabin the master-at-arms and the sailor; for a rumor that both of them had been seen to enter it and neither of them had been seen to emerge, this rumor had got abroad upon the gun decks and in the tops, the people of a great warship being in one respect like villagers, taking microscopic note of every outward movement 292 or non-movement going on. When therefore, in weather not at all tempestuous, all hands were called in the second dogwatch, a summons under such circumstances not usual in those hours, the crew were not wholly unprepared for some announcement extraordinary, one having connection too with the continued absence of the two men from their wonted haunts.

There was a moderate sea at the time; and the moon, newly risen and near to being at its full, silvered the white spar deck wherever not blotted by the clear-cut shadows horizontally thrown of fixtures and moving men. On either side the quarter-293 deck the marine guard under arms was drawn up; and Captain Vere, standing in his place surrounded by all the wardroom officers, addressed his men. In so doing, his manner showed neither more nor less than that properly pertaining to his supreme position aboard his own ship. In clear terms and concise he told them what had taken place in the cabin: that the master-at-arms was dead, that he who had killed him had been already

tried by a summary court and condemned to death, and that
the execution would take place in the early morning watch. The
word *mutiny* was not named in what he said. He refrained too
from making the occasion an opportunity for any preachment
as to the maintenance of discipline, thinking perhaps that under
existing circumstances in the navy the consequence of violating
discipline should be made to speak for itself.

Their captain's announcement was listened to by the throng
of standing sailors in a dumbness like that of a seated congregation of believers in hell listening to the clergyman's announcement of his Calvinistic text.

At the close, however, a confused murmur went up. It began
to wax. All but instantly, then, at a sign, it was pierced and
suppressed by shrill whistles of the boatswain and his mates.
The word was given to about ship.

To be prepared for burial Claggart's body was delivered to
certain petty officers of his mess. And here, not to clog the sequel
with lateral matters, it may be added that at a suitable hour,
the master-at-arms was committed to the sea with every funeral
honor properly belonging to his naval grade.

In this proceeding as in every public one growing out of the
tragedy strict adherence to usage was observed. Nor in any
point could it have been at all deviated from, either with respect to Claggart or Billy Budd, without begetting undesirable
speculations in the ship's company, sailors, and more particularly men-of-war's men, being of all men the greatest sticklers
for usage. For similar cause, all communication between Captain Vere and the condemned one ended with the closeted interview already given, the latter being now surrendered to the
ordinary routine preliminary to the end. His transfer under
guard from the captain's quarters was effected without unusual
precautions—at least no visible ones. If possible, not to let the
men so much as surmise that their officers anticipate aught
amiss from them is the tacit rule in a military ship. And the
more that some sort of trouble should really be apprehended,

298 the more do the officers keep that apprehension to themselves, though not the less unostentatious vigilance may be augmented. In the present instance, the sentry placed over the prisoner had strict orders to let no one have communication with him but the chaplain. And certain unobtrusive measures were taken absolutely to insure this point.

24

299 In a seventy-four of the old order the deck known as the upper gun deck was the one covered over by the spar deck, which last, though not without its armament, was for the most part exposed to the weather. In general it was at all hours free from hammocks; those of the crew swinging on the lower gun deck and berth deck, the latter being not only a dormitory but also the place for the stowing of the sailors' bags, and on both sides lined with the large chests or movable pantries of the many messes of the men.

300 On the starboard side of the *Bellipotent*'s upper gun deck, behold Billy Budd under sentry lying prone in irons in one of the bays formed by the regular spacing of the guns comprising the batteries on either side. All these pieces were of the heavier caliber of that period. Mounted on lumbering wooden carriages, they were hampered with cumbersome harness of breeching and strong side-tackles for running them out. Guns and carriages, together with the long rammers and shorter linstocks lodged in loops overhead—all these, as customary, were painted black; and the heavy hempen breechings, tarred to the same tint, 301 wore the like livery of the undertakers. In contrast with the funereal hue of these surroundings, the prone sailor's exterior apparel, white jumper and white duck trousers, each more or less soiled, dimly glimmered in the obscure light of the bay like a patch of discolored snow in early April lingering at some up-

land cave's black mouth. In effect he is already in his shroud, or the garments that shall serve him in lieu of one. Over him but scarce illuminating him, two battle lanterns swing from two massive beams of the deck above. Fed with the oil supplied by the war contractors (whose gains, honest or otherwise, are in every land an anticipated portion of the harvest of death), with flickering splashes of dirty yellow light they pollute the pale   *302* moonshine all but ineffectually struggling in obstructed flecks through the open ports from which the tampioned cannon protrude. Other lanterns at intervals serve but to bring out somewhat the obscurer bays which, like small confessionals or side-chapels in a cathedral, branch from the long dim-vistaed broad aisle between the two batteries of that covered tier.

Such was the deck where now lay the Handsome Sailor. Through the rose-tan of his complexion no pallor could have shown. It would have taken days of sequestration from the winds and the sun to have brought about the effacement of that. But the skeleton in the cheekbone at the point of its   *303* angle was just beginning delicately to be defined under the warm-tinted skin. In fervid hearts self-contained, some brief experiences devour our human tissue as secret fire in a ship's hold consumes cotton in the bale.

But now lying between the two guns, as nipped in the vice of fate, Billy's agony, mainly proceeding from a generous young heart's virgin experience of the diabolical incarnate and effective in some men—the tension of that agony was over now. It survived not the something healing in the closeted interview with Captain Vere. Without movement, he lay as in a trance,   *304* that adolescent expression previously noted as his taking on something akin to the look of a slumbering child in the cradle when the warm hearth-glow of the still chamber at night plays on the dimples that at whiles mysteriously form in the cheek, silently coming and going there. For now and then in the gyved one's trance a serene happy light born of some wandering remi-

305   niscence or dream would diffuse itself over his face, and then wane away only anew to return.

The chaplain, coming to see him and finding him thus, and perceiving no sign that he was conscious of his presence, attentively regarded him for a space, then slipping aside, withdrew for the time, peradventure feeling that even he, the minister of Christ though receiving his stipend from Mars, had no consolation to proffer which could result in a peace transcending that which he beheld. But in the small hours he came again. And the prisoner, now awake to his surroundings, noticed his approach, and civilly, all but cheerfully, welcomed him. But it 306 was to little purpose that in the interview following, the good man sought to bring Billy Budd to some godly understanding that he must die, and at dawn. True, Billy himself freely referred to his death as a thing close at hand; but it was something in the way that children will refer to death in general, who yet among their other sports will play a funeral with hearse and mourners.

307   Not that like children Billy was incapable of conceiving what death really is. No, but he was wholly without irrational fear of it, a fear more prevalent in highly civilized communities than those so-called barbarous ones which in all respects stand nearer to unadulterate Nature. And, as elsewhere said, a barbarian Billy radically was—as much so, for all the costume, as his countrymen the British captives, living trophies, made to march in the Roman triumph of Germanicus. Quite as much so as those later barbarians, young men probably, and picked 308 specimens among the earlier British converts to Christianity, at least nominally such, taken to Rome (as today converts from lesser isles of the sea may be taken to London), of whom the Pope of that time, admiring the strangeness of their personal beauty so unlike the Italian stamp, their clear ruddy complexion and curled flaxen locks, exclaimed, "Angles" (meaning *English*, the modern derivative), "Angles, do you call them? And is it because they look so like angels?" Had it been

later in time, one would think that the Pope had in mind Fra Angelico's seraphs, some of whom, plucking apples in gardens of the Hesperides, have the faint rosebud complexion of the more beautiful English girls.

309

If in vain the good chaplain sought to impress the young barbarian with ideas of death akin to those conveyed in the skull, dial, and crossbones on old tombstones, equally futile to all appearance were his efforts to bring home to him the thought of salvation and a Savior. Billy listened, but less out of awe or reverence, perhaps, than from a certain natural politeness, doubtless at bottom regarding all that in much the same way that most mariners of his class take any discourse abstract or out of the common tone of the workaday world. And this sailor way of taking clerical discourse is not wholly unlike the way in which the primer of Christianity, full of transcendent miracles, was received long ago on tropic isles by any superior *savage*, so called—a Tahitian, say, of Captain Cook's time or shortly after that time. Out of natural courtesy he received, but did not appropriate. It was like a gift placed in the palm of an outreached hand upon which the fingers do not close.

310

But the *Bellipotent*'s chaplain was a discreet man possessing the good sense of a good heart. So he insisted not in his vocation here. At the instance of Captain Vere, a lieutenant had apprised him of pretty much everything as to Billy; and since he felt that innocence was even a better thing than religion wherewith to go to Judgment, he reluctantly withdrew; but in his emotion not without first performing an act strange enough in an Englishman, and under the circumstances yet more so in any regular priest. Stooping over, he kissed on the fair cheek his fellow man, a felon in martial law, one whom though on the confines of death he felt he could never convert to a dogma; nor for all that did he fear for his future.

311

Marvel not that having been made acquainted with the young sailor's essential innocence the worthy man lifted not a finger to avert the doom of such a martyr to martial discipline. So to do

312

would not only have been as idle as invoking the desert, but would also have been an audacious transgression of the bounds of his function, one as exactly prescribed to him by military law as that of the boatswain or any other naval officer. Bluntly put, a chaplain is the minister of the Prince of Peace serving in the host of the God of War—Mars. As such, he is as incongruous as a musket would be on the altar at Christmas. Why, then, is he there? Because he indirectly subserves the purpose attested by the cannon; because too he lends the sanction of the religion of the meek to that which practically is the abrogation of everything but brute Force.

25

313   The night so luminous on the spar deck, but otherwise on the cavernous ones below, levels so like the tiered galleries in a coal mine—the luminous night passed away. But like the prophet in the chariot disappearing in heaven and dropping his mantle to Elisha, the withdrawing night transferred its pale robe to the breaking day. A meek, shy light appeared in the East, where

314   stretched a diaphanous fleece of white furrowed vapor. That light slowly waxed. Suddenly *eight bells* was struck aft, responded to by one louder metallic stroke from forward. It was four o'clock in the morning. Instantly the silver whistles were heard summoning all hands to witness punishment. Up through the great hatchways rimmed with racks of heavy shot the watch below came pouring, overspreading with the watch already on deck the space between the mainmast and foremast including that occupied by the capacious launch and the black booms tiered on either side of it, boat and booms making a summit of

315   observation for the powder-boys and younger tars. A different group comprising one watch of topmen leaned over the rail of that sea balcony, no small one in a seventy-four, looking down

on the crowd below. Man or boy, none spake but in whisper, and few spake at all. Captain Vere—as before, the central figure among the assembled commissioned officers—stood nigh the break of the poop deck facing forward. Just below him on the quarter-deck the marines in full equipment were drawn up much as at the scene of the promulgated sentence.

At sea in the old time, the execution by halter of a military *316* sailor was generally from the foreyard. In the present instance, for special reasons the mainyard was assigned. Under an arm of that yard the prisoner was presently brought up, the chaplain attending him. It was noted at the time, and remarked upon afterwards, that in this final scene the good man evinced little or nothing of the perfunctory. Brief speech indeed he had with the condemned one, but the genuine Gospel was less on *317* his tongue than in his aspect and manner towards him. The final preparations personal to the latter being speedily brought to an end by two boatswain's mates, the consummation impended. Billy stood facing aft. At the penultimate moment, his words, his only ones, words wholly unobstructed in the utterance, were these: "God bless Captain Vere!" Syllables so unanticipated coming from one with the ignominious hemp about his neck—a conventional felon's benediction directed aft towards the quarters of honor; syllables too delivered in the clear melody of a singing bird on the point of launching from *318* the twig—had a phenomenal effect, not unenhanced by the rare personal beauty of the young sailor, spiritualized now through late experiences so poignantly profound.

Without volition, as it were, as if indeed the ship's populace were but the vehicles of some vocal current electric, with one voice from alow and aloft came a resonant sympathetic echo: "God bless Captain Vere!" And yet at that instant Billy alone must have been in their hearts, even as in their eyes.

At the pronounced words and the spontaneous echo that voluminously rebounded them, Captain Vere, either through *319* stoic self-control or a sort of momentary paralysis induced by emotional shock, stood erectly rigid as a musket in the ship-armorer's rack.

The hull, deliberately recovering from the periodic roll to leeward, was just regaining an even keel when the last signal, a preconcerted dumb one, was given. At the same moment it chanced that the vapory fleece hanging low in the East was shot through with a soft glory as of the fleece of the Lamb of God *320* seen in mystical vision, and simultaneously therewith, watched by the wedged mass of upturned faces, Billy ascended; and, ascending, took the full rose of the dawn.

In the pinioned figure arrived at the yard-end, to the wonder of all no motion was apparent, none save that created by the slow roll of the hull in moderate weather, so majestic in a great ship ponderously cannoned.

26

321 When some days afterwards, in reference to the singularity just mentioned, the purser, a rather ruddy, rotund person more accurate as an accountant than profound as a philosopher, said at mess to the surgeon, "What testimony to the force lodged in will power," the latter, saturnine, spare, and tall, one in whom a discreet causticity went along with a manner less genial than polite, replied, "Your pardon, Mr. Purser. In a hanging scientifically conducted—and under special orders I myself directed how Budd's was to be effected—any movement following the completed suspension and originating in the body suspended, *322* such movement indicates mechanical spasm in the muscular system. Hence the absence of that is no more attributable to will power, as you call it, than to horsepower—begging your pardon."

"But this muscular spasm you speak of, is not that in a degree more or less invariable in these cases?"

"Assuredly so, Mr. Purser."

"How then, my good sir, do you account for its absence in this instance?"

"Mr. Purser, it is clear that your sense of the singularity in this matter equals not mine. You account for it by what you call will power—a term not yet included in the lexicon of science. For me, I do not, with my present knowledge, pretend to account for it at all. Even should we assume the hypothesis that at the first touch of the halyards the action of Budd's heart, intensified by extraordinary emotion at its climax, abruptly stopped—much like a watch when in carelessly winding it up you strain at the finish, thus snapping the chain—even under that hypothesis how account for the phenomenon that followed?"

"You admit, then, that the absence of spasmodic movement was phenomenal."

"It was phenomenal, Mr. Purser, in the sense that it was an appearance the cause of which is not immediately to be assigned."

"But tell me, my dear sir," pertinaciously continued the other, "was the man's death effected by the halter, or was it a species of euthanasia?"

"*Euthanasia*, Mr. Purser, is something like your *will power:* I doubt its authenticity as a scientific term—begging your pardon again. It is at once imaginative and metaphysical—in short, Greek.—But," abruptly changing his tone, "there is a case in the sick bay that I do not care to leave to my assistants. Beg your pardon, but excuse me." And rising from the mess he formally withdrew.

27

The silence at the moment of execution and for a moment or two continuing thereafter, a silence but emphasized by the regular wash of the sea against the hull or the flutter of a sail caused by the helmsman's eyes being tempted astray, this emphasized silence was gradually disturbed by a sound not easily to be verbally rendered. Whoever has heard the freshet-wave of a torrent suddenly swelled by pouring showers in tropical mountains, showers not shared by the plain; whoever has heard the first muffled murmur of its sloping advance through precipitous woods may form some conception of the sound now heard. The seeming remoteness of its source was because of its murmurous indistinctness, since it came from close by, even from the men massed on the ship's open deck. Being inarticulate, it was dubious in significance further than it seemed to indicate some capricious revulsion of thought or feeling such as mobs ashore are liable to, in the present instance possibly implying a sullen revocation on the men's part of their involuntary echoing of Billy's benediction. But ere the murmur had time to wax into clamor it was met by a strategic command, the more telling that it came with abrupt unexpectedness: "Pipe down the starboard watch, Boatswain, and see that they go."

Shrill as the shriek of the sea hawk, the silver whistles of the boatswain and his mates pierced that ominous low sound, dissipating it; and yielding to the mechanism of discipline the throng was thinned by one-half. For the remainder, most of them were set to temporary employments connected with trimming the yards and so forth, business readily to be got up to serve occasion by any officer of the deck.

Now each proceeding that follows a mortal sentence pronounced at sea by a drumhead court is characterized by promptitude not perceptibly merging into hurry, though bordering that. The hammock, the one which had been Billy's bed when alive, having already been ballasted with shot and otherwise prepared to serve for his canvas coffin, the last offices of the sea undertakers, the sailmaker's mates, were now speedily completed. When everything was in readiness a second call for all hands, made necessary by the strategic movement before mentioned, was sounded, now to witness burial.

The details of this closing formality it needs not to give. But when the tilted plank let slide its freight into the sea, a second strange human murmur was heard, blended now with another inarticulate sound proceeding from certain larger seafowl who, their attention having been attracted by the peculiar commotion in the water resulting from the heavy sloped dive of the shotted hammock into the sea, flew screaming to the spot. So near the hull did they come, that the stridor or bony creak of their gaunt double-jointed pinions was audible. As the ship under light airs passed on, leaving the burial spot astern, they still kept circling it low down with the moving shadow of their outstretched wings and the croaked requiem of their cries.

Upon sailors as superstitious as those of the age preceding ours, men-of-war's men too who had just beheld the prodigy of repose in the form suspended in air, and now foundering in the deeps; to such mariners the action of the seafowl, though dictated by mere animal greed for prey, was big with no prosaic significance. An uncertain movement began among them, in which some encroachment was made. It was tolerated but for a moment. For suddenly the drum beat to quarters, which familiar sound happening at least twice every day, had upon the present occasion a signal peremptoriness in it. True martial discipline long continued superinduces in average man a sort of impulse whose operation at the official word of command much resembles in its promptitude the effect of an instinct.

The drumbeat dissolved the multitude, distributing most of them along the batteries of the two covered gun decks. There, as wonted, the guns' crews stood by their respective cannon erect and silent. In due course the first officer, sword under arm and standing in his place on the quarter-deck, formally received the successive reports of the sworded lieutenants commanding the sections of batteries below; the last of which reports being made, the summed report he delivered with the customary salute to the commander. All this occupied time, which in the present case was the object in beating to quarters at an hour prior to the customary one. That such variance from usage was

330

331

332

333

authorized by an officer like Captain Vere, a martinet as some deemed him, was evidence of the necessity for unusual action implied in what he deemed to be temporarily the mood of his men. "With mankind," he would say, "forms, measured forms, are everything; and that is the import couched in the story of Orpheus with his lyre spellbinding the wild denizens of the wood." And this he once applied to the disruption of forms going on across the Channel and the consequences thereof.

334

At this unwonted muster at quarters, all proceeded as at the regular hour. The band on the quarter-deck played a sacred air, after which the chaplain went through the customary morning service. That done, the drum beat the retreat; and toned by music and religious rites subserving the discipline and purposes of war, the men in their wonted orderly manner dispersed to the places allotted them when not at the guns.

And now it was full day. The fleece of low-hanging vapor had vanished, licked up by the sun that late had so glorified it. And the circumambient air in the clearness of its serenity was like smooth white marble in the polished block not yet removed from the marble-dealer's yard.

28

335

The symmetry of form attainable in pure fiction cannot so readily be achieved in a narration essentially having less to do with fable than with fact. Truth uncompromisingly told will always have its ragged edges; hence the conclusion of such a narration is apt to be less finished than an architectural finial.

How it fared with the Handsome Sailor during the year of the Great Mutiny has been faithfully given. But though properly the story ends with his life, something in way of sequel will not be amiss. Three brief chapters will suffice.

336

In the general rechristening under the Directory of the craft originally forming the navy of the French monarchy, the *St. Louis* line-of-battle ship was named the *Athée* (the *Atheist*). Such a name, like some other substituted ones in the Revolutionary fleet, while proclaiming the infidel audacity of the ruling power, was yet, though not so intended to be, the aptest name, if one consider it, ever given to a warship; far more so indeed than the *Devastation*, the *Erebus* (the *Hell*), and similar names bestowed upon fighting ships.

On the return passage to the English fleet from the detached cruise during which occurred the events already recorded, the *Bellipotent* fell in with the *Athée*. An engagement ensued, during which Captain Vere, in the act of putting his ship alongside the enemy with a view of throwing his boarders across her bulwarks, was hit by a musket ball from a porthole of the enemy's main cabin. More than disabled, he dropped to the deck and was carried below to the same cockpit where some of his men already lay. The senior lieutenant took command. Under him the enemy was finally captured, and though much crippled was by rare good fortune successfully taken into Gibraltar, an English port not very distant from the scene of the fight. There, Captain Vere with the rest of the wounded was put ashore. He lingered for some days, but the end came. Unhappily he was cut off too early for the Nile and Trafalgar. The spirit that 'spite its philosophic austerity may yet have indulged in the most secret of all passions, ambition, never attained to the fulness of fame.

Not long before death, while lying under the influence of that magical drug which, soothing the physical frame, mysteriously operates on the subtler element in man, he was heard to murmur words inexplicable to his attendant: "Billy Budd, Billy Budd." That these were not the accents of remorse would seem clear from what the attendant said to the *Bellipotent*'s senior officer of marines, who, as the most reluctant to condemn of the members of the drumhead court, too well knew, though here he kept the knowledge to himself, who Billy Budd was.

29

340 Some few weeks after the execution, among other matters under the head of "News from the Mediterranean," there appeared in a naval chronicle of the time, an authorized weekly publication, an account of the affair. It was doubtless for the most part written in good faith, though the medium, partly rumor, through which the facts must have reached the writer served to deflect and in part falsify them. The account was as follows:

"On the tenth of the last month a deplorable occurrence took
341 place on board H.M.S. *Bellipotent*. John Claggart, the ship's master-at-arms, discovering that some sort of plot was incipient among an inferior section of the ship's company, and that the ringleader was one William Budd; he, Claggart, in the act of arraigning the man before the captain, was vindictively stabbed to the heart by the suddenly drawn sheath knife of Budd.

"The deed and the implement employed sufficiently suggest that though mustered into the service under an English name the assassin was no Englishman, but one of those aliens adopting
342 English cognomens whom the present extraordinary necessities of the service have caused to be admitted into it in considerable numbers.

"The enormity of the crime and the extreme depravity of the criminal appear the greater in view of the character of the victim, a middle-aged man respectable and discreet, belonging to that minor official grade, the petty officers, upon whom, as none know better than the commissioned gentlemen, the efficiency of His Majesty's navy so largely depends. His function was a responsible one, at once onerous and thankless; and his fidelity
343 in it the greater because of his strong patriotic impulse. In this instance as in so many other instances in these days, the character of this unfortunate man signally refutes, if refutation were needed, that peevish saying attributed to the late Dr. Johnson, that patriotism is the last refuge of a scoundrel.

[[*130*]]

"The criminal paid the penalty of his crime. The promptitude of the punishment has proved salutary. Nothing amiss is now apprehended aboard H.M.S. *Bellipotent*."

The above, appearing in a publication now long ago super-   *344*
annuated and forgotten, is all that hitherto has stood in human record to attest what manner of men respectively were John Claggart and Billy Budd.

30

Everything is for a term venerated in navies. Any tangible ob-   *345*
ject associated with some striking incident of the service is converted into a monument. The spar from which the foretop-man was suspended was for some few years kept trace of by the bluejackets. Their knowledges followed it from ship to dockyard and again from dockyard to ship, still pursuing it even when at last reduced to a mere dockyard boom. To them a chip of it was as a piece of the Cross. Ignorant though they were of the secret facts of the tragedy, and not thinking but that the penalty was somehow unavoidably inflicted from the naval point of view, for all that, they instinctively felt that Billy was a sort of man   *346*
as incapable of mutiny as of wilful murder. They recalled the fresh young image of the Handsome Sailor, that face never de-formed by a sneer or subtler vile freak of the heart within. This impression of him was doubtless deepened by the fact that he was gone, and in a measure mysteriously gone. On the gun decks of the *Bellipotent* the general estimate of his nature and its un-conscious simplicity eventually found rude utterance from an-other foretopman, one of his own watch, gifted, as some sailors are, with an artless *poetic* temperament. The tarry hand made some lines which, after circulating among the shipboard crews   *347*
for a while, finally got rudely printed at Portsmouth as a ballad. The title given to it was the sailor's.

BILLY IN THE DARBIES

348   Good of the chaplain to enter Lone Bay
And down on his marrowbones here and pray
For the likes just o' me, Billy Budd.—But, look:
Through the port comes the moonshine astray!
It tips the guard's cutlass and silvers this nook;
But 'twill die in the dawning of Billy's last day.
A jewel-block they'll make of me tomorrow,
Pendant pearl from the yardarm-end
Like the eardrop I gave to Bristol Molly—

349   O, 'tis me, not the sentence they'll suspend.
Ay, ay, all is up; and I must up too,
Early in the morning, aloft from alow.
On an empty stomach now never it would do.
They'll give me a nibble—bit o' biscuit ere I go.
Sure, a messmate will reach me the last parting cup;
But, turning heads away from the hoist and the belay,
Heaven knows who will have the running of me up!
No pipe to those halyards.—But aren't it all sham?
A blur's in my eyes; it is dreaming that I am.
A hatchet to my hawser? All adrift to go?

350   The drum roll to grog, and Billy never know?
But Donald he has promised to stand by the plank;
So I'll shake a friendly hand ere I sink.
But—no! It is dead then I'll be, come to think.
I remember Taff the Welshman when he sank.
And his cheek it was like the budding pink.
But me they'll lash in hammock, drop me deep.

351   Fathoms down, fathoms down, how I'll dream fast asleep.
I feel it stealing now. Sentry, are you there?
Just ease these darbies at the wrist,
And roll me over fair!
I am sleepy, and the oozy weeds about me twist.

Notes & Commentary

"Peace, peace, thou ass of a commentator."
(*Melville's marginal notation on an editor's footnote to Shakespeare.*)
"Ye gods!" (*The same.*)

To facilitate cross-references within this edition, the editors have employed for purposes of citation a new foliation of the *Billy Budd* manuscript, adopted by the Houghton Library of Harvard University in 1961. Numerals designating the successive manuscript leaves appear both in headings within the Genetic Text and in the margins of the Reading Text, where they are printed on the same lines as the words with which each leaf begins. In the following notes, numerals preceding catch-lines indicate the manuscript leaf on which the passage under discussion occurs, and references to other passages of *Billy Budd* made within notes also include leaf numbers.

With respect to Melville's other prose fiction, the editors have cited the novels by chapter (*Pierre* by book and chapter) and the shorter pieces by title rather than by giving page references applicable only to a single edition. Citation of *Clarel* is by book and canto plus the line numbers appearing in the text edited by Walter E. Bezanson (New York, 1960). Citation of the shorter verse includes not only the title but a parenthetical reference to page numbers in the most widely available edition: *Collected Poems*, ed. Howard P. Vincent (Chicago, 1947). Melville's journal entries are cited simply by date and his correspondence by date and addressee; for these passages in context see Leyda, *The Melville Log* (1951), or the following standard editions:

Journal of a Visit to London and the Continent by Herman Melville, 1849–1850, ed. Eleanor Melville Metcalf. Cambridge: Harvard University Press, 1948.

Journal of a Visit to Europe and the Levant, October 11, 1856–May 6, 1857, by Herman Melville, ed. Howard C. Horsford. Princeton: Princeton University Press, 1955.

The Letters of Herman Melville, ed. Merrell R. Davis and William H. Gilman. New Haven: Yale University Press, 1960.

Books from Melville's library are cited not only by author and title but also according to their numbering in Merton M. Sealts, Jr., "Mel-

TITLE

ville's Reading: A Check-List of Books Owned and Borrowed," *Harvard Library Bulletin*, Vols. II, III, IV (1948–50), and "Melville's Reading: A Supplementary List . . . ," *ibid.*, Vol. VI (1952). Books and manuscripts now in the Harvard College Library are designated "HCL."

Since a selected bibliography of criticism and scholarship bearing upon *Billy Budd* appears on pp. 203–12, these notes employ only abbreviated citations of materials included there, giving the author's last name and the date of publication plus page references where appropriate.

[TITLE.] (*An inside narrative*): Anderson (1940), p. 338, first suggested that in writing *Billy Budd* Melville had in mind "an inside story of the *Somers* mutiny" from the point of view of his cousin Guert Gansevoort. Other readings internalize the action of the novel: Montale (1942, translated 1960), p. 421, mentions but dismisses the interpretation of its three principal characters "as narcissistic projections of the three ages of the author"; Braswell (1957) sees reflected a tragic conflict "inside" Melville's own spiritual life; Lesser (1957) holds that the story may induce resolution of intrapsychic conflict in its readers. Kaplan (1957), explicating "An inside narrative" in terms of the work itself, finds in it "no mystery," arguing that Melville is saying only that "this is no yarn, no salty tale, no 'mere' external narrative, but 'the *inside* story' of what *really* happened."

Kaplan's explanation is in line with statements made in the manuscript itself. A remark on Leaf 49 describes the story as "restricted . . . to *the inner life* of one particular ship and the career of an individual sailor" (italics added); an earlier subtitle in fact read "What befell [Billy Budd] in the year of the Great Mutiny &c" (Leaf [1a]352). Ch. 29 implies that the tale is designed to show for the first time what really took place aboard ship, since the distorted account ostensibly appearing in an authorized "naval chronicle of the time" (Leaf 340) is "all that hitherto has stood in human record to attest what manner of men respectively were John Claggart and Billy Budd" (Leaf 344).

A somewhat similar pattern appears in Melville's remarks about *White-Jacket*. In a discarded manuscript preface (HCL), the earlier book is said to furnish "some idea of the interior life in a man-of-war"; in the narrative itself, and particularly in its later pages, Melville develops larger implications of his subtitle, "The World in a Man-of-War." Recurring in the final chapter to the figure of the ship as a microcosm of society, he makes this general observation: "Outwardly regarded, our craft is a lie; for all that is outwardly seen of it is the clean-swept deck, and oft-painted planks comprised above the water-line; whereas, the vast mass of our fabric, with all its store-rooms of secrets, forever slides along far under the surface."

LEAVES 2-3

Readers of fiction, Melville observed in Ch. 33 of *The Confidence-Man*, "look ... for more reality, than real life itself can show." Hence the need in *Billy Budd* for "inside narrative" to probe within what is "outwardly seen."

2. *a stroller along the docks:* this is the first of a number of passages in *Billy Budd* so closely resembling passages in Melville's earlier works as to raise the question whether he was deliberately borrowing from them or had read them so recently that he unconsciously echoed even their phrasing. The two opening paragraphs of Ch. 1 bear a close topical and verbal similarity to the first four paragraphs of *Moby Dick*, Ch. 6, where Ishmael takes a stroll through the streets of New Bedford: "In thoroughfares nigh *the docks, any considerable seaport* will frequently offer to view the queerest looking nondescripts from foreign parts ..." (italics added). These nondescripts are enumerated, paralleling the "assortment of tribes and complexions" (Leaf 5) that in *Billy Budd* accompanies the handsome Negro sailor: "It makes a stranger stare." Both contexts also embody a description of the sailor dandy.

Among other parallels in theme and phrasing between *Billy Budd* and Melville's earlier works, those recorded in notes to the following passages are particularly striking: Leaf 28, *But now, when the boat ...* ; 72, *stand with drawn swords;* 75, *under Rodney ...* ; 88, *the master-at-arms;* 90, *Titus Oates ...* and *his eye ...* ; 91, *pallor ...* ; 97, *an old pensioner ...* ; 105, *formal gangway-punishment;* 107-8, *a veteran ...* ; 114, *the sweet and pleasant young fellow;* 134, *lunacy ...* ; 137, *his significant personal beauty;* 143, *Down among the groundlings;* 145, *"Squeak";* 150, *Guy Fawkes ...* ; 155-56, *a narrow platform ...* ; 162, *instinctively ...* ; 178, *like the man of sorrows;* 235, *Was he unhinged?;* 281, *the U.S. brig-of-war* Somers; 289, *the agony of the strong;* 305, *The chaplain ...* ; 329, *certain larger seafowl.*

3. *like Aldebaran:* a star of the first magnitude, "eye" of the constellation Taurus, the Bull: further allusions in succeeding paragraphs to the "grand sculptured Bull" (Leaf 6) and "the horns of Taurus" (Leaf 8) belong to the same sequence of images. Four references to Aldebaran appear in Melville's *Mardi*, Ch. 75, 136, 161, 184; astronomical figures recur throughout his writings, as in the ensuing comparison of Claggart's career with "a comet's travels" (Leaf 101 below).

3. *In Liverpool, now half a century ago:* Melville himself had been in Liverpool, as a sailor aboard the American ship *St. Lawrence*, from July 2 until August 13, 1839. In *Redburn*, the book based in part on his Liverpool voyage, which includes several chapters on Prince's Dock and its environs, he had made no mention of the Negro described here as seen at the dock on "a hot noon in July," though in Ch. 41, noting "the absence of negroes" in Liverpool, he remarked upon "the looks of interest with which negro-sailors" such as the ship's steward "are regarded" in the city.

This is the first of several directly autobiographical reminiscences on Melville's part which, while fitting the retrospective theme of the novel, incidentally tend to discredit the view advanced by Thompson (1952) and others that in *Billy Budd* he was deliberately creating a "narrator" other than his own person. (Compare, for example, the recollection on Leaf 97 of an encounter with "an old pensioner . . . at Greenwich," which is corroborated by an entry Melville had made in his journal while in England in 1849.) Tindall (1956) and Cramer (1957) differ markedly from Thompson in assessing the effect upon the tone of the novel of this "I" who tells the story.

4. *the unadulterate blood of Ham:* the descendants of Ham, son of Noah, were cursed by Noah because Ham had mocked him (Genesis 9:22–25). Popularly, the curse was taken to be a black skin. In *Mardi*, Ch. 157 and 162, Negro slaves are said to belong to the tribe of "Hamo" (Ham); in Ch. 168, Africa is alluded to as "Hamora."

4. *A Highland bonnet with a tartan band:* sailors in *Omoo*, Ch. 61, and *Redburn*, Ch. 47, similarly wear "a Scotch cap"; in *Israel Potter*, Ch. 14, Melville is historically accurate in describing John Paul Jones in "a Scotch bonnet, with a gold band." The recurrence in several books of such matter-of-fact details would seem to cast doubt on Chase's suggestion that the bonnet here recalls specifically from *Pierre* "the emblem of Lucy Tartan," symbolizing "the illuminating grace of consciousness" (1948, p. 1213; 1949, p. 259).

5. *Anacharsis Cloots:* Jean Baptiste du Val-de-Grâce, Baron de Cloots (1755–94), of Prussian extraction. Melville was familiar with the account in Carlyle's *French Revolution*, Pt. II, Bk. I, Ch. 10, of how Cloots presented an aggregation of men of various countries to the French National Assembly as representatives of the human species. In *Moby Dick*, Ch. 27, adopting Carlyle's spelling "Clootz," Melville describes the *Pequod*'s crew as an "Anacharsis Clootz deputation from all the isles of the sea, and all the ends of the earth"; similarly in *The Confidence-Man*, Ch. 2, the *Fidèle*'s passengers are "an Anacharsis Cloots congress of all kinds of that multiform pilgrim species, man"; and a draft version of the ballad "Billy in the Darbies" (Leaf [347c], reproduced in Plate IV above) incorporates the same idea of sailors "from every shore— / Countrymen, yes, and Moor & Swede, / Christian Pagan Cannibal breed." As Matthiessen remarks (1941), p. 410, "this thought is an integral part of Melville's conception of the world as 'a ship on its passage out.' "

5. *this black pagod of a fellow:* similar images of a "barbaric" fellow towering above a procession occur in "Naples in the Time of Bomba" (*Poems*, p. 363) and in *Clarel*, I.v.145, where "Each sheik" appears "a pagod on his tower." (The *New English Dictionary* glosses "pagod" not only as "An idol temple" but also as "An image of a deity, an idol. . . .")

7. *a nautical Murat:* Joachim Murat (1767?–1815), made King of Naples by Napoleon; noted for his dandyism. There is an earlier allusion to "plumed Murat" in *Mardi*, Ch. 36.

7. *the tempestuous Erie Canal:* ironic, like the well-known songs about a terrible storm on "The Raging Can-all"; so in *White-Jacket,* Ch. 91, ten of the waisters, landsmen at heart, "mean to club together and buy a *serving-mallet boat* . . . ; and if ever we drown, it will be in the 'raging canal!'" Melville himself had undoubtedly traveled on the canal en route to Illinois in 1840. In *Moby Dick,* Ch. 54 ("The Town-Ho's Story," which has affiliations with *Billy Budd*), Ishmael describes the waterway as "one continual stream of Venetianly corrupt and often lawless life."

8. *It was strength and beauty:* so to the hero of *Pierre,* in Bk. 2.3, his grandfather's portrait declares "that man is a noble, god-like being . . . made up of *strength and beauty*" (italics added). Melville had similarly associated beauty with strength in "Hawthorne and His Mosses" and in *Moby Dick,* Ch. 86; the latter passage instances "the carved Hercules," to which Billy is likened on Leaf 38 below (see note).

8. *Close-reefing topsails* . . . : the procedure is explained by Felix Riesenberg, *Standard Seamanship for the Merchant Service* (2d ed.; New York, 1936), pp. 179–80: "Men go out on a yard by means of the *foot ropes,* held up by *stirrups.* The footrope extending from inside of the sheave hole to the yard arm is called the *flemish horse.* When hauling out on a weather or lee earing, a sailor must go out on the famous steed, straddle the yard and keep one arm around the lift." Melville similarly describes the operation in *Redburn,* Ch. 24 and 59, where he notes that in reefing, "the extreme weather-end of the topsail-yard"—the position referred to here—is "accounted the post of honor."

8. *young Alexander* . . . *the fiery Bucephalus:* in *Mardi,* Ch. 29, Melville writes: "you fancy a fiery steed . . . as young Alexander fancied Bucephalus; which wild horse, when he patted, he preferred holding by the bridle." Another allusion to Alexander in *The Confidence-Man,* Ch. 26—one possibly to be taken ironically—may be relevant to Melville's subsequent description of Billy as "little more than a sort of upright barbarian" (Leaf 44): "Though held . . . a barbarian, the backwoodsman would seem to America what Alexander was to Asia—captain in the vanguard of conquering civilization."

8. *tossed* . . . *by the horns of Taurus:* so in *Mardi,* Ch. 13: "flying into the air, as if tossed from Taurus' horn."

10. *welkin-eyed:* in Melville's poem "The Blue-Bird" (*Poems,* p. 265) "welkin-blue" is a "heavenly tint," a "clear ethereal hue"; the phrase "welkin eyes" occurs below on Leaf 140. Chase (1950), p. xv, suggests a source in the "welkin eye" of Shakespeare's *The Winter's Tale,* I.ii.136.

10. *having been impressed:* "*that* was a period," Melville had written of this same era in Ch. 36 of *White-Jacket,* "when the uttermost resources of England were taxed to the quick; . . . when British press-gangs . . . boarded their own merchantmen at the mouth of the Thames"; subsequently discussing "The Manning of Navies" in Ch. 90, he treated impressment in some detail, citing

several historical references. In Ch. 74 of the same work the old Negro Tawney tells how he and other Americans had been impressed during the War of 1812 by a British frigate "upon the high seas, out of a New England merchantman"; in *Israel Potter*, Ch. 13, Israel is "kidnapped" at Dover "into the naval service of . . . George III . . . and, ere long," becomes "a foretopman" like Billy, aboard H.M.S. *Unprincipled*.

10. *the Narrow Seas:* the channels separating Great Britain from the Continent and from Ireland. Describing the sights of Liverpool in *Redburn*, Ch. 40, Melville had mentioned "the various black steamers (so unlike the American boats, since they have to navigate the boisterous Narrow Seas) plying to all parts of the three kingdoms"; in *White-Jacket*, Ch. 71, he alluded to Admiral Blake, who "in Cromwell's time . . . swept the Narrow Seas of all the keels of a Dutch admiral [Van Tromp; see Leaf 60 below] who insultingly carried a broom at his foremast. . . . "

19-20. *the buffer of the gang:* i.e., the boxer, or fighter; see John S. Farmer, *Slang and Its Analogues* (London, 1890), I, 355.

23. *Some of 'em do his washing:* so in *Mardi*, Ch. 3, old Jarl was the narrator's voluntary "laundress and tailor."

26. *Put your duds in a bag:* Admiral W. H. Smyth, *The Sailor's Word-Book* (London, 1867), p. 267, glosses *duds* as "a cant term for clothes or personal property," observing that the word is "old, but still in common use."

27. *the* Rights-of-Man . . . *Paine* . . . *Burke's arraignment:* Thomas Paine published *The Rights of Man* in 1791 as a rejoinder to Edmund Burke's *Reflections on the Revolution in France* (1790); the opposing positions of the two men concerning the doctrine of abstract natural rights lie behind the dialectic of *Billy Budd*. As early as *White-Jacket*, Ch. 5, Melville had seen an anomaly in the situation of such a man as Jack Chase: while ashore "a stickler for the rights of man, and the liberties of the world," though "bowing to naval discipline afloat." Ishmael, in *Moby Dick*, discussing "Fast-fish and Loose-fish" in Ch. 89, asks: "What are the Rights of Man and the Liberties of the World but Loose-Fish?"

27. *Stephen Girard of Philadelphia:* Girard (1750-1831), merchant, banker, and philanthropist, who had lived in his native France until he was twenty-seven, named his finest ships *Montesquieu, Rousseau, Voltaire*.

28. *But now, when the boat swept under the . . . stern:* Billy's transfer by cutter from merchantman to warship is reminiscent of a similar episode in *Omoo*, Ch. 27, where the "mutineers" are transferred from the whaleship *Julia* to a French frigate. First, the same point about sea-chests is made: "Armed ships allow nothing superfluous to litter up the deck; . . . our chests and their contents [must] be left behind." Then comes the departure by cutter, with cheering farewell to the ship: " 'Good-by, *Little Jule*,' cried Navy Bob, as we swept under the bows." " 'Give her three more!' cried Salem, springing

to his feet and whirling his hat round." Finally, Salem's words and gesture draw a reprimand and blow from "the lieutenant of the party."

30. *by no means of a satirical turn:* Billy is thus like Melville's Captain Amasa Delano, characterized in "Benito Cereno" as "a man of such native simplicity as to be incapable of satire or irony." Such men are likely to be "singularly undistrustful" (note to Leaf 154), in direct contrast to the sardonic and suspicious Claggart, to be introduced below.

30. *sinister dexterity:* Melville's phrase (added to the passage in revision) strikes Tindall (1956), p. 76, as sounding "like something from *Finnegans Wake,* where, indeed, it reappears." Compare an earlier reference to "ambidextrous double-dealers" in the opening paragraph of "To Major John Gentian," one of the Burgundy Club sketches composed by Melville *circa* 1876.

31. *practically a fatalist:* so the title character of Melville's "John Marr" recalls his youthful fellow sailors of long ago: "Taking things as fated merely, / Child-like though the world ye spanned . . ." (*Poems*, p. 165).

31. *rated as an able seaman:* as explained in *Redburn*, Ch. 12, "sailors are of three classes—*able-seaman, ordinary-seaman,* and *boys.* . . . And the able seamen in the Highlander had such grand notions about their seamanship, that I almost thought that able seamen received diplomas, like those given at colleges. . . ." (In his own sailing career, Melville had been rated at different times in all three classes: as boy on the *St. Lawrence* in 1839, as able seaman on the slack whaler *Lucy Ann* in 1842, but as ordinary seaman on the frigate *United States* in 1843.)

By specifying Billy's rating here, Melville is reiterating his earlier point that Billy is "a proficient in his perilous calling" (Leaf 8); the subject of his thorough sailorly competence recurs in a later reference to his "qualities as a 'sailor-man'" (Leaf 209 and note). Critics of the novel have tended to overlook Billy's manly strength and skill while emphasizing such attributes as his beauty and his childlike simplicity—perhaps taking too literally his nickname "Baby" (Leaf 112). His "important variations" from the typical Handsome Sailor (Leaf 10) were certainly not shortcomings in professional aptitude and proficiency.

31. *the starboard watch of the foretop:* as shown by his draft headnote from which the story developed, Melville had originally thought of Billy as "Captain of a gun's crew in a seventy-four." The change of station, as Melville developed the character, perhaps had some relation to his own partiality for the tops, and to his conviction, expressed in *White-Jacket,* Ch. 12, concerning the influence of the station on the topmen's tempers: "Who were more liberal-hearted, lofty-minded, gayer, more jocund, elastic, adventurous, given to fun and frolic, than the top-men of the fore, main, and mizzen masts? The reason of their liberal-heartedness was, that they were daily called upon to expatiate themselves all over the rigging. The reason of their lofty-mindedness was, that

they were high lifted above the petty tumults, carping cares, and paltrinesses of the decks below."

The title character of *White-Jacket*—a dramatization of Melville himself— is assigned to the starboard watch on the *main*top (Ch. 3), captained by his admired Jack Chase—to whom *Billy Budd* is dedicated (Leaf 1 above). The title character of *Israel Potter*, impressed into the British navy as was Billy, also becomes a foretopman (Ch. 13); Israel, however, lacks the "genial happy-go-lucky air" which had been part of Melville's conception of Billy from the beginning: in the draft headnote Billy was similarly described as "genial in temper, and sparklingly so."

Melville's account of the foretopmen in *White-Jacket*, Ch. 3, also stresses their active seamanship, which sets them apart from such other crewmen as the waisters and afterguardsmen; in *Billy Budd*, Claggart, Billy's persecutor, had been a waister before his appointment as master-at-arms (Leaf 102 and note, *the least honorable section . . .*), and Claggart's agent sent to tempt Billy is an afterguardsman (Leaves 160–64 and note to 160, *the afterguard . . .*). This assignment of Billy to a station in the foretop further marks Melville's conception of him as a thorough sailor even though a moral novice, whereas Claggart and Claggart's underlings are clearly to be taken as lesser men.

38. *the Saxon strain:* characters of this same physical type, with "clear ruddy complexion and curled flaxen locks," as Melville describes the ancient Britons on Leaf 308 below, recur in his earlier writings. The admirable Jack Chase, hailed in Ch. 4 of *White-Jacket* as a particularly fine "specimen of the island race of Englishmen," was evidently of the same stamp. Other examples range from "Shorty" in *Omoo*, Ch. 53, a "good-looking" blue-eyed and fair-haired young rover of twenty-five, cheeks "dyed with the fine Saxon red," who like Billy (Leaf 42) is "quite illiterate," to the multifarious title character of *The Confidence-Man*, appearing in Ch. 1 as a person of "singularly innocent" aspect whose "cheek was fair, his chin downy, his hair flaxen" (the "mute"); in Ch. 36 of the latter book the "mystic" is "a blue-eyed man, sandy-haired, and Saxon-looking."

38. *his heroic strong man, Hercules:* originally written ". . . the Farnese Hercules." Melville, having seen this statue in Naples, remarked in his journal entry for February 21, 1857, on its size and its "gravely benevolent face." Later in that same year, lecturing on "Statues in Rome," he anticipated the phrasing of the present passage ("that *humane* look of reposeful *good nature*") by observing that the Farnese Hercules "in its simplicity and good nature reminds us of cheerful and humane things. This statue is not of that quick, smart, energetic strength [of] the powerful Samson or the mighty Hercules; but rather of a character like that of the large ox, confident of his own strength but loth to use it" (quoted from contemporary newspaper reports in Sealts, *Melville as Lecturer* [Cambridge, Mass., 1957], p. 147).

Perhaps the association in Melville's mind between this particular statue

and "the large ox" led him in *Billy Budd* to generalize his comparison by
deleting "the Farnese." Then too, the Farnese Hercules, an idealized image
of mature strength, may have seemed out of keeping with his conception of
the youthful Billy: "Young" is the first adjective applied to Billy in the set-
description on Leaf 34; "young" is the epithet consistently attached to the
heroes with whom Billy is compared—"young Alexander" (Leaf 8), "young
Achilles" (Leaf 116), "young David" (Leaf 140), "young Joseph" (Leaf 213),
"young Isaac" (Leaf 288), and especially "young Adam before the Fall" (Leaf
208; compare Leaf 44).

38. *another and pervasive quality:* the present passage grew out of the very
earliest paragraph Melville wrote of what became the story of Billy Budd;
in the draft headnote to the ballad (see Plate I) he had specified Billy's
"features, ear, foot, and in a less degree even his sailor hands but more
particularly his frame and natural carriage" as "indicating a lineage contradicting his lot." Several characters in previous works have similar physical
attributes, notably Harry Bolton of *Redburn*, described in Ch. 44 and 56, and
the "nobly robust" clergyman Falsgrave of *Pierre*, Bk. 5.4. Noting in Ch. 56
of *Redburn* that small fingers are as characteristic of Limaean paupers as of
Lord Byron, Melville called it foolish "to think that a gentleman is known
by his finger-nails . . . or that the badge of nobility is . . . the smallness of the
foot"; yet subsequently in *Pierre* he remarked that "in countries like America,
where there is no distinct hereditary caste of gentlemen," such "daintiness
of the fingers" as Falsgrave's, "when united with a generally manly aspect,
assumes a remarkableness unknown in European nations."
  The seafaring character of higher birth than his station is a familiar figure
in Melville: in addition to Harry Bolton there are Doctor Long Ghost of
Omoo, the title character of *Redburn*, and the narrator of *Mardi*, who declares
in Ch. 3 that on shipboard it is vain "to assume qualities not yours; or to
conceal those you possess"; because of marks of birth and breeding "that
could not be hidden," he explains, "aboard of all ships in which I have sailed,
I have invariably been known by a sort of drawing-room title." And in *Moby
Dick*, Ch. 1, Ishmael finds the transition "from a schoolmaster to a sailor"
especially keen, "particularly if you come of an old established family in the
land" (such, presumably, as the Melvilles and the Gansevoorts).

38. *dyed to the orange-tawny of the toucan's bill:* in Ch. 14 of *Redburn* the
title character finds his hands "stained all over of a deep yellow" from tarring
canvas. The "Imperial Toucan" is described in *White-Jacket*, Ch. 56 ("a
magnificent, omnivorous, broad-billed bandit bird of prey . . ."), and is used
for comparison in Ch. 24 of *The Confidence-Man*.

41. *a foundling, a presumable by-blow:* "sailors are mostly foundlings and
castaways," according to *Mardi*, Ch. 29; throughout his works Melville presented in orphans and foundlings appropriate images for man's estrangement
in the universe: Lem Hardy in *Omoo*, Harry Bolton and Carlo in *Redburn*,

LEAVES 41–44

Ishmael in *Moby Dick,* Isabel in *Pierre,* and more recently the title character of *John Marr and Other Sailors,* published in 1888. "Where is the foundling's father hidden?" he had asked in *Moby Dick,* Ch. 114. "Our souls are like those orphans whose unwedded mothers die in bearing them: the secret of our paternity lies in their grave, and we must there to learn it." Jack Chase, according to *White-Jacket,* Ch. 4, "must have been a by-blow of some British admiral of the blue."

41. *the wisdom of the serpent:* "Behold, I send you forth as sheep in the midst of wolves: be ye therefore wise as serpents, and harmless as doves" (Matthew 10:16). The allusion recurs in *Pierre,* Bk. 5.4; *Israel Potter,* Ch. 8; and *Clarel,* II.xxxii.97–98.

42. *knowing little more of the land than as a beach:* "sailors only go *round* the world, without going *into* it," Melville observed in Ch. 28 of *Redburn;* "and their reminiscences of travel are only a dim recollection of a chain of tap-rooms surrounding the globe": in Ch. 39 he speaks of the "abandoned neighborhoods" they frequent in Liverpool. The term *fiddler's green,* used in the present passage to denote such an area, is glossed in Smyth, *The Sailor's Word-Book,* p. 293, as "a sort of sensual Elysium."

43. *that manufacturable thing known as respectability:* Melville had observed scornfully to James Billson in a letter of December 20, 1885, that in the modern world the reputation of a writer "can be manufactured to order, and sometimes is so manufactured"; as for the "thing known as respectability," it had drawn his fire in such earlier writings as "The Two Temples" (*circa* 1854), with its ironic thrusts at "social and Christian respectability," and "Jack Gentian" (*circa* 1876), in which Gentian incurs the suspicion of "respectable society" and particularly a "respectable vestryman" (Melville published neither manuscript). When the title character of *The Confidence-Man* manifests himself as "the man with the weed" in Ch. 4, he seems both "clean and respectable"; in *Billy Budd,* the "natural depravity" of a Claggart similarly "folds itself in the mantle of respectability" (Leaf 131). Yet elsewhere in the novel Captain Graveling is said, evidently with no irony, to be "the sort of person whom everybody agrees in calling 'a respectable man' " (Leaf 13).

44. *a sort of upright barbarian:* the epithet is in keeping with the recollections of old shipmates Melville had attributed to John Marr (*Poems,* p. 166):

> "Ye float around me, form and feature:—
> Tattooings, ear-rings, love-locks curled;
> Barbarians of man's simpler nature,
> Unworldly servers of the world."

Note that the Negro sailor described at the beginning of the novel possesses "barbaric good humor" (Leaf 4), and also that on Leaf 307 below occurs the reiterated statement that "a barbarian Billy radically was." As Matthiessen (1941) remarked, p. 501, Melville himself "had thought of unspoiled barbarism at every stage of his writing since *Typee*." Here, the narrator's likening of the "upright barbarian" Billy to unfallen Adam anticipates Vere's analogy for Billy on Leaf 208: "young Adam before the Fall."

44. *the doctrine of man's Fall:* in 1850 Melville had written, in "Hawthorne and His Mosses," of "that Calvinistic sense of Innate Depravity and Original Sin, from whose visitations, in some shape or other, no deeply thinking mind is always and wholly free. For, in certain moods, no man can weigh this world, without throwing in something, somehow like Original Sin, to strike the uneven balance." Specific tokens of such "visitations" are recurrent not only in Melville's subsequent writings (e.g., *Pierre*, Bk. 16.1; *The Confidence-Man*, Ch. 22, 26; *Clarel*, IV.xxii.34–43) but also in the marks and notes he made in books from his library that touch upon these topics. Matthiessen (1941), pp. 502–3, tracing Melville's preoccupation with the Fall, holds that the present passage "dovetails in" with his response to Schopenhauer, whom he was reading in 1891 (Sealts Nos. 443–48), notably to a statement by Schopenhauer marked in *Studies in Pessimism:* that the story of the Fall is "the sole thing that reconciles me to the Old Testament."

On Melville's reading of Schopenhauer in relation to *Billy Budd*, consult Freeman (1948), pp. 120–23; Olive Fite, "The Interpretation of Melville's *Billy Budd*" (Northwestern University, 1956)—see *Dissertation Abstracts*, XVII (1957), 354; and Sutton (1960)—see notes to Leaves 321, *a hanging scientifically conducted*, and 334, *the clearness of its serenity*.

45. *prior to Cain's city and citified man:* "And Cain went out . . . and . . . builded a city" (Genesis 4:16–17). Pitch in *The Confidence-Man*, Ch. 24, notes that the first city was built following the first murder; in *Battle-Pieces*, the battlefield of the Wilderness is a "site for the city of Cain" (*Poems*, p. 64). Conversely, in *Pierre*, Bk. 1.2 and 2.2, the still-innocent Pierre and Lucy have strong affiliations for the country rather than the city. In the present context, as elsewhere in *Billy Budd*, Melville's awareness of word roots seems evident in his likening of Billy to innocent Adam "ere the *urbane* Serpent wriggled himself into his company."

45. *Caspar Hauser:* a mysterious foundling (1812?–33), perhaps a victim of amnesia, who appeared "wandering dazed" in Nuremberg in 1828. Melville had alluded to "the lot of Caspar Hauser" in *Pierre*, Bk. 18.1; in *The Confidence-Man*, Ch. 2, a bystander facetiously identifies the "mute" as Hauser.

46. *the good-natured poet's famous invocation:* Martial, *Epigrams*, I.iv.1–2; Melville's quotation below is from the Cowley translation, in the Bohn edition (1865 *et seq.*), p. 179. The Bohn Introduction, p. vii, cites the younger Pliny's comment on Martial's "agreeable spirit of wit and satire, conducted . . . with great candour and good nature."

46. *one of Hawthorne's minor tales:* "The Birthmark," in which Hawthorne describes the mark on Georgiana's cheek as "the fatal flaw of humanity which Nature, in one shape or another, stamps ineffaceably on all her productions."

Freeman (1948), pp. 117–20, and Stewart (1957), pp. 258–59, discuss *Billy Budd* with reference to Hawthorne's story; Olson (1949), pp. 65–66, finds Hawthorne's influence on the novel an unfortunate one.

46. *a vocal defect:* in describing Billy's stutter as an "organic hesitancy" the narrator employs a characteristic Melvilleian adjective ("organic causes," "organic disorder," etc.); in *White-Jacket*, Ch. 89, Melville had termed "organic evils . . . incurable, except when they dissolve with the body they live in." Bond (1953), pp. 364–65, has suggested that Billy's "defect" may derive from the speech impediment of a character in one of Melville's favorite books: Sam, the flogged sailor in Dana's *Two Years before the Mast* (1869 ed.). As early as 1839 Melville himself had drawn a character unable to speak: in his second "Fragment from a Writing-Desk," the mysterious lady proves at the last to be both deaf and dumb. In another juvenile composition of 1838 Melville had asked: "what doth it avail a man[,] though he possesses all the knowledge of a Locke or a Newton, if he know not how to communicate that knowledge[?]" (see William H. Gilman, *Melville's Early Life and Redburn* [New York, 1951], p. 262). The title character of *The Confidence-Man* first manifests himself in the opening chapter as a mute; in a canceled and superseded passage of *Billy Budd*, Leaf [229a]355, there is a reference to Billy himself as "the young mute." (For other affiliations between Billy and the mute of *The Confidence-Man*, see notes to Leaf 38, *the Saxon strain*; Leaf 45, *Caspar Hauser*, and Leaf 300, *behold Billy . . . lying prone in irons*.)

With Billy's stutter, the "one thing amiss" in him, Anderson (1940), p. 344, compares the "one thing wanting" in Jack Chase, a missing finger (*White-Jacket*, Ch. 4); Richard Chase, who includes both Jack Chase and Billy among Melville's "maimed" characters, suggests (1949), p. 277, that Billy's "stammering is Melville's own." For Olson (1947), p. 104, Melville's men generally, after Ahab in *Moby Dick*, are flawed in "mean" ways; here, Billy's "stutter is the plot. . . . It all finally has to do with the throat, SPEECH."

49. *the seventy-four . . . the absence of frigates:* the *Bellipotent*, mounting seventy-four guns, was of the commonest class of the line-of-battle ships. "Three-deckers," mentioned just below, were of a larger class mounting ninety guns or more. Frigates, mounting from thirty-two to thirty-eight guns, were used for reconnaissance, convoy, and general duties, but formed no part of the line of battle.

Absence of frigates is mentioned several times in Robert Southey's *Life of Nelson*, Ch. 5, where Nelson is quoted as writing to the Admiralty in 1798: "Were I to die this moment, *want of frigates* would be found stamped on my heart! No words of mine can express what I have suffered, and am suffering, for want of them." The swift-sailing frigates were the eyes and ears of the fleet.

Melville's copy of the *Life* (New York, 1855) carries a notation in Mrs. Melville's hand: "This book is kept for reference from 'Billy Budd'—(unfinished)"; there is no indication of the date of acquisition (Sealts No. 481, HCL). The use made of Southey in the novel may be gauged to some degree by the parallels pointed out here and in notes to Leaves 51, 57, 58, 62, 64, 65, 70, 313, 316, 338, and 345; a further reference to "want of frigates" occurs on Leaf 189.

49. *the inner life:* in a letter to Melville of July 21, 1886, the English novel_ ist W. Clark Russell, acknowledging Melville's earlier praise of *Two Years before the Mast,* mentioned "Dana's portraiture of the homely inner life of a little brig's forecastle"; his letter is quoted in Leyda (1951), II, 799. Compare also the phrasing of Melville's subtitle: "(An inside narrative)".

50. *Spithead . . . the Nore:* the uprisings in the British fleet to which Melville alludes began on April 15, 1797, at Spithead, a roadstead in the English Channel between Portsmouth and the Isle of Wight, and on May 20, at the Nore, a sandbank at the mouth of the Thames. Melville's notation of the exact dates appears on one of two library call-slips fastened to Leaf 364 of the *Billy Budd* manuscript; the slips also bear additional notes made in the course of his writing the novel. Melville's interest in British naval history of this period goes back to *White-Jacket,* where the uprisings are mentioned in Ch. 36 and 85; "the great mutiny of the Nore," as he remarked in Ch. 36, ". . . for several weeks jeopardized the very existence of the British navy."

The essential accuracy of Melville's historical background in the present novel was established by Anderson (1940); as he notes, p. 334, several small mutinies broke out in the Mediterranean during July and September of 1797, causing British officers to fear repetition of the widespread revolts at Spithead and the Nore; "one of the most serious of these, resulting in the execution of three ringleaders, had occurred in the squadron off Cádiz, the locale of Melville's story." In the West Indies occurred the seizure of the frigate *Hermione* by her mutinous crew, an event which Melville had cited in Ch. 36 of *White-Jacket.* Brief notes about this case made on one of the library call-slips suggest that at one time he considered alluding to it in *Billy Budd* also, though the *Hermione* is unnamed in the manuscript proper as he left it.

As Freeman has pointed out (1948), p. 30, Melville's stress upon the intense unrest of the times makes plausible the apprehensions of Captain Vere regarding possible mutiny and thereby provides a basis for his conduct with respect to Budd's trial.

51. *what it was that . . . England expected:* Nelson's famous signal at the Battle of Trafalgar is given in Southey's *Life,* p. 294, as "England expects every man to do his duty!"

53. *Dibdin:* Charles Dibdin (1745–1814), English dramatist and songwriter, whose name and whose ballads, including "Poor Jack" below, appear also in Melville's *Typee,* Ch. 29, *Redburn,* Ch. 30, and *White-Jacket,* Ch. 23 and 90. Leyda (1952), pp. xviii–xix, aptly remarking that when an examination is made of "the British poets who attracted Melville, the modest songs of Charles Dibdin will get their due," suggests that "Dibdin's 'Poor Tom

LEAF 53

Bowling, the darling of our crew,' may have waked the old memory that produced Melville's last book":

> "His form was of the manliest beauty,
> His heart was kind and soft,
> Faithful below he did his duty,
> And now he's gone aloft. . . ."

What Melville himself wrote of Dibdin in Ch. 90 of *White-Jacket* bears upon the present context. After pointing out that navies, both to work ships under sail and to man their batteries, must enlist not only "volunteer landsmen and ordinary seamen of good habits" but also "a multitude of persons, who, if they did not find a home in the navy, would probably fall on the parish, or linger out their days in a prison," he observed that these among others are "the men into whose mouths Dibdin puts his patriotic verses, full of sea-chivalry and romance. . . . I do not unite with a high critical authority in considering Dibdin's ditties as 'slang songs,' for most of them breathe the very poetry of the ocean. But it is remarkable that those songs—which would lead one to think that man-of-war's-men are the most care-free, contented, virtuous, and patriotic of mankind—were composed at a time when the English navy was principally manned by felons and paupers. . . . Still more, these songs are pervaded by a true Mohammedan sensualism; a reckless acquiescence in fate, and an implicit, unquestioning, dog-like devotion to whoever may be lord and master. Dibdin was a man of genius; but no wonder Dibdin was a government pensioner at £200 per annum."

53. *did not "impartiality forbid fastidiousness"*: the acknowledged but slightly inaccurate quotation here affords a unique opportunity to observe Melville's use of notes taken by him from source material. "The subject is a melancholy one," wrote the British historian William James in *The Naval History of Great Britain* (6 vols.; London, 1860), II, 26, at the close of his first paragraph concerning the uprising at Spithead, "and one which we would fain pass over; but historical impartiality forbids any such fastidiousness. At the same time, the subject not being an international one, nor one of which the details have acquired any permanent interest, we may, consistently with our plan, abridge the account." Melville's condensed version of James's words, written on one of the library call-slips fastened to Leaf 364 of the *Billy Budd* manuscript, includes the phrase ascribed to James in the manuscript proper: "The subject is a melancholy one—would fain pass it over; but historical impartiality forbids fastidiousness. But the subject not being international, nor one where the details have acquired any permanent interest, we may, according to our plan, abridge &c"; there is no reference made on the slip either to James or to the *Naval History*.

The present text corrects Melville's wording of the parenthetical reference to James that occurs in the first sentence of this paragraph. After writing the phrase "one of them" he inserted, above the line, "(James)"; still later he added before the inserted parenthesis not "William" but "G. P. R[.]"—an error pointed out by Freeman (1948), p. 31 n., who reprints James's accounts of the uprisings and discusses Melville's use of them (pp. 31–38, 38–40). Thompson (1952), pp. 368–69, taking his cue from Freeman's note, holds that Melville was deliberately "pretending to stumble into this mistake," possibly for "the gain of a sly joke" at the expense of his "officer-honoring narrator." But study of the growth of the manuscript suggests that Melville's mistake was simply an unintentional oversight, one occurring several years after he had briefly consulted the *Naval History* at a library—a mistake perhaps induced by his personal acquaintance with G. P. R. James, the British historical novelist (1799–1860), whom he had probably met when the two were neighbors in the Berkshires in 1852 (see Leyda [1951], I, 455).

54. *less a narration than a reference:* Melville's statement here that James's account has "to do *hardly at all with details*" and his prior remark on Leaf 49 that *Billy Budd* is "*restricted . . . to* the inner life of one particular *ship* and the career of an *individual* sailor" may include verbal reminiscences of James, who in the *Naval History,* II, 115, declared his intention "to be *sparing of details* in cases of mutiny, especially where *restricted to individual ships*" (italics added).

54. *Like . . . events . . . befalling states . . . including America:* as an author Melville had never "passed over" such reproaches to American "national pride" as exploitation and abuse of common sailors and mistreatment of Polynesian natives abroad and of Indians and Negroes at home. Here, circled at the bottom of the leaf is his notation for a projected addition, taken from American military history, that he never completed: "Do we publish / no medicines pass the lines / &c"; the allusion, as in *Clarel,* IV.ix.116–17, is evidently to the Union's "blockades / Of medicine" and surgical instruments during the Civil War.

56. *the marine corps:* in *White-Jacket,* Ch. 89, Melville had explained and commented bitterly upon the function of the marine corps in a man-of-war. The naval officers, he said, reason thus: "Secure of this antagonism between the marine and the sailor, we can always rely upon it, that if the sailor mutinies, it needs no great incitement for the marine to thrust his bayonet through his heart; if the marine revolts, the pike of the sailor is impatient to charge. Checks and balances, blood against blood, *that* is the cry and the argument."

57. *a coronet . . . the naval crown of crowns:* Southey, devoting several pages of the fifth chapter of his *Life of Nelson* to the honors bestowed on Nelson following the great victory of the Nile, mentions the feeling at the time— shared by Nelson himself—that he might well have been made a viscount or an earl rather than a baron; "It depended upon the degree of rank," as Southey observes, "what should be the fashion of his coronet. . . ." Considering Melville's consciousness of root meanings and the extent of his use of Southey elsewhere in the novel, it seems possible that this passage in the *Life*

may have suggested the antithesis developed here between the coronet (a small crown) granted by the British government and "the naval crown of crowns" won for him at Trafalgar, where Nelson's "most magnificent of all victories" was "crowned by his own glorious death" (Leaf 66).

Melville considered particularizing his acknowledgment of the gallantry in battle of Nelson's sailors. His circled penciled notation "the Aggamenon?" (*Agamemnon*) appears in the manuscript below "the tars" in the opening sentence of this paragraph. The ship itself, which Nelson once commanded, is mentioned later in the text (Leaf 109).

58. *some bypaths have an enticement:* as analysis of the manuscript reveals, Melville debated whether his "divergence" should perhaps be excluded from an "inside narrative." In the novel as he left it, this is one of three chapters (4, 12, 26) carrying projected titles: here, "Concerning 'the greatest sailor since the world began.'" The allusion is to Tennyson, "Ode on the Death of the Duke of Wellington," line 86, which reads not "the world" but "our world"; the quotation on Leaf 66 below has been corrected accordingly. (Following the chapter title in the manuscript is Mrs. Melville's penciled query: "Tennyson?"). Melville marked a similar tribute to Nelson in his copy of Southey's *Life*, p. 307: a "great naval hero—the greatest of our own, and of all former times."

The significance of Melville's treatment of Nelson has been variously assessed, particularly in relation to the ensuing characterization of Captain Vere in Ch. 6 and 7. Glick (1953) holds that "the digression on Nelson, though it intrudes upon the plot, is central to an understanding of Melville's final resolution" of his old problem, "the eternal conflict between absolute morality and social expediency" (p. 103): Nelson, by transcending the merely expedient, provides an immortal example of "supreme heroism, conformable to the highest ideals governing human behavior" (p. 109). Barrett (1955), pp. 622–23, takes the chapter as "really a statement of the theme of the whole story, ... that measured form [Leaf 333 below; see note] makes it possible for man to live" with such "ambiguities"; Nelson, in exposing himself to danger and death at Trafalgar, "is both captain and condemned man, both Vere and Billy Budd, and his act is an assertion of form." But Noone (1957), p. 261, argues conversely that "whereas Vere equates successful leadership with complete submission to form, Nelson is noted for his daring departures from forms.... As against Vere's belief in force as the best preventive of mutiny," Nelson possessed "that feeling for primitive instincts which ... led him ... to expose himself in battle." Barrett and Noone agree, however, in seeing Nelson as an ideal figure in whom head and heart, reason and instinct, are fused.

Stern (1957), pp. 206–10, similarly finds Melville's "bypath" a "direct road into the center of this 'inside narrative,'" leading to "a statement of the kind of heroism that ... may lead to salvation"—for Stern, the heroism of "the Governor." Nelson is "a political and moral administrator" who offers "the sacrifice of self to the possible victory that the combined head and heart may achieve." But where Stern sees a "perfectly complete parallel between Nelson and Vere" (p. 209), Bowen (1960), p. 229, thinks the virtues here attributed to Nelson "bring the lesser man's own qualities, by the force of contrast, unavoidably to mind." In this connection see note to Leaf 65 below, *prudence . . . glory . . . duty.*

58-59. *inventions . . . change in sea warfare:* "Nor brave the inventions that serve to replace / The openness of valor while dismantling the grace": so Melville had written in "Bridegroom Dick" (*Poems*, p. 181), published in the *John Marr* volume of 1888. In the earlier *Battle-Pieces* a series of poems deals with the introduction of ironclads during the Civil War (*Poems*, pp. 34–40). One of these pieces, "A Utilitarian View of the Monitor's Fight," concludes as follows:

> "War yet shall be, but warriors
> Are now but operatives; War's made
> Less grand than Peace,
> And a singe runs through lace and feather."

60. *such naval magnates:* Don John of Austria (1547–78) was the naval commander of the Holy League at Lepanto in 1571; Andrea Doria (1468?–1560) freed Genoa from the Turks; Maarten [Van] Tromp (1597–1653) commanded Dutch fleets against Spain, Portugal, and Britain; Jean Bart (1651?–1702) sailed privateers against the Netherlands; Stephen Decatur (1779–1820) led American naval forces against the Tripoli pirates and against British ships (e.g., H.M.S. *Macedonian:* note to Leaf 72) in the War of 1812.

61. *at Portsmouth, Nelson's* Victory: seen by Melville on Christmas Day in 1849, as noted in his journal at the time; the star inserted in her quarterdeck is mentioned in Ch. 8 of *Moby Dick* as well as in the succeeding paragraph here. The present passage embodies themes and language recurrent in Melville's poetry. A dirge for "the departed three-deckers of De Ruyter and Van Tr[o]mp" is found in "At the Hostelry," a poem that laments displacement of "the Picturesque" by modern progress: now "Utility reigns . . . / And bustles along in Bentham's shoes" (*Poems*, pp. 324, 317). So Melville had included "A Utilitarian View of the Monitor's Fight" in *Battle-Pieces;* references to "martial utilitarians" and "the Benthamites of war" occur below (Leaves 62, 64). The narrator's preference for "the old battleships" of the Past rather than "the *Monitors* and yet mightier hulls" of "the Present" is shared by Melville's Bridegroom Dick (*Poems*, p. 182):

> "Aloof, bless God, ride the war-ships of old,
> A grand fleet moored in the roadstead of fame;
> Not submarine sneaks with *them* are enrolled;
> Their long shadows dwarf us, their flags are as flame."

62. *publication of his person in battle:* Melville's conjectures regarding the "priestly motive" for Nelson's choice of battledress go beyond his sources, as noted by Freeman (1948), p. 45. Southey's *Life of Nelson*, p. 294, states

that on the day of his death Nelson wore, "*as usual*, his admiral's frock coat, bearing on the left breast four stars, of the different orders with which he was invested. Ornaments which rendered him so conspicuous a mark for the enemy, were beheld with ominous apprehensions by his officers. It was known that there were riflemen on board the French ships; and it could not be doubted but that his life would be particularly aimed at" (italics added); Beatty's *Death of Lord Nelson* gives similar information. Melville himself, while in London in 1849, had seen the "coats of Nelson in glass cases" at Greenwich Hospital (journal, November 21, 1849). In "Cock-A-Doodle-Doo!" he compares the cock to "Lord Nelson with all his glittering arms on, standing on the Vanguard's quarter-deck going into battle"; in *Battle-Pieces* he recalls "The Victory, whose Admiral / With orders nobly won, / Shone in the globe of the battle glow" ("The Temeraire," *Poems*, p. 38).

64. *his sagacious dying injunctions:* in his copy of Southey's *Life of Nelson*, Melville marked with a marginal line the latter sentences of the passage on pp. 301–2 dealing with the admiral's death: "And then, in a stronger voice, he said, 'Anchor, Hardy; anchor.' Hardy, upon this, hinted that Admiral Collingwood would take upon himself the direction of affairs. 'Not while I live, Hardy,' said the dying Nelson, ineffectually endeavouring to raise himself from the bed: 'do you anchor.' His previous order for preparing to anchor had shown how clearly he foresaw the necessity of this. . . ." An exact parallel to Melville's phraseology occurs in the account given by Joseph Allen in *Battles of the British Navy* (2 vols.; London, 1852), II, 148, referring to "the benefit which *might have* resulted had the *dying injunction* of Lord Nelson been attended to" (italics added). (What may be a citation of this work occurs on the cover of the folder leaf Melville used to enclose the second Vere chapter—Leaf 363: see Plate VII.)

65. *buoying the deadly way . . . as at Copenhagen:* the reference is to Nelson's preparations for the Battle of Copenhagen in 1801. Southey's *Life of Nelson*, p. 213, gives the following account (unmarked in Melville's copy): "The channel was little known, and extremely intricate; all the buoys had been removed, and the Danes considered this difficulty as almost insuperable, thinking the channel impracticable for so large a fleet. Nelson himself saw the soundings made, and the buoys laid down, boating it upon this exhausting service, day and night, till it was effected. When this was done, he thanked God for having enabled him to get through this difficult part of his duty. 'It had worn him down,' he said, 'and was infinitely more grievous to him than any resistance which he could experience from the enemy.' " The same episode is treated briefly in James's *Naval History*, III, 46.

65. *prudence . . . glory . . . duty:* the point being established in rebuttal to "these martial utilitarians" (Leaf 62) is like that made ironically in "A Utilitarian View of the Monitor's Fight" (*Poems*, p. 40):

LEAVES 65-70

"Hail to victory without the gaud
Of glory; zeal that needs no fans
Of banners; plain mechanic power
Plied cogently. . . ."

With reference to the remark here concerning Nelson, that "Personal prudence . . . surely is no special virtue in a military man," Glick (1953), pp. 106–8, notes that Melville rings changes throughout the story on the theme of prudence. Thus a dutiful Captain Graveling, though rightfully credited with "much prudence, much conscientiousness" (Leaf 14), is of course no Nelson. Claggart, who in his depravity "has everything to hide," has made habitual an "uncommon prudence" (Leaf 148); experience has taught the Dansker "that bitter prudence which never interferes in aught and never gives advice" (Leaf 169); the "prudent surgeon," who is so disturbed by Captain Vere's excited manner (Leaf 231), would refer judgment of Billy to the admiral (Leaf 234). As for Vere himself, the time is admittedly "very critical to naval authority, demanding from every English sea commander two qualities not readily interfusable—prudence and rigor" (Leaf 238). Vere is depicted below as "an officer mindful of the welfare of his men, but never tolerating an infraction of discipline; . . . intrepid to the verge of temerity, though never injudiciously so" (Leaves 74–75). But unlike Nelson, he is "undemonstrative," he wears "no pronounced insignia" (Leaf 76), and though morally "exceptional" (Leaf 214 and note) he is nevertheless "one who whatever his sterling qualities was without any brilliant ones" (Leaf 79).

66. *Alfred:* Lord Tennyson; see note to Leaf 58. Use of the given name here, if not a solecism, would imply depreciation or disparagement.

66. *crowned by . . . death:* the idea of death as "life's crown" occurs also in Melville's Civil War poem "At the Cannon's Mouth" (*Poems*, pp. 82–83); compare "the naval crown of crowns" won by Nelson at Trafalgar (Leaf 57 above).

68. *as late as Mansfield:* William Murray, Earl of Mansfield (1705–93), who became Lord Chief Justice of Britain in 1756.

70. *One instance:* Melville's source here is Southey's *Life of Nelson*. On p. 104 of his copy he checked passages concerning Nelson's meeting the Spanish fleet on February 13, 1797 ("the same year with this story"), and his subsequent transfer to the *Captain*. On p. 110 he marked these sentences, which as Freeman notes (1948), p. 42, are virtually echoed in the present passage: "Sir Horatio, who had now hoisted his flag as rear-admiral of the blue, was sent to bring away the troops from Porto Ferrajo: having performed this he shifted his flag to the Theseus. That ship had taken part in the mutiny in England, and being just arrived from home, some danger was apprehended from the temper of the men. This was one reason why Nelson was removed to her." References to both pages are included among Melville's notations on

the back flyleaves of the *Life:* "110 Mutiny &c" and "104 Jervis' victory / *Feb.* 1797 / Nelson Rear Admiral."

In view of Melville's attention to dates and circumstances in dealing with this background material, it is curious that in the manuscript here, despite both Southey and his own note, he referred to Nelson as being in 1797 "then Vice-Admiral," and on Leaf 109 incorrectly termed him "Sir Horatio" at a period "some two years prior"; the present text corrects both errors.

72. *stand with drawn swords:* "Nor seems it a practice warranted by the Sermon on the Mount," Melville had written in *White-Jacket,* Ch. 74, "for the officer of a battery, in time of battle, to stand over the men with his drawn sword." The context concerns an order to this effect reputedly given officers of H.M.S. *Macedonian* during her battle with the American frigate *United States* in the War of 1812.

75. *under Rodney ... in ... victory over De Grasse:* the British admiral George Brydges, Baron Rodney (1719–92), defeated the French admiral De Grasse off Dominica in April, 1782: an account of the battle is part of the "Professor's" lecture on naval tactics in *White-Jacket,* Ch. 83. Anderson (1940), pp. 332–33, cites parallels between Melville's account of Edward Fairfax Vere and the naval career of Sir William George Fairfax, who played a distinguished part in the engagement.

75. *scarce ... taken him for a sailor:* "It is often observable," according to *White-Jacket,* Ch. 73, "that, in vessels of all kinds, the men who talk the most sailor lingo are the least sailor-like in reality. ... [W]hen not actively engaged in his vocation, you would take the best specimen of a seaman for a lands-man." Melville's comments on the garb and demeanor of Captain Vere closely parallel those of James Fenimore Cooper on Admiral Bluewater in Ch. 4 of *The Two Admirals;* there is a further point of comparison with Vere in Bluewater's habit of "abstracted" thought (Ch. 17), described as "a sort of dreaming of his own" (Ch. 11). Other similarities in phrasing and situation are frequent enough to suggest that Melville may have been reading Cooper's naval fiction during the period of his work on *Billy Budd.*

76. *officers retiring to leeward:* the same naval usage is noted in *White-Jacket,* Ch. 6: "At the first sign of those epaulets of [the Commodore's] on the weather side of the poop, the officers there congregated invariably shrunk over to leeward. ..."

79. *a copy of Andrew Marvell's poems:* in his annotated copy of Marvell's *Poetical Works* (Boston, 1857; Sealts No. 351, HCL) Melville marked lines 721–24 of "Appleton House," quoted below; on the back fly-leaf he wrote "Starry Vere" and the page number of the passage, 31. In the poem it-self the lines refer to the education of Mary Fairfax (1638–1704), whom Marvell had tutored, the daughter of Thomas and Anne Vere Fairfax; the mother is "the starry Vere" of the poem. "Appleton House" suggested to Melville not only the surname and appellation "Starry Vere," as Anderson

noted (1940), pp. 332–33, but also the name of Vere's "kinsman, Lord Denton": line 73 mentions *Denton*, another seat of the Fairfaxes 30 miles from Nun Appleton.

For speculative discussion of possible "allegorical value" in "Vere" and "Starry Vere," see Chase (1948), p. 1215; Chase (1949), p. 261; Thompson (1952), pp. 369–70; and Withim (1959), p. 125.

80. *"Give ye joy, Ed . . . !"*: in Ch. 39 of *White-Jacket* the narrator finds himself named a substitute crewman in the captain's gig: "Come, White-Jacket . . .; you are a gig-man, my boy—give ye joy!" In "Benito Cereno" Captain Delano, addressing Don Benito, says: "I give you joy."

82. *leisure . . . falling . . . to commanders*: *White-Jacket*, Ch. 6, notes the Commodore's "abundance of leisure," remarking on "how indefinitely he might have been improving his mind." On Melville's own sea voyages, especially when he sailed as a passenger, he himself carried a "library, compact but of the best."

83. *like Montaigne . . . philosophize upon realities*: "My philosophy," declared Montaigne in "On Some Verses of Virgil" (*Essays*, Bk. 3), "is in action, in natural and present practice, little in fancy." Among a half-dozen references to Montaigne by name in Melville's other writings, a passage in *White-Jacket*, Ch. 13, characterizes White-Jacket's friend Nord as "a reader of good books" who "seized the right meaning of Montaigne. I saw that he was an earnest thinker; . . . my heart yearned toward him." Kilbourne (1962), who discusses the present passage in detail, argues that in *Billy Budd* Melville used Montaigne's philosophy as a guide to Vere's action and may also have taken Montaigne himself as a model for parts of his delineation of Vere.

84. *disinterestedly*: perhaps a reflection of Melville's close reading of Matthew Arnold, advocate of "disinterestedness." A seeming disparity between "the disinterestedness of Captain Vere's mental processes" as described here and his later concern over "the 'practical consequences' if Budd is not immediately hanged" (Leaf 280) was pointed out by T. T. E. (1943); Hillway (1945) replied that this "should not be regarded as an oversight" on Melville's part; "nor is it necessarily 'one of the essential ambiguities in the story.' Vere's 'disinterestedness' is discussed . . . chiefly in relation to the social and political reforms of his day," which "form only a vivid backdrop" for the "spiritual drama." This exchange foreshadowed the vigorous debate among critics of the 1950's over the primary focus of *Billy Budd*.

84. *insusceptible of embodiment*: Vere's middle-of-the-road position is not unlike that taken in the anonymous "scroll" quoted at length in *Mardi*, Ch. 161, which declares that "though . . . great reforms, of a verity, be needed; nowhere are bloody revolutions required. Though it be the most certain of remedies, no prudent invalid opens his veins, to let out his disease with his life. And though all evils may be assuaged; all evils can not be done away. For evil is the chronic malady of the universe. . . ."

86. *'Spite the gazettes:* Melville's " 'spite" in the *Billy Budd* manuscript, found—without the apostrophe—here and on Leaf 338 (" 'spite its philosophic austerity"), is clearly intended as a contraction of "despite"; compare "Spite this clinging reproach" in the prose Supplement to *Battle-Pieces* (*Poems*, p. 462). In his earlier writing, however, "spite" occurs in a shortened form of the phrase "in spite of": as in "Hawthorne and His Mosses" ("spite of all the Indian-summer sunlight") and *Moby Dick*, Ch. 9 ("spite of all his pains and pangs").

88. *the master-at-arms:* described in *White-Jacket*, Ch. 6, as "a sort of high constable and schoolmaster, wearing citizen's clothes, and known by his official rattan. He it is whom all sailors hate. His is the universal duty of a universal informer and hunter-up of delinquents. . . . It is indispensable that he should be a very Vidocq in vigilance. But as it is a heartless, so is it a thankless office. . . ." Both the present passage and *White-Jacket*, Ch. 44, term the master-at-arms a "chief of police."

Melville's use of William McNally's *Evils and Abuses in the Naval and Merchant Service* . . . (Boston, 1839) is pointed out in the Introduction (pp. 31–32). This book was exhibited by Mr. Hayford as a major source of *White-Jacket* and *Billy Budd* at the Newberry Library meeting of the Melville Society, Chicago, December 27, 1955. It has since been discussed by Thomas Philbrick, "Another Source for *White-Jacket*, "*American Literature*, XXIX (January, 1958), 431–39.

90. *beardless as Tecumseh's:* Tecumseh (1768?–1813), the Shawnee Indian chief; mentioned in *The Confidence-Man*, Ch. 25.

90. *Titus Oates . . . the alleged Popish Plot:* Oates (1649–1705) concocted in 1678 the story of a supposed Catholic plot to massacre English Protestants and to burn London. A previous allusion to Oates in *Omoo*, Ch. 46, also concerns policemen: in Tahiti, "kannakippers," or "religious police," are "sent out with rattans" on Sunday mornings "as whippers-in of the congregation." "To be reported by one of these officials . . . is as much dreaded as the forefinger of Titus Oates was, levelled at an alleged papist."

90. *his eye could cast a tutoring glance:* so with Jackson, Claggart's prototype in *Redburn*, Ch. 12: "one glance of his squinting eye" is "as good as a knockdown," being "the most deep, subtle, infernal looking eye, that I ever saw lodged in a human head. . . . I would give much to forget that I have ever seen it; for it haunts me to this day." The present passage in *Billy Budd* is the first of a series of references to Claggart's eyes (Leaves 178–80, 213, 221–22) culminating in the accusation scene. There Claggart "mesmerically" looks upon Billy as he makes his charge, his "first mesmeristic glance" being "one of serpent fascination; the last . . . as the paralyzing lurch of the torpedo fish."

90. *phrenologically associated:* "Phrenologically," Bland in *White-Jacket*, Ch. 44, "was without a soul." Bland, master-at-arms of the *Neversink*, is another prototype of Claggart.

LEAVES 90-95

On Melville's interest in phrenology, see Tyrus Hillway, "Melville's Use of Two Pseudo-Sciences," *Modern Language Notes*, LXIV (March, 1949), 145–50; Howard P. Vincent, *The Trying-Out of Moby-Dick* (Boston, 1949), pp. 265–67.

91. *pallor tinged with . . . amber:* in *White-Jacket*, Ch. 3, the "holders"— crew members stationed below in the hold—are likewise "pale," for "they seldom come on deck to sun themselves." Here, as perceptively suggested by Fiedler (1960), pp. 434–35, the amber shading in the complexion of the master-at-arms, "akin to the hue of time-tinted marbles of old," recalls Melville's earlier association in *Redburn*, Ch. 55, of the tawny-skinned Jackson with the Roman emperor Tiberius. The present passage seems to embody impressions of a bust of Tiberius that Melville saw in Rome: his journal entry for February 26, 1857, notes its look of "sickly evil"; Claggart's color similarly hints of "something defective or abnormal in the constitution and blood." The bust depicts "intellect without manliness & sadness without goodness"; the depraved Claggart possesses "more than average intellect," his forehead is "shapely and intellectual-looking" (Leaf 226), and men of his type "invariably are dominated by intellectuality" (Leaf 131). Melville's lecture on "Statues in Rome" emphasized the deceptive appearance of Tiberius, "handsome, refined, and even pensive in expression" (Sealts, *Melville as Lecturer*, p. 135); here, Claggart's "aspect and manner were so suggestive of an education and career incongruous with his naval function that . . . he looked like a man of high quality, social and moral, who . . . was keeping incog." (Long Ghost in *Omoo*, Ch. 60, is considered "some illustrious individual . . . going incog"; Vine in *Clarel*, II.x.104–5, is taken for "some lord who fain would go / For delicate cause, incognito.")

93. *a* chevalier *. . . arraigned:* sailor speculations concerning the past lives of shipmates "of easy manners and polite address" occur also in *Redburn*, Ch. 23 and 50, where their sea-going is "almost invariably" imputed to "an irresistible necessity . . . to evade the constables," and in *Moby Dick*, Ch. 9, where Father Mapple's sermon mentions the circulation of similar rumors concerning Jonah's past. Claggart, "who never made allusion to his previous life ashore," is like Nord in *White-Jacket*, Ch. 13, who "never made allusion to his past career—a subject upon which most high-bred cast-aways in a man-of-war are very diffuse."

By "chevalier" Melville evidently meant what the *New English Dictionary* terms a *"Chevalier of fortune:* one who lives by his wits, an adventurer, swindler, sharper"; among the *Fidèle's* passengers in Ch. 1 of *The Confidence-Man* are "certain chevaliers" who clearly fit this description.

95. *the London police:* on the verso of one of the library call-slips on which he took notes for *Billy Budd* (Leaf 364) Melville copied the words italicized in the following passage from James, *Naval History of Great Britain*, II, 73: "It is notorious, that a custom had long prevailed for the London police, when

LEAVES 95 – 102

a culprit *possessed wit enough for his roguery just* to elude the letter of the law, rather than discharge him that he might commit, with increased confidence, fresh depredations upon society, to *send him on board a ship of war.*"

97. *an old pensioner . . . at Greenwich, a Baltimore Negro:* in his journal entry for November 21, 1849, describing Greenwich Hospital near London, Melville had written: "The negro. . . . Walked in Greenwich Park . . . talk with an old pensioner there." Here, the book that Melville "cannot recall" may be either his own *White-Jacket* or a source for its Ch. 36: Thomas Philbrick, "Melville's 'Best Authorities,' " *Nineteenth-Century Fiction*, XV (September, 1960), 175–76, shows that Melville was drawing on a review by Francis Jeffrey in the *Edinburgh Review*, XLVII (1828), 405, when he wrote that "jails and alms-houses throughout . . . Great Britain" were "in Collingwood's time . . . swept clean of the last lingering villain and pauper to man his majesty's fleets."

99. *us graybeards:* compare *White-Jacket*, Ch. 26: "Graybeards! thank God [Cape Horn] is passed"; the proverb in "Apathy and Enthusiasm," in *Battle-Pieces* (*Poems*, p. 9): *"Grief to every graybeard / When young Indians lead the war"*; "L'Envoi" (*Poems*, p. 310): "Wiser in relish, if sedate / Come gray-beards to their roses late."

99. *Camoëns' Spirit of the Cape:* Adamastor, in the *Lusiads* of Luiz Vaz de Camões (1524–80), the Portuguese poet, is a monster, embodying the terror and danger of natural forces, who attempts to destroy Da Gama and his crew. In *White-Jacket*, Ch. 65, Melville had emphasized the devotion of Jack Chase to Camoëns and his translator Mickle; in 1867 he himself acquired a copy of the Strangford translation (Sealts No. 116).

99. *Napoleon's unexampled conquests:* in *Mardi*, Ch. 168, Babbalanja terms Napoleon "the Mars and Moloch of our times. . . . Thou god of war! who didst seem the devouring Beast of the Apocalypse . . ."; among other allusions is the remark in Ch. 55 of *Redburn:* "If Napoleon were truly but a martial murderer, I pay him no more homage than I would a felon."

101. *quidnuncs:* these same busybodies figure in *White-Jacket*, Ch. 91, where "the gossiping smokers" discuss the ship's "interior affairs": rumors about the private lives of officers and crew are said there to prove "inexhaustible topics for our quidnuncs."

102. *the least honorable section . . . embracing the drudgery:* i.e., the *waisters*, "always stationed on the gun-deck," according to *White-Jacket*, Ch. 3. "These haul aft the fore and main-sheets, besides being subject to ignoble duties; attending to the drainage and sewerage below hatches." Similarly in *Israel Potter*, Ch. 20, the waisters are described as "the vilest caste of an armed ship's company, mere dregs and settlings—sea-Pariahs, comprising all the lazy, all the inefficient, all the unfortunate and fated, all the melancholy, all the infirm, all the rheumatical scamps, scapegraces, ruined prodigal sons, sooty faces, and swine-herds of the crew, not excluding those with dismal wardrobes."

104. *the topmen:* "always . . . active sailors," according to *White-Jacket*, Ch. 3; Ch. 4 describes "the tops of a frigate" as "quite spacious and cosy. They are railed in behind so as to form a kind of balcony, very pleasant of a tropical night. From twenty to thirty loungers may agreeably recline there, cushioning themselves on old sails and jackets. We had rare times in that top. We accounted ourselves the best seamen in the ship. . . ."

Here, the sketch of the topmen "lounging at ease . . . , spinning yarns like the lazy gods, and . . . amused with what was going on in the busy world . . . below," appears to embody a reminiscence of Melville's poetry. In *Clarel*, III.iv.1–21, a Cypriote sings of the "Noble gods"

"Superb in their leisure—
Lax ease—
Lax ease after labor divine!"

("Ever blandly adore them," he admonishes; "But spare to implore them: / They rest, they discharge them from time.") On January 29, 1888, during the composition of *Billy Budd*, Melville enclosed a copy of the song, under the title "Ditty of Aristippus," with his reply to a request from E. C. Stedman for autograph material to be reproduced in Stedman's *Poets of America;* the occasion may well have suggested the simile "like the lazy gods" in the present paragraph.

105. *formal gangway-punishment:* in a note to Ch. 29 of *Omoo*, Melville had written: "I do not wish to be understood as applauding the flogging system practiced in men-of-war. As long, however, as navies are needed, there is no substitute for it. War being the greatest of evils, all its accessories necessarily partake of the same character; and this is about all that can be said in defense of flogging." The attitude toward naval discipline so expressed may be closer to Melville's position at the time of *Billy Budd* than is the all-out rhetorical assault on flogging in Ch. 33–36 of *White-Jacket*, with which *Billy Budd* is usually compared. "To the sensitive seaman," according to the first of those chapters, the summons to witness a flogging "sounds like a doom." Like Billy, both White-Jacket himself and his friend Nord resolve to conduct themselves so as "never to run the risk of the scourge" (Ch. 13), but White-Jacket barely escapes the dreaded degradation (Ch. 67). (His imputed offense is exactly that of the novice afterguardsman whose flogging horrifies Billy: being absent from his assigned post when the ship was being put about.) The title character of "Bridegroom Dick," on which Melville was at work in 1887, puts the issue as follows:

"Discipline must be; the scourge is deemed due.
But ah for the sickening and strange heart-benumbing,
Compassionate abasement in shipmates that view. . . ."

He is recalling an incident at sea when all hands are summoned to witness punishment (the details resemble the execution scene in *Billy Budd*), only to have the captain spare the lash with the words "Submission is enough" (*Poems*, pp. 176–78).

LEAVES 105–110

Written in Melville's hand on the back fly-leaf of a copy of Volume I of the first English edition of *White-Jacket* (London, 1850) are these notations: "192 / 214 Flogging" (the volume, bearing Mrs. Melville's name, is in the collection of Mrs. Henry K. Metcalf). Leyda (1951), II, 812, suggests that Melville was referring to this copy of *White-Jacket* while writing *Billy Budd*.

107. *bully boy:* "A good fellow (1815)" (Farmer, *Slang and Its Analogues*, I, 371). The phrase recurs in a canceled passage on Leaf 346 drafted for the final chapter.

107–8. *a veteran . . . mainmastman . . . an old Dansker:* similar to several characters in Melville's earlier works. In *White-Jacket*, Quoin in Ch. 11 has a complexion like the Dansker's, resembling "a gun-shot wound after it is healed"; the gunner in Ch. 31, "Old Combustibles," has "a frightful scar" resulting from a sabre cut; an old mainmastman in Ch. 68, also a veteran, has a "scarred, blackened forehead, chin, and cheeks," his face being "seamed with three sabre cuts." Ahab in *Moby Dick* (Ch. 28) and the title characters of *Israel Potter* (Ch. 26) and "Daniel Orme" are also scarred. The expression "Board-Her-in-the-Smoke," the Dansker's nickname here, is termed "a fighting phrase" in *Mardi*, Ch. 28; it occurs also in Ch. 144 of *Mardi* and Ch. 91 of *White-Jacket*.

Freeman (1944), pp. 208–11, discusses the relationship of the Dansker to Old Combustibles and Daniel Orme; his treatment of the "Daniel Orme" manuscript is in error, however. Walter E. Bezanson, in his edition of *Clarel* (1960), p. 531, adds Jarl in *Mardi* and Agath in *Clarel*, III.xii.32–34, to this sequence of "weird, oracular old sea-dogs."

109. *Haden's etching:* "Breaking up of the 'Agamemnon,'" the masterpiece of Sir Francis Seymour Haden (1818–1910); the etching had been widely known since its first publication in 1870 and its large immediate sale.

110. *the old Merlin's equivocal merriment:* the Dansker's first reaction to the Handsome Sailor recalls the statement on Leaf 37 above that "something about [Billy] provoked an ambiguous smile in one or two harder faces among the bluejackets." Such passages may carry implications reminiscent of *White-Jacket*, Ch. 89, where Melville had made guarded but unmistakable reference to the existence of homosexual practices in the naval service. But critics too narrowly preoccupied with an element in *Billy Budd* first discussed by Grant Watson (1933)—what he termed its "suggestive shadows of primal, sexual simplicities" (p. 324)—may ignore the emphasis here on Billy's own naïveté and inexperience, which to the Dansker seem "oddly incongrous" in terms of "the warship's environment." So in *The Confidence-Man*, Ch. 1, the "singularly innocent" aspect of the mute aboard the *Fidèle* is taken by the crowd as "somehow inappropriate to the time and place"; in *Clarel*, I.viii.73–74, it is remarked, with reference to the innocent and childlike Nehemiah, that "say what cynic will or can, / Man sinless is revered by man." Elsewhere in *Clarel*, I.xliv.32–46, is a situation directly parallel to that

presented here. Just as the Dansker assesses young Billy against his environment, so a character termed the Black Jew gravely watches a procession of pilgrims, among them one young man "elate / In air Auroral, June of life, / With quick and gay response . . ."; the following lines pertain to the Black Jew's reaction:

> "Experienced he, the vain elation gone;
> While flit athwart his furrowed face
> Glimpses of that ambiguous thought
> Which in some aged men ye trace
> When Venture, Youth, and Bloom go by;
> Scarce cynicism, though 'tis wrought
> Not all of pity, since it scants the sigh."

Similarly here, the Dansker's initial expression of "equivocal merriment" gives way to one of "speculative query as to what might eventually befall a nature like [Billy's], dropped into a world not without some mantraps and against whose subtleties simple courage lacking experience and address, and without any touch of defensive ugliness, is of little avail. . . ."

114. Jemmy Leggs: "Jemmy Leggs" or "Jimmy Leggs," an old sailor term for the master-at-arms, is still in use in the American navy. Although in *White-Jacket* the expression is not applied to Bland, master-at-arms of the *Neversink*, a subordinate who had been "a turnkey attached to 'The Tombs' in New York" is known among the sailors as "Leggs" (Ch. 73).

114. *the sweet and pleasant young fellow:* the ironic overtones of what is later called "Claggart's own phrase" (Leaf 122) are obvious enough to the Dansker but have evidently escaped Billy himself; he is presumably unaware that the Red Whiskers, in the words of Captain Graveling, had "mockingly designated him to the others" (originally "to his face") aboard the *Rights-of-Man* as "a 'sweet and pleasant fellow' " who "could hardly have the spirit of a gamecock" (Leaf 20).

The phrase as used elsewhere in Melville normally carries implications of chaffing, mockery, or even of disdain; it frequently occurs in association with olfactory imagery. In *Mardi*, Ch. 121, Media calls upon his "sweet and pleasant poet" Yoomy for a "pipe song" ("Puff! Puff! / More musky than snuff. . . ."); in Ch. 123, included among Oh-Oh's collection of ancient manuscripts is "A most Sweet, Pleasant, and Unctuous Account of the Manner in which Five-and-Forty Robbers were torn asunder by Swiftly-Going Canoes." In *Redburn*, Ch. 26, the men on deck, calling the watch below "in a most provoking but mirthful and facetious style," address them as "my lively hearties" and "my sweet and pleasant fellows." In *White-Jacket*, Ch. 47, the purser's steward twice applies the adjectives "sweet and pleasant" to "a suspicious-eyed waister," who from the nature of his "ignoble duties" (see Leaf 102 above and the accompanying note, *the least honorable section . . .*) surely would be none too sweet, however pleasant he might be. And in *Moby Dick*,

Ch. 91, Stubb jokingly addresses as "my sweet and pleasant fellow" the chief mate of the *Rose-bud*, who is cutting into a "blasted" whale that emits a most unsavory odor; Stubb subsequently tricks both the mate and the even more unsophisticated captain.

Melville's association of "sweet" and "pleasant" may derive from his recollection of Proverbs 9:17 ("Stolen waters are sweet, and bread eaten in secret is pleasant"), to which he alludes in Ch. 10 of *Omoo*, or 16:24. A possible implication of his recurrent olfactory imagery is suggested by a passage in *Pierre*, Bk. 5.3, that terms as one of Pierre's "own little femininenesses—of the sort sometimes curiously observable in very robust-bodied and big-souled men, as Mohammed, for example—" his trait of being "very partial to all pleasant essences."

115–16. *the old sea Chiron . . . his young Achilles:* Chiron the centaur in Greek myth was the wise teacher of Aesculapius, Achilles, and Hercules (see Leaf 38: "his heroic strong man, Hercules").

117. *to spill the entire contents of his soup pan:* in *White-Jacket*, Ch. 6, it is pointed out that aboard a man-of-war the master-at-arms "reigns supreme" on the berth deck, "spying out all grease-spots made by the various cooks of the seamen's messes." In the present passage, Grant Watson (1933), pp. 324–25, was the first of a number of critics to detect possible sexual symbolism.

119. *handsome is as handsome did it:* as Melville specifically notes on Leaf 137, Claggart has "applied to the sailor the proverb 'Handsome is as handsome does' "; the expression occurs as early as 1670.

120. *laugh "with counterfeited glee":* in "The Deserted Village," lines 197–202, Oliver Goldsmith describes the village schoolmaster, "severe . . . and stern to view," whose trembling students had

> "learn'd to trace
> The day's disasters in his morning face;
> Full well they laugh'd, with counterfeited glee,
> At all his jokes, for many a joke had he. . . ."

Similarly, the sailors in *Redburn*, Ch. 12, feel bound to laugh "whenever Jackson said any thing with a grin."

125. *Radcliffian romance:* Melville had referred to "romantic Mrs. [Ann] Radcliffe" (1764–1823) in "The Apple-Tree Table" and to "her curdling romances" in his journal for 1856–57; in "The South Seas" he declared that the rites of the "taboo" are so horrible as to "far transcend any of Mrs. Radcliffe's stories." On Melville's own fondness for "the mysterious" in gothicism, see Newton Arvin, "Melville and the Gothic Novel," *New England Quarterly*, XXII (March, 1949), 33–48, and Fiedler (1960), pp. 433–35, 538–42.

125. *antipathy: Redburn*, Ch. 51, had noted "the natural antipathy with which almost all seamen . . . regard the inmates of the cabin." The subject

of antipathy and its opposite attracted Melville in his later reading of James Howell's *Instructions for Forreine Travell* (London, 1869), a copy of which he bought in 1870 (Sealts No. 285b, HCL). On p. 34 he marked the following passage, underlining the words "inexplicable termes": "And to fly to the ordinary termes of *Sympathy* and *Antipathy*, I know it is the *common refuge of the ignorant, when being not able to conceive the true reason of naturall Actions and Passions in divers things, they fly to indefinite generality, and very often to these inexplicable termes of* Sympathy *and* Antipathy." On p. 37 Melville also marked Howell's conclusion that such reactions are attributable not merely to such causes as the stars or the climate but to the Devil, "for *the least advantage in the World is sufficient for him to infuse his venom when he finds hearts never so little disposed to receive it* either by *naturall* or *contingent* causes."

125. *irritating juxtaposition of . . . personalities . . . at sea:* "No school like a ship," according to *Mardi*, Ch. 3, "for studying human nature"; *White-Jacket*, Ch. 53, develops the topic further with reference to officers "cherishing personal malice against so conventionally degraded a being as a sailor." Human nature is the same regardless of title, rank, wealth, and education; "its only differences lie in the different modes of development. At sea, a frigate houses and homes five hundred mortals in a space so contracted that they can hardly so much as move but they touch. Cut off from all those outward passing things which ashore employ the eyes, tongues, and thoughts of landsmen, the inmates of a frigate are thrown upon themselves and each other, and all their ponderings are introspective. A morbidness of mind is often the consequence, especially upon long voyages. . . . Nor does this exempt from its evil influence any rank on board. . . ."

126. *Jonah's toss:* "So they took up Jonah, and cast him forth into the sea" (Jonah 1:15); the words are echoed in Father Mapple's sermon in *Moby Dick*, Ch. 9. In *Omoo*, Ch. 24, there is a cry to "give him a sea-toss! . . . Overboard with him!"

126. *"the deadly space between":* Melville's reference here remains elusive.

127. *an honest scholar, my senior:* actually a spokesman invented in order to dramatize a point of view, like the optician "Hilary, my companionable acquaintance," in the "Inscription Epistolary" to the *John Marr* volume published in 1888 (*Poems*, p. 468). So in earlier works Melville had repeatedly professed to be quoting sentencious documents of various kinds—scrolls, sermons, pamphlets; *Moby Dick*, Ch. 2, cites an unnamed "old writer—of whose works I possess the only copy extant," and "The Bell-Tower" includes epigraphs taken "from a private MS." In the Burgundy Club sketches, begun in the 1870's, occur such aliases as "B. Hobbema Brown," supposedly a landscape painter, and "the Burgundy's eccentric philosopher," who is unnamed. The "writer whom few know" appearing later in *Billy Budd* (Leaf 282 and note) is evidently of the same stamp. (See Introduction, p. 38.)

128. *an average man of the world:* the present passage invites comparison with "Rammon," written *circa* 1887–88, recently studied by Miss Tilton (1959; the page references which follow are to Miss Tilton's text). In "Rammon," Tardi is described as "little more than a highly agreeable man-of-the-world, and as such, unconsciously pledged to avert himself in a light-hearted way, from entire segments of life and thought" (pp. 73–74). "Rammon," however, suggests a somewhat qualified view of "that finer spiritual insight" said here to be found in such "recluses" as the Hebrew prophets: to Rammon, in his "lack of experience and acquired knowledge . . . it had never occurred . . . as a conjecture, much less as a verity that the more spiritual, wide-seeing, conscientious and sympathetic the nature, so much the more is it spiritually isolated, and isolation is the mother of illusion" (p. 62).

129. *Coke and Blackstone:* Sir Edward Coke (1552–1634), Sir William Blackstone (1723–80), noted British jurists.

129–30. *that lexicon . . . based on Holy Writ:* though Miss Wright (1949), p. 129 n., suggests that Melville may have been thinking here of a particular work, such as Thomas Wilson's *Complete Christian Dictionary* (1612), it would appear that the reference is rather to the special vocabulary of biblical theology, just as he refers below to the characteristic terminology of philosophy. So the ship's surgeon is to speak of "the lexicon of science" as excluding such layman's terms and concepts as those employed by the purser (Leaf 322). A pattern of similar antitheses runs throughout the novel: in discussing Nelson, Melville had contrasted the discourse of "martial utilitarians" with the language of "great epics and dramas" (Leaves 62, 67); in the concluding chapters an "authorized" version of Billy's story immediately precedes the "artless" ballad of "Billy in the Darbies."

On the general difficulties of defining and denominating, compare the "inconclusive debate" mentioned in one of the headnotes in "At the Hostelry" (*Poems*, p. 317) "as to the exact import of a . . . term . . . whereof the lexicons give definitions more lexicographical than satisfactory."

130. *the authentic translation of Plato:* presumably the Bohn edition of Plato's works, 6 vols., first published in 1848–54, in which "Natural depravity" is defined as "a badness by nature, and a sinning in that, which is according to nature" (VI, 143); Whewell's and Jowett's later nineteenth-century translations do not include the "list of definitions" cited by Melville as does the sixth volume of the Bohn text.

As early as *Mardi*, Melville had speculated that men "are governed by their very natures," the corollary following that "it is easier for some men to be saints, than for others not to be sinners" (Ch. 143). In *White-Jacket*, Ch. 44, Claggart's prototype Bland, the master-at-arms of the *Neversink*, is by nature "an organic and irreclaimable scoundrel, who did wicked deeds as the cattle browse the herbage, because wicked deeds seemed the legitimate operation of his whole infernal organization." Written in Melville's copy of Arnold's

Essays in Criticism (Sealts No. 17, HCL), p. 99, is his observation that men are "influenced . . . by the very fibre of the flesh, & chalk of the bones. We are what we are made." To Mortmain in *Clarel*, II.xxxvi.96–103, the explanation of human wickedness lies

> " 'Nearer the core than man can go
> Or Science get—nearer the slime
> Of nature's rudiments and lime
> In chyle before the bone. Thee, thee,
> In thee the filmy cell is spun—
> The mould thou art of what men be:
> Events are all in thee begun—
> By thee, through thee!' "

131. *no vulgar alloy of the brute:* so Claggart's depravity "partakes nothing of the sordid or sensual" (Leaf 132); his envy of Billy is "no vulgar form of the passion" (Leaf 139). The present reflections on depravity recall a passage in *Clarel* where Ungar, obsessed by the "ever-upbubbling wickedness" of men, complains that the term has been perverted from its full meaning (IV. xxii.34–43):

> " 'This wickedness
> (Might it retake true import well)
> Means not default, nor vulgar vice,
> Nor Adam's lapse in Paradise;
> But worse: 'twas this evoked the hell—
> Gave in the conscious soul's recess
> Credence to Calvin. What's implied
> In that deep utterance decried
> Which Christians labially confess—
> Be born anew?' "

Elsewhere in the poem Mortmain, pondering what the wickedness might be that brought destruction upon the biblical cities of the plain (II.xxxvi.30–73),

> "Urged that those malefactors stood
> Guilty of sins scarce scored as crimes
> In any statute known, or code—
> Nor now, nor in the former times:
> Things hard to prove: decorum's wile,
> Malice discreet, judicious guile;
> Good done with ill intent—reversed:
> Best deeds designed to serve the worst;
> And hate which under life's fair hue
> Prowls like the shark in sunned Pacific blue.
> '. . . 'Twas not all carnal harlotry,
> But sins refined, crimes of the spirit. . . .'
> '. . . Few dicers here, few sots,
> Few sluggards, and no idiots.' "

134. *lunacy . . . evoked by some special object:* this "monomania" in Claggart "—if that indeed it were" (Leaf 188) invites comparison with the affliction of another "more than average intellect," Ahab in *Moby Dick*, Ch. 41: "Human madness is oftentimes a cunning and most feline thing. . . . Ahab's full lunacy subsided not, but deepeningly contracted. . . . But, as in his narrow-flowing monomania, not one jot of Ahab's broad madness had been left behind; so in that broad madness, not one jot of his great natural intellect had perished. That before living agent, now became the living instrument. . . . Ahab had some glimpse of this, namely: all my means are sane, my motive and my object mad. Yet without power to kill, or change, or shun the fact; he likewise knew that to mankind he did long dissemble. . . . But that thing of his dissembling was only subject to his perceptibility, not to his will determinate."

135. *Dark sayings:* "the sage lawgiver Yamjamma" in *Mardi*, Ch. 104, "disdained to be plain. . . . Like all oracles, he dealt in dark sayings." As Thompson remarks (1952), p. 456, n. 7, "Melville knows when he quotes the Bible without quotation marks"—in these instances, from Psalms 78:2: "I will open my mouth in a parable: I will utter dark sayings of old."

135. *"mystery of iniquity"*: 2 Thessalonians 2:7: "the mystery of iniquity doth already work"; Vere uses the same phrase in the trial scene (Leaves 258-59). In *Mardi*, Ch. 144, the sorcerers of the isle of Minda wax eloquent "in elucidating the mysteries of iniquity." In *Clarel*, II.xxxv.23-24, Piranezi's prints, fabling the labyrinths of man's mind, intimate "Paul's 'mystery of iniquity' "; this allusion precedes Mortmain's speculations concerning the sins of the biblical cities of the plain (quoted above in note to Leaf 131).

137. *his significant personal beauty:* in *Redburn*, Ch. 12, the sailor Jackson, conscious of his own "miserable, broken-down condition," eyes young Redburn with "malevolence. . . . For I was young and handsome"; similarly, Jackson cordially hates a young Irishman "because of his great strength and fine person, and particularly because of his red cheeks"—note Billy's "rose-tan" here. In *Moby Dick*, Ch. 54 ("The Town-Ho's Story"), the mate Radney, "ugly as a mule," hates the "tall and noble" sailor Steelkilt, for "it is not seldom the case in this conventional world of ours—watery or otherwise; that when a person placed in command over his fellow-men finds one of them to be very significantly his superior in general pride of manhood, straightway against that man he conceives an unconquerable dislike and bitterness; and if he have a chance he will pull down and pulverize that subaltern's tower, and make a little heap of dust of it." The principle is illustrated both by Claggart and by Shakespeare's Iago, who in *Othello*, V.i.19-20, observes that Cassio "hath a daily beauty in his life / That makes me ugly" (the passage is not marked in Melville's set of Shakespeare, Sealts No. 460, HCL).

Heilman (1956), p. 37, drawing upon *Billy Budd* in his analysis of *Othello*, points out the "truly extraordinary parallels" between Iago and Claggart, which are especially prominent in this and the following chapter; there are also numerous verbal echoes of *Othello* here and elsewhere in the novel. The conception below of Envy as a "monster," for example, may well recall the words of the play applying to jealousy: "the green-ey'd monster, which doth mock / The meat it feeds on" (III.iii.166–67) and "a monster / Begot upon itself, born on itself" (III.iv.151–62); see also notes to Leaves 148, 188, and 211.

137. *envy and antipathy:* in the manuscript, Melville entitled this chapter (12) "Pale ire, envy and despair," alluding to the situation of Satan in *Paradise Lost*, IV.114–17 (but misconstruing "pale" as an adjective):

> "each passion dimm'd his face
> Thrice chang'd with pale, ire, envie, and despair,
> Which marr'd his borrow'd visage, and betraid
> Him counterfet. . . ."

(For discussion of the relationship between Milton's Satan and Claggart, see Pommer [1950], pp. 83–90.) In an earlier version of the present analysis (Leaf [135f]230v) occur these words: "Spencer depicts envy as a ghastly hag forever chewing a poisonous toad [see *The Faerie Queene*, Book I, IV.xxx; Book V, XII.xxx–xxxi]. 'Pale ire, envy, and despair' is Miltonic. Behind these frescoed walls of flesh it is the closeted skeleton. . . ." Envy is first introduced into *Billy Budd* with Captain Graveling's conjecture that the Red Whiskers was moved "out of envy, perhaps," of Billy to pick a fight with him (Leaf 20); Billy's stutter is termed a mark left by "the arch interferer, the envious marplot of Eden" (Leaf 48).

137. *Chang and Eng:* the famous "Siamese Twins" (1811–74), whom Melville presumably saw on their visit to Pittsfield in August of 1853, during his residence there; previous allusions occur in *Israel Potter*, Ch. 19; *The Confidence-Man*, Ch. 21; *Clarel*, III.xiii.56.

140. *jealousy that marred Saul's visage:* the comeliness of young David and the growing jealousy of Saul are described in I Samuel 16:18, 18:8 ff., where David's military prowess and popularity are specified as the causes of Saul's envy. The phrasing here suggests that Melville may have had a drawing or painting in mind as well as the biblical narrative.

140. *the reactionary bite of that serpent:* Melville uses "reactionary" here in a special way, as attested by earlier versions of his sentence. Developing Claggart's response to Billy's young innocence, he wrote that Billy's nature, unlike Claggart's, had "never willed malice or felt unavailing remor[s]e." For the last four words he then substituted "or experienced the reacting bite of that serpent" (having in mind the derivation of "remorse" from the Latin *remordere:* to bite again, strike back, attack in return?). Finally, he changed "reacting" to "reactionary."

Claggart's "reactionary" thoughts are thus like those of Ahab in *Moby*

Dick, Ch. 44, whose thinking "created a creature" in him that fed upon its creator in the manner of Prometheus' vulture. The serpent imagery applied to Claggart here and in his death scene (Leaf 227) suggests not classical but rather biblical or Miltonic associations, however. Claggart's mingled "disdain of innocence" and aesthetic appreciation of its charm parallel the mixed emotions of Satan in *Paradise Lost*, IV.388–92, who "melts" at the "harmless innocence" of Adam and Eve but feels compelled nevertheless "To do what else though damnd I should abhorre"; Claggart "would have shared" Billy's innocence, "but he despaired of it" (Leaf 141). The ensuing statement that such a nature has no recourse "but to *recoil upon itself*" (Leaf 142) echoes a recurrent Miltonic phrase, as Freeman (1948) points out, pp. 91–92: compare such passages as *Comus*, lines 593–97, and *Paradise Lost*, IV.15–18, IX.171–73, etc. (Melville's own John Marr, rebuffed in his attempts to communicate with his inland neighbors, "would soon recoil upon himself and be silent"—*Poems*, p. 161.)

140. *as from windows:* so in *Moby Dick*, Ch. 2: "these eyes are windows, and this body of mine is the house."

142. *like the scorpion:* compare *Clarel*, IV.iv, "An Intruder," in which the tail of a "crabbed scorpion" is likened to "a snake's wroth neck and head / Dilating when the coil's unmade" (lines 7–8). Cries Rolfe (lines 23–29):

> " 'O small epitome of devil,
> Wert thou an ox couldst thou thus sway?
> No, disproportionate is evil
> In influence. *Evil* do I say?
> But speak not evil of the evil:
> Evil and good they braided play
> Into one cord.' "

The theme of moral accountability and responsibility, which is of major importance in *Billy Budd*, long occupied Melville's thought; "who is to blame in this matter?" he had asked in *White-Jacket*, Ch. 44, writing of the "organic and irreclaimable scoundrel" Bland. His treatment of the scorpion here and in *Clarel* recalls earlier discussions of the nature of sharks in *Moby Dick*, Ch. 64 and 66, and rattlesnakes in *The Confidence-Man*, Ch. 36, where the latter are termed "perfectly instinctive, unscrupulous, and irresponsible" by the "mystic"; if such creatures are "accountable," the "cosmopolitan" observes, it is "neither to you, nor me, nor the Court of Common Pleas, but to something superior." So Melville depicts the title character of *Timoleon*, published in 1891, as "Arraigning heaven as compromised in wrong: / To second causes why appeal?" (*Poems*, p. 214); here, "the Creator alone is responsible" for the scorpion.

The reference below to the "part allotted" a Claggart is reminiscent of Ishmael's speculations in *Moby Dick*, Ch. 1, about "those stage managers, the Fates," having "put me down for this shabby part of a whaling voyage" and "cajoling me into the delusion that it was a choice resulting from my own . . . freewill and . . . judgment." Similarly, the poem "On the Slain Collegians" includes these lines (*Poems*, p. 105): "But well the striplings bore their fated parts / (The heavens all parts assign). . . ." The roles given Claggart, Billy, and even Vere in *Billy Budd* are all thought of as determined by their respective "natures" and the circumstances into which they are unwittingly "dropped" (Leaf 111); their situations are thus comparable to the "parts" previously assigned the bedeviled Babbalanja in *Mardi*, the organically wicked Bland, and the "fated" Ishmael, Ahab, and Pierre.

143. *Down among the groundlings:* so in *Moby Dick*, Ch. 26: "to meanest mariners, and renegades and castaways," Ishmael engages to "ascribe high qualities, though dark, [and to] weave round them tragic graces," affirming that "perchance the most abased . . . shall at times lift himself to the exalted mounts. . . ." Similar imagery of the theater recurs in *Israel Potter*, Ch. 24 and 25, where after remarking that "man, 'poor player,' succeeds better in life's tragedy than comedy," Melville promises—ironically—to abridge the account of Israel's squalid sufferings, for the "gloomiest and truthfulest dramatist seldom chooses for his theme the calamities . . . of inferior and private persons; least of all the pauper's," since few can bear to consider them. (Israel is in fact described as among the "rakers of the garbage": he even "wrangl[es] with rats for prizes in the sewers"!)

As for "circumstances . . . trivial or mean," Pommer (1950), p. 157, n. 85, compares Hamlet's finding "quarrel in a straw / When honour's at the stake" (*Hamlet*, IV.iv.55–56); the phrasing here echoes that of a discussion in "Benito Cereno" of "the circumstance which had provoked" Captain Delano's distrust.

For contrasting views of the present passage see Matthiessen (1941), pp. 500–501, and Chase (1949), p. 271.

145. "*Squeak*": in *White-Jacket*, Ch. 73, Bland, the master-at-arms, has two corporals known as "Leggs" and "Pounce"; while Bland is suspended from his office, a suspected informer called "Sneak" takes his place, proving most persevering "in ferreting out culprits." (On Leaf 102 above, Claggart is said to have "a peculiar ferreting genius.")

148. *an injury but suspected:* as on Leaf 137 above, the tenor and language of the passage carry reminiscences of *Othello;* compare I.iii.395–96: "Yet I, for mere *suspicion* in that kind, / Will do as if for *surety*" (italics added). Other seeming echoes on Leaves 148–50 are as follows:

"monstrous disproportion"	" 'Tis monstrous." (II.iii.217)
	"O monstrous world!" (III.iii.377)
	"O monstrous! monstrous!" (III.iii.427)
	"Foul disproportion" (III.iii.233)
"an inordinate usurer"	"Every inordinate cup" (II.iii.311)

"lawyer to his will"	"Our bodies are our gardens, to the which our wills are gardeners" (I.iii.323)
"ogres of trifles"	"Trifles light as air / Are to the jealous confirmations strong / As proofs of holy writ" (III.iii.322-24)

149. *the scriptural devils who "believe and tremble"*: as in James 2:19: "the devils also believe, and tremble."

150. *Guy Fawkes ... the hid chambers*: Fawkes (1570–1606), a Roman Catholic, was arrested in London on November 5, 1605, upon discovery of the "Gunpowder Plot" to blow up the Houses of Parliament. As early as Ch. 9 of *Omoo* Melville had mentioned "the gleamings of Guy Fawkes's lantern in the vaults of the Parliament House"; in *White-Jacket*, Ch. 31, the actions of a gunner, "as if ... laying a train of powder," suggest "Guy Fawkes and the Parliament house" and speculation about "whether this gunner was a Roman Catholic." (There are other allusions in Melville's journal for November 5, 1849—Guy Fawkes Day, and in Ch. 24 of *Israel Potter*, "Benito Cereno," and "Portrait of a Gentleman.")

Melville's recurrent allusions to such historical figures as Fawkes and Titus Oates (Leaf 90 above) not only reveal characteristic patterns of association, but also raise the question of whether in later years he was rereading his own earlier writings.

154. *the weaknesses inseparable from essential good nature*: like Billy, Captain Delano in "Benito Cereno" is described as "a person of a singularly undistrustful good-nature, not liable, except on extraordinary and repeated incentives, and hardly then, to indulge in personal alarms, any way involving the imputation of malign evil in man. Whether, in view of what humanity is capable, such a trait implies, along with a benevolent heart, more than ordinary quickness and accuracy of intellectual perception, may be left to the wise to determine." *The Confidence-Man* continues Melville's exploration of this same issue.

155-56. *a narrow platform ... his private oratory*: a similar passage occurs in Ch. 76 of *White-Jacket*, "The Chains," where another "Nonconformist old tar" likewise appears. This "aged seaman" was "a sheet-anchor-man, an earnest Baptist," whose withdrawal to the chains for his solitary devotions is like "St. Anthony going out into the wilderness to pray."

The platform is "screened by the great deadeyes and ... lanyards": a *deadeye* is a round, flat block of wood with holes for the *lanyards*, shorter ropes which fasten the shrouds. *Shrouds* are sets of ropes stretching between the side of a ship and the masthead; *backstays* extend aft from the mast.

158. *g—g—go where you belong*: a "holder" in *Israel Potter*, Ch. 20, similarly tells Israel to "go where you belong—on deck."

158. *the booms*: light spars used to extend the foot of sails; they were stored between foremast and mainmast, as noted on Leaf 314.

LEAVES 159-164

159. *marry to the gunner's daughter:* i.e., to flog, the *gunner's daughter* being "the gun to which boys were lashed for punishment" (Farmer and Henley, *Slang and Its Analogues,* III, 236).

160. *forecastlemen . . . resenting territorial encroachments:* so in *Israel Potter,* Ch. 20, the captain of the forecastle, an "old veteran," pushes Israel "ignominiously off the forecastle, as some unknown interloper from distant parts of the ship."

160. *the afterguard . . . in no wise competent:* as pointed out in Ch. 26 of *Redburn,* some sailors can merely "run aloft, furl sails, haul ropes, and stand at the wheel," but the qualified able seaman, in actually "working at the rigging," must be "a sort of Jack of all trades" who can perform such complicated tasks as setting *deadeyes* and using *marlinspikes* and other "special tools peculiar to his calling." Freeman (1948), pp. 51–52, compares with the present passage Melville's slighting treatment of the afterguard in *White-Jacket,* Ch. 3; according to a contemporary, Admiral Thomas O. Selfridge, who had been a midshipman on the *United States* when Melville served aboard her in 1843–44, Melville himself was stationed in the afterguard rather than the maintop.

162. *instinctively knew must involve evil:* in *Moby Dick,* Ch. 42 ("The Whiteness of the Whale"), "the instinct of the knowledge of the demonism in the world" finds illustration "even in a dumb brute"—specifically, a "strong young colt," like the "young horse" here.

163. *allotted to the pipe:* as explained in Ch. 91 of *White-Jacket,* "Smoking-Club in a Man-of-War . . . ," "the galley, or cookery, on the gun-deck is the grand centre of gossip and news among the sailors. Here crowds assemble to chat away the half hour elapsing after every meal. The reason . . . is this: in the neighborhood of the galley alone, and only after meals, is the man-of-war's-man permitted to regale himself with a smoke."

Though Stern (1958), pp. 270–71, would locate Billy "aloft in the foretop when he espied below the man he sought," it is evident that both Billy and the afterguardsman must necessarily be among the crowd gathered below, on the "forward part of the upper gun deck." In "a seventy-four of the old order," as noted on Leaf 299, "the upper gun deck was the one *covered over* by the spar deck, which last . . . was for the most part exposed to the weather" (italics added).

The *first dogwatch* was the first of "the half-watches of two hours each, from 4 to 6, and from 6 to 8, in the evening," as Smyth explains. "By this arrangement an uneven number of watches is made—seven instead of six in the twenty-four hours; otherwise there would be a succession of the same watches at the same hours throughout the voyage or cruise" (*The Sailor's Word-Book,* p. 256).

164. *something of a rattlebrain:* in *The Confidence-Man,* Ch. 42, Morpheus, god of dreams, is termed "an arrant rattlebrain, who, though much listened to by some, no wise man would believe under oath."

[[*169*]]

165. *the evening promenade:* "In the dog-watches at sea, during the early part of the evening," according to Ch. 13 of *White-Jacket,* "the main-deck is generally filled with crowds of pedestrians, promenading up and down past the guns, like people taking the air in Broadway. At such times, it is curious to see the men nodding to each other's recognitions . . . ; exchanging a pleasant word . . . ; making a hurried appointment . . . , or passing . . . without deigning the slightest salutation." So in "Bridegroom Dick" is a recollection of "the press o' men / On the gunned promenade where rolling they go, / Ere the dog-watch expire and break up the show" (*Poems,* p. 174).

168. *a cat's-paw:* the Dansker's equivoque employs the term in two special nautical senses, the second being close to common usage: "A light air perceived at a distance in a calm, by the impressions made on the surface of the sea, which it sweeps very gently, and then passes away, being equally partial and transitory. . . . Also, good-looking seamen employed to entice volunteers" (Smyth, *The Sailor's Word-Book,* p. 172). "Cat's-paw" in the sense of "a light air" occurs also in *Mardi,* Ch. 16; *Redburn,* Ch. 60; "Benito Cereno"; and *Israel Potter,* Ch. 10.

Beside this passage in the manuscript Melville wrote in pencil the circled query "flaw?"—taken by Freeman (1948), pp. 15, 52, to apply to the entire paragraph. (Because "the Dansker's enigmatic reply to Billy's questions about the afterguardsman" is insufficiently explained in the paragraph, Freeman holds, "Melville's suspicion of a flaw in his tale of Billy Budd is justified.") What Melville presumably had in mind, however, was the possible substitution of a more technical term for the phrase "light puff of air." "Flaw" in very much this same sense occurs both in *Clarel* (I.i.156–58, I.xiv.128–31, II.xxxvi.48–50) and in the poem "Pebbles" (*Poems,* p. 205), though elsewhere the word refers to a wind blowing suddenly and with more violence, as in *Redburn,* Ch. 16, and *Israel Potter,* Ch. 14, where "a sudden flaw of wind . . . came nigh capsizing them." In his set of Shakespeare (Sealts No. 460, HCL), VII, 374, Melville checked and queried a gloss-note to the phrase "winter's flaw" in *Hamlet,* V.i, that defines "flaw" as "a violent gust of wind." Here, his indecision between "light puff of air" and "flaw" may reflect his uncertainty as to the exact shade of meaning that would be suggested by "flaw." Such concern for phrasing shows Melville's meticulous regard not only for words themselves but for natural fact—a regard too often overlooked, as evidenced by those critics who see *Billy Budd* only as a treatment of abstract good and evil.

170. *a child's . . . innocence is but its blank ignorance:* Billy as "a child-man" resembles the "child-like" sailors remembered so fondly by John Marr (*Poems,* p. 165)—and to "ignorant men, such as sailors generally are," according to *Redburn,* Ch. 19, "the likelihood of great calamities occurring, seldom obtrudes . . ; for the things which wise people know, anticipate, and guard against, the ignorant can only become acquainted with, by meeting them face to face. And even when experience has taught them, the lesson only serves for that

day. . . ." Here, an allusion seems intended to Locke's "celebrated comparison of . . . the human mind at birth to a sheet of blank paper," as in "The Tartarus of Maids."

174. *unless . . . he exercise a distrust:* contrary to the doctrine ascribed to Benjamin Franklin as portrayed in *Israel Potter*, Ch. 7: " 'An indiscriminate distrust of human nature is the worst consequence of a miserable condition, whether brought about by innocence or guilt. And though want of suspicion more than want of sense sometimes leads a man into harm, yet too much suspicion is as bad as too little sense.' " The antithetical themes of suspicion and trustfulness that dominate *The Confidence-Man* suggest that Melville's own attitude in the mid-1850's was far less sanguine than that attributed to Franklin. More recently, in his playful "Inscription Epistolary" for *John Marr,* Melville had declared himself "reluctantly led to distrust" the perspicacity of his optician friend Hilary, who is "lacking more or less in cautionary self-skepticism" (*Poems*, p. 468). Here, the ensuing remarks on "men of the world" may be compared with the opinion of the "honest scholar" of Leaf 127: that "constant rubbing" with the world "blunts that finer spiritual insight indispensable to the understanding of . . . certain exceptional characters. . . .' "

178. *like the man of sorrows:* in Isaiah 53:3 the Lord's servant is said to be "despised and rejected of men; a man of sorrows, and acquainted with grief"; the phrase is commonly applied to Christ, as in *Moby Dick*, Ch. 96: "The truest of all men was the Man of Sorrows." Claggart's "meditative and melancholy expression" here resembles the "sad and musing air" Melville had remarked in the bust of Tiberius he had seen at Rome: "to some . . . it might convey the impression of a man broken by great afflictions, of so pathetic a cast is it. Yet . . . Tiberius was melancholy without pity, and sensitive without affection. He was, perhaps, the most wicked of men" (Sealts, *Melville as Lecturer*, p. 135). On Claggart and Tiberius, see note to Leaf 91, *pallor tinged with . . . amber.*
Claggart's alternative look, "pinching and shriveling [his] visage," recalls that of the herb-doctor in *The Confidence-Man*, Ch. 21, who wears "a kind of pinched expression, mixed of pain and curiosity, as if he grieved at his state of mind"; Seneca's bust as described in "Statues in Rome" presents a face "pinched and grieved"; and in "The Haglets" a fading moon is "pinched in visage" (*Poems*, p. 189).

178. *could even have loved Billy:* Milton's Satan, on beholding Adam and Eve in Eden, "could love" and "could pity" them (*Paradise Lost*, IV.363, 374). Melville himself wrote in Ch. 4 of *White-Jacket* that "he who could not love" Jack Chase "would thereby pronounce himself a knave"; in *Omoo*, Ch. 50, he had remarked that "to be hated cordially, is only a left-handed compliment." Hawthorne, in the concluding chapter of *The Scarlet Letter*, deals in similar terms with Roger Chillingworth's attitude toward Arthur Dimmesdale: "It is a curious subject of observation and inquiry, whether hatred and

love be not the same thing at bottom. Each . . . renders one individual dependent for the food of his affections and spiritual life upon another. . . . Philosophically considered, . . . the two passions seem essentially the same, except that one happens to be seen in a celestial radiance, and the other in a dusky and lurid glow" (Ch. 24).

In *Billy Budd*, though the envious hostility of the Red Whiskers toward Billy had given way to love (Leaf 22), Claggart's "yearning" is checked "by fate and *ban*"; in "Timoleon," published in 1891, Melville twice uses "ban" as a noun meaning a decree of outlawry ("censorship and ban," *Poems*, p. 209) or a curse ("heavy as a mother's ban," p. 213). Billy himself is to be termed by Vere "Fated boy" (Leaf 226).

179. *dental satire of a Guise:* of the French ducal family, the conspiratorial Henri de Guise (1550–88) is best known; as Hamlet says of Claudius, "one may smile, and smile, and be a villain" (*Hamlet*, I.v.108). Here, the "red light" sometimes flashing forth from Claggart's eye may recall the "glare of red light" in the eyes of Chillingworth in *The Scarlet Letter*, Ch. 14.

181. *thews:* in the manuscript a question mark (added by Mrs. Melville) stands beside this word, possibly because the writing seemed unclear or perhaps to suggest a substitution. Melville had used the word previously, in the sense of muscles or sinews, in *Mardi*, Ch. 98; *Pierre*, Bk. 25.3 and 4; and in "Stonewall Jackson" (*Poems*, p. 53).

181. *the "too fair-spoken man"*: the exact phrase is unlocated; Melville may have intended a generalized allusion to such biblical passages as Proverbs 26:24–25 ("When he speaketh fair, believe him not"), Jeremiah 12:6, and Romans 16:18.

183. *by naval usage messmates:* into the same mess, according to *White-Jacket*, Ch. 6, "the usage of a man-of-war thrusts . . . the master-at-arms, purser's steward, ship's corporals, marine sergeants, and ship's yeomen, forming the first aristocracy above the sailors."

188. *a subterranean fire . . . eating its way:* "Dangerous conceits are . . . poisons" which "Burn like the mines of sulphur" (*Othello*, III.iii.326–29); in *Moby Dick*, Ch. 41, is a reference to the "subterranean miner that works in us all."

189. *the English squadron up the Straits:* the Mediterranean squadron. Melville kept a manuscript "Journal up the Straits" in 1856, when he sailed through the Straits of Gibraltar en route to Constantinople and beyond.

192. *cap in hand by the mainmast:* as Melville had explained in *White-Jacket*, Ch. 32, this is "the only place where the sailor can hold formal communication with the captain and officers. If any one has . . . aught important for the executive of the ship to know—straight to the main-mast he repairs; and stands there—generally with his hat off—waiting the pleasure of the officer of the deck. . . ."

203. *secret mines and dubious side:* in the manuscript the words "secret . . . dubious" replace "darker"; in *Moby Dick*, Ch. 127, Ahab is so "far gone . . . in the dark side of earth, that its other side, the theoretic bright one, seems but uncertain twilight." The antithesis of "dark side" and "bright side" recurs in "The Fiddler," the second sketch of "The Encantadas," and "Misgivings" (*Poems*, pp. 3-4).

207. *A mantrap:* the expression occurs in *Redburn*, Ch. 43; *The Confidence-Man*, Ch. 31; and on Leaf 111 above. The notion of peril beneath the surface of natural beauty is a repeated one in Melville's work, notably in *Moby Dick*, Ch. 42 ("The Whiteness of the Whale"): "all deified Nature absolutely paints like the harlot, whose allurements cover nothing but the charnel-house within." Even "the sweet tinges of . . . butterfly cheeks" are thus "but subtile deceits, . . . only laid on from without." Melville wrote but later discarded a striking metaphor of similar purport in his analysis of Claggart's "envy and antipathy" (Leaf 137; see note above): "Behind these frescoed walls of flesh it is the closeted skeleton. . . ."

209. *qualities as a "sailor-man":* for seamen the term has a special significance that Melville has in mind here, in "Bridegroom Dick" (*Poems*, p. 177), and in Ch. 26 of *Redburn*, where he explains it as distinguishing a thoroughly qualified "artist in the rigging" from less competent sailors who merely "*hand, reef, and steer.*" By this time, in other words, Billy's performance of duty aboard the *Bellipotent* has justified to the captain the initial rating of "able seaman" given him as a skilled professional (Leaf 31).

210. *a "King's bargain":* "King's Bargain: Good or Bad" is applicable to a seaman's "activity and merit, or sloth and demerit" (Smyth, *The Sailor's Word-Book*, p. 422).

211. *"mantrap under the daisies":* Melville revised Claggart's antecedent remark about Billy (Leaf 207) from "Your honor, . . . there is a pitfall under his ruddy clover" to "A man-trap may be under the ruddy-tipped daisies". He neglected, however, to make the corresponding revision in the manuscript on this late leaf (211) from "pitfal [*sic*] under the clover" to "man-trap under the daisies". Though some editors have been content to note rather than to correct the discrepancy, we have emended the present passage so as to carry through Melville's clear intention.

211. *cite me an act or spoken word:* Claggart's demeanor as he accuses Budd is not unlike Iago's as he works up his accusation of Desdemona in *Othello*, III.iii; Vere's response is akin to Othello's demand for

> "the ocular proof;
> Or, by the worth of man's eternal soul,
> Thou hadst been better have been born a dog
> Than answer my wak'd wrath!" [lines 360-63]

"I'll have some proof," Othello repeats (line 386); "Give me a living reason she's disloyal" (line 409).

213. *the envious children of Jacob:* "And they took Joseph's coat, and killed a kid of the goats, and dipped the coat in the blood; And they sent the coat of many colours, and they brought it to their father; and said, This have we found: know now whether it be thy son's coat or no" (Genesis 37:31-32).

214. *something exceptional in the moral quality of Captain Vere:* it is by now apparent that Vere, Claggart, and Billy are all to be thought of as extraordinary men, just as Rolfe and Vine in *Clarel,* I.xxxi.45, are termed "Exceptional natures." Though in a previous passage Vere is described as "one who whatever his sterling qualities was without any brilliant ones" (Leaf 79), he is nevertheless "an exceptional character" (Leaf 81), a man with "something exceptional in [his] moral quality." Being "a veritable touchstone of [another] man's essential nature," as stated here, he doubtless possesses "that finer spiritual insight indispensable to the understanding of the essential in certain [other] exceptional characters, whether evil ones or good" (Leaf 129)— e.g., Claggart and Budd. Claggart too has an "exceptional" nature (Leaf 132); he and presumably Vere are "perhaps" the only two men in the ship "intellectually capable of adequately appreciating the moral phenomenon . . . in Billy" (Leaf 141), since to understand "such a character" as Budd's "something more, or rather something else than mere shrewdness is perhaps needful" (Leaf 187). Though Billy too is an extraordinary specimen both physically and morally, the machinations of a Claggart are said to be "beyond the construing of such a nature," for he lacks "that sort of sensitive spiritual organization which in some cases instinctively conveys to ignorant innocence an admonition of the proximity of the malign" (Leaves 180-81).

220. *to make me his coxswain:* as stated on Leaf 209, Vere has already thought of promoting Billy to the captaincy of the mizzentop. The practice of selecting outstanding crewmen to man commodore's barge and captain's gig or to become quartermaster is mentioned in *White-Jacket,* Ch. 39; *Israel Potter,* Ch. 14-15; and "Bridegroom Dick" (*Poems,* pp. 167-68), whose title character in his youth is a figure much like Billy.

221. *mesmerically looking him in the eye:* so in *The Confidence-Man,* Ch. 43, Melville had alluded to the "cosmopolitan's" manner as like that, "fabled or otherwise, of certain creatures . . . which have the power of persuasive fascination—the power of holding another creature by the button of the eye, as it were, despite the serious disinclination, and, indeed, earnest protest, of the victim." Here and on Leaf 222, the allusions to mesmerism are late additions.

222. *the paralyzing lurch of the torpedo fish:* the expression "torpedo-fish thrill" occurs in Melville's letter to Hawthorne of June 1[?], 1851; in *Clarel,* I.xxiii.78-80, a coldly hostile rabbi is like "a torpedo-fish, with mind / Intent to paralyze."

226. *quick as the flame from a discharged cannon:* Braswell (1957), p. 137, comparing Billy with Ahab, notes that "Melville uses the same figure, a firing cannon, to express the terrific feeling of the two men against their opponents. ... Ahab's chest is compared to a mortar which bursts his 'hot heart's shell' upon the White Whale" (*Moby Dick*, Ch. 41). Ahab would "strike the sun if it insulted me" (Ch. 36); *Pierre*, Bk. 9.3, interprets *Hamlet* as signifying "that all meditation is worthless, unless it prompt to action; ... that in the earliest instant of conviction, the roused man must strike, and, if possible, with the precision and the force of the lightning-bolt." "Quick as lightning" Billy had struck the insulting Red Whiskers (Leaf 21); here, though he strikes quickly, the blow comes only after his "vocal impediment" prevents his complying with Vere's injunction: "Speak! Defend yourself!"

Unhesitating in his response to a primarily physical assault, Billy is clearly at a loss when confronting less tangible challenges such as his "petty trouble" with the ship's corporals (Leaf 106) and the unwelcome overtures of the afterguardsman. Though "his vocal infirmity somewhat intruded" during the scene in the forechains (Leaf 157), he had repulsed the afterguardsman with a physical threat, but remaining "nonplussed" by the incident (Leaf 162), he subsequently failed in "his duty as a loyal bluejacket" to report the matter (Leaves 166, 253). The earlier passages in *Billy Budd* constitute Melville's careful preparation for the present scene.

228. *The father ... the military disciplinarian:* the young hero of *Redburn*, according to Ch. 14, "had heard that some sea-captains are fathers to their crew; and so they are; but such fathers as Solomon's precepts tend to make— severe and chastising fathers, fathers whose sense of duty overcomes the sense of love, and who every day, in some sort, play the part of Brutus, who ordered his son away to execution, as I have read in our old family Plutarch."

231. *the divine judgment on Ananias:* "Peter said, Ananias ... thou hast not lied unto men, but unto God. And Ananias hearing these words fell down, and gave up the ghost ..." (Acts 5:3–5).

232. *"Struck dead by an angel of God! Yet the angel must hang!"*: Vere's "passionate interjections"—which so "discompose" the surgeon—reveal him as having already made up his mind concerning Billy's fate.

233. *a drumhead court:* a court-martial held in the field for immediate trial of offenses committed during military operations (originally, an upturned drum was used for a table); in *Billy Budd*, "a summary court" of the *Bellipotent*'s own officers, Captain Vere "electing the individuals composing it" (Leaf 245).

According to Ch. 21 (Leaves 243–45), Vere would have preferred to hold Billy prisoner until the matter could be laid before the admiral, but sensing "the urgency of the case" he is "glad *it would not be at variance with usage* to turn the matter over to a summary court of his own officers" (italics added). This passage was inscribed at Stage *Fa*. But in Ch. 20, subsequently inscribed after Stage *G* during Melville's late pencil revision, the idea of appointing a drumhead court strikes the surgeon "as impolitic, if nothing more" (Leaf 234); unlike Vere, the surgeon, the lieutenants, and the captain of marines all think "such a matter should be referred to the admiral" (Leaf 236), though they offer no direct challenge to the decision of their superior. Given the circumstances of the case, however, the point at issue—as British naval officers of the period would certainly have known—is a matter not of "usage," as Vere is said to consider it, but of law.

According to statute (22 George II, Cap. 33, Sect. VIII), it was then provided that "in case any Commander in Chief of any Fleet or Squadron . . . in Foreign Parts shall detach any Part of such Fleet or Squadron, every Commander in Chief shall, and he is hereby authorized and required, by Writing under his Hand, to impower the Chief Commander of the Squadron or Detachment so ordered on such separate Service . . . to hold Courts Martial during the Time of such separate Service . . . " (*A Collection of the Statutes Relating to the Admiralty, Navy, Shipping, and Navigation* . . . [London, 1810], p. 157). Though the *Bellipotent* is currently "on detached service," being "almost at her furthest remove from the fleet" (Leaves 190, 191), Vere is but the captain of a single vessel rather than "the Chief Commander of the Squadron or Detachment" mentioned in the statute. John McArthur, *Principles and Practice of Naval and Military Courts Martial* (4th ed.; 2 vols.; London, 1813), I, 162–63, observing that there were no inferior or divisional courts-martial in the British navy analogous to regimental or garrison courts-martial in the army, states that "by the 4th article of the Old Printed Instructions [*Rules of discipline and good government, to be observed on board his majesty's ships of war*, in effect until 1806], a captain was not authorized to punish a seaman beyond 12 lashes upon his bare back, with a cat-of-nine-tails; but, *if the fault should deserve greater punishment, he was directed to apply for a court martial*" (italics added). That is, a captain on foreign station was required to refer such a case to his "Chief Commander" as the convening authority.

The evidence here and elsewhere suggests that Melville simply had not familiarized himself with statutes of the period concerning administration of British naval justice. Observe the size and composition of the "court" that Vere appoints (Leaf 245); Vere's statement that "We proceed under the law of the Mutiny Act" (Leaf 273); his decision to carry out the court's sentence "without delay" (Leaf 284) before the findings can be submitted to higher authority for review.

235. *Was he unhinged?:* the same word occurs in *Clarel* with reference to quite unlike characters, Nathan and Cyril. In I.xvii.99–100, dealing with Nathan's earlier career, there is no implication of permanent mental derangement: "This reminiscence of dismay, / These thoughts unhinged him." But the monk Cyril, once a soldier, has become a monomaniac: "[W]hat grief or zeal," asks Clarel in III.xxiv.79–80, "Could so unhinge him?" Madness itself, Melville had once written in his copy of Shakespeare, is "undefinable. It & right reason extremes of one"; as with Pip in *Moby Dick*, Ch. 93, "man's insanity" may even be "heaven's sense." A passage in *Pierre*, Bk. 11.4, is

especially applicable here in view of the further development of the surgeon's character in his dialogue with the purser on Leaves 321–24 below. Concerning the "wild, perverse" reactions observable in "minds of a certain temperament" while undergoing "unusual affliction," this comment is made: "The cool censoriousness of the mere philosopher would denominate such conduct as . . . temporary madness; and perhaps it is, since, in the inexorable and inhuman eye of mere undiluted reason, all grief, whether on our own account, or that of others, is the sheerest unreason and insanity."

As pointed out by Anderson (1940), pp. 339–41, magazine discussion of the *Somers* case (see Leaf 281 and note) in the late 1880's stressed the "trepidation" of Captain Mackenzie "as amounting almost to a mania"; some critics find parallels between Mackenzie and Vere—even between Mackenzie and Claggart (see Leaves 134, 188, on Claggart's state of mind).

239. *innocence and guilt . . . in effect changed places:* in such chapters of *Moby Dick* as "The Try-Works" and "The Chase—Third Day" (Ch. 96, 135), and throughout *Pierre*, which he subtitled "The Ambiguities," Melville had presented somewhat comparable reversals of values. *Pierre*, Bk. 9.1, observes that "even the less distant regions of thought are not without their singular introversions," and Bk. 18.2, taking issue with the conventional idea that this is "a very plain, downright matter-of-fact, plodding, humane sort of world," forcefully controverts the everyday view that "scorns all ambiguities, all transcendentals, and all manner of juggling" (note "the jugglery of circumstances" specified here). In Bk. 19.2 the despairing Pierre takes even "Virtue and Vice" themselves to be but meaningless terms—"two shadows cast from one nothing."

For similar reversals in *Billy Budd*, compare the rendering of events in the "three brief chapters" that conclude the novel. Under "News from the Mediterranean" in an "authorized" naval chronicle (Leaf 340) is a version of the affair as "navally regarded."

241–42. *The maintenance of secrecy . . . Peter the Barbarian:* this sentence is nearer than any other in *Billy Budd* to indicating disapproval of Vere's course of action. It parallels strikingly a passage in *White-Jacket*, Ch. 72, that indignantly attacks courts-martial: "What can be expected from a court whose deeds are done in the darkness of the recluse courts of the Spanish Inquisition? . . . when an oligarchy of epaulets sits upon the bench, and a plebian top-man, without a jury, stands judicially naked at the bar?" Three paragraphs later in *White-Jacket* occurs Melville's condemnatory reference to the *Somers* case of 1842 (to which a deliberately noncommittal allusion is made on Leaves 280–82 below); in that case a council of officers—not a court—met privately, without announcement even to the three men whose lives were at stake. Here, the reference above to Vere's "cousin Jack Denton" may perhaps suggest that Melville had in mind the situation of his own cousin, Guert Gansevoort, first lieutenant of the *Somers* and the officer presiding at the council.

The association of Vere with "Peter the Barbarian" (Peter the Great of

Russia, 1672–1725, who founded St. Petersburg in 1703) appears to constitute another reversal of values within the story: in previous passages Vere has been related to organized society while the term "barbarian" has been applied— with favorable connotations—to Billy. References to Peter the Great and to Russian czars generally in Melville's earlier works, especially *Redburn*, Ch. 33 of *Moby Dick*, and "I and My Chimney," had laid stress on their autocratic rule: Ch. 52 of *Redburn* describes emigrant passengers aboard the *Highlander* as being "under a sort of martial-law," their affairs "regulated by the despotic ordinances of the captain [named *Riga!*]. And though ... to a certain extent this is necessary, and even indispensable; yet, as at sea no appeal lies beyond the captain, he too often makes unscrupulous use of his power. And as for going to law with him at the end of the voyage, you might as well go to law with the Czar of Russia."

244. *a conscientious disciplinarian:* Vere, though "mindful of the welfare of his men," is described as "never tolerating an infraction of discipline" (Leaf 74); he evidently follows "that icy though conscientious policy" said in "Benito Cereno" to be "more or less adopted by all commanders of large ships." Yet "in a world so full of all dubieties as this," to quote *Pierre*, Bk. 3.2, "one can never be entirely certain whether another person, however carefully and cautiously conscientious, has acted in all respects ... for the very best." ("Here he may or may not have erred"—Leaf 241.) Relevant to the present paragraph is a superseded passage (Leaf [229c]357) concerning the surgeon's reaction to Vere's course: "he could not help thinking how more than futile the utmost discretion sometimes proves in this human sphere subject as it is to unfor[e]seeable fatalities; the prudent method adopted by Captain Vere to obviate publicity and trouble having resulted in an event that necessitated the former, and, under existing circumstances in the navy indefinit[e]ly magnified the latter."

As for "the perils of moral responsibility" confronting Vere, compare *White-Jacket*, Ch. 72: "White-Jacket is not unaware ... that the responsibility of an officer commanding at sea ... is unparalleled by that of any other relation in which man may stand to man." But, the chapter continues, "modern sea-commanders and naval courts-martial" have "powers which exceed the due limits of reason and necessity." Principles "right and salutary ... in themselves ... have been advanced in justification of things, which in themselves are ... wrong and pernicious."

245. *the individuals composing it:* as pointed out above, British naval regulations in effect at this period made no provision for a drumhead court (note to Leaf 233). According to statute, moreover, regular naval courts-martial consisted of commanders and captains (Stat. 22 George II, Cap. 33, Sect. VI, as quoted in *A Collection of the Statutes Relating to the Admiralty, Navy, Shipping, and Navigation* ... [London, 1810], p. 157); on Leaf 205, however, it is said that Vere had served on "a court-martial ashore ... when a lieutenant."

LEAVES 245-262

The inclusion of the marine captain and the sailing master in Vere's "court" is doubly a deviation "from general custom" (Leaf 246). In the words of C. Northcote Parkinson, *Portsmouth Point: The British Navy in Fiction, 1793–1815* (Cambridge, Mass., 1949), p. 27, "Marine officers had less to do than perhaps anyone else on board. In the literature of the period they are always represented as dividing their time between gluttony and sleep. As few of them could rise above the rank of captain, which was equal to lieutenant in the navy, and none above the rank of major, they were seldom men of either birth or talent. The master, whose principal function was as navigational expert, had almost invariably been in the merchant service. He was not a commissioned officer but, like the purser, he held his warrant from the Admiralty."

At Stage *X* Melville had thought of a four-man court; in later reducing the number to three and substituting here "the captain of marines" for "a lieutenant of minor grade" he overlooked certain resulting inconsistencies that remain standing in the manuscript. Immediately below, on Leaf 246, is a reference to "the sea lieutenants," emended in the present text to "the sea lieutenant and the sailing master." On Leaf 275 is a reference to "the junior lieutenant," emended to "the sailing master": since by that point both the marine officer and the lieutenant have participated in the discussion, it must be the sailing master who speaks there "for the first." And on that same leaf, we have accordingly emended Vere's reply to begin not with "Lieutenant" but with "Gentlemen".

253. *the heaviest of penalties:* "If any person in the fleet shall conceal any traiterous or mutinous practice, or design, being convicted thereof by the sentence of a court martial, he shall suffer death, or such other punishment as a court martial may think fit; and if any person, in or belonging to the fleet, shall conceal any traiterous or mutinous words, spoken by any, to the prejudice of his Majesty or government, or any words, practice, or design, tending to the hindrance of the service, and shall not forthwith reveal the same to the commanding officer; or being present at any mutiny or sedition, shall not use his utmost endeavours to suppress the same, he shall be punished, as a court martial shall think he deserves" (Article of War XX, as quoted in McArthur, *Principles and Practice of Naval and Military Courts Martial*, I, 332–33).

257. *a dog of generous breed:* "Of self-consciousness he seemed to have . . . about as much as we may reasonably impute to a dog of Saint Bernard's breed" (Leaf 42).

262. *the monotonous blank of the twilight sea:* Vere's repeated gazing at the "blank sea" (Leaf 78) suggests comparison with the "blank ocean" of "In the Desert" (*Poems*, p. 253) and with the remark in "Pebbles" (*Poems*, p. 205) that

"echo the seas have none;
Nor aught that gives man back man's strain—
The hope of his heart, the dream in his brain."

263. *deters some minds from addressing any popular assemblies:* before revision this passage read: "deters some superior minds from taking part in popular assemblies; under which head is to be classed most legislatures in a Democracy." Compare "Major Gentian and Colonel J. Bunkum," in which, when Gentian's "insistent friends" run him "for the legislature," Bunkum attacks him for tendencies considered aristocratic or even monarchical. Of his own position Melville had written to Hawthorne on June 1[?], 1851: "It seems an inconsistency to assert unconditional democracy in all things, and yet confess a dislike to all mankind—in the mass." Throughout his subsequent writing runs a marked antithesis between what he called in the same letter his "ruthless democracy on all sides" and his evident pride of family, respect for tradition, and regard for those men who stand out from the mass, as do his own principal characters. In a discussion of Ahab in *Moby Dick*, Ch. 33, it is observed that "a man's intellectual superiority . . . can never assume the practical, available supremacy over other men, without the aid of some sort of external arts . . . more or less paltry and base. This it is, that for ever keeps God's true princes . . . from the world's hustings; and leaves the highest honors . . . to those men who become famous more through their infinite inferiority to the choice hidden handful of the Divine Inert, than through their undoubted superiority over the dead level of the mass."

In Vere is "a virtue aristocratic in kind" (Leaf 77); both Billy and Claggart as well as the captain possess "exceptional" qualities (note to Leaf 214, *something exceptional in the moral quality* . . .).

264. *unshared studies . . . an active career:* "Though given to study," Rolfe in *Clarel*, I.xxxi.17–21, was "no scholastic partisan . . . / But supplemented Plato's theme / With daedal life in boats and tents, / A messmate of the elements."

268. *allegiance . . . to Nature:* in *Israel Potter*, Ch. 15, John Paul Jones seems "as much to bear the elemental commission of Nature, as the military warrant of Congress."

268. *the ocean, . . . where we move and have our being:* in the Lord "we live, and move, and have our being" (Acts 17:28); compare "Pebbles" (*Poems*, p. 206): "On ocean where the embattled fleets repair, / Man, suffering inflictor, sails on sufferance there."

270. *the heart . . . , sometimes the feminine in man:* a recurrent analogy in Melville's depiction of characters dominated by imagination and compassion: e.g., "an imaginative and feminine sensibility," in *The Confidence-Man*, Ch. 13.

272. *according to the Articles of War, a capital crime:* "If any officer, mariner, soldier, or other person in the fleet, shall strike any of his superior officers, or draw, or offer to draw, or lift any weapon against him, being in the execution of his office, *on any pretence whatsoever*, every such person being convicted of such offence, by the sentence of a court martial, shall suffer death . . ." (Article XXII, as quoted in McArthur, *Principles and Practice of Naval and Military*

Courts Martial, I, 333 [italics added]; *White-Jacket*, Ch. 70, quotes its American counterpart as of 1850, Article XIV).

273. *the Mutiny Act:* the first Mutiny Act was voted by Parliament in 1689 as a temporary measure to punish mutineers and deserters from the English *army;* successive Mutiny Acts relating to the land forces were passed annually, with some brief exceptions, for nearly two hundred years (McArthur, I, 23; James Snedeker, *A Brief History of Courts-Martial* [Annapolis, 1954], pp. 17–19). The British *navy* in 1797 was operating under an entirely separate Act of 1749, one that consolidated and clarified prior naval laws, together with the *King's Regulations and Admiralty Instructions* of 1772 (Snedeker, p. 47). Vere's statement here that "We proceed under the law of the Mutiny Act" is therefore incorrect unless Melville thought of the captain as deliberately applying military rather than naval law to the case at hand.

273. *forced to fight ... against their will:* in Ch. 74 of *White-Jacket* an old Negro, Tawney, an American impressed into the British navy during the War of 1812, is represented as recalling how he had vainly sought permission to remain neutral during a battle with an American ship. "But when a ship of any nation is running into action," Melville commented, "it is no time for argument, small time for justice, and not much time for humanity." Similarly, Danes in the British navy were unwilling to fight against Denmark at the Battle of Copenhagen: Melville marked a relevant passage in his copy of Southey's *Life of Nelson*, p. 204. (In *Israel Potter*, Ch. 13, when the impressed Israel complains to his kidnappers that he is "no Englishman," his jailers reply: " 'Oh! that's the old story. . . . There's no Englishman in the English fleet. All foreigners. You may take their own word for it.' ")

281. *the U.S. brig-of-war* Somers: Melville's previous allusions to the *Somers* case in *White-Jacket* occur in the context of an impassioned dissertation on the Articles of War, which Ch. 71 denounces as "an importation from . . . Britain" (compare "modeled upon the English Mutiny Act" below). Ch. 70, discussing enforcement of "these bloodthirsty laws" even in time of peace, asks: "What happened to those three sailors on board an American armed vessel a few years ago, quite within your memory, White-Jacket; yea, while you yourself were yet serving on board this very frigate, the *Neversink* [the *United States*]? What happened to . . . those three sailors, even as you, who once were alive, but now are dead? 'Shall suffer death!' those were the three words that hung those three sailors." Ch. 72 cites the "well-known case of a United States brig" as "a memorable example, which at any moment may be repeated. Three men, in a time of peace, were then hung at the yard-arm, merely because, in the captain's judgment, it became necessary to hang them. To this day the question of their complete guilt is socially discussed." In "Bridegroom Dick" Melville makes further allusion to the case through the character of "Tom Tight" (*Poems*, pp. 174–75), who is clearly intended to stand for his cousin Guert Gansevoort, first lieutenant of the *Somers* at the time of the hanging:

LEAF 281

"Tom was lieutenant in the brig-o'-war famed
When an officer was hung for an arch-mutineer,
But a mystery cleaved, and the captain was blamed,
And a rumpus too raised, though his honor it was clear.
And Tom he would say, when the mousers would try him,
And with cup after cup o' Burgundy ply him:
'Gentlemen, in vain with your wassail you beset,
For the more I tipple, the tighter do I get.'
No blabber, no, not even with the can—
True to himself and loyal to his clan."

That *Billy Budd* derives from Melville's knowledge and opinion of the *Somers* affair has been suggested by a number of scholars, notably Anderson (1940) and Arvin (1948); for the fullest background on the case see Hayford (1959). As Arvin points out, p. 55 n., Melville is mistaken in his statement in the manuscript that "a midshipman and two petty officers" were executed; Philip Spencer was an acting midshipman; Samuel Cromwell "was in fact the boatswain's mate, but the other, Elisha Small, was a plain 'seaman.' " (The present text is emended to read "a midshipman and two sailors.") He is also mistaken in asserting here that their execution was resolved upon under the Articles of War; the commander, Alexander Slidell Mackenzie, recognized that these gave him no authority to try or to hang the men, and he declared, "In the necessities of my position I found my law, and in them also I must trust to find my justification" (see Hayford [1959], p. 42; also pp. 123, 149–53). When Melville wrote the passage quoted above from *White-Jacket*, Ch. 72, he was aware that "the letter of the code was not altogether observed" and that "necessity" was the commander's plea. Not only was Mackenzie's act vindicated by the naval court of inquiry, as Melville states, but he was also acquitted of the charge of murder (and other charges) in a subsequent court-martial. Melville's inaccuracies here indicate that he did not have the details of the case clearly in mind and that he had not recently, as has sometimes been asserted, "examined all that he could find about the alleged mutiny plot on the *Somers*" (Leyda [1952], p. 636).

Richard T. Stavig in his unpublished doctoral dissertation, "Melville's *Billy Budd*—A New Approach to the Problem of Interpretation" (Princeton University, 1953; see *Dissertation Abstracts*, XIV [1954], 822–23), argues strongly for the *Somers* case as the major determinant of Melville's handling of *Billy Budd*. According to Stavig, "the way in which Melville used the *Somers* material and his attitude toward Mackenzie's action (he called it 'murder' at one time) suggest the general trend of the book, an interpretation which internal evidence supports. . . . I believe Melville was making a bitter protest against blind and complete obedience—in this case to naval law, rather than to a superior officer. Man must never sacrifice his humanity, Melville is saying . . ." (letter to Hanson W. Baldwin, quoted in the latter's *Sea Fights and Shipwrecks* [Garden City, 1955], p. 202).

Though recollections of the *Somers* affair were certainly in Melville's mind during the writing of *Billy Budd*, his attitude toward it is by no means clear, as the passage at hand and that cited above from "Bridegroom Dick" indicate; and the present editors conclude both from their detailed study of the case and from their analysis of the novel's genesis that the hanging aboard the *Somers* should not be taken as its primary "source." What survives of the ballad and draft headnote from which *Billy Budd* grew, and the manner of its growth, show clearly enough that at first Melville was not thinking specifically of the historical incident of 1842. (See Introduction, pp. 28-30.)

282. *a writer whom few know:* doubtless Melville himself, who in his later years depreciated " 'fame' . . . especially of the literary sort," to use the language of his letter to James Billson of December 20, 1885. (An earlier version of the passage here read "a writer whom nobody knows, and who being dead recks not of the oblivion.") On Melville's device of invented spokesmen, see note to Leaf 127, *an honest scholar, my senior;* the letter to Billson also professes to quote "a waggish acquaintance."

284. *follows without delay:* according to McArthur, *Principles and Practice of Naval and Military Courts Martial,* I, 67-68, "*The offences relating to mutinous assemblies, sedition, &c.* are punished by the articles of war with death; or otherwise, as a court martial shall think fit. By stat. 22 Geo[rge] II. cap. 33. sect. 19. sentences of death by naval courts martial, in cases of mutiny, may be put in execution, within the narrow seas or on foreign stations, without reporting the proceedings of the courts martial either to the lords commissioners of the admiralty, or the commander in chief abroad, where such sentence was passed. But no sentence of death, *for other crimes specified in the articles of war,* can be put in execution till after the report of the proceedings of the said court shall have been made to the lords commissioners of the admiralty, or to the commander of the fleet or squadron in which the sentence was passed, and their or his directions shall have been given therein" (italics added). See note to Leaf 233, *a drumhead court.*

288. *what remains primeval in our formalized humanity:* Glick (1953), pp. 107-8, holds that Vere "did not earn Melville's highest accolade . . . until he let himself 'melt back' " as he does here, forgetting temporarily his sense of duty, his prudence (see note to Leaf 65, *prudence . . . glory . . . duty*); such a view argues that Vere is not the mere formalist that some critics take him to be (see note to Leaf 333, *forms, measured forms*). Lesser (1957), pp. 92-93, stresses Billy's response to Vere: "No less instinctively than he had recoiled from Claggart's hostile assault, Billy submits to his sentence because he feels that Captain Vere has decreed it in love." Thus the novel "at the deepest level" is "a legend of reconciliation between an erring son and a stern but loving father-figure." For evidence of Billy's regard for Vere, however, Lesser depends upon "Billy's expression as he sleeps before his execution" and his subsequent dying benediction upon the captain (Leaf 317)—which some readers

take ironically. As for the present encounter, other commentators, though recognizing its importance to the story, detect a failure of artistry in its rendering. Thus Gettmann and Harkness (1955), p. 74, charge that Melville "simply evades this scene, and that he felt embarrassed in doing so is suggested by the fact that he substitutes for it a paragraph of thin summarized conjecture about Vere's part in the interview." Billy's reaction rather than Vere's troubles Goldsmith (1961), who thinks the Coxe-Chapman play of *Billy Budd* an improvement upon the novel: by adding a dramatized "discovery scene" at this point in the action, he argues, the authors are able to show a "kinetic" Billy in the process of reaching, with Vere's help, an understanding of his fate.

288. *Abraham . . . Isaac . . . the exacting behest:* "God did tempt Abraham, and said . . . Take now thy son, thine only son Isaac, whom thou lovest, . . . and offer him . . . for a burnt offering. . . . And Abraham . . . bound Isaac his son, and laid him on the altar upon the wood. And Abraham stretched forth his hand, and took the knife to slay his son. And the angel of the Lord . . . said, Lay not thine hand upon the lad, neither do thou any thing unto him: for now I know that thou fearest God. . . . And . . . saith the Lord, . . . I will bless thee . . . because thou hast obeyed my voice" (Genesis 22:1-18).

289. *each diviner magnanimity:* "In me divine magnanimities are spontaneous and instantaneous," Melville had written to Hawthorne on November 17[?], 1851; "—catch them while you can." Berthoff (1960), pp. 344-49, finds in the concept of magnanimity held by Aristotle and by Milton a clue to what is meant by the "rarer qualities of our nature" said to be shared by Billy and Vere (Leaves 285-86): he cites as illustrative Melville's discussion of Nelson in Ch. 4 above and notes that on an earlier occasion Billy is credited with "novice magnaminity" (Leaf 167).

289. *the agony of the strong:* the paragraph recalls Melville's earlier comment in *Pierre*, Bk. 10.2, concerning the "inevitable keen cruelty in the loftier heroism. It is not heroism only to stand unflinched ourselves in the hour of suffering; but it is heroism to stand unflinched both at our own and at some loved one's united suffering; a united suffering, which we could put an instant period to, if we would but renounce the glorious cause for which ourselves do bleed, and see our most loved one bleed."

294. *the clergyman's announcement:* Melville considered naming a specific individual; his penciled marginal notation here reads "Jonathan Edwards".

295. *The word . . . to about ship:* in the *Fa* fair copy the murmur of the crew was "pierced and suppressed by the boatswain and his Mates piping down one watch." In his late pencil revision, Melville wrote in a marginal notation, "Another order to be given here in place of this one," and supplied the substitute order: "the word was given to about ship". The point of the substitution, apparently, is that this order would require both watches to prepare for tack-

ing the ship by being at their stations, whereas piping down one watch would leave the men of that watch unoccupied.

300. *behold Billy . . . lying prone in irons:* the sleeping Billy is somewhat reminiscent of the mute sleeping on the deck of the *Fidèle* at the conclusion of the initial chapter of *The Confidence-Man*; Richard and Rita Gollin (1957), p. 514, compare the chained prisoner in one of the suggested sources of *Billy Budd*, the play *Black-Ey'd Susan* by Douglas Jerrold.

304. *the look of a slumbering child: Mardi*, Ch. 49, suggests that the idea of pre-existence "may have originated in one of those celestial visions . . . stealing over the face of a slumbering child"; *Redburn*, Ch. 13, recalls the "happy, careless, innocent look" of "an infant in the cradle"; *Moby Dick*, Ch. 87, speaks of infants "spiritually feasting upon some unearthly reminiscence"; *Pierre*, Bk. 7.8, alludes to "that angelic childlikeness, which our Savior hints is the one only investiture of translated souls; for of such—even of little children—is the other world."

305. *The chaplain . . . Christ . . . Mars:* "Good of the chaplain to enter Lone Bay," begins the ballad "Billy in the Darbies" (Leaf 348). Here and in the ballad Billy is facing death, as do the speakers in the opening pieces of the *John Marr* volume with which the ballad was originally associated; the present passage, like the prose headnotes to those pieces, stands in the present tense: "behold Billy. . . . In effect he is already in his shroud. . . . Over him . . . two battle lanterns swing. . . ." Not only the material of this passage but even the form of its presentation derives from Melville's earliest conception of Billy and his situation.

The incongruous position of a "minister of Christ . . . receiving his stipend from Mars," as the chaplain's role is described here, is strongly developed in Ch. 38 of *White-Jacket*, which pointedly asks: "How can it be expected that the religion of peace should flourish in an oaken castle of war? How can it be expected that the clergyman, whose pulpit is a forty-two-pounder, should convert sinners to a faith that enjoins them to turn the right cheek when the left is smitten? . . . Where the Captain himself is a moral man, he makes a far better chaplain for his crew than any clergyman can be"—as in *Billy Budd* it is inferred that Vere may have more "consolation to proffer" Billy than does the chaplain. That "worthy man" who "lifted not a finger to avert" Billy's doom as "a martyr to martial discipline" (Leaf 312) is like the passive chaplain at the flogging scene in "Bridegroom Dick," being himself "disciplined and dumb" (*Poems*, p. 177). In *Clarel*, III.xiii.108–29, still another "Good chaplain" reflects upon his situation as "Priest in ship with saintly bow / War-ship named from Paul and Peter"—a ship incongruously christened *The Apostles*. For Melville, the fundamental incongruity appeared to lie in "our man-of-war world" itself, to borrow a phrase from *White-Jacket*, a world in which the sacred and secular establishments, like "peace" and "war," present characteristics that appear at least outwardly similar. As in his vows "a true

[[*185*]]

military officer is . . . like a true monk" (Leaf 243 above), so an entire warship is a "Grim abbey on the wave afloat," governed with "cenobite dumb discipline," its crew pacing "Black cloisters of the god of war" (*Clarel*, IV.vii.5–12). See also notes to Leaves 311, 312.

307. *his countrymen the British captives:* in reviewing Parkman's *The California and Oregon Trail* for the *Literary World* of March 31, 1849, Melville had similarly mentioned "the naked British barbarians sent to Rome to be stared at more than 1500 years ago." Germanicus Caesar (15 B.C.–A.D. 19) received a triumph at Rome in A.D. 17.

308. *the Pope of that time:* Melville's reference is obviously to Gregory the Great (540?–604), of whom this anecdote is told in Bede's *Ecclesiastical History of the English People*, Bk. 2, Ch. 1; Bede, however, dates the incident *before* Gregory became Pope in 590.

308. *Fra Angelico's seraphs:* Giovanni da Fiesole, "Fra Angelico" (1387–1455), whose work Melville had presumably seen at the Accademia delle Belle Arti while in Florence during 1857; there are references to him in "At the Hostelry" (*Poems*, p. 332) and to his frescoes in *Clarel*, I.xviii.29.

310. *the primer of Christianity . . . received . . . on tropic isles:* in *Omoo*, Ch. 45, where Melville had enlarged upon the constitutional incapacity of the Tahitians to receive the gospel, he noted that "the missionaries give them the large type, pleasing cuts, and short and easy lessons of the primer." (Here, the word "pioneer" appears in the manuscript above "primer," written in Mrs. Melville's hand—presumably her conjectural reading of "primer"; Ch. 48 of *Omoo* speaks of the early missionaries to Tahiti as "pioneers" of the faith.) In *Omoo* as in *Typee* and the later lecture on "The South Seas" Melville scandalized some of his contemporaries by the tenor of his remarks on the missionary enterprise and exploitation of natives by allegedly civilized white men. Queequeg in *Moby Dick*, a "superior *savage*, so called," who is conspicuously more religious than his white shipmates, is virtually a missionary in reverse from the Pacific Islands to Christian, civilized America; according to Rolfe in *Clarel*, IV.xviii.45–56, "Tahiti should have been the place / For Christ in advent."

"Captain Cook's time" in Tahiti began in 1769, when Captain James Cook (1728–79) observed the transit of Venus there; he returned in the course of his second Pacific voyage of 1772–75.

311. *the young sailor's essential innocence:* at the foot of this leaf is Melville's marginal phrase "an irruption of heretic thought hard to suppress"; this we interpret as a notation referring to his own "irruption" on two leaves which at Stage *Fa* immediately followed here but which at Stage *F/G* he did in fact "suppress," partly by revision and partly by omission of Leaf *Fa* 76 ("76 omitted" is noted on Leaf 312). The content presumably involved further remarks on the anomaly of a chaplain in a warship.

Freeman (1948), on the contrary (see facsimile of *Fa* 74, facing p. 262 of his book), interpreted this phrase not as a notation but as a comment on the chaplain's thoughts and as intended for insertion, and accordingly he placed it in the text thus: "Marvel not that having been [made] acquainted with the young sailor's essential innocence (an irruption of heretic thought hard to suppress) the worthy man lifted not a finger. . . ." But the phrase when placed in that context could scarcely refer to what precedes it there. Vere and the members of the court perceived his "essential innocence" in the sense referred to here, that is, in relation to his "crime"; indeed, it is of just this aspect of Billy's situation as a condemned man that the chaplain has been informed. Such a perception, therefore, could scarcely constitute "an irruption of heretic thought hard to suppress" on the chaplain's part. The phrase might indeed make some sense as a comment on the previous paragraph, but it is not marked for insertion there. All in all, its most likely reference is to what followed on the next two leaves at *Fa* and was in fact "suppressed" by the *F/G* revision. (We take Melville's reason for the suppression to be as much or more the irrelevance here of any more extensive an irruption on this old foible of his than its heretical quality.)

312. *a musket . . . on the altar:* Melville did not develop a projected revision here: "that musket of Beecher [*Freeman:* Blücher] &c"; the present text restores his original wording. He presumably had in mind an incident of 1856 when the Rev. Henry Ward Beecher, in the words of Paxton Hibben, "pledged Plymouth Church to contribute twenty-five rifles" to a group of colonists in order to "promote the just and peaceful settlement of the Kansas issue. . . . Frivolous people called Sharp's rifles 'Beecher's Bibles' and the irreligious dubbed Plymouth Church 'the Church of the Holy Rifles.' " See Hibben's *Henry Ward Beecher: An American Portrait* (New York, 1942), p. 134.

In *The Confidence-Man,* Ch. 3, Melville introduces—to typify the paradox of the "Church Militant"—"a Methodist minister, . . . a tall, muscular, martial-looking man, . . . who in the Mexican war had been volunteer chaplain to a volunteer rifle-regiment." In *Billy Budd,* compare the boarding lieutenant's reference to the *Bellipotent*'s guns as "fighting peacemakers" (Leaf 24); see also note to Leaf 305.

313. *the prophet in the chariot:* "there appeared a chariot of fire, and horses of fire, and parted them both asunder; and Elijah went up by a whirlwind into heaven. And Elisha . . . took up . . . the mantle of Elijah that fell from him . . ." (II Kings 2:11–13). Though the allusion is not an uncommon one, there may have been lingering in Melville's mind, as he wrote this passage, the eloquent final paragraph of Southey's *Life of Nelson,* p. 308, which reads in part: "The most triumphant death is that of the martyr; the most awful, that of the martyred patriot; the most splendid, that of the hero in the hour of victory; and if the chariot and the horses of fire had been vouchsafed for Nelson's translation, he could scarcely have departed in a brighter blaze of glory. He has left us, not indeed his mantle of inspiration, but a name and an example. . . ."

LEAVES 313-317

Here, the transition from "luminous night" to the "meek, shy light" of the breaking day is similar to the movement in "Aurora-Borealis" (*Poems*, p. 98), where the Northern Lights give way to "pale, meek Dawn." The poem commemorates the dissolution of the armies of the Civil War, God "Decreeing and commanding" their "muster and disbanding."

316. *generally from the foreyard:* like other examples of Melville's seemingly detailed knowledge of naval custom "in the old time," this observation may derive from a passage in Southey's *Life of Nelson*, where in Ch. 6 Prince Francesco Caraccioli is sentenced to be hanged "at the fore-yard-arm."

316. *for special reasons the mainyard was assigned:* Freimarck (1957) suggests that the "special reasons" may have been, on Vere's part, a sensitive avoidance of the foreyard as the scene of Billy's faithful service and, on Melville's own part, the symbolic significance of the cruciform structure of mainmast and mainyard. It would appear, however, that the captain's motive was simply precautionary: the phrase "for special reasons," which is an insertion, previously read "for strategic reasons."

317. *"God bless Captain Vere!"*: this, "the most famous single sentence in *Billy Budd*" (Arvin [1948], p. 55) and for some critics "the high point" of the story (Stewart [1959], p. 285), has been variously interpreted over the years. Representative of earlier views is Watters' observation (1945), pp. 48–49, that Billy's words "show that he not only forgave the captain and condoned the judgment, but glorified the whole act, since under his influence the entire crew ... returned a sympathetic echo of the same words. In short, at the moment of his death Billy healed any breach his execution might have caused in the respect and affection of the crew for the captain." More recent critics, however, have taken issue with readings of this nature, pointing to such evidence as the statement on Leaf 327 below concerning the possible "revocation on the men's part of their involuntary echoing of Billy's benediction." The "famous sentence" is seen as ironic by those who interpret *Billy Budd* in the vein of Schiffman (1950) and Thompson (1952). " 'God bless Captain Vere!' Is this not piercing irony?" asks Schiffman, p. 133. "As innocent Billy utters these words, does not the reader gag? The injustice of Billy's hanging is heightened by his ironic blessing of the ironic Vere." To Thompson, pp. 406–7, "Billy's last words are indeed fitting and proper, in either the Christian or the ironically anti-Christian frame of reference. [They] can supply the supreme irony of the entire narrative, because they are so palpably at odds with the dark facts of the situation...."

Differing implications are also seen in the words by those who approach *Billy Budd* in terms of its possible historical or literary sources and analogues. Arvin (1948), pp. 54–55, quoting Thurlow Weed, points out that one of "the alleged mutineers" of the *Somers*, Elisha Small, "a great favorite with the crew, exclaimed 'God bless the flag!' " [though not, as Weed says, "at the moment he was run up to the yard-arm"]; Melville, Arvin speculates, had

LEAF 317

heard of Small's words, possibly from his cousin Guert Gansevoort, from their mutual acquaintance Weed, or from Weed's *Autobiography* (1883), which discusses the case and reveals a previously unpublished and rather inaccurate reminiscence of Gansevoort's role in it. But McElderry, adducing earlier literary treatments of "the *Billy Budd* theme" (1955), has greatly broadened the context of discussion. With particular reference to Freeman (1948), pp. 120–24, McElderry presents his conclusions as follows (pp. 256–57): " 'God bless Captain Vere!' may be, as some critics insist, the key to Melville's final philosophy, but beyond question it is the essence of the popular nautical hero. *Billy Budd* has usually been discussed as if it were unique in theme, a strange, unprecedented story. Future discussion must take into account the fact that Billy Budd himself is distilled from a well-established type, the nautical hero for whom duty, no matter how unfair or unreasonable it may appear, is nevertheless the voice of God. If one recognizes this, 'God bless Captain Vere!' becomes first of all what Melville said it was: 'a conventional felon's benediction directed aft towards the quarters of honor. . . .' It is the traditional ritual of the condemned man forgiving the official who is duty bound to order his death. Melville's achievement was to make real and convincing an attitude and a speech which for centuries has been a staple of popular accounts of executions."

317. *a conventional felon's benediction:* as the passage now stands, construction of the word "conventional" appears open to interpretation. (1) "Conventional" may be construed with "felon's," implying that Billy is a felon only because of the conventions that have declared him one—compare use of the word on Leaf 42 above, where Billy's "unconventional rectitude" is mentioned, and also on Leaf 48, where Billy "is not presented as a conventional hero"; in *White-Jacket* occur such expressions as "so conventionally degraded a being as a sailor" (Ch. 53) and "conventional and social superiors" (Ch. 72). (2) "Conventional" may be construed with "benediction," since there does exist the long-standing convention whereby a felon with his last words blesses some person or thing—compare Melville's phrase "this conventional world" (*Moby Dick*, Ch. 54, quoted in note to Leaf 137 above, *his significant personal beauty*) and witness the findings of McElderry (1955) and of Richard and Rita Gollin (1957), who observe that in the hanging scene of Jerrold's analogous play *Black-Ey'd Susan* the protagonist William cries "Bless you! bless you all——." Reference to the manuscript suggests that Melville himself intended "conventional" to be taken with "felon's": he originally wrote "a benediction" but made successive changes to "a felon's" and finally "a conventional felon's" while altering the beginning of the sentence from "So unanticipated a benediction" to "Syllables [s]o unanticipated"; i.e., the words of "a conventional felon" were "unanticipated" from Billy.

It will be noted that Billy's "benediction" echoes his previous words to Vere: "God will bless you for that, your honor!" (Leaf 251). There the pattern followed is simply that of the inferior blessing the superior who has treated him kindly—e.g., in Cooper's *Wing-and-Wing*, Ch. 20, where the master's mate, Clinch, acknowledges the magnanimous behavior toward him of his captain: "God bless you, Captain Cuffe; God bless you, sir. . . ." *Israel Potter* offers several instances of this nature: "God bless you for that, Mr. Millet" (Ch. 4); "God bless your Majesty!" (Ch. 5); "the King behaved handsomely towards me; . . . God bless him for it" (Ch. 14). Also relevant are Rolfe's examples in *Clarel*, I.xxxvii.104–9, of the unfortunate mariner who "Praised heaven, and said that God was good, / And his calamity but just," and Sylvio Pellico, who, when released from prison, cried: "Grateful, I thank the Emperor."

The earliest of the surviving draft leaves of the ballad of Billy Budd contains the reading "I bless his [the chaplain's] story, / The Good Being hung and gone to glory" (Leaf [347a], now Leaf 17v of "Daniel Orme").

317–18. *a singing bird on the point of launching:* Billy "could not read, but he could sing, and like the illiterate nightingale was sometimes the composer of his own song" (Leaf 42 above). The repeated bird images may survive from that period in which Melville thought of Billy himself as singing the ballad of Billy Budd, before development of the execution scene made it necessary to assign the ballad to another sailor-author. Other implications of the imagery also deserve examination.

Wagner (1958), p. 171, holds that since Billy's stutter occurred only "under sudden provocation of strong heart-feeling" (Leaf 47), and since his last words here are "wholly unobstructed in the utterance," the reader is "supposed to think, then, that there was no heart in Billy's words." But "Not in a spirit of foolish speculation altogether," Melville had written in Ch. 49 of *Redburn*, did Socrates "fancy the human soul to be essentially a harmony." So Billy's voice is said to be normally "musical, as if expressive of the harmony within" (Leaf 47); his occasional stutter (e.g., Leaves 157–59, 223–26) must therefore express some inner discord. Stewart (1959), p. 285, argues that his delivery of "God bless Captain Vere!" in "clear melody" symbolizes attainment of an inward peace, a state of mind and heart prepared for in his interview with the captain. According to this line of interpretation, Billy's last words are spoken sincerely and without intentional irony or satire (compare Leaf 30 above, and note); Melville's own attitude is of course another matter.

As for the likening of "welkin-eyed Billy" (Leaf 10) to a bird "launching from the twig," compare the concluding stanzas of "The Blue-Bird" (*Poems*, p. 265), which imply that death is followed by a form of transfiguration—not necessarily personal survival:

> "Too soon he came;
> On wings of hope he met the knell;
> His heavenly tint the dust shall tame;
> Ah, some misgiving had been well!
>
> But, look, the clear ether[e]al hue
> In June it makes the Larkspur's dower;

It is the self-same welkin-blue—
The Bird's transfigured in the Flower."

319. *the vapory fleece . . . seen in mystical vision:* so in *Clarel*, I.xxxv.96–99, the palmer Arculf describes the Palestinian sky on Ascension Eve:

" 'Olivet gleams then much the same—
Caressed, curled over, yea, encurled
By fleecy fires which typic be:
O lamb of God, O light o' the world!' "

As Miss Wright (1949) points out, p. 163, these passages combine two visions from the New Testament, the Ascension of Jesus and the Lamb on the throne, linked by "comparison of the clouds, into which Jesus disappeared, to the fleece of the lamb." In *Moby Dick*, Ch. 42 ("The Whiteness of the Whale"), is an allusion to "the Vision of St. John," in which "the Holy One" appears "white like wool" (Revelation, 1:14); a footnote speaks of "the fleece of celestial innocence and love." *Pierre*, 3.3, discusses the "angelicalness" of "the fleecy Lucy." *Clarel*, I.xvii.75–76, uses the conventional figure of lambs as "Innocents—and the type of Christ / Betrayed."

320. *ascending, took the full rose of the dawn:* in the manuscript, "rose" is a late pencil revision for "shekinah". Compare a passage in *Clarel*, IV.ix.33–47, recalling the vision of the shepherds on the morning of Christ's birth, who

"Beheld a splendor diaphanic—
Effulgence never dawn hath shot,
Nor flying meteors of the night;
And trembling rose, shading the sight;
But heard the angel breathe—*Fear not.*
So (might one reverently dare
Terrene with heavenly to compare),
So, oft in mid-watch on that sea
Where the ridged Andes of Peru
Are far seen by the coasting crew—
Waves, sails and sailors in accord
Illumed are in a mystery,
Wonder and glory of the Lord,
Though manifest in aspect minor—
Phosphoric ocean in shekinah."

The poem "In the Desert" similarly presents the sun as God's "fiery standard," its light "Of God the effluence of the essence, / Shekinah intolerably bright!" (*Poems*, pp. 253–54). But elsewhere in *Clarel*, I.xv.1–13, the troubled Celio expressly repudiates any cosmic significance in a "superb" dawn. Addressing the sun as "thou orb supreme," he continues:

" ' 'Tis Olivet which thou ascendest—
The hill and legendary chapel;

LEAVES 320-321

Yet how indifferent thy beam!
Awe nor reverence pretendest:
Dome and summit dost but dapple
With gliding touch, a tinging gleam:
Knowest thou the Christ? believest in the dream?' "

As to the implications of the present passage, the critics are in wide disagreement. Miss Wright (1940), p. 194 n., and (1949), p. 135, finds "a suggestion of the Ascension and of the doctrine of the Atonement"; Campbell (1951), pp. 379–80, though agreeing that "there is a reference to the ascension of Christ" in this paragraph, finds "overwhelming evidence for the ironical pessimism" of the story in the hanging scene as a whole: Billy's "ascension is only to the yard-end," says Campbell, "and the peaceful beauty in the 'full rose of the dawn' by contrast makes this solemn fact all the more horribly evident." Both Campbell and Miss Wright take note of Melville's revisions in the manuscript here and at the beginning of Ch. 27 ("execution" for "ascension," Leaf 325), but draw opposite conclusions from the evidence; similar differences persist among subsequent commentators.

320. *the slow roll of the hull:* as copied and revised, the passage once read "the slow roll of the hull, in moderate weather so majestic in a great ship ponderously cannoned." Then with the marginal notation "put on previous page" Melville marked "in moderate . . . cannoned" for transfer to Leaf 319 (there to follow "the periodic roll to leeward"), first substituting "ship" for "hull" and then replacing "slow roll of the ship" with "ship's motion." Still later he decided against the transfer, striking out the notations concerning it on both affected leaves but without correcting the vestigial reading "the ship's motion in moderate . . . cannoned." We have returned to the original reading as Melville himself presumably intended doing, since what is "so majestic" here is particularly the ship's "slow roll" rather than its "motion" generally.

321. *the purser: White-Jacket,* Ch. 48, describes the duties and status of a purser, who has "under his charge all the financial affairs of a man-of-war"; "usage seems to assign him a conventional station somewhat above that of his equals in navy rank—the chaplain, surgeon, and professor."

Here, the purser's discussion with the surgeon is an expansion at copy Stage *Ga* of a single paragraph which stood at this same point in the manuscript at copy Stage *Fa;* still later, in pencil, Melville set off the expanded passage as a separate chapter headed "A digression." To Freeman (1948), p. 14, the episode is merely an unfortunate attempt at humor, but for Chase (1948), p. 274, it "universalizes the theme of the story by presenting two opposite mythical types of man lingering, as it were, over the body." Miss Foley (1961) rightly recognizes that with Ch. 26 begins an interrelated series of five concluding chapters, each in its way a "digression," which present sharply divergent impressions of Billy and his story. The series, Miss Foley observes, p.

164, fulfills a dual function: structurally, to "echo the novel's basic conflict between metaphysical and external form"; thematically, to "demonstrate the impossibility of reducing truth to a single formal standard."

321. *the surgeon:* the role of this unnamed official is essentially that of a professional needed first to certify that Claggart is dead and later to supervise Billy's execution. His appearances as a commentator upon Vere's mental state (Leaf 234) and, in terms of "the lexicon of science" (Leaf 322), on Billy's death, are relatively late additions to the manuscript that radically alter his characterization and especially his function in the story. In these added scenes his attitude is reminiscent of the "heartless" scientist found in Melville's previous writings—particularly Cadwallader Cuticle, surgeon of the fleet, who is broadly satirized in *White-Jacket*, Ch. 61–63.

321. *a hanging scientifically conducted:* in London on November 13, 1849, when in the company of his friend Dr. Franklin Taylor, Melville had witnessed the public execution by hanging of the Mannings, a husband and wife convicted of murder: "All in all, a most wonderful, horrible, & unspeakable scene," runs the comment in his journal. (Leyda [1951], I, 331, reproduces a portion of a broadside Melville bought at the time and prints a stanza of a street ballad on the execution.)

Here, the absence of motion in Billy's "pinioned figure" (Leaf 320) has provoked critical comments as diverse as the views of purser and surgeon. Chase holds (1948), p. 1217, that there is no muscular spasm—no orgasm—in the body because Billy has been "unmanned" by Melville himself; subsequently Chase adds (1949), pp. 274–75, that "Billy's vitality or 'virtue' has been symbolically transferred to Vere," noting that at Billy's benediction Vere had "stood erectly rigid as a musket" (Leaf 319). Casper (1952), pp. 151–52, remarks that "obviously" the purser is using "euthanasia" in the Greek sense of "wilful sacrifice of one's self for one's country; the fact that the death was willed was supposed to induce pleasure." Giovannini (1955), p. 492, sees in the narrative the suggestion of "a providential death which ironically cheats the gallows"; his interpretation has been strongly challenged, however, by Campbell (1955), who represents those critics who interpret the novel as sustained irony. See Introduction, pp. 26–27.

Sutton (1960), p. 131, arguing for the influence of Schopenhauer on *Billy Budd* (see note to Leaf 44 above, *the doctrine of man's Fall*), notes that Schopenhauer equates the word "euthanasia" with "the Buddhist term *Nirvana*. In his *Counsels and Maxims*"—read by Melville in 1891 (Sealts Nos. 443, 444) —"he describes euthanasia as 'an easy death, not ushered in by disease, and free from all pain and struggle.' For Schopenhauer, as for the Buddhist, death in this form is not an evil but the highest consummation of life." For Sutton, Billy's "strange bodily quiescence" is suggestive of just such a "mental acceptance of death." Sutton's position, with respect to the entire novel as well as to the point at issue here, recalls the influential interpretation of *Billy Budd* by Grant Watson (1933) as a "testament of acceptance"; to approach the work in 1960 as Sutton does is to challenge those critics of the 1950's who read it as ironic social protest—a "testament of resistance," in Withim's phrase (1959). But here, it should be emphasized, neither the purser nor the surgeon is necessarily advancing the views of the author—indeed, the deliberate juxtaposition of contrasting attitudes found in this and the remaining chapters is itself a factor that argues against taking any one of them exclusively as Melville's own.

326. *its murmurous indistinctness:* in Ch. 23 of *The Scarlet Letter* Hawthorne had written similarly of the reaction to Arthur Dimmesdale's "final word": "The multitude, silent till then, broke out in a strange, deep voice of awe and wonder, which could not as yet find utterance, save in this murmur that rolled so heavily after the departed spirit."

329. *the last offices:* in *White-Jacket,* Ch. 80 and 81, dealing with a burial at sea, the activities of the sailmaker's mates are treated at some length.

329. *certain larger seafowl:* Freeman (1948), p. 50, compares the fowl appearing at the burial of Shenly in *White-Jacket,* Ch. 81. The sky-hawk of the final chapter of *Moby Dick,* the three gulls of the Timoneer's story in *Clarel,* III.xii, and as Fogle suggests (1960), p. 204, the three fatal birds of "The Haglets" (*Poems,* pp. 185–94) are also analogous.

The sentence here will serve as an example of Melville's more chaotic syntax. Before emendation it read: "But when the tilted plank let slide its freight into the sea, a second strange human murm[u]r was heard, blended now with another inarticulate sound proceeding from certain larger sea-fowl whose attention having been attracted by the peculiar commotion in the water resulting from the heavy sloped dive of the shotted hammock, into the sea flew screaming to the spot." We have emended "sea-fowl whose attention having been attracted . . . sea flew screaming" to "seafowl who, their attention having been attracted . . . sea, flew screaming".

331. *the drum beat to quarters: White-Jacket,* Ch. 69, describes the ceremony in some detail, including the prayers at the guns; in "The Haglets" (*Poems,* p. 192), even as the doomed ship strikes,

> "a drum-beat calls
> And prompt the men to quarters go;
> Discipline, curbing nature, rules—
> Heroic makes who duty know:
> They execute the trump's command,
> Or in peremptory places wait and stand."

331. *a sort of impulse:* the manuscript at this point reads "impulse docility"; previous editors, by supplying a supposedly missing "of" so as to read "impulse of docility," have concocted a basically incongruous phrase. Though "impulse *or* docility" might be a preferable emendation, the problem here arises not from lack of a word that will link the two nouns but rather from

an unresolved choice between them posed by Melville in revising a much-altered sentence. Had he completed the revision by settling on the word more appropriate to its context he would presumably have preferred "impulse" to "docility."

332. *The drumbeat dissolved the multitude:* something of a parallel to the scene described here is found in "Naples in the Time of Bomba," VII (*Poems*, pp. 357-63). There the boy Carlo improvises a lyric that catches "the wafted roll / Of Bomba's barbarous tom-toms thumped," illustrating the effect of the drumbeat upon the chattering Neapolitan crowd: "Drubs them *dumb!* . . . All is *glum! . . .* For, look, they *come!*"

333. *forms, measured forms:* Vere's attitude here recalls Melville's own response to the world of Greece and Rome during his Mediterranean trip of 1856-57, reflected in his lecture "Statues in Rome" and his poems headed "Fruit of Travel Long Ago" in the *Timoleon* volume of 1891. "Greek Architecture" (*Poems*, p. 248) is especially relevant:

"Not magnitude, not lavishness,
But Form—the Site;
Not innovating wilfulness,
But reverence for the Archetype."

Barrett (1955), arguing that Melville himself "had discovered that form . . . is life-giving and . . . that forms, measured forms, are the resolution of the dissociation of sensibility" (p. 622), holds that "*Billy Budd* is an assertion of order and form" (p. 621); he takes direct issue with those who read the novel as irony. Gross (1956), p. 165, asserts flatly that it "implicitly repudiates revolution and defends fixed forms, tradition, order, and historical community." (See notes to Leaves 58, 65, 288 above for additional comments on this point.)

On the other side of the argument are the "ironist" critics who see *Billy Budd* primarily as a novel of social protest and who assert that Melville himself mocked at Vere's devotion to "measured forms." Thus Zink (1952), p. 136, interprets the captain's words here as "the climactic, ironic cap" to the crew's "feelings of outrage—this easy, learned explanation, heightened by the classical allusion which betrays the great age of the entrenched power of the forms." But Fogle (1958), p. 109, though granting that there is "perhaps a lurking irony" in the present passage, finds it signifying "not a total reversal of its ostensible meaning but a consciousness of its incompleteness. As with all general maxims, it leaves something more to be said." As in the novel as a whole, the irony "magnifies and intensifies, it deepens and enriches, rather than diminishing by a mere irony of wailing mockery" (p. 113).

Concerning Melville's own attitude toward revolutionary "disruption of forms," even his earlier *White-Jacket*, with its thoroughgoing demands for abolition of undemocratic naval abuses, takes account in Ch. 54 of "the lamentable effects of suddenly and completely releasing 'the people' of a man-of-war from arbitrary discipline. It shows that, to such, 'liberty,' at first, must be administered in small and moderate quantities, increasing with the patient's capacity to make a good use of it." And among his poems, the "treatment of Law and the People" in "The House-Top" (*Poems*, p. 57), as Fogle observes (1959), p. 75, "has a strong bearing" upon interpretation of *Billy Budd*. The poem deals with the New York draft riots of 1863 in such condemnatory terms as "the Atheist roar of riot" and "red Arson": the city, having been taken over "by its rats—ship-rats / And rats of the wharves," is finally "redeemed" by the arrival of militia regiments, and so

> "Gives thanks devout; nor, being thankful, heeds
> The grimy slur on the Republic's faith implied,
> Which holds that Man is naturally good,
> And—more—is Nature's Roman, never to be scourged."

Neither in *Battle-Pieces* nor in *Billy Budd*, it would seem, did Melville himself depart from the injunction he had previously embodied in the concluding paragraph of *White-Jacket:* "whatever befall us, let us never train our murderous guns inboard; let us not mutiny with bloody pikes in our hands."

333. *the story of Orpheus:* compare *The Merchant of Venice*, V.i.71–82: if "a wild and wanton herd" but

> "hear perchance a trumpet sound,
> Or any air of music touch their ears,
> You shall perceive them make a mutual stand,
> Their savage eyes turn'd to a modest gaze,
> By the sweet power of music: therefore the poet
> Did feign that Orpheus drew trees, stones, and floods;
> Since naught so stockish, hard, and full of rage,
> But music for the time doth change his nature."

Among several allusions to Orpheus in Melville's earlier works, that in Ch. 56 of *Redburn* is closest to the present passage. There, after noting the delight of sailors "even with the rudest minstrelsy," Melville describes the singing Harry Bolton as sitting "among them like Orpheus among the charmed leopards and tigers."

334. *toned by music and religious rites:* the headnote to the ninth section of "Naples in the Time of Bomba" (*Poems*, p. 365) observes that the power of the church "proves of far more efficacy in bringing a semi-insurgent populace to their knees than all the bombs, bayonets, and fusilades of the despot of Naples."

334. *the clearness of its serenity:* the imagery of this paragraph and its possible implications deserve special attention in view of the climactic position of the passage; there are characteristic patterns of image and theme here and in comparable scenes to be found in Melville's earlier works.

In *Moby Dick* the alluring "serenity" of nature—beheld in the "exasperating sunlight" (Ch. 41), "the weather" (Ch. 51), "the tropical sea" (Ch. 133), or even in the White Whale himself (Ch. 133)—is repeatedly characterized as deceptive, its "quietude but the vesture of tornadoes" (Ch. 133). In the later poetry the indifference of man's environment to his fate is repeatedly stressed: in "Pebbles" the sea is "Implacable most when most . . . serene" (*Poems*, p. 206); in "Off Cape Colonna" the architectural columns look down impassively on shipwreck and disaster, "Over much like gods! Serene" (*Poems*, p. 248), as in "Pausilippo" the "bland untroubled heaven" gazes "listlessly" upon the wronged Silvio Pellico (*Poems*, p. 245). In "The Berg," subtitled "A Dream" (*Poems*, pp. 203–4), "a ship of martial build," described as "infatuate," "impetuous," and "Directed as by madness mere," is seen to steer against "a stolid iceberg" and go down. The ship does not "budge" the iceberg: except for "one avalanche" that "crashed the deck" of the doomed vessel there is no responsive movement along its "dead indifference of walls." And in *Clarel*, III.v, a discussion of "The spleen of nature and her love" (line 32) takes place "While unperturbed over deserts riven / Stretche[s] the clear vault of hollow heaven" (lines 207–8).

Here the sun has "licked up" the "fleece" it had previously "glorified"; in *Clarel* a fading into the light of common day repeatedly follows upon the appearance of some natural phenomenon that at first glance had seemed to embody cosmic meaning or promise. Thus "that prose critic keen, / The daylight" (IV.xiii.105–6), continually challenges any of the pilgrims who seek signs or portents in a rainbow or a dawning day, just as Celio dismisses as "vain" and "idle" the "pageant" of a sunrise: "When one would get at Nature's will— / To be put off by purfled shows!" (I.xv.3–5). A phrase of Rolfe's, "nature with her neutral mind" (I.xxxvii.48), like the earlier reference in Ch. 17 of *Israel Potter* to nature's "stoical imperturbability," recapitulates the prevalent theme of the foregoing citations, just as a couplet elsewhere in the poem (IV.xxviii.17–18) epitomizes the tone of the present passage: "But Nature never heeded this: / To Nature nothing is amiss."

Looking to the recurrent imagery of sun and cloud in Ch. 25 and 27 for intimations of Billy's personal survival following his execution would therefore seem to be expecting a departure from the patterns of Melville's earlier thought and art. For the Melville of this period, Miss Tilton has concluded in her study of "Rammon" (1959), p. 86, "The only paradise is the paradise recollected." Apposite here are the words given Babbalanja forty years earlier in Ch. 69 of *Mardi*: "All vanity, vanity, . . . to seek in nature for positive warranty to these aspirations of ours. Through all her provinces, nature seems to promise immortality to life, but destruction to beings. Or, as old Bardianna has it, if not against us, nature is not for us." More relevant to the present passage than belief in personal survival is Melville's old fascination with animism and pantheism, ideas recurrent in his writing since *Mardi*, and his exploration of the concept of Nirvana in such late compositions as "Rammon" and "Buddha" (*Poems*, pp. 411–16, 232). (Miss Tilton, pp. 83–85, discusses both "Buddha" and *Billy Budd* with reference to "the stoical attitude and ethic" of Vere; Sutton [1960] sees in poem and novel the influence of Schopenhauer's philosophy of negation.)

In "Buddha" occur these lines: "Nirvana! absorb us in your skies, / Annul us into thee"; as an epigraph to the poem Melville prefixed a verse from the New Testament that may well have suggested the figure of the "low-hanging vapor" that vanishes after Billy's death: "For what is your life? It is even a vapour, that appeareth for a little time, and then vanisheth away" (James 4:14; an allusion to the same passage concludes Ch. 31 of *White-Jacket*). With the "licking up" of the "fleece" and its disappearance into "the circumambient air" may be compared Isabel's desire in *Pierre*, Bk. 6.4, "to feel myself drank up into the pervading spirit animating all things."

In likening the air to "smooth white marble" the passage is close to a paragraph in the prose section of "Rip Van Winkle's Lilac" (*Poems*, pp. 287–88; italics added) where an "artist" feels "the difference between dead planks [a church steeple] or dead iron smeared over with white-lead . . . and *white marble* . . . new from the quarry *sparkling* with the minute mica in it, or, mellowed by ages, taking on another . . . tone endearing it to that *Pantheistic antiquity* . . . felt or latent in every one of us. In visionary flash he saw . . . the perfect temples of Attica *flushed with Apollo's rays*. . . . For the moment, in this paganish dream* he quite lost himself." The Greek landscape of the artist's "paganish dream" is celebrated by Melville himself in the poems grouped as "Fruit of Travel Long Ago" in the *Timoleon* volume of 1891, in which "Buddha" was also included.

335. *the conclusion . . . is apt to be less finished:* so in *Pierre*, Bk. 7.8: "while . . . common novels laboriously spin vails of mystery, only to complacently clear them up at last; and . . . common dramas do but repeat the same; yet the profounder emanations of the human mind . . . never unravel their own intricacies, and have no proper endings; but in imperfect, unanticipated, and disappointing sequels (as mutilated stumps), hurry to abrupt intermergings with the eternal tides of time and fate." As for a narration "having less to do with fable than with fact," Ch. 14 of *The Confidence-Man*, referring to the "requirement" that "fiction based on fact should never be contradictory to it," similarly argues that novelists are justified in drawing characters embodying inconsistencies because in real life human nature, "in view of its inconsistencies, . . . is past finding out." A reference to "the symmetry of this book" begins the prose Supplement to *Battle-Pieces* (*Poems*, p. 460). See Introduction, pp. 38–39.

Of the present passage, Wright Morris remarks: "This observation, no matter how we construe it, sums up the state of the American imagination after a century of engagements, most of them inconclusive, with the raw material of American experience. If what you want is the truth, with its ragged edges, stick to the facts. And the *facts?* You will find them recorded in the past." See Morris, *The Territory Ahead* (New York, 1958), p. 77.

LEAVES 336-338

336. *rechristening under the Directory:* "in this matter of christening ships of war," according to *Mardi*, Ch. 28, "Christian nations are but too apt to be dare-devils"; a series of examples follows to reinforce the point. The present subject of "names bestowed upon fighting ships" recurs also in *White-Jacket*, Ch. 71, *Israel Potter*, Ch. 13, and *Clarel*, III.xiii.107–9. A parallel to the discussion here is found in Cooper's *Wing-and-Wing*, Ch. 13, where Nelson, represented as commenting on the French and their infidelity, instances the "sort of names they give their ships . . . now they have beheaded their king, and denounced their God!"

The name *Athée* or *Atheist* appears to be of Melville's own coinage; Anderson (1940), p. 332, notes that there was no French warship of that name. In Melville's earlier writing the term "atheist" has unfavorable connotations, as in *Battle-Pieces*: "the Atheist roar of riot," slavery as "an atheistical iniquity" (*Poems*, pp. 57, 465); in Ch. 28 of *The Confidence-Man* the plausible but deceptive "cosmopolitan" holds misanthropy and infidelity to be "co-ordinates. For . . . , set aside materialism and what is an atheist, but one who does not, or will not, see in the universe a ruling principle of love . . . ?"

The various ship-names in *Billy Budd*—*Rights-of-Man, Bellipotent, Athée*—are appropriately connotative. Ch. 28 of the manuscript, inscribed at Stage *F/G*, is one of the two sections in which *Bellipotent* appears as the name of Vere's ship, reflecting Melville's comparatively late decision to substitute *Bellipotent* for *Indomitable*; his creation of the episode here may have influenced the change. See Introduction, pp. 20–21.

336. *the* Athée *(the* Atheist*)*: in Melville's preliminary notes for this part of the narrative (Plate VIII) the ship's name is the *Directory;* in the manuscript itself, at this point and again on Leaf 337, he left a blank space for the name. In the margin of each leaf he wrote "Athéiste" in pencil, perhaps as a reminder to verify the correct French equivalent of the English "atheist" before supplying the title in the text itself. Instead of the proper form, *Athée*, Mrs. Melville later inserted "Atheiste" in the two blank spaces. The present text substitutes the correct form, here supplying the English word in parentheses as Melville himself in the next sentence follows "the *Erebus*" with "(the *Hell*)."

338. *the Nile and Trafalgar:* Nelson's great victories over the French took place in 1798 and 1805, respectively. Melville seems to have had in mind here a clear contrast between Vere and Nelson, who—as Southey demonstrated throughout his *Life*—hungered jealously for fame and attained it: Ch. 4 above, in discussing Nelson, declares "an excessive love of glory" to be the first virtue in a military man (Leaf 65).

The subjects of fame and ambition, which had long concerned Melville, appear frequently in his late poetry, as Freeman notes (1948), pp. 11–18. Discussing fame in a letter to James Billson on December 20, 1885, he called it "this 'vanity of vanities' "; sometime in 1891 he checked a quotation from Tacitus in his copy of Schopenhauer's *Wisdom of Life* (HCL): "The lust of fame is the last that a wise man shakes off."

LEAVES 339-343

339. *"Billy Budd, Billy Budd"*: the present passage is cited by those who take Billy to have been Vere's natural son—an idea advanced by Anderson (1940), p. 345. Stewart (1959), p. 285, compares the dying words of Pierre's father in *Pierre*, Bk. 4.2: "My daughter! my daughter!"

340. *a naval chronicle of the time:* despite "extensive search for the authority here cited," Anderson (1940), p. 334, found only an authorized monthly publication of a later date, 1799–1818: *The Naval Chronicle*, which lacks a section headed "News from the Mediterranean" and sheds "no further light on the problem of the reality of events in *Billy Budd.*" Beyond adding "an air of authenticity" to the narrative, as Anderson suggests, the device of the "authorized" account actually embodies an ironic reversal of "the facts." Billy, an Englishman of "the Saxon strain" without "any Norman or other admixture" (Leaf 38), is said here to be "no Englishman," while Claggart, who "might" have been "an Englishman" though "possibly he was not such by birth" (Leaf 92), is by implication of "his strong patriotic impulse" truly English. The lofty sentence about "aliens adopting English cognomens" (Leaves 341–42) glosses over the notorious fact that both Englishmen and foreign nationals were "caused to be admitted" into the service not voluntarily but through forcible impressment.

Note that the "chronicle" makes no reference to Vere by name, nor to the engagement during which he received his mortal wound, though this significant episode is said above to have taken place on "the return passage to the English fleet from the detached cruise during which occurred the events already recorded" (Leaf 337)—i.e., the deaths of Claggart and Budd reported here. The explanation, confirmed by analysis of the manuscript, is that the substance of the present chapter actually antedates Melville's whole elaboration of the character evidently at first identified not by name but only as "the commander" or "the captain," as here. Again, in its statement that the treatment of Billy afforded by the "chronicle" is "all that hitherto has stood in human record" (Leaf 344) the chapter contradicts the assertion below that "Billy in the Darbies" was "printed at Portsmouth as a ballad" (Leaf 347). These inconsistencies, growing out of changes in Melville's plans concerning the development of the story and the ordering of its closing chapters, are evidence that *Billy Budd* was literally "unfinished"—Mrs. Melville's term (see note to Leaf 49 above, *the absence of frigates*)—at the time of his death.

343. *attributed to the late Dr. Johnson:* Samuel Johnson had died in 1784. Boswell's *Life of Johnson* (1791) reports under date of April 7, 1775, his apothegm "Patriotism is the last refuge of a scoundrel," explaining that Johnson's reference was to "that pretended patriotism which so many, in all ages and countries, have made a cloak for self-interest." Though Claggart is credited above with a "certain austere patriotism" (Leaf 102), it is rumored in Ch. 8 that he "had volunteered into the King's navy by way of compounding for some mysterious swindle" (Leaf 93); to the irritated Vere his "patriotic zeal" appears "rather supersensible and strained" (Leaf 205).

NOTES & COMMENTARY

LEAVES 344-347

344. *John Claggart and Billy Budd:* by Stage D the following penciled addition, later canceled, followed at this point: "Here ends a story not unwarranted by what sometimes happens in this [one undeciphered word] world of ours—Innocence and infamy, spiritual depravity and fair repute". (The undeciphered word is given as "incongruous" by Weaver and "incomprehensible" by Freeman; neither reading is satisfactory. See Plate VIII.)

345. *for a term venerated:* Weaver's reading of the penciled phrasing of the manuscript here is "for a season remarkable"; Freeman and other subsequent editors read "for a term remarkable." There is no doubt that Melville wrote "term" rather than "season," but a question remains concerning the predicate adjective that follows. The word given in all previous editions, "remarkable," is unsatisfactory; the present reading, "venerated," though more appropriate to a context dealing with objects converted into monuments or relics, is not entirely beyond conjecture.

345. *as a piece of the Cross:* though the comparison is cited by those who see analogies between Billy's story and the Crucifixion, the figure may be given undue weight; in other contexts Melville had used the same not uncommon expression with merely casual intent. *White-Jacket,* Ch. 3, mentions old tars "who spin interminable yarns about Decatur, Hull, and Bainbridge; and carry . . . bits of 'Old Ironsides,' as Catholics do the wood of the true cross"; *Moby Dick,* Ch. 14, would have it that "pieces of wood in Nantucket are carried about like bits of the true cross in Rome." The passage here resembles Southey's statement in the concluding chapter of his *Life of Nelson* that sailors preserved "as relics of Saint Nelson" pieces of the leaden coffin in which he was brought home, and also fragments of his flag (p. 307).

347. *printed at Portsmouth as a ballad:* while in Liverpool on his first voyage Melville had encountered sailor ballad-singers, described in Ch. 39 of *Redburn:* "after singing their verses," they "hand you a printed copy, and beg you to buy"; in London, ten years later, he witnessed a hanging commemorated by a street ballad and a printed broadside (note to Leaf 321 above, *a hanging . . .*). The Gollins (1957) note that in Jerrold's *Black-Ey'd Susan* the hanged William likewise inspires a ballad among the crew.

347. BILLY IN THE DARBIES: a prose sketch of Billy (see Plate I) introducing an earlier version of the ballad constituted the starting-point for what became *Billy Budd, Sailor.* In the sketch Billy is nicknamed "the Jewel," an expression that survives in Captain Graveling's reference to him on Leaf 18 above as "my best man . . . , the jewel of 'em." So originally Melville had Billy punning on his nickname in the seventh line of the ballad: "A jewel-block they'll make of me tomorrow"—jewel-blocks, which hang from the ends of yards where studding-sails are hoisted, carry those sails to the extreme ends of the yards; in Cooper's *Red Rover,* Ch. 19, and *Wing-and-Wing,* Ch. 15, bodies similarly hang from yards "like . . . jewel-blocks." The words "all is up; and I must up too" (involving another play on words) have further affilia-

[[201]]

tions with the prose sketch. The third surviving draft leaf of the ballad (Plate IV) follows this line with "Early in the morning the deed they will do / Our little game's up they must needs obey." "Our little game" presumably refers to the "incipient mutiny" for which Billy, as ringleader, was to be hanged, according to the sketch. The word-plays and the "little game," as well as the further play on words in the line "O, 'tis me, not the sentence they'll suspend," stem from Melville's earlier conception of Billy when he was evidently not so simple and innocent and when "to deal in double meanings" was not "quite foreign to his nature" (Leaf 30).

A discussion of the ballad as a dramatic monologue appears in Rosenthal and Smith (1955), pp. 372-75.

351. *these darbies:* "Darbies: an old cant word for irons or hand-cuffs; it is still retained" (Smyth, *The Sailor's Word-Book*, p. 233). The word "darbies" rsu cocin *White-Jacket*, Ch. 58, and "double-darbies" in Ch. 56.

Bibliography

The following entries cover published criticism and scholarship that bear directly upon *Billy Budd* and other closely related works of the Melville canon. Only those editions, reprints, and translations of *Billy Budd* are listed that offer introductory material of particular critical or scholarly significance. Foreign-language titles, not all of which we have been able to examine, have been taken from LELAND R. PHELPS, *A Preliminary Check-List of Foreign Language Materials on the Life and Works of Herman Melville*, Melville Society Special Publication Number II (mimeographed), [Evanston, Ill.:] Northwestern University, 1960.

ABEL, DARREL. " 'Laurel Twined with Thorn': The Theme of Melville's *Timoleon*," *The Personalist*, XLI (Summer, 1960), 330–40.

ANDERSON, CHARLES ROBERTS. "The Genesis of *Billy Budd*," *American Literature*, XII (November, 1940), 329–46.

ANDERSON, QUENTIN. "Second Trip to Byzantium," *Kenyon Review*, XI (Summer, 1949), 516–20.

ARVIN, NEWTON. *Herman Melville*. New York: William Sloane Associates, 1950. Pp. 292–99. Reprinted, New York: Viking Press, 1957.

———. "A Note on the Background of *Billy Budd*," *American Literature*, XX (March, 1948), 51–55.

AUDEN, W. H. *The Enchafèd Flood: or The Romantic Iconography of the Sea*. New York: Random House, 1950. Pp. 144–49.

———. "Herman Melville," in *Collected Poems of W. H. Auden*. New York: Random House, 1945. Pp. 146–47.

BAIRD, JAMES. *Ishmael*. Baltimore: Johns Hopkins Press, 1956. Pp. 249–51, 272–73, 405, 426–27. Reprinted, New York: Harper & Brothers, 1960.

BALDINI, GABRIELE. "Il Silenzio di Billy Budd," in *Melville O Le Ambiguità*. Milano, Napoli: Riccardo Ricciardi Editore, 1952. Pp. 179–205.

BARNET, SYLVAN. "The Execution in *Billy Budd*," *American Literature*, XXXIII (January, 1962), 517–19.

BARRETT, LAURENCE. "The Differences in Melville's Poetry," *PMLA*, LXX (September, 1955), 606–23.

BEHL, C. R. W. *"Billy Budd* und *Benito Cereno," Die Literatur,* XL (August, 1938), 691–92.

BERTHOFF, WARNER. " 'Certain Phenomenal Men': The Example of *Billy Budd," ELH,* XXVII (December, 1960), 334–51.

BERTI, LUIGI. "Melville e *Billy Budd,"* in *Boccaporto secondo.* Firenze: Parenti, 1944. Pp. 196–98.

BLACKMUR, R. P. (ed.). *American Short Novels.* New York: Thomas Y. Crowell Co., 1960. Pp. 5–8.

BOND, WILLIAM H. "Melville and *Two Years before the Mast," Harvard Library Bulletin,* VII (Autumn, 1953), 362–65.

BOOTH, WAYNE C. *The Rhetoric of Fiction.* Chicago: University of Chicago Press, 1961. Pp. 178, 215, 365.

BOWEN, MERLIN. *The Long Encounter: Self and Experience in the Writings of Herman Melville.* Chicago: University of Chicago Press, 1960. Pp. 216–33.

BRASWELL, WILLIAM. "Melville's *Billy Budd* as 'An Inside Narrative,' " *American Literature,* XXIX (May, 1957), 133–46.

———. *Melville's Religious Thought: An Essay in Interpretation.* Durham, N.C.: Duke University Press, 1943. Pp. 122–24. Reprinted, New York: Pageant Books, 1959.

BROWN, JOHN MASON. "Hanged from the Yardarm," in *As They Appear.* New York: McGraw Hill Book Co., 1952. Pp. 186–92.

BRUMM, URSULA. "The Figure of Christ in American Literature," *Partisan Review,* XXIV (Summer, 1957), 403–13.

CAMERON, KENNETH W. *"Billy Budd* and 'An Execution at Sea,' " *Emerson Society Quarterly,* No. 2 (First Quarter, 1956), pp. 13–15.

CAMPBELL, HARRY MODEAN. "The Hanging Scene in Melville's *Billy Budd, Foretopman," Modern Language Notes,* LXVI (June, 1951), 378–81.

———. "The Hanging Scene in Melville's *Billy Budd:* A Reply to Mr. Giovannini," *Modern Language Notes,* LXX (November, 1955), 497–500.

CARPENTER, FREDERIC I. *American Literature and the Dream.* New York: Philosophical Library, 1955. Pp. 73–82, 199–207.

———. "Melville: The World in a Man-of-War," *University of Kansas City Review,* XIX (Summer, 1953), 257–64. Incorporated in Carpenter, *American Literature and the Dream,* 1955.

CASPER, LEONARD. "The Case against Captain Vere," *Perspective,* V (Summer, 1952), 146–52.

CHASE, RICHARD. "An Approach to Melville," *Partisan Review,* XIV (May–June, 1947), 285–94.

————. "Dissent on *Billy Budd*," *Partisan Review*, XV (November, 1948), 1212–18. Expanded in Chase, *Herman Melville*, 1949.

————. "Innocence and Infamy," in *Herman Melville: A Critical Study*. New York: Macmillan Co., 1949. Pp. 258–77, 298, *et passim*.

————. "A Note on *Billy Budd*," in *The American Novel and Its Tradition*. Garden City: Doubleday & Co., 1957. Pp. 113–15.

———— (ed.). *Selected Tales and Poems by Herman Melville*. New York: Rinehart & Co., 1950. Pp. xiii–xvi.

CLIVE, GEOFFREY. *The Romantic Enlightenment*. New York: Meridian Books, 1960. Pp. 161–65.

————. " 'Teleological Suspension of the Ethical' in Nineteenth-Century Literature," *Journal of Religion*, XXXIV (April, 1954), 75–87. Incorporated in Clive, *The Romantic Enlightenment*, 1960.

COWIE, ALEXANDER. "Herman Melville," in *The Rise of the American Novel*. New York: American Book Co., 1948. Pp. 394–95, 399.

COXE, LOUIS O., and ROBERT CHAPMAN. *Billy Budd: A Play in Three Acts*, with "Foreword" by BROOKS ATKINSON. Princeton: Princeton University Press, 1951.

CRAMER, MAURICE B. "*Billy Budd* and *Billy Budd*," *Journal of General Education*, X (April, 1957), 78–91.

CUNLIFFE, MARCUS. *The Literature of the United States*. Harmondsworth, Middlesex: Penguin Books, 1954. Pp. 118–19.

E————, T. T. "Melville's *Billy Budd*," *Explicator*, Vol. II (December, 1943), Query 14.

EKNER, REIDER. [Notes on *Billy Budd*.] Stockholm: Raben & Sjögren, 1955.

FEIDELSON, CHARLES, JR. *Symbolism and American Literature*. Chicago: University of Chicago Press, 1953. Pp. 212, 344–45. Reprinted, 1959.

FIEDLER, LESLIE A. *Love and Death in the American Novel*. New York: Criterion Books, 1960. Pp. 359, 362, 434–35.

FOGLE, RICHARD HARTER. "*Billy Budd*—Acceptance or Irony," *Tulane Studies in English*, VIII (1958), 107–13.

————. "*Billy Budd*: The Order of the Fall," *Nineteenth-Century Fiction*, XV (December, 1960), 189–205.

————. "Melville and the Civil War," *Tulane Studies in English*, IX (1959), 61–89.

FOLEY, MARY. "The Digressions in *Billy Budd*," in WILLIAM T. STAFFORD (ed.), *Melville's Billy Budd and the Critics*. San Francisco: Wadsworth Publishing Co., 1961. Pp. 161–64.

FORSTER, E. M. *Aspects of the Novel.* New York: Harcourt, Brace & Co., 1927. Pp. 204–6. Reprinted, 1954.

———. "Letter," *The Griffin* [The Readers' Subscription, Inc.], I (1951), 4–6.

———, and ERIC CROZIER. Libretto for *Billy Budd: Opera in Four Acts.* Music by BENJAMIN BRITTEN. London: Boosey & Hawkes, 1951.

FREEMAN, F. BARRON. "The Enigma of Melville's 'Daniel Orme,' " *American Literature,* XVI (November, 1944), 208–11.

——— (ed.). *Melville's Billy Budd.* Cambridge, Mass.: Harvard University Press, 1948. Pp. vii–xii, 1–126.

FREEMAN, JOHN. *Herman Melville.* London and New York: Macmillan Co., 1926. Pp. 131–36.

FREIMARCK, VINCENT. "Mainmast as Crucifix in *Billy Budd,*" *Modern Language Notes,* LXXII (November, 1957), 496–97.

GABRIEL, RALPH H. "Melville, Critic of Mid-Nineteenth Century Beliefs," in *The Course of American Democratic Thought.* New York: Ronald Press Co., 1940. Pp. 67, 74, 75, 77, 243.

GEROULD, GORDON HALL. *The Patterns of English and American Fiction: A History.* Boston: D. C. Heath & Co., 1942. Pp. 354, 358.

GETTMANN, ROYAL A., and BRUCE HARKNESS. "*Billy Budd, Foretopman,*" in *Teacher's Manual for "A Book of Stories."* New York: Rinehart & Co., 1955. Pp. 71–74.

GIOVANNINI, G. "The Hanging Scene in Melville's *Billy Budd,*" *Modern Language Notes,* LXX (November, 1955), 491–97.

GLICK, WENDELL. "Expediency and Absolute Morality in *Billy Budd,*" *PMLA,* LXVIII (March, 1953), 103–10.

GOLDSMITH, ARNOLD L. "The 'Discovery Scene' in *Billy Budd,*" *Modern Drama,* III (February, 1961), 339–42.

GOLLIN, RICHARD and RITA. "Justice in an Earlier Treatment of the *Billy Budd* Theme," *American Literature,* XXVIII (January, 1957), 513–15.

GROSS, JOHN J. "Melville, Dostoevsky, and the People," *Pacific Spectator,* X (Spring, 1956), 160–70.

HAYFORD, HARRISON. "The Sailor Poet of *White-Jacket,*" *Boston Public Library Quarterly,* III (July, 1951), 226–27.

——— (ed.). *The Somers Mutiny Affair.* Englewood Cliffs: Prentice-Hall, 1959.

HEILMAN, ROBERT. *Magic in the Web: Action and Language in Othello.* Lexington: University of Kentucky Press, 1956. Pp. 37, 43.

BIBLIOGRAPHY

HILLWAY, TYRUS. "Billy Budd: Melville's Human Sacrifice," *Pacific Spectator*, VI (Summer, 1952), 342–47.

——. "Melville's *Billy Budd*," *Explicator*, Vol. IV (November, 1945), Item 12.

HOWARD, LEON. *Herman Melville: A Biography*. Berkeley and Los Angeles: University of California Press, 1951. Pp. 324–28. Reprinted, 1958.

——. *Literature and the American Tradition*. Garden City: Doubleday & Co., 1960. Pp. 181–83, 310.

JAFFE, ADRIAN H., and HERBERT WEISINGER (eds.). *The Laureate Fraternity: An Introduction to Literature*. Evanston: Row, Peterson & Co., 1960. Pp. 142–43.

JOSEPHSON, MATTHEW. "The Transfiguration of Herman Melville," *Outlook*, CL (September 19, 1928), 809–11, 832, 836.

KAPLAN, SIDNEY. "Explication," *Melville Society Newsletter*, XIII, No. 2 (Summer, 1957), [3].

KAZIN, ALFRED. "Ishmael in His Academic Heaven," *New Yorker*, XXIV (February 12, 1949), 84, 87, 88–89.

KILBOURNE, W. G., JR. "Montaigne and Captain Vere," *American Literature*, XXXIII (January, 1962), 514–17.

KNOX, G. A. "Communication and Communion in Melville," *Renascence*, IX (Autumn, 1956), 26–31.

KRIEGER, MURRAY. *The Tragic Vision: Variations on a Theme in Literary Interpretation*. New York: Holt, Rinehart & Winston, 1960. Pp. 256, 260, 263–64.

LANG, HANS-JOACHIM. "Melvilles 'Billy Budd' und seine Quellen: Eine Nachlese," in *Festschrift für Walther Fischer*. Heidelberg: Carl Winter, 1959. Pp. 225–49.

LANZINGER, KLAUS. *Primitivismus und Naturalismus in Prosaschaffen Herman Melvilles*. Innsbruck: Universitätsverlag Wagner, 1959. Pp. 108–13.

LESSER, SIMON. *Fiction and the Unconscious*. Boston: Beacon Press, 1957. Pp. 92–93.

LEVIN, HARRY. *The Power of Blackness*. New York: Alfred A. Knopf, 1958. Pp. 194–97. Reprinted, New York: Vintage Books, 1960.

LEWIS, R. W. B. *The American Adam: Innocence, Tragedy, and Tradition in the Nineteenth Century*. Chicago: University of Chicago Press, 1955. Pp. 146–52. Reprinted, 1959.

LEYDA, JAY. *The Melville Log: A Documentary Life of Herman Melville, 1819–1891*. 2 vols. New York: Harcourt, Brace & Co., 1951.

LEYDA, JAY (ed.). *The Portable Melville.* New York: Viking Press, 1952. Pp. xviii–xix, 635–36, 743.

LEYRIS, PIERRE. "Préface," *Billy Budd, Gabier de Misaine.* Neuchâtel et Paris: Attinger, 1935. Pp. 9–24. Reprinted, Paris: Gallimard, 1937.

MCELDERRY, B. R., JR. "Three Earlier Treatments of the *Billy Budd* Theme," *American Literature,* XXVII (May, 1955), 251–57.

MASON, RONALD. *"Billy Budd* and the Victory of Innocence," in *The Spirit above the Dust: A Study of Herman Melville.* London: John Lehmann, 1951. Pp. 245–60.

MATTHIESSEN, F. O. "Billy Budd, Foretopman," in *American Renaissance: Art and Expression in the Age of Emerson and Whitman.* New York: Oxford University Press, 1941. Pp. 500–514.

MAYOUX, JEAN JACQUES. *Melville.* Translated by JOHN ASHBERY. New York: Grove Press, 1960. Pp. 124–29.

MILLER, JAMES E., JR. *"Billy Budd:* The Catastrophe of Innocence," *Modern Language Notes,* LXXIII (March, 1958), 168–76.

———. "Melville's Search for Form," *Bucknell Review,* VIII (December, 1959), 260–76.

MONTALE, EUGENIO (trans.). *La Storia di Billy Budd, di Herman Melville.* Milano: Bompiani, 1942. Introduction translated as "An Introduction to *Billy Budd* (1942)," *Sewanee Review,* LXVIII (Summer, 1960), 419–22.

MUMFORD, LEWIS. *Herman Melville.* New York: Harcourt, Brace & Co., 1929. Pp. 353–57.

MURRY, JOHN MIDDLETON. "Herman Melville's Silence," *Times Literary Supplement,* No. 1173 (July 10, 1924), p. 433. Reprinted in *John Clare and Other Studies.* London: Peter Neville, 1950. Pp. 209–12.

———. "Quo Warranto?" *Adelphi,* II (August, 1924), 194.

NOONE, JOHN B., JR. *"Billy Budd:* Two Concepts of Nature," *American Literature,* XXIX (November, 1957), 249–62.

OKAMOTO, HIDOO. "Billy Budd, Foretopman as Melville's Testament of Acceptance," *Studies in English Literature* (published by the English Literary Society of Japan), XXXV, No. 2 (March, 1959), 225–43.

OLSON, CHARLES. *Call Me Ishmael.* New York: Reynal & Hitchcock, 1947. Pp. 48, 90, 104–5. Reprinted, New York: Grove Press, [1958].

———. "David Young, David Old," *Western Review,* XIV (Fall, 1949), 63–66.

PALMER, R. R. "Herman Melville et la Révolution Française," *An-*

nales Historiques de la Révolution Française, XXVI (July–September, 1954), 254–56.

PAUL, SHERMAN. "Melville's 'The Town-Ho's Story,'" *American Literature,* XXI (May, 1949), 212–21.

PEARSON, NORMAN HOLMES. "Billy Budd: 'The King's Yarn,'" *American Quarterly,* III (Summer, 1951), 99–114.

PHELPS, LELAND R. "The Reaction to *Benito Cereno* and *Billy Budd* in Germany," *Symposium,* XIII (Fall, 1959), 294–99.

PLOMER, WILLIAM (ed.). "Introduction," *Billy Budd, Foretopman.* London: John Lehmann, 1946. Pp. 7–10.

POMMER, HENRY F. *Milton and Melville.* Pittsburgh: University of Pittsburgh Press, 1950. Pp. 83–85, 87–90.

QUASIMODO, SALVATORE. "Oratorio per Billy Budd," *Inventario,* II (Estate, 1949), 109–21, 155. Reprinted: *Billy Budd: Un atto di H. Melville; Musica di Giorgio Federico Ghedini.* Milano: Edizioni Suvini Zerboni, 1949.

REED, HENRY. "Books in General," *New Statesman and Nation,* XXXV (May 31, 1947), 397.

ROSENTHAL, M. L., and A. J. M. SMITH. *Exploring Poetry.* New York: Macmillan Co., 1955. Pp. 372–75.

ROUDIEZ, LEON S. "Strangers in Melville and Camus," *French Review,* XXXI (January, 1958), 217–26.

SALE, ARTHUR. "Captain Vere's Reasons," *Cambridge Journal,* V (October, 1951), 3–18.

SCHIFFMAN, JOSEPH. "Melville's Final Stage, Irony: A Re-examination of *Billy Budd* Criticism," *American Literature,* XXII (May, 1950), 128–36.

SCHNEIDER, HERBERT W. "At Sea," in *A History of American Philosophy.* New York: Columbia University Press, 1946. Pp. 293–301.

SEDGWICK, WILLIAM ELLERY. "Billy Budd," in *Herman Melville: The Tragedy of Mind.* Cambridge, Mass.: Harvard University Press, 1944. Pp. 231–49.

SHORT, RAYMOND W. (ed.). *Four Great American Novels.* New York: Henry Holt & Co., 1946. Pp. xxxi–xxxiii.

———. "Melville as Symbolist," *University of Kansas City Review,* XV (Autumn, 1948), 38–46.

SIMON, JEAN. *Herman Melville, marin, métaphysicien et poète.* Paris: Boiven & Cie, 1939.

SNYDER, OLIVER. "A Note on 'Billy Budd,'" *Accent,* XI (Winter, 1951), 58–60.

SPANGLER, EUGENE R. "Harvest in a Barren Field: A Countercomment," *Western Review*, XIV (Summer, 1950), 305–7.

SPILLER, ROBERT E. *The Cycle of American Literature: An Essay in Historical Criticism.* New York: Macmillan Co., 1955. Pp. 95, 99, 112. Reprinted, New York: New American Library, 1957. Pp. 80, 83, 93.

STAFFORD, WILLIAM T. (ed.). *Melville's Billy Budd and the Critics.* San Francisco: Wadsworth Publishing Co., 1961.

STALLMAN, R. W., and R. E. WATTERS (eds.). *The Creative Reader.* New York: Ronald Press Co., 1954. Pp. 334–38.

STEIN, WILLIAM BYSSHE. " 'Billy Budd': The Nightmare of History," *Criticism*, III (Summer, 1961), 237–50.

———. "The Motif of the Wise Old Man in *Billy Budd*," *Western Humanities Review*, XIV (Winter, 1960), 99–101.

STERN, MILTON R. "Billy Budd," in *The Fine Hammered Steel of Herman Melville.* Urbana: University of Illinois Press, 1957. Pp. 206–39; also 26–27.

——— (ed.). *Typee and Billy Budd.* New York: E. P. Dutton & Co., 1958. "Introduction," pp. xx–xxv. "A Note about the Text," pp. 269–74.

STEWART, RANDALL. *American Literature and Christian Doctrine.* Baton Rouge: Louisiana State University Press, 1958. Pp. 98–102.

———. "Moral Crisis as Structural Principle in Fiction," *Christian Scholar*, XLII (December, 1959), 284–89.

———. "The Vision of Evil in Hawthorne and Melville," in NATHAN A. SCOTT, JR. (ed.), *The Tragic Vision and the Christian Faith.* New York: Association Press, 1957. Incorporated in Stewart, *American Literature and Christian Doctrine*, 1958.

STONE, GEOFFREY. "Herman Melville: Loyalty to the Heart," in HAROLD C. GARDINER, S.J. (ed.), *American Classics Reconsidered.* New York: Charles Scribner's Sons, 1958. Pp. 227–28.

———. *Melville.* New York: Sheed & Ward, 1949. Pp. 306–19.

SÜHNEL, RUDOLF. "Melvilles *Billy Budd*," *Sprache und Literatur Englands und Amerikas*, III, 125–44. Tübingen: Niemeyer, 1959.

SUNDERMANN, K. H. *Herman Melvilles Gedankengut.* Berlin: Collignon, 1937.

SUTTON, WALTER. "Melville and the Great God Budd," *Prairie Schooner*, XXXIV (Summer, 1960), 128–33.

TAYLOR, ROBERT H., and HERMAN W. LIEBERT. *An Address . . . by Robert H. Taylor at . . . an Exhibition of Literary Manuscripts . . . with a Catalogue . . . by Herman W. Liebert and Facsimiles of . . .*

Exhibits. New York: Grolier Club, 1957. P. 40, and two facsimile leaves, No. 37.

TAYLOR, WALTER FULLER. *A History of American Letters.* New York: American Book Co., 1936. P. 139.

THOMPSON, LAWRANCE. "Divine Depravity," in *Melville's Quarrel with God.* Princeton: Princeton University Press, 1952. Pp. 355–414 *et passim.*

THORP, WILLARD. "Herman Melville," in ROBERT E. SPILLER, WILLARD THORP, THOMAS H. JOHNSON, and HENRY SEIDEL CANBY (eds.). *Literary History of the United States.* 3 vols. New York: Macmillan Co., 1948. I, 464, 468–71. Revised ed., 1 vol., 1953.

────── (ed.). *Herman Melville: Representative Selections.* New York: American Book Co., 1938. P. lxxxiv.

TILTON, ELEANOR M. "Melville's 'Rammon': A Text and Commentary," *Harvard Library Bulletin,* XIII (Winter, 1959), 50–91.

TINDALL, WILLIAM YORK. "The Ceremony of Innocence," in R. M. MACIVER (ed.), *Great Moral Dilemmas in Literature, Past and Present.* New York: Harper & Brothers, 1956. Pp. 73–81.

VAN DOREN, CARL. *The American Novel 1789–1939.* (Revised ed.) New York: Macmillan Co., 1940. Pp. 100, 101.

────── (ed.). *"Billy Budd," "Benito Cereno" and "The Enchanted Isles."* New York: Readers Club, 1942. "Foreword," pp. viii–ix.

──────. "A Note of Confession," *Nation,* CXXVII (December 5, 1928), 622.

WAGENKNECHT, EDWARD. "The Ambiguities of Herman Melville," in *Cavalcade of the American Novel.* New York: Henry Holt & Co., 1952. Pp. 79–81.

WAGNER, VERN. "Billy Budd as Moby Dick: An Alternate Reading," in A. DAYLE WALLACE and WOODBURN O. ROSS (eds.), *Studies in Honor of John Wilcox.* Detroit: Wayne State University Press, 1958. Pp. 157–74.

WARNER, REX (ed.). *Billy Budd and Other Stories.* London: John Lehmann, 1951. "Introduction," pp. vii–xi.

WATSON, E. L. GRANT. "Melville's Testament of Acceptance," *New England Quarterly,* VI (June, 1933), 319–27.

WATTERS, R. E. "Melville's 'Isolatoes,' " *PMLA,* LX (December, 1945), 1138–48.

──────. "Melville's Metaphysics of Evil," *University of Toronto Quarterly,* IX (January, 1940), 170–82.

──────. "Melville's 'Sociality,' " *American Literature,* XVII (March, 1945), 33–49.

WEAVER, RAYMOND. *Herman Melville: Mariner and Mystic.* New York: George H. Doran Co., 1921. Pp. 239–40, 381. Reprinted, New York: Pageant Books, 1960, and New York: Cooper Square Publishers, 1961.

——— (ed.). *The Shorter Novels of Herman Melville.* New York: Horace Liveright, 1928. "Introduction," pp. xlix–li. Various reprints.

WEIR, CHARLES, JR. "Malice Reconciled: A Note on Melville's *Billy Budd*," *University of Toronto Quarterly*, XIII (April, 1944), 276–85.

WEST, RAY B., JR. "Primitivism in Melville," *Prairie Schooner*, XXX (Winter, 1956), 369–85.

———. "The Unity of 'Billy Budd,'" *Hudson Review*, V (Spring, 1952), 120–28.

WHITE, ERIC WALTER. "Billy Budd," *Adelphi*, XXVIII (First Quarter, 1952), 492–98.

WINTERS, YVOR. *Maule's Curse: Seven Studies in the History of American Obscurantism.* Norfolk: New Directions, 1938. Pp. 86–87. Reprinted in WINTERS, *In Defense of Reason.* New York: The Swallow Press and William Morrow & Co., 1947. Pp. 230–31.

WIRZBERGER, KARL-HEINZ. *Vortoppmann Billy Budd und andere Erzählungen.* Leipzig: Dieterich, 1956. Pp. 482–88.

WITHIM, PHIL. "*Billy Budd:* Testament of Resistance," *Modern Language Quarterly*, XX (June, 1959), 115–27.

WRIGHT, NATHALIA. "Biblical Allusion in Melville's Prose," *American Literature*, XII (May, 1940), 185–99.

———. *Melville's Use of the Bible.* Durham, N.C.: Duke University Press, 1949. Pp. 126–36.

ZINK, KARL E. "Herman Melville and the Forms—Irony and Social Criticism in 'Billy Budd,'" *Accent*, XII (Summer, 1952), 131–39.

Textual Notes

As stated in the Preface, the Reading Text embodies the *wording* (the "substantive" or "verbal" elements of the story) that in the editors' judgment most closely approximates Melville's final intention had a new fair copy of *Billy Budd, Sailor,* been made without his engaging in further expansion or revision. His inconsistent spelling, capitalization, hyphenation, paragraphing, and punctuation (the "accidentals" of the manuscript) have here been standardized—within the limits imposed by his own characteristic syntax—in accordance with present-day usage.

The ensuing discussion and listing cover all categories of *substantive* emendations made in the body of the Reading Text; the editors are depositing a complete list of emendations, including accidentals as well as substantives, in the Houghton Library of Harvard University. Each item is listed in terms of the manuscript leaf on which it appears: leaf numbers are those of the 1961 foliation of the manuscript, as in the margins of the Reading Text.

TREATMENT OF SUBSTANTIVES

The principles followed in six categories of substantive emendations can be summarized briefly.

1. The editors have excluded all verbal elements not intended by Melville himself, at the time of the latest copy stage, to be an intrinsic part of the novel. Examples range from marginal notations and queries written by both Melville and his wife, which are recorded in our Notes and Commentary, to those fragments discussed at some length under History of the Text in the Introduction: a draft title leaf, a so-called "Preface," and a superseded chapter.

2. We have supplied chapter numbers wherever Melville designated chapter divisions. In our Notes and Commentary, though not in the body of the text, we give the titles that Melville himself projected for three of the thirty chapters: in the present edition, those numbered 4, 12, and 26. (See notes to Leaves 58; 137, *envy and antipathy;* 321, *the purser.*)

3. We have rectified those obvious slips of Melville's pen that produced actual substantive errors, we have eliminated inadvertent mechanical repetitions, and we have corrected minor grammatical oversights. The instances, by leaf number, are as follows:

LEAF	READING TEXT	MANUSCRIPT
5	frequently	frequent
8	foot in the . . . as	foot the . . . as in
45	of these	of of these
65	in fight	in in fight
69	ships	ship
77	which shown	and which shown
79	to fall upon	to fall to upon
88	Captain Vere's	Captain's Vere
88	landsmen	landsman
97	lend	lends
105	by a . . . a novice afterguardsman	by by a . . . a novice an after-guardsman
106	through	though
109	which dismantled	and which dismantled
119	down to	down to to
121	smile,	smile, and
131	within	within in
134	Claggart	Claggart Claggart
135	savor of	savor of of
141	capable of	capable of of
143	a palatial	a a palatial
145	a grizzled	a a grizzled
151	was started	were started
151	even . . . into plausible	even [*inserted*] . . . into even [*second even uncanceled*] plausible
152	than aught	that aught
153	among	and among
153	the foremast	from the foremast
154	there," and disappearing	there"; and disappeared
154	to negative	to to negative
156	took him, . . . for one	took him to be, . . . for one
157	husky. "See	husky, th see
159	hair who	hair, and who
160	turn	turning
161	ever	even
162	spare buttons	buttons spare buttons
162	discomfited	discomforted
162	trying	tries
166	were so	was so
168	exclamation, whether	exclamation, which, whether
173	juvenility, this	juvenility. And this
176	As	While, as
181	an admonition	a admonition

187	may so	may so so
194	Vere's	Vere
196	under	inder
210	have not	having not
217	captain's	Captain
222	accuser's	accuser'
229	and, interrupting	and and interrupting
231	the surgeon's	the the Surgeon's
232	Again	But again
266	case is	case is is
273	Majesty's	Magesty
280	man-of-war's man's	man-of-war's-man
287	captain's	Captain
287	an exterior	a exterior
308	taken	and taken
311	one whom	one who
317	a conventional	a a conventional
318	even as in	even as he in
319	a soft	a a soft
325	was gradually	was gradually was
329	offices	office
329	now	and now
329	who, their	whose
332	wonted	wont
335	than an	that an
342	a responsible	an responsible
346	foretopman	foretopmen
350	lash	lash me
351	these	this

Certain changes listed here—"through" for "though" (Leaf 106), "than" for "that" (Leaves 152, 335)—correct slips of the pen that resulted in actual substantive errors. Not appearing above but included in our complete list of emendations are our silent corrections of such other mistakes as "experiend" instead of "experienced" (Leaf 16), "encoutering" instead of "encountering" (Leaf 195), "largety" instead of "largely" (Leaf 273), etc. Like Melville's outright misspellings—"prescence" (Leaf 72), "proceding" (Leaf 134), "hypothosis" (Leaf 323), etc.—mistakes of this nature do not constitute true substantive errors.

4. We have corrected any relatively minor verbal inaccuracy or error of fact that a copy editor would or should recognize in an original manuscript. Thus we have emended Melville's inexact quotations from

Tennyson (Leaf 66: "our world" for "the world") and from a translation of Martial (Leaf 46: "hath thee" for "has Thee"). Where in Mrs.
Melville's hand the manuscript reads "the Atheiste" and *"Atheiste"*
(Leaves 336, 337) we have substituted "the *Athée* (the *Atheist)"* and
"Athée" (employing the preferable French word). We have remedied
mistakes in names and titles: "Haden's" for "Hayden's" (Leaf 109),
"(William James)" for "G. P. R[.] (James)" (Leaf 53), "Rear Admiral" Sir Horatio Nelson for "Vice Admiral" (Leaf 70), and "still
captain" for "but Sir Horatio" (Leaf 109). And we have corrected
an error of fact in Melville's reference to the affair of the *Somers*
mutiny in 1842 (Leaf 281: "two sailors" for "two petty officers"). But
we have made no changes that would remove the material inconsistencies between Ch. 29 and passages that precede it (see note to Leaf 340),
or conceal the repeated departures from eighteenth-century British
statutes in Melville's treatment of the drumhead court and its proceedings (see notes to Leaves 233, 245, 273, 284). Our responsibility
here was that of a commentator rather than a copy editor.

5. Like the previous editors of *Billy Budd*, we have occasionally
been obliged to supply one or more words not found in a given sentence
of the manuscript as it stands but necessary to the sense of the passage.
Where such omissions have resulted from Melville's inadvertent cancellations, as in certain heavily revised passages, we have simply restored the essential words.

LEAF	READING TEXT	MANUSCRIPT
10	to be called	to be [calld *canceled*]
57	display and	display, [and *canceled*]
113	Dansker, do tell me	Dansker, [do tell *canceled*] me
140	went along with	[went *canceled*] [along with *canceled and restored*]
151	the private mentor of	the [private mentor *canceled*] of
155	commensurate to the hull's	commensurate [to the ample *canceled*] hull's
173	upon the junior	upon [the *canceled*] junior
181	the young	for [the *canceled*] young
187	shrewd ones may	shrewd [one *canceled*] may
270	any instances	any [instances *canceled*]

Where such omissions have resulted from Melville's cancellation of
both the original word or words and a tentative substitution, we have
restored the original.

LEAF	READING TEXT	MANUSCRIPT
24	lieutenant	[lieutenant *canceled* / officer *canceled*]
51	the fire brigade	[the *canceled* / her *canceled*] fire-brigade
72	mere presence and heroic personality	mere prescence & heroic [personality *canceled* / prescence *canceled*]
112	the name by	the [name *canceled* / knickname prefix *canceled*] by
150	Pharisee is	Pharisee [is *canceled* / being *canceled*]
223	horror of the accuser's eyes	horror [of *canceled* / at *canceled*] the accuser eyes

Where the omissions have resulted not from cancellations but from Melville's errors in drafting and copying, thus requiring an editor to supply altogether new words, we have been guided in our selection by the immediate context and by Melville's characteristic usage in similar passages.

LEAF	READING TEXT	MANUSCRIPT
17	he dismally	dismally
17	same time	same
24	now was	now
56	corps and	corps
87	as he would be to cite	air that he would cite
102	an ingratiating	ingratiating
134	as much as to	as much to
134	is never	never
168	or a	or
179	would flash forth	would forth
184	that came from	that
201	events in the fleet	events the Fleet
207	at all hazards	all hazards
211	voice demanded	voice
222	were gelidly	gelidly
238	That the	The
247	obesity—a man who	obesity. man who
251	immediately he	immediatly

6. Though Melville's intention in drafting manuscript revisions and additions is usually clear, he did not always fully carry through his projected changes. As a general rule we have applied the principle that an author's latest intention is to be honored, wherever the time-

sequence can be determined, even though he himself did not completely effect the changes he began. But where Melville failed to make his ultimate intention sufficiently clear, or in a few cases where his projected changes would actually obscure the sense of a passage, we have retained or restored the original wording—as explained here or in the Notes and Commentary.

One major substantive change has resulted from application of the principle that the author's latest intention will govern. In line with Melville's practice in the latest fair copy stage, we have uniformly given *Bellipotent* rather than *Indomitable* as the name of Captain Vere's ship. Thus the Reading Text prints "*Bellipotent*" for Melville's "*Indomitable*" and "Indomitable" (Leaves 11, 24, 31, 35, 49, 81, 156, 170, 239, 282, 341, 343, and 346), and "*Bellipotent*'s" for his "*Indomitable*'s" and variants (" '*Indomitable*'s' " or "Indomitable's" or "Indomitables"; Leaves 15, 80, 100, 109, 231, 240, 243, 300, and 310). Parenthetically, the same principle applied to accidentals has led us to prefer "Jemmy Legs" to the variant "Jimmy Legs" (Leaves 114, 120).

Where Melville himself made substitutions or restorations but did not cancel the phrasing thereby replaced, we have normally printed the words that he evidently wrote last, or ultimately restored.

LEAF	READING TEXT	MANUSCRIPT
4	Highland	Scotch / Highland
53	patriotic devotion . . . tar	[patriotic *inserted*] devotion . . . tar [*without cancellation of* , that is, to his country]
76	cabin	retreat / cabin
89	sword or	sword and/or
104	in such society	in that / such society
133	atrocity	[atrocity *canceled*] malignity / atrocity [*restored without cancellation of* malignity]
134	method . . . proceeding are	method . . . proceding is / are
170	blank	[blank *canceled*] utter / blank [*restored without cancellation of* utter]
205	perjurous	perjured / perjurous
229	character	man / character
229	take him aback	surprise, / take him aback
296	ended	closed / ended
306	close	near / close
314	*eight bells*	*one* / eight *bells*

There are six exceptions to this procedure, however, three of them involving words written not by Melville but by Mrs. Melville. On Leaf 310 we have retained his word "primer" even though above it in the manuscript Mrs. Melville wrote "pioneer"—presumably her conjectural reading of the word rather than an actual substitution; similarly on Leaf 199 we have retained his "the testifier's" though she wrote "a witness' " above it. On Leaf 132, in a puzzling instance, we read "them. It is never . . . avaricious." where the manuscript reads "them. from anything [from anything *inserted in pencil by Mrs. Melville*] Never . . . avaricious [and so forth *canceled*]". For the sake of clarity we have restored Melville's original wording on Leaf 150 to read "some natures like Claggart's" for "[some natures like *canceled*] the Claggart"; and on Leaf 235 we have restored the noun of his original sentence to read "can the surgeon" for "can he". On Leaf 198 we omit a superfluous "Whereof" written above "Quite lately".

We have made other emendations to effect more extensive changes called for though not actually completed by Melville himself. On Leaf 295, even though he made no cancellation in the text, we have his specific authority for revising the wording of one sentence: in a marginal notation he wrote "Another order to be given here in place of this one" (to pipe down one watch), and later he added, also in the margin, the actual phrasing desired ("the word was given to about ship"). On Leaf 211, where the situation is somewhat different, we have changed "pitfal[l] under the clover" to "mantrap under the daisies" in order to bring the passage into conformity with Melville's revision of Claggart's antecedent remark on Leaf 207. In both instances the author's ultimate intentions require the editorial changes we have made, though only the one alteration is guided by Melville's own specific notation. Similarly, we have made minor changes on Leaves 246 ("sea lieutenant and the sailing master" for "sea lieutenants") and 275 ("sailing master" for "junior Lieutenant" and "Gentlemen" for "Lieutenant") to carry through Melville's latest change in the size and composition of the drumhead court (see note to Leaf 245).

In still other instances, however, we have retained or restored Melville's original wording where he partially revoked a tentative change (see note to Leaf 320, *the slow roll of the hull*) or failed to develop a projected revision or expansion. Thus on Leaf 262, where above a canceled "stood" Melville wrote only "(sitting)", we have simply restored "stood"; and on Leaf 316, where after first writing that Billy was brought up under "an arm" of the foreyard, he inserted the later notation "weather or lee" above "an arm", we have left "an arm" unchanged, finding no basis in the manuscript itself for reading either "the weather arm" or "the lee arm". Additional instances of this kind are discussed at some length in individual notes to Leaves 54, *Like . . . events . . .* ; 57; 168; 181, *thews* (queried); 311; 312; and 331, *a sort of impulse.*

TREATMENT OF ACCIDENTALS

In general terms, we have in the Reading Text expanded Melville's customary abbreviations (&, Rev^d, tho', thro') and silently emended his mistakes, omissions, inconsistencies, and redundancies in spelling, capitalization, hyphenation, paragraphing, and punctuation. Apart from his characteristic vagaries of spelling, many of these instances were merely incidental to the process of revising and amplifying the *Billy Budd* manuscript over a period of years, and would in most instances have been caught and corrected by the author himself or by his copyist had the manuscript reached the stage of a final fair copy.

Comparison of passages in the Reading and Genetic Texts will indicate the nature and scope of the changes made in accidentals; every modification appears in the complete list of editorial emendations we have prepared for deposit in the Houghton Library. Since it was imperative to normalize on some basis, we determined to modernize the text rather than to impose upon Melville's latitudinarian usage the principles of some arbitrarily selected nineteenth-century stylebook. Making due allowance for the structural idiosyncrasies of his prose, we have therefore followed present-day editorial practice in styling the Reading Text for a twentieth-century public.

THE
GENETIC TEXT

Analysis of the Manuscript

THE MANUSCRIPT

The manuscript of *Billy Budd* is now in the Houghton Library of Harvard University, with the designation "Ms Am 188 (363)". A few additional leaves bearing superseded *Billy Budd* matter are among other Melville manuscripts with the designation "Ms Am 188 (369)". At present a new arrangement and boxing of all the Melville manuscripts is in progress.

PAPER

Most of the leaves Melville used in the *Billy Budd* manuscript are of the same cream laid paper, with no watermark. A few leaves, however, though of similar paper, are of more weight and deeper shade. Miss Tilton (1959), p. 53, is correct in distinguishing the two shades of paper as lighter and darker and in finding that "the use of the lighter paper appears generally to have followed the use of the darker."

The leaves are not altogether uniform in size, having been torn or cut from sheets. The measurements vary slightly around $7'' \times 5\frac{5}{8}''$. We have made much use of the physical evidence of matching edges (whether cut, or scissored, or torn), and of the position of chain-lines, in determining whether or not clips originally belonged to the same leaf. A thorough study of the physical properties of the paper in all Melville's late manuscripts will eventually have great value in the intricate process of establishing their chronological interrelationships.

HANDWRITING CHARACTERISTICS AND MEDIA

The handwriting of the manuscript is Melville's own, but four other hands appear. The earliest of these alien hands is that of Melville's wife, Elizabeth Shaw Melville, which appears in several notations and at various points within the text. Previous editors have not distinguished it from Melville's hand, though the distinction has important consequences for the final text. The second alien hand appears only in a foliation evidently that of Raymond Weaver, the first editor of *Billy Budd*. The third hand appears only in the Houghton Library designation "Ms Am 188 (363)" which has been penciled on a number of leaves; the fourth appears in the new Houghton Library foliation inscribing the lower left corner of each leaf with the leaf number assigned in the present edition. The second hand (Weaver's) has some significance as indicating what leaves were in the manuscript when he foliated it. The third and fourth hands are of no analytical significance.

Melville's own handwriting varies conspicuously from passage to passage in the size and shaping of letters and in the spacing of words and of lines of writing. These variations, taken with concomitant variations in media and with the content, often provide a basis for identifying passages as first drafts, revisions, or fair copies; and at times they make it possible to bring separated passages back together.

The media in which Melville wrote on the leaves vary considerably. Among the three types of media, ink predominates. It is of several distinguishable colors or intensities (black, brown, blue, gray); Melville evidently used several different pens, in ways that left observable differences, especially when the color of ink, particular pen, and style of handwriting are considered together. Pencil appears frequently: in first-draft material, in revisions, in cancellations, and in marginal notations. Finally, crayons of green, red, orange, brown, and blue were used by Melville for foliation and cancellations, in ways sufficiently consistent to allow valid deductions, particularly in the number sets. All of these media, taken in relation to each other and to further evidence, help make possible the assignment of segments of the writing to one or another of the stages and substages of composition, revision, or copying.

NUMBER AND CONTENT OF LEAVES

There are in all 370 leaves with *Billy Budd* matter written on or attached to them. These may be subdivided into two classes. In the first class, 351 leaves stand in Melville's final manuscript; that is, they stand in a sequence carrying the dedication and the text of the story. Also on some of these leaves, both recto and verso, there are superseded passages. In the second class there are nineteen leaves, standing outside this final sequence: five of these are associated leaves bearing notations of some sort, and fourteen are superseded worksheets (the versos of four of the latter were re-used later for "Daniel Orme").

As mentioned above, some of the leaves in the final sequence have earlier inscription on their versos. In some cases such inscription is superseded matter from *Billy Budd* itself, in some cases matter from other prose or poetry. The superseded *Billy Budd* matter belonged to earlier stages; after its supersession Melville turned the leaves over and re-used their backs for passages standing in the final sequence. The unrelated writing is mostly passages of verse from the *John Marr* and *Timoleon* volumes; the consistency of its distribution is significant confirmatory evidence in fixing stages of composition. (See "Leaves with Inscribed Versos," pp. 430–42.)

Also included in the manuscript are numerous part-leaves—that is, pieces which Melville cut from whole-leaves. Almost all of these were pinned (and often later glued) to whole-leaves which stand in the final sequence. Some of these part-leaves bear passages Melville salvaged by clipping them from *earlier* leaves merely to avoid copying them; these we call "clips." Others bear revisions or insertions *later* than the copy stage of the leaves to which they are fastened; these we call "patches." In some instances Melville attached such clips or patches to leaves which bear no other writing (except perhaps folio numbers) and which serve simply as mounts to bring the part-leaves up to uniform leaf size. In our numbering we have included the clips and patches as part of the leaves to which they are attached, but in the Genetic Text we have recorded the distinction by separate symbols for clips (*) and patches (†).

As evidence of the process of composition, both the whole-leaves and their contents are of great importance. Considering the leaves as such—that is, their physical separateness—their value as evidence lies in the fact, discussed below, that Melville carried forward many individual leaves intact from stage to stage of inscription, and that as he did so he had to identify them with folio numbers, which varied for the same leaf in successive stages.

An essential distinction crucial at a later phase of the analysis must be made and maintained between the leaves *as such* and the writing on them. For, on the one hand, upon the number of leaves present in given copy stages will turn much of the process of reasoning about the topics present in those stages; but, on the other hand, the *number* of leaves bears no necessary or exact relation to either the exact *amount* or the exact verbal *content* of the writing on those leaves. That is to say, while we may with reasonable assurance make inferences concerning the *number* of leaves, we cannot assume that the verbal *content* of the leaves has remained altogether the same, though it seems safe enough to assume that the *topic* has remained the same. For example, the fact that at a given point one copy stage had three leaves, later supplanted and destroyed, and that at the corresponding point the next stage also had three leaves, now extant, does not constitute grounds for a certain inference that the same words were on the earlier leaves that are now on the later ones—indeed, the fact that the earlier leaves were recopied forward indicates that Melville had substantially revised them, while conversely the survival of leaves from one stage to another indicates that he had made so few revisions on them that he could carry them forward without recopying their matter.

FOLIATION

There are three peculiarities in Melville's foliation of the manuscript:

1. *Discontinuous foliation:* Though there are six different sets of folio numbers, no single set runs continuously through the entire manuscript. As Melville left it, the order of its leaves was designated by his numbers in six successive sequences from five different sets, as shown in the tabulation below. (A few stray vestigial numbers outside any of these sets also appear, together with minor sets for short sequences of leaves.)

2. *Overlapping leaf numbers:* Leaf numbers of some of the six sets very often overlap; that is, a single leaf may carry numbers from more than one of the six sets. (See Figure 1, p. 227.)

3. *Added numbers:* Frequently Melville modified a leaf number by adding to it a number circled or in parentheses (which we indicate by superscripts), and sometimes he numbered several consecutive leaves in this manner: . . . 48, 49^1, 49^2, 50^1, 50^2, 50^3, 50^4, 50^5, 50^6, 50^7, 51. . . . Obviously, these "added numbers" were necessitated when Melville inserted leaves into the series after he had already numbered past the point of insertion. (But the leaves so designated were not always those which he inserted, since in the process he sometimes altered the numbers of leaves already present, giving them "added numbers" while assigning unqualified numbers to leaves which he was adding.)

The following tabulation shows the order in which Melville's six number sets carry the final narrative. It does not show the *time order* in which he composed the matter on them, or the *time order* in which he inscribed and numbered the leaves—these are major questions which remain to be determined in the ensuing analysis. (The leaf numbers are those assigned in the present edition and by the Houghton Library.)

Set I: [Leaves 2–118] "Left Green" (LG). This set appears in broken series, numbered 1–81, in green crayon on the upper left corner. The set was superseded by the "Red" set, and hence does not carry Melville's final numbering for these leaves.

Set II: [Leaves 2–142] "Red." Numbered 1–151 in "red" crayon (so referred to in the manuscript notations; actually varying red, orange, and brown crayons), on the upper right corner of leaves.

Set III: [Leaves 143–177] "Left-Corner Pencil" (LCP). Numbered 16^3 to 41 in pencil, on the upper left corner of leaves. Begins with top-marginal notation (by Mrs. Melville), "Follows 151 *red*", and ends with Melville's notation, "48 *green* follows".

Set IVa: [Leaves 178–188] "Middle Green" (MG). Numbered 48–51 (with added numbers) in green crayon on the middle-top of leaves.

Set V: [Leaves 189–251] "Middle-Right Pencil" (MRP). Numbered 1–56 in pencil, on the middle-right margin of leaves. Begins with Melville's notations, *"follows 51 green"* and "See [right-hand] side for Number of Page". Ends with notation (by Mrs. Melville), "16 on left side of page follows". Its last nine leaves (49–56) are the first nine leaves of the following set.

Set VI: [Leaves 243–339] "Middle-Left Pencil" (MLP). Numbered 7–101 in pencil, on the middle-left margin of leaves. (7–15 are the last nine leaves of Set V.)

Set IVb: [Leaves 340–351] "Middle Green" (MG). Numbered 75^2 to 84 in green crayon (and pencil), on the middle-top of leaves. This is a continuation of Set IV, to which it belongs. Begins with Mrs. Melville's notation, "follows 101 on side in pencil".

LCP [C] LG [D]	MG [B]	Red [E]
MLP [F]		MRP [G]

Fig. 1.—The leaf displays the positions of the six number-sets in Melville's foliation of the manuscript. In brackets following the abbreviated labels for the number sets (MG, LCP, LG, Red, MLP, MRP) are the alphabetical labels designating their relative time-order.

In the ensuing analysis, these sets are referred to by the abbreviated labels, assigned above, which are based on the medium and position of their number sets: LG, Red, LCP, MG, MRP, MLP. Upon completion of the analysis, they are reassigned labels in an alphabetical series showing the relative *time-order* of their inscription: [A], B, C, D, [X], E, F, G, p. (A, X, and p are letters we have added to designate three other sequences or stages for which no number sets survive.) These alphabetical labels are used in the Genetic Text and in discussion of the stages of composition corresponding to the copy stages. (See Figure 1, above.)

The nature of these six number-sets is obvious: each set was used by Melville to foliate a sequence of leaves which at a given stage stood together as a unit of some sort. Inspection shows that, as a matter of fact, what each set foliated was a fair-copy sequence. When Melville had brought the manuscript to the state in which it finally stood, with the constituent leaves in narrative order, he did not re-number them all from first to last, but simply made use of the number sets already on the successive fair-copy sequences, and added some marginal notations (Mrs. Melville added others later) to indicate the transitions from one set to the next. In short, except for a few late pencil-draft leaves, the manuscript consists of leaves from a number of fair-copy sequences which Melville inscribed *at various times, not in narrative order;* and the foliation is that of the separate fair-copy sequences, not of the manuscript as a whole.

The next step in analysis, therefore, is to ascertain the time order in which Melville inscribed the fair-copy sequences bearing the six number-sets. Thus far, to repeat, the sets have been presented only in their order relative to the sequence of the narrative. The question now becomes: In what *time order* were they inscribed?

TIME ORDER OF THE NUMBER SETS

As it turns out, the time order of the number sets can be ascertained, finally and fully, only by a rather intricate use of nearly all the existing kinds of manuscript evidence enumerated in the foregoing sections.

The first major clue, however, is the overlapping leaf numbers described and tabulated above. The immediately observable fact, as stated, is that many leaves bear more than one number. The numbers were placed in different positions on the leaves, as indicated on the hypothetical leaf represented in Figure 1, though no single actual leaf bears numbers in all the positions.

The general explanation of these overlapping numbers is clear enough: any leaf which bears numbers from more than one set belonged at different times to each of those sequences. This situation arose because when Melville was inscribing his fair-copy sequences he did not copy every leaf but retained and carried forward all the earlier leaves that were still fairly clear of revisions, putting them into the new sequence and numbering them in its new number set. Thus they would bear numbers from both old and new sets, and any of them that similarly survived into a still later copy stage would receive still a third number. The resulting situation in the manuscript poses two problems. The first problem is to assign all surviving leaves, in their numbered order, to every sequence in which they belonged at any time. The second problem, still, is to determine the time order in which the sets, as such, received their numbering. As it happens, one fairly simple device goes a long way toward solving both problems at once.

As first recognized by Freeman (1948), p. ix, the leaf numbers can readily be tabulated in a way that will simultaneously show which leaves belonged in each number set and reveal the relative time-order in which at least some of the sets were numbered. A vertical column is allotted for each of the six number-sets. These vertical columns are arranged parallel to each other so that numbers from each set run down the table in their appropriate columns, while at the same time all the numbers which appear on a single leaf are ranged in a horizontal row across the columns. Thus, all leaf numbers belonging in a given set are sorted into a single vertical column, and also the pattern formed by the leaf numbers of the overlapping numbered leaves is revealed. (Since the resulting table is long and complex, and since it is at once subject to rearrangement when the time order has been determined, only a rearranged final version of this table is presented, giving the sets in time order from left to right. In this final table, individual leaves and part-leaves have been assigned to the stage or substage of their actual inscription, when even further evidence has shown that Melville gave them numbers of a different stage or substage than that at which he inscribed them.)

When the table has been thus constructed, several significant facts at once emerge, relating both to the order of materials in the narrative and to the time order of the numberings. (The ensuing analysis should be read with constant reference to Figure 2 and to the final table, pp. 241–69, in both of which the number sets have been arranged in their relative time order as ascertained by the ensuing analysis.)

Inspection of the vertical columns (into which the six number-sets have been separated) reveals three facts:

1. Down every one of the columns the numbers follow each other in ascending, though often interrupted, arithmetic order. Since this is true for all six sets, the first striking fact comes out: *in the whole course of observable composition (with one major and a few minor exceptions) Melville did not change the relative order of the materials in the narrative enough to throw the surviving leaf numbers in any set out of arithmetic order.* That is, Melville did not engage in re-ordering episodes, or in wholesale shifting-about of materials. (This fact negates Freeman's conjecture, p. 70, concerning re-arrangements in the story order.) That Melville did not do so, needless to say, enormously simplifies the already complicated analysis of the growth of the manuscript.

2. The second fact revealed is that not one of the six number-sets, as they run down the columns, forms a closed series: they all have gaps—that is, some of their numbers, at the ends or within the series, are missing. Further, some

Leaf	MG [B]	LCP [C]	LG [D]	[X]	Red [E]	MLP [F]	MRP [G]	[p]
2	⟨1⟩		1		1			
10								
20								
30	7⁷							
40								
51	⟨11⟩		⟨37⟩		44			
61	16⁵							
70	17⁴							
80								
90	18⁶		54		102			
100	⟨25⟩							
110								
118	31⁶	⟨1⟩	81		126			
130								
143		16³			149			
150								
160								
170								
178	48	41						
188	50⁵						1	
200								
210								
221	66						29	
230						⟨1⟩		
243						7	49	
251						15	56	
260								
270								
280								
290								
300								
310								
320								
330								
339	75²					101		
351	⟨85⟩							

Fig. 2.—This diagram shows (a) the range of numbers within each of the six number-sets; (b) the portion of the manuscript included in the copy sequence numbered by each set; (c) the overlappings and intersections of the sets. The heavy vertical lines indicate the six successive sequences from five number-sets that carry the final foliation, as discussed, pp. 226–27. Broken vertical lines indicate discontinuous sequences. Apparent disproportions in the scale result from the gaps and the "added numbers" within the sets; these occur especially in MG [B]. The relative time order and position of Stage X and the late pencil revision stage, p, are also shown.

leaves numbered only one unit apart are separated from each other by leaves with numbers from other sets. And finally, some numbers occur on leaves first numbered in another set. The significance of these observations is that *the process of composition observable was fundamentally a process of expansion,* as Freeman recognized from his similar analysis.

3. The third fact revealed is that *only one set, MG, has numbers running (though intermittently) through the whole manuscript.* Two other sets, LG and Red, both begin at the first story leaf, but both end in the midst of the story. The other three sets, LCP, MRP, and MLP, in that order, begin as well as end their numberings at different points within the body of the story. This fact has a significant bearing on the problem of the time order of the number sets, a problem to whose solution the horizontal columns provide the leading clue.

Discovery of the time order of the number sets begins with inspection of the horizontal columns. These display a more complicated situation than the vertical columns. And unfortunately, on their evidence alone not all the six number-sets can be placed in time order relative to each other—the reason being, as the accompanying diagram (Figure 2) shows, that they do not all overlap. So far as usable overlappings do occur, the manuscript falls into two segments, roughly the first and last halves of the story. The first segment (Leaves 2–177) carries overlapping numbers of LG, Red, LCP, and MG. The second segment (Leaves 189–351) carries overlapping numbers of MG, MRP, and MLP. The only set which appears in both segments is MG. And not only does MG have numbers in both segments, it also supplies the leaves between the two segments; for the two segments are connected by a "bridge" sequence of eleven leaves (Leaves 178–188) carrying *only* MG numbers. The upshot of this segmentation of the manuscript is that the number overlappings supply evidence sufficient to reveal—with one exception—the time order of the sets that lie *within* each of the two segments, but not evidence sufficient to reveal that of all six sets relative to each other. Therefore, determination of the complete order of all six sets becomes a further problem, one which depends for its solution upon supplementary evidence, chiefly that of the various inks. (It may be stated here that all of the conclusions as to time order presented below on the evidence of the horizontal columns are in fact confirmed by further evidence, of ink, paper, contents, etc.)

Taking the two segments separately, then: In the first segment (Leaves 2–177), the sets are revealed to have been inscribed in the time order MG, LCP, LG, and Red. The evidence establishing this order is clear.

First, LG, Red, and (evidently) MG all began their number series at the same leaf, the first page of the story. Since they thus had a common starting-point, and since Melville, as already shown, was *expand-ing* the story, it follows that when numbers from all three of these sets occur on a single leaf (as they frequently do), the lowest number must have been the earliest one Melville placed there, the intermediate number must have been second, and the highest number must have been last. (For example, Leaf 52 bears the numbers MG 12, LG 38, and Red 45; that is, in three successive stages, as Melville expanded the story and increased the number of leaves, this was at first Leaf 12, then Leaf 38, and then Leaf 45.) This interpretation is confirmed by the evidence of all leaves where numbers from all three sets occur, since their relationship on all such leaves remains consistent. So we arrive at the conclusion that in the first segment (Leaves 2–177) MG, LG, and Red were numbered in that order.

Now in the first segment LCP remains to be placed in relation to those three. The evidence places the numbering of LCP earlier than Red and later than MG.

1. LCP is placed as earlier than Red by the fact that the Red num-bering runs into the numbering of LCP, overlapping with it on Leaf 143 where the Red set ends with 149 and the extant leaves of the LCP set begin with 16^3. The obvious inference from this conjunction of numbers is that the first sixteen leaves of LCP ($\langle 1–16 \rangle$), plus the "added-number" leaves they may have included, were replaced by the copying and numbering process that carried the Red sequence that many leaves into the LCP numbering. That is, as Melville was inscribing and numbering the Red sequence he did not stop when he came to the leaf already numbered LCP 1, but kept on copying—now copying from LCP leaves and replacing them by Red leaves—and also kept on numbering in the Red set, until he got to the leaf already numbered LCP 16^3, which he let stand, along with the rest of the LCP sequence from there on, ending the Red copying and numbering at this leaf—Red 149. Hence, it is clear that LCP was already in exist-ence as a number set before the Red numbering took place.

2. Further: In relation to MG, the LCP number set is placed as *later* by the fact that numbers in the MG set occur both before the beginning of LCP and after its ending, as well as overlapping some of its numbers; thus LCP represents an expansion stage whose leaves ($\langle 1 \rangle$–41) bear materials expanded from and added to materials origi-nally carried by the leaves of MG between about MG $\langle 35 \rangle$ and MG 48.

3. In relation to LG, however, LCP cannot be placed by the same evidence of overlapping, since their numbers do not overlap at all. But by two other types of evidence LCP is placed as *earlier* than LG.

For one thing, we may advance the inferences that the LG and LCP sequences probably intersected originally at about Leaf 121 or 122, and that the prior existence of the LCP sequence, beginning at this point, would account for the termination of the LG series here; whereas if LG had preceded LCP Melville would have had no good reason for discontinuing rather than going on with the LG number series when he made the new fair-copy sequence he numbered as LCP. For a second thing, going beyond the present class of evidence, the ink and the copy-relations within the two sequences both confirm the priority of LCP to LG.

In sum, the evidence thus places MG, LCP, LG, and Red in that time order within the first segment of the manuscript.

In the second segment (Leaves 189–351), consisting of leaves with overlapping numbers of three sets, the sets are revealed to stand in the time order MG, MLP, and MRP. (1) MG stands first because it straddles and overlaps both MLP and MRP (just as it does LCP in the first segment): this fact shows that both MLP and MRP bear material expanded from and added to material originally appearing in MG. (2) As to the time relation of MLP and MRP, the evidence is similar to that for LCP and Red in the first segment: MLP was numbered before MRP, as evidenced by the fact that MLP now begins its numbering with MLP 7, where MRP joins MLP (MLP 7 and MRP 49 occur on the same leaf). That is, as Melville inscribed and numbered copy-sequence MRP, he kept on copying and numbering when he came to MLP ⟨1⟩, and replaced MLP leaves ⟨1–6⟩ with MRP 41–48— this fact being made more evident by the further fact that he continued MRP numbering up to 56 on the MLP leaves without replacing them.

Now the evidence has been presented which establishes the time order of the sets *within* each of the two segments:

First segment: MG, LCP, LG, Red

Second segment: MG, MLP, MRP

Here immediately, on the basis of evidence already presented, a cardinal revelation of the whole chronological analysis emerges: *the surviving leaves of the MG set carry the remains of the earliest version of the story represented in the final manuscript.* For the MG set is clearly the earliest of all the numberings present, by two counts. (1) MG numbers are earliest in both segments, and they also supply the "bridge" (Leaves 178–88) between the two segments, where only MG numbers occur. (2) MG is the only set whose numbers span the whole length of the manuscript. The MG numbers are present intermittently from so near the beginning that it is evident that the series must have begun there, to the very end. Patently, the MG set numbered the earliest version of the story from which leaves still survive in the final manuscript; and from this version the finally much longer story was expanded. Therefore, the MG leaves provide the foundation upon which we may base the whole analysis of the several stages of composition—our ultimate objective.

Unfortunately, however, beyond placing MG as the earliest number-set of all, the evidence supplied by the horizontal columns is not sufficient, in itself, to fix the relative time-order of all the other sets. At this point evidence supplied by the various inks must be employed.

By evidence of the inks, MRP is placed as the last number-set of all; and MLP is closely linked to MRP in time as the set *immediately* preceding it. The proof is as follows. The ink of MRP leaves is of two shades. The first, and basic, ink of the MRP sequence is of a distinctive blue, which is not the basic ink of any other sequence. Melville's use of this blue ink in revisions and additions on leaves numbered by the Red number set establishes MRP as belonging to a later time-stage than Red. A second, distinguishable ink also appears in the MRP sequence, an ink which links the MRP leaves closely to those of MLP while placing MLP as the number set that just preceded MRP. This second ink is of a pale charcoal or blue-gray, at times mottled in a way that suggests it is actually the same blue ink when its level had fallen low in the inkwell and its density had thereby been increased. This blue-gray ink occurs as the basic ink of only the first three leaves (Leaves 189–91) of the sequence, MRP 1, 2^1, and the top and top clip on 2^2, after which blue ink takes over. But this same blue-gray ink also appears as the basic ink of the *later* leaves of MLP, whose own basic ink in its first and longest ink sequence (MLP 7–74; Leaves 243–311) is of heavy brown. Revising and adding to these earlier MLP leaves, the blue-gray ink appears on MLP 75 (Leaf 312), which is a recopied and inserted leaf with the notation "76 omitted". The blue-gray ink soon reappears as the ink of MLP 85, 86^1, 86^2, 86^3 (Leaves 321–24), leaves which constitute Ch. 26 (which was a later insertion, expanded from material of the last lines of MLP 84 and on the replaced ⟨85–86⟩). This ink appears again on MLP 91 (Leaf 329), where it takes over from the heavy-brown ink at a paragraph-break in mid-page, and from there it continues to the end of the sequence, MLP 91–101 (Leaves 329–39), with varying shades of blue, gray, and black which seemingly resulted from the decreasing level of the ink in the inkwell and the varying depths within it to which Melville dipped his pen. The interpretation of this distribution of inks seems clear enough. Melville inscribed MLP ⟨*1*⟩–91 in heavy-brown ink.

When he came to finish inscribing the sequence, he used the blue-gray ink. In this ink he replaced original brown ink MLP ⟨75–76⟩ with a single new leaf numbered 75. He expanded a passage on MLP 84 and set it off as a new chapter, MLP 85–86^3, in this ink. And then he took up copying at MLP 91, where he had left off with brown ink, and completed the sequence to MLP 101 (since at that point he came to the end of the pencil draft from which he was copying, and arrived at ink fair-copy leaves belonging to MG). Then—and this is what links MRP to the end of MLP—he went back in the narrative to the beginning of Ch. 18, and in the same blue-gray ink began copying down, and revising, the sequence which he simultaneously numbered with the MRP number-set. In this ink he wrote only the first two-and-a-third leaves of MRP 1, 2^1, 2^2, and on MRP 2^2 the ink shades into blue for the rest of the MRP sequence—perhaps because of a refilling of his inkwell.

A further peculiarity links certain late leaves of MLP (99, 101; Leaves 337, 339) with certain early leaves of MRP (1, 2^1, 5, 10; Leaves 190, 191, 194, 200). On these leaves the name of the British warship, elsewhere always *Indomitable*, is given as *Bellipotent*. The linking of these leaves by their use of the name *Bellipotent* confirms the inference from the ink colors also linking them: Melville, upon finishing the MLP sequence, went back directly to begin on the MRP sequence in the same ink; for this procedure accounts for the six uses of *Bellipotent* as having been put on paper all within fifteen leaves of each other as Melville was inscribing them, though they are separated by some 150 leaves in narrative sequence.

Thus, by the evidence of both the inks as well as by the evidence of the name *Bellipotent*, MLP is linked directly to MRP and is shown to stand as the number set immediately preceding it in time order of inscription.

Up to this point, the time order of the six number-sets has been established as: first, MG; fifth, MLP; sixth, MRP. Already, moreover, on the evidence of the horizontal columns, both LCP and LG have been shown to have preceded Red, in that order; hence LCP, LG, and Red are established as second, third, and fourth in the time order. At this point, therefore, determination of the time order of all the six number-sets—and hence of their fair-copy sequences—is complete: MG, LCP, LG, Red, MLP, MRP.

We may now simplify the designation of the six sets and make their time order clear by assigning them alphabetical labels in place of those used thus far: MG, *B;* LCP, *C;* LG, *D;* Red, *E;* MLP, *F;* MRP, *G.* These alphabetical labels have immediate reference to the number sets of the several foliations. By extension, as noted, they refer as well to the fair-copy sequences which the number sets foliated. And since they indicate the time order in which these sequences were inscribed, they may be employed to designate as well the fair-copy stages—that is, the *stages of inscription*.

Further analysis of the manuscript necessitates the addition of three more alphabetical labels, A, X, and p (late pencil revision), to designate further important stages of inscription for which no separate or extended copy sequences and number sets survive, as explained below in the tabulation of stages. The time order of all nine stages is: A, B, C, D, X, E, F, G, p.

On the basis of the chronological ordering thus established for the number sets and their fair-copy sequences—as well as the added stages A, X, and p—we may now go on to the two major objectives of the analysis. The immediate objective is to assign all writing to the proper stages and substages of *inscription*. The second, and ultimate, objective is to determine the time of *composition* of the matter on the leaves and to trace the stages in the growth of the story, so far as these may be inferred from the manuscript evidence. Both of these objectives offer problems whose solution involves more intricate use of the evidence than can be reported in detail here, but the general lines of analysis may be stated briefly.

STAGES AND SUBSTAGES OF INSCRIPTION

The next objective in the analysis is to assign all leaves, part-leaves (clips and patches), passages, and revisions to the stages and substages of their actual inscription. A problem at once arises in such assignment when inspection shows that not all of the leaves standing within any one of the six copy-sequences were actually inscribed at the same time, or in their numbered order, or even at the stage indicated by their numbering. As reflection would suggest, in this heavily revised manuscript of a story developed by gradual expansion there are various classes of leaves within each of the sequences: some leaves were brought forward from earlier copy stages, as indicated by their earlier foliation; some leaves carry clips brought forward from earlier stages; some leaves were inscribed at the time the sequence was foliated; some leaves were inscribed later at substages, and even sub-substages; some leaves were inscribed and inserted at later stages, though foliated in the sequence; other leaves carry patches inscribed at later stages; and almost all leaves carry revisions made after their inscription.

As already discussed above, there are several kinds of evidence by which to define stages and substages of inscription and to assign individual leaves and passages to them. First, and fundamental, there are the numbers and added numbers; second, there are the various inks (and pens) and other media of inscription and numbering; and finally, there is the local physical as well as contextual evidence. The results of our analysis are presented in the Table of Foliations and in the Genetic Text. A brief account is given here of the characteristics distinguishing the nine stages and their substages, to which each leaf, clip, patch, and passage of revision has been assigned.

Stage *A:* This stage is defined as embracing all the writing before Stage *B*—that is, from the beginning up to the inscription of the fair-copy leaves of Stage *B*, which are the earliest leaves standing in the final manuscript. Only four leaves, all in pencil draft, survive from Stage *A*. (See "Stage A Leaves" below, Plates I–IV, and Introduction, pp. 3–6; also Extra-textual Leaves, Nos. 1, 2.)

Stage *B:* This was a fair-copy stage distinguished by the MG number-set. Within Stage *B* three substages, *Ba*, *Bb*, and *Bc*, are generally (though not always certainly) distinguishable by the combination of pens and black ink employed in each, respectively "heavy," "fine," and "dark," and by local contextual interrelations. The same factors indicate occasional further local distinctions of sub-substages: *Bba*, *Bbb*, within *Bb;* and *Bca*, *Bcb*, within *Bc.*

Stage *C:* This was a fair-copy stage distinguished by the LCP number-set. Within it substages *Ca*, *Cb*, *Cc* are distinguished by the numbers and added numbers, while local sub-substages *Caa* and *Cab*, *Cba* and *Cbb*, and *Cca* are further distinguished by contextual relationships. The inscription of *Ca* was in the same "dark" ink and pen as that of *Bc*, and internal relations also indicate that the time stage of their inscription was the same; hence at some points we employ both letters together, thus: *Bc[C]* to indicate the whole stage of both and also to indicate that segment foliated by the MG numbers, and *[Bc]Ca* to indicate that segment foliated with the LCP numbers.

Stage *D:* This was a fair-copy stage distinguished by the LG number-set. Its ink is pale black, almost gray. Its unmodified numbers define substage *Da;* its added numbers and contextual relations indicate substage *Db*, as well as the local subdivision of *Da* into *Daa* and *Dab.*

Stage *X:* This was an extensive pencil-draft composition stage which supplied much of the matter incorporated by the fair-copy stages *F* and *G*. (The letter *X* was assigned to indicate its distinction from the fair-copy stages designated by the letters *B* through *G*.) Several of its pencil-draft leaves survive, three in the final manuscript sequence;

they carry folio numbers and matter that indicate there were many substages of pencil-draft composition within X but no fair copy in ink before the incorporation of X by Stages F and G. A few notations and revisions on leaves of other stages also survive from Stage X.

Stage E: This was a fair-copy stage distinguished by the Red number-set. Within it there were several copy and revision sequences distinguishable with some certainty by their inks and pens, by the varying shades of the "red" (red, orange, brown) numbering crayons, and by contextual relations. The initial sequence Ea (Ch. 1–2), in gray-black ink, has the substage Eab, distinguished by the added numbers and by local contextual relations. Next Eb, the chief sequence (Ch. 3–12), inscribed in similar ink with a fine sharp pen, is revised and at points supplanted by Ec. Ec is distinguished by the added numbers and (Ch. 9) by a somewhat coarser pen and is associated with a brown numbering crayon. Ed (in Ch. 11) is a minor local substage. Ee/F revised and replaced some of Eb (Ch. 11–12) in the brown ink of F, as did E/G in the blue ink of G. Nothing of consequence has been deduced from the more or less tenuous distinctions between Ea and Eb, which do not overlap; the clear distinctions in time stages are between Ea and Eab, Eb and Ec; Eb and Ee/F; and Eb and E/G.

Stage F: This was a fair-copy stage distinguished by the MLP number-set and by the brown ink and blunt pen of its inscription. Its substages, Fa and Fb, both in the same medium, are distinguished respectively by the unqualified folio numbers and by the added numbers. As indicated above, the brown ink of F revised and replaced some E leaves at Ee/F.

Stage G: This was a fair-copy stage distinguished by the MRP number-set and by its blue ink. A significant variation in this blue ink is discussed above, pp. 234–35. Within Stage G, the substage Ga is distinguished by the unqualified numbers, Gb by the added numbers and local contextual relations. The blue ink of G revised some passages and replaced several leaves of earlier stages.

Stage p, or late pencil revision stage: Most of the leaves carry pencil revisions, all of which we label p. These fall into two classes. (1) The first class are those revisions made *prior* to the latest ink revisions on the leaf, as indicated either by their own erasure and incorporation, or other involvement, in later ink revisions.* Such pencil revisions are designated by p, either added to the proper stage label (Dap, Gbp), or placed before the stage label of the ink that incorporated the revision

---

* Most erased words are still visible under close scrutiny, though we have not recovered quite all of them, and not all show in photographic reproductions such as the plates in this volume.

(*p Da, p Gb*), or simply by *p* alone when the ink revision immediately follows separately labeled. (2) The second class of pencil revisions are those made *later* than any ink revisions on the leaf. On most leaves of each of the fair-copy sequences there are such "late pencil" revisions. Since theoretically these may have been made on the leaves of the separate sequences at various times later than that of the ink inscription of each sequence, and hence cumulatively at quite different stages or random times, we have not assigned them all a single letter parallel to the others (for example, *H* or *P*) but have conservatively used the designation *p* and the synonymous term "late pencil" for all such revisions. On the other hand, it is possible that all or the larger part of these "late pencil" revisions were made at a single stage, later than the last fair-copy stage in each segment of the manuscript. Such we believe, for several reasons, was in fact the case. Our major reason is that all standing pencil revisions must be later than the inscription of *E* in the first segment (now Leaves 2–177), since the purpose of the *E* stage was to put that segment into fair-copy form and it would therefore have incorporated all pencil revisions then standing on earlier leaves it retained. Similarly, the purpose of the immediately succeeding inscription stages *F* and *G* was to incorporate the second segment (now Leaves 189–351), consisting mostly of pencil draft leaves of *X*, into a fair copy. Therefore, we may reasonably hypothesize that when Melville finished inscribing fair-copy sequences *F* and *G* he had a complete fair copy of both segments—that is, of the whole length of his story—one not carrying a random accumulation of pencil revisions made in the meanwhile. Since he was aiming at a complete fair copy, in other words, we may infer that he would not have marred it with pencil revisions. If he had such a complete fair copy, he subsequently undertook a comprehensive late pencil revision that affected words and phrases on most leaves, supplied various patches, and substituted a number of whole leaves, notably the passage affecting the surgeon and Captain Vere. Although we believe the evidence as well as fair inference supports this interpretation, we are too well aware of Melville's habit of constant revision to have incorporated the interpretation in the labels of our analysis or our definition of the late pencil stage.

Such are the nine major stages of inscription with their substages, which we distinguish primarily on the basis of the number sets. One further word of explanation may clarify a possible ambiguity in our usage of the alphabetical labels: the stage letter may refer either to the *whole stage* or, at times, to its earliest phase—thus *B* may include all the substages, *Ba, Bb, Bc,* or may be used as synonymous with *Ba.* Which reference is intended is usually clear from the context. A further, more general use of the stage letters to refer to stages of composition and stages in the growth of the story, is discussed below.

STAGES OF COMPOSITION AND GROWTH

By a final extension the alphabetical labels designating the time order of the number sets, and hence of the fair-copy sequences and the stages of inscription, may be employed to refer to stages of composition and stages in the growth of the story. Such use of the labels is possible because the fair-copy stages bear a direct correlation to the stages of composition and growth; what each fair-copy stage incorporated was not only the materials existing at the corresponding previous copy stage but also the new materials added to it by the intervening revision and expansion which necessitated a new fair copy. Hence, each fair-copy stage also marked a stage in the growth of the story. The alphabetical labels, when used to designate the stages of composition and growth, must be taken in a generalized sense; they cannot be altogether precise, or equally precise at all points, in their reference.

Although matter composed at each of the stages, thus defined, can be identified in the manuscript, it is obviously not possible to recover *verbatim* what stood in the story at each stage. Nevertheless, it is possible to infer, to a surprising extent, what topics were present at each stage, when they were introduced, and how their proportions were affected as the story expanded. The process of reasoning from the parallel columns of number sets and the writing itself is simpler to demonstrate than to describe in abstract terms. The ensuing discussion of the Foliations will make clear its own rationale.

Table & Discussion
of Foliations

This table of Foliations includes all the extant manuscript leaves and fragments (except Stage *A*), in the order followed in the Genetic Text. (The construction of the table and the basis on which the editors assigned alphabetical stage-letters to the foliations and leaves are explained in the foregoing Analysis of the Manuscript. See pp. 229–39.)

What the table reveals about the genesis of *Billy Budd* is indicated in the accompanying discussion. For convenience the discussion takes up groups of leaves by chapters in the final story, but it must be emphasized that these chapter divisions were of course not present from the beginning but were made at various stages as the story developed.

Horizontally, the columns show the successive folio numbers that appear on each leaf.

Vertically, the columns show the numbers (and hence the leaves) that survive from each stage, and also the surviving clips (*) and patches (†).

Note that *the italicized numbers in broken brackets are not numbers that appear on the leaves.* Such a number indicates the *hypothetical* number of the superseded leaf that carried corresponding material at the earlier stage designated. The table does not show all the hypothetical numbers that might be inferred, but supplies a few to assist inferences about earlier stages.

In addition to the symbols used in the Genetic Text (see pp. 271–73), the following symbols and conventions are employed:

112   boldface type indicates leaf was inscribed at stage designated;

[*18*⁴]   italicized numbers in square brackets are inferential;

⟨*26*⟩   italicized numbers in broken brackets are those of hypothetical leaves that carried corresponding material at stage designated;

S   superseded leaf survives with foliation from stage designated;

Lf   leaf was inscribed at stage designated;

Is   inscription on leaf belongs to stage designated;

?   query is raised about placing of item at stage designated.

For consistency, entries under "Topic" are normalized with respect to accidentals as in the Reading Text. Entries under "Leaf" are given here only the number assigned to show their place relative to the final sequence (i.e., [58a]233v is given as [58a], and [334a]361 as [334a]).

Leaf	Topic	B			D		E		Others
		Ba	Bb	Bc[C]	Da	Db	Ea	Eab	
1 [Ch. 1]	Dedication.								X^+p
2	Handsome Sailor.	⟨*1*⟩			1		1		
3	"	⟨*2*⟩			*2	2^1	2		
4	Negro sailor.					⟨2^2⟩	3		
5	"					*[2^3]		3^2	
6	"						4		
7	"					2^4	5		
8	Handsome Sailor.	⟨*3*⟩			3		6		
9	"	⟨*4*⟩			4		7		
10	BB introduced.	⟨*5*⟩			5		8		
11	BB impressed.	⟨*6*⟩			6		9		
12	Lt. chooses BB.		⟨6^2⟩		7		10		
13	Captain's attitude.				*8	8^1	11		
14	His character.					8^2	12		
15	Lt. takes drink.					8^3	13		
16	"		⟨6^3⟩		*[9]	8^4	14		
17	Captain serves.				⟨10⟩		15		
18	B "the jewel"—	⟨7⟩			⟨11⟩		16		
19	ensured peace.	⟨7^1⟩			12		17		
20	Red-Whiskers must needs pick a row.				*13	D/Ea 13^1	18	18^1	
21	Angers B by dig in ribs—is quickly					D/Ea ⟨13^2⟩		18^2	
22	drubbed; loves B.		⟨7^2⟩	?*	14		19		
23	"My peacemaker."		?7^3		15		20		
24	Of guns and peace.	⟨7^2⟩		?*	16		21		
25	Shipmasters resent.	⟨7^3⟩		⟨7^5⟩	17		22		
26	"Here he comes."	⟨7^4⟩	*[7^4]	⟨7^6⟩	⟨18⟩		23		
27	Embark to leave *Rights* (Paine).	⟨7^5 *I	7^5	7^7	19		24		
28	While officer and all note name,	Is *II	Lf	7^8	20		25		
29	salutation by B.	7^6		7^9	21		26		
30	He means no slur.	⟨7^7⟩	†	⟨8^1⟩	22		27		
31	Enters new life.	7^8		8^2	23		28		
32	Right at home.			⟨8^3⟩	⟨24⟩		29		
33	Entire family, self.						30		

The earliest *B* stage, preceding *Ba* and perhaps all surviving leaves, had only seven or eight leaves here, none of which survive. It already had the major topics: the Handsome Sailor type; Billy Budd; and Billy's impressment, told but not yet dramatized. In *Ba* the impressment was somewhat dramatized, on leaves added to *B* ⟨7⟩. (*Ea* 16, corresponding to our hypothetical ⟨7⟩, refers to Billy as a "jewel"—his original nickname in the draft headnote of *A*.) Also in *Ba* was Billy's good-bye to the *Rights-of-Man;* parts of it survived on *Ba* leaves through all stages (see also Leaf 207). *Bb* and *Bc* elaborated the dramatization, on leaves added to *B* ⟨6⟩ and on more leaves added to *B* ⟨7⟩, probably in terms of the lieutenant's drinking and the merchant captain's account to him of Billy and the Red Whiskers.

In *D*, which was the fair-copy tidying-up stage that began on November 16, 1888, Melville was copying those *B* leaves he had cluttered by his revisions, and was putting on his new *D* foliation to supplant the *B* foliation he had confused by layers of added numbers. In this chapter his new *D* foliation included (with its six *Db* added numbers) thirty-one leaves, of which the first nineteen were new fair-copy leaves and most of the rest were all or in part leaves he held over from *B*. In *Db* he made two brief additions: the Negro sailor, 2^2, 2^3, 2^4; and the characterizations of the captain and lieutenant, 8^1 to 8^4, as well as the name Graveling.

At *E*, for the most part, in Ch. 1–5, Melville merely added its new foliation, since his chief concern in doing Stage *E* was not with these early chapters—whose leaves he had pretty much put in their final form at *D*—but with Ch. 6–12, where he built up Vere and then once again reworked his analysis of Claggart. Even so, he added at *E* a few new leaves here and there in these earlier chapters. In Ch. 1 he recopied several leaves and elaborated on three matters: the handsome Negro sailor, adding 3^2; the Red Whiskers again, 18^1, 18^2; and—in Ch. 2—Billy's reception aboard the warship, 31, 32^1.

A significant genetic clue appears on the verso of one leaf Melville inserted during *E*. In elaborating on the Red Whiskers, 18^1, he used the clear side of Leaf 20, whose verso he had used earlier in the pencil draft of Vere's speech to the court, $[260c]Xp$ 10, 9^2. Still earlier the same verso had carried the foliation *B* 71 and clip(s) but no *B* inscription. This previous use is one of many clues indicating that Stage *X*, in which Melville radically developed Vere and his part, had come subsequent to *B* and *D* and just prior to *E*.

Leaf	Topic	B			D		E		Others
		Ba	Bb	Bc[C]	Da	Db	Ea	Eab	
[Ch. 2]									
34	No cynosure now.							31	
35	His rose, tanned.							32^1	
36	Rustic beauty.	$*[8^x]$	$?8^5$	$?8^5$	26		32	32^2	
37	Its effect.				27		33		
38	His shapeliness.				28		34		
39	Lineage: "Father?"				29	29^1	35	35^1	
[39]	"God knows, but I don't."					S 29^2	S 36		
40	"God knows."							35^2	
41	B a foundling.				*	$[29^2]$		36	
42	Composed own song.	**	8^{D7}	8^8	30		37		
43	No vices.						38		
44	Upright barbarian.				31	31^2	39††		
45	His virtues alien to cities.				*32	Lf Is	40		
46	One thing amiss.				33		41		
47	Sometimes he would stutter.						**42	E/Gp 42^1	G†
48	Not a conventional hero.							E/Gp 42^2	G†

The whole chapter, describing Billy's person and character, grew directly out of the draft headnote of A (see p. 275), of which some topics and phrasing survive on Leaves 38 and 39. This means that genetically the material of Ch. 2 (though not its final form) is earlier than the material on the Handsome Sailor, the merchant ship, and Billy's impressment, now standing before it in Ch. 1.

Where this chapter finally occupies fifteen leaves, the earliest B stage had only two or three $(?\langle 8\rangle, \langle 9\rangle, \langle 10\rangle)$. Most of the expansion came at Ba and Bb on leaves added to $\langle 8\rangle$, up to at least 8^9, so that Bb ran to some ten leaves. Just how the expansion developed within these additions to $\langle 8\rangle$ is not clear from the distribution of the surviving numbers. Bc and the later stages each made some elaborations. That involving the interchange between the officer and Billy about his paternity illustrates the general pattern of dramatizing expository statements. Even at A, Melville conceived Billy as of "a lineage contradicting his lot." This idea he later dramatized by the interchange, which probably came in at Bc and was further developed in Db and Eab. Billy's reply to "Who was your father?" was elaborated from merely "God knows, Sir, but I don't. I was found, but where I don't know," into more significant terms: ". . . I have heard that I was found in a basket of oakum hanging one morning from the knocker of a good man's door in Bristol." And finally, in the pencil revision after E, the "basket of oakum" became "a pretty silk-lined basket"— a detail suggesting a high-born mother in the "lineage contradicting his lot," whereas the "basket of oakum" it replaced would more likely have suggested that his mother though "favored by Love and the Graces" was some sailor's daughter and that his "no ignoble" blood stemmed from his father alone.

A second still visible expansion, that concerning Billy's stutter, was made at the final Stage G, which not only revised the version of Eaa but added the whole last leaf (Leaf 48). However, since this "vocal defect" had already been present in Da (33, $\langle 34\rangle$), most likely it was also in the dramatized Bb, Bc stages. The defect probably came into the story as a motivating factor along with the development in A that changed Billy's crime from being ringleader of an incipient mutiny to striking and killing a superior officer.

Leaf	Topic	B			D	E		Others
		Ba	Bb	Bc[C]	Da	Eb	Ec	
[Ch. 3]								
49	The ship.					*43I	43¹	
50	Summer of 1797.					*43II	43²	
51	Nore Mutiny.	$\langle 11?\rangle$	**Bx		$\langle 37\rangle$	44		
52	Flag of revolt.		$\begin{cases}\text{Bx}\\12\end{cases}$	$\begin{cases}\text{Bx}^+\\\dagger\dagger\dagger\end{cases}$	38	45		
53	From France.		$\begin{cases}\text{Lf Is}\\*13\ ?*\end{cases}$		39	46		
	Dibden, James.							
54	Details not easily		$\begin{cases}?*13²,\\14\end{cases}$		40	47		
	found in libraries.							
55	Concessions.	*	13, 15		41	48		
56	Suppression.	*	?16¹		42	49		
57	Trafalgar, Nelson.		16²		43	50		p†

In broad terms, the development of Ch. 3, 4, and 5 is quite clear. The four main topics are the mutinies of 1797, the abuses (including impressment) that led to them, their relation to the Revolutionary era, and Nelson. Of these, the first three were present in earliest *B*, *Ba* stages (on *B* leaves ⟨*11–17*⟩). Evidently these topics stem from somewhere in the *A* stage. The fourth topic, Nelson, was not in those early *B* stages, however, and hence not in *A*, but was added at later *Ba* (*cf.* Leaf 62) and developed at *Bb*.

The exact developments within Ch. 3 cannot be ascertained because the indeterminate inks and writing hands do not allow dependable assignment of the various *B* stages. Nevertheless, certain features seem clear. At *Bb* Melville reworked the original *B* leaves 11–16 in a way that added a leaf at 13 and another at 16. The indication is that his reworking and additions came after he had sought "in the libraries" (Leaf 54) for details about the mutinies to bolster his originally more general account, and had found James's work from which he took the phrase quoted on Leaf 53. (See discussion of the library slips, "Extra-Textual Leaves," No. 5, p. 428, and notes to Leaves 53–54.) The *Bb* addition to 16 extended into what became Ch. 4.

At *Da* Melville merely refoliated the existing *B* leaves. At *Eb* he supplied two fair-copy leaves, with no expansion, supplanting *Da* ⟨36, 37⟩. At *Ec* he inserted a new paragraph into *Eb* 43, making the division into *Ec* 43^1 and 43^2.

Leaf	Topic	B			D	E		Others
		Ba	Bb	Bc[C]	Da	Eb	Ec	
[Ch. 4]								
58	Bypath, lured by genius of Nelson.							G p 1
[58a]	Naval gallantry now out of date.		S 16^5					
59	Inventions have changed warfare.							G p 2
60	Nobler qualities not obsolete.							G p 3
61	Past, Present, *Victory, Monitor.*		16^5, 16^6					p 4
62	Utilitarians may	*	16^7					p 5
63	blame Nelson.		16^8					p 6
64	His dying injunctions overruled.		*16^7, 16^9					G p 7
65	N's foresight; love of glory.		*					G p 8
66	N's name trumpet. Tennyson.							G p 9
67	N adorned self for altar at Traf.							G p 10

Melville was led into this "divergence" about Nelson at *Bb*, on some nine leaves added to 16, four of which still stand. At fair-copy Stage *Da* he decided to exclude it, as shown by the *Da* foliation in which he allowed no numbers for it—or perhaps only 44^1. At this time, evidently, he withdrew it from the the sequence and placed it in a separate folder (see "Extra-Textual Leaves,"

No. 3, p. 427). At *Eb* he seems to have wavered, but he neither restored nor rejected it, for in the *E* foliation, without numbering its leaves he went from *E* 50 just before it to *E* 60 just after it, and numbered the following leaves (now Ch. 5) 60, 70, 80, 90, 91, by this device both supplying a continuous *E* series and allowing space for the possibility of a later reinsertion of the Nelson material. At *G*, resolving on its restoration, he revised and recopied some of the leaves. On the new *G* opening leaf (Leaf 58), he confessed the "literary sin" to which he was now once again deliberately succumbing, "beckoned by the genius of Nelson." He foliated the Nelson leaves 1–10 in pencil but, perhaps again wavering, still did not insert them into the manuscript or assign them the *E* numbers for which he had allowed, but left them in their separate folder. Perhaps still weighing final inclusion, he passed on to revise the scene between Vere and the surgeon. That he did revise that scene shortly after revising the Nelson chapter is indicated by his use of the verso of superseded *Bb* leaf 16⁵ (which he had replaced by the new Nelson leaf *G* 3) for the new leaf 41 in post-*G* pencil, in the revised Vere-surgeon scene. Although he did not finally insert the leaves into the manuscript we concur with Weaver and Freeman in judging that his intention was to do so, since he revised it in the latest copy stage, *G*, and in late pencil revisions.

Leaf	Topic	B			D	E		Others
		Ba	Bb	Bc[C]	Da	Eb	Ec	
[Ch. 5]								
68	Impressment still.		?17²		44	60		
69	Needed by fleet.	?17	17³		45	70		
70	Discontent; N shifts to *Theseus*,		*17⁴ I	Lf Is	46	80		
71	which had been in the mutiny;		*17⁴ II	Lf Is	47	90		
72	N to win crew.		17⁵		48	91		

The material of this chapter, like that of Ch. 4, was developed by Melville at *Bb* on leaves added to *Ba* 17, which already had to do with the mutinies and impressment; and like the additions to 16, these also related to Nelson. Since the Nelson material here came largely from Southey, perhaps it was the reading of Southey that set off the additions.

In the later stages, Melville did not replace or substantially revise these leaves, though at *Eb* he foliated them 60, 70, 80, 90, 91—possibly an indication that he thought any reworking of the Nelson episode might include their material.

Leaf	Topic	B			D	E		Others
		Ba	Bb	Bc[C]	Da	Eb	Ec	
[Ch. 6]								
73	No air of danger on B's ship.					*92	Lf Is 92	

Leaf	Topic	B			D	E		Others
		Ba	Bb	Bc[C]	Da	Eb	Ec	
74	Captain Vere.					93		
75	His demeanor.					*94	94^1	
76	Undemonstrative,					Is	Lf	
	inconspicuous.					*94	94^2	
77	Modesty a virtue					*95		
	aristocratic.					I	95^1	
[77a]	V would stand					S		
	gazing at sea.					?†		
78	V practical but					Is	Lf	
	would gaze. . . .					II	95^2	
79	"Starry Vere"—					96		p†
80	How he got name.					97		

Captain Vere played no developed role at any of the stages through *D*. The evidence is clear that Melville created his present significant role in the post-*D* expansion Stage *X*, which developed his part in the scenes of confrontation and killing and invented the trial and argument scenes for him. The evidence is also clear that subsequently Melville came back to this point and worked up a presentation of Vere's character in what became Ch. 6 and 7, his object being to prepare the reader for those later scenes already drafted, though not yet copied into *F* and *G* fair copy. The material of these two chapters, then, is largely the product of *E*. Earlier, at *Ba*, he perhaps had one leaf here, *Ba* ⟨18⟩, but probably not even that leaf, since apparently original *Ba* 18 carried Claggart material in what became Ch. 8. At *Bb* Melville evidently built Vere up to the extent of the three leaves ⟨18^1⟩, ⟨18^2⟩, ⟨18^3⟩ that followed 17^5 and preceded 18^4, on which Claggart is introduced. At copy Stage *D* there were still only three leaves, *Da* ⟨49⟩, ⟨50⟩, ⟨51⟩, later supplanted. (Later, Mrs. Melville added *Da/p* numbers 49–56, which have no analytical significance and which we have not shown.) Melville's important additions to Vere, as stated, came at *E*.

At *Eb* Melville increased the number of leaves to eight (*Eb* 92–99), recopying all three *B* (or *D?*) leaves, so that it is impossible to tell what material was on them and what he added to it at *Eb*. Next, in *Eb* ink he added a second chapter (Ch. 7) on Vere, somehow incorporating *Eb* 98, 99 as discussed below. Subsequently, at *Ec*, he came back to revise Ch. 6 further, increasing the number of leaves to eight while introducing several important sentences strengthening Vere's character.

Leaf	Topic	B			D	E		Others
		Ba	Bb	Bc[C]	Da	Eb	Ec	
[Ch. 7]								
81	To fill out on V.					Lf Is		p 1
82	V loved books on							p 1^2,
	men & events—					Lf Is		2

Leaf	Topic	B			D	E		Others
		Ba	Bb	Bc[C]	Da	Eb	Ec	
83	writers like							p 3
	Montaigne.					Lf Is		p†
84	V's convictions,							p 4¹, 4
	disinterested.					Lf Is		p†
85	V found dry—					*		p 5
86	pedantic—					Lf Is		p 6
87	he would cite the							p 7
	ancients.					Lf Is		p†

Even while Melville developed Vere's character somewhat in Ch. 6, at *Eb*, he felt that still more was needed: "In view of the part that the Commander . . . plays in scenes shortly to follow, it may be well to fill out a little that passing sketch of him outlined in a previous chapter" (Leaf 81). He drafted at this time another chapter (now Ch. 7) incorporating *Eb* ⟨*98*⟩, ⟨*99*⟩, and in the same *Eb* ink made a fair copy. In this chapter he treated Vere's intellectual characteristics. He did not foliate the chapter with *E* numbers, but kept it apart in a separate folder. (See "Extra-Textual Leaves," No. 4, p. 427.) Possibly he did so because he had not decided just where to insert it—consider the phrase "a previous chapter" and the notation on *Eb* 97, "100 *red* follows", with the paired notation on *E/p* 100, "follows 97 *red*". He may have thought of inserting it just before the confrontation scene or the trial scene (*cf.* "in scenes shortly to follow"). Its own penciled foliation contains some vestigial numbers (which we have not reported in the Table) on the first four leaves. These numbers suggest that several other leaves came before the chapter at one time, possibly with matter now in the previous chapter or in a later chapter to which he tentatively annexed it, and possibly with matter later dropped —as matter was dropped following its last leaf (7), which ends without a chapter-ending mark, in the midst of a canceled sentence. In any case, Melville later revised the chapter heavily at the late pencil stage, making some excisions and inserting some important passages on patches. It seems likely that materials in this chapter (as in Ch. 6) were transferred to or interchanged with passages in the *X* draft, since closely related materials and cross-references are included on Leaves [229d–f], 236 ff., 241, 262–65, and 333. But though he probably drew upon the chapter thus as a quarry, he did not use it up (as he used up Leaves 353 and 354, "Lawyers, Experts, Clergy"), but salvaged its remains, grafting in substantial pencil-revision patches. These patches he made soon after his *F* fair copy of draft *X* had engrossed Vere's argument, thus superseding its draft leaves, two of the versos of which he employed for his patches on Leaves 83 and 87.

Though Melville never inserted the chapter, he labeled its folder for insertion, and later Mrs. Melville put it into the manuscript, changing "a previous chapter" to "the previous chapter" (Leaf 81). (See Plate VII.)

Leaf	Topic	Ba	Bb	Bc[C]	Da	Eb	Ec	Others
[Ch. 8]						E/p		
88	Master-at-arms, John Claggart.		*[18⁴]		⟨52⟩	100		
89	His function.		18⁵		53	101		
90	Description of C.	*18	18⁶		54	102		
91	"	*	19¹		55	103		
92	A person of quality going incog.	*19 I	19²		56	104		
93	In gun-deck gossip C a swindler.	Is *19 II	Lf 19³		57	105		
94	C's past, mystery.	*20	20¹		58	106 †		
95	Gossip not absurd.		⟨20²⟩		59	107		
96	Navy a haven.	⟨21⟩			60	107²		
97	Old Negro's story.	⟨22⟩			61¹	108	†	
98	Drafts from jails.	⟨23⟩				109	†	
99	Napoleonic era.	⟨24⟩				110		
100	M-at-A unpopular.	⟨25⟩				111		
101	How men took C.	⟨26⟩				112		
102	His rise in navy.		27		64	113		
103	C's power.	*[28]			⟨65⟩	114		

Melville's development of Vere at Stage *E*, already discussed, follows his earlier pattern in developing Claggart at *Bc*. In each case the expansion, based on existing materials, resulted in two chapters: an initial chapter of relatively exterior materials, partly from the *Ba* and *Bb* stages, followed by a more interior analysis. For Vere this process eventuated in the paired chapters 6 and 7; for Claggart it gave rise to a sequence of chapters, beginning here with Ch. 8 and developing more detailed analysis through Ch. 11–13 and 17 (with interspersed episodes about the operation of Claggart's plot against Billy, in Ch. 9–10 and 14–16).

The main burden of Ch. 8, on Claggart and his background in the era, was already present in *Ba*, which occupied some eleven leaves (⟨?18–28⟩) where the chapter finally has sixteen. From these eleven, *Bb* expanded to probably fifteen, building up the account of Claggart's office, 18⁽⁴⁾⁻⁵, his physical description, 19¹⁻³, and his rumored background, 20¹. Thus by the end of the *B* stages the matter ran to virtually the present length of the chapter. The exact substance, however, may not have been altogether the same, since just what happened at the *D* and *E* stages is not entirely evident. *Da*, it would seem, required fewer leaves than *Bb* for the matter it copied onto *Da* 59 ff., even though it perhaps added matter, while *Eb*, in copying onto its 109–12, apparently also added matter and increased the number of leaves over *Da*. What was added by each is not revealed in the distribution of surviving numbers, but the topics show some fairly clear divisions that allow one to speculate.

Leaf	Topic	B			D	E		Others
		Ba	Bb	Bc[C]	Da	Eb	Ec	
[Ch. 9]								
104	B at home in tops.						115^1	
105	Cause of alacrity—						115^2	
106	horror of flogging.						116	
107	B's troubles begin.						117	
108	Old Dansker.						118	
109	Description of D.						119	
110	D's view of Billy.						120	
111	D took to Billy.						121	
112	D says "Baby."						122	p†
113	B consults D.						123	
114	"Jemmy Legs is down on you."						*124 / {Ec/G 124^1	
115	B incredulous; D says no more.						{Ec/G 124^2	
116	Incident next day.						125^1	

In general, the material of the first four leaves may be assigned to *Ba, Bb;* the rest, involving the Dansker, to *Bc,* by the following reasoning. Although no leaves at all survive here from the *B* stages or *D,* since all the leaves were inscribed at *Ec,* their topics and development can be inferred. At the earliest *B* stage presumably three leaves ($\langle 29$–$31\rangle$) fell here, between 27–$\langle 28\rangle$ at the end of the previous chapter and $\langle 32\rangle$ below (setting aside the additions to $\langle 31\rangle$). In later *Bc,* which had 31^5 for 31^2, it would seem that three more ($\langle 31\rangle$, with added $\langle 31^{2,\ 3,\ 4}\rangle$) must have fallen here as well, giving *Bc* at least six leaves. Whether there were further *Bb* or *Bc* leaves, as additions to $\langle 29\rangle$, $\langle 30\rangle$, becomes the question. As to *Da:* reasoning as above from the gap between *Da* 64–$\langle 65\rangle$ and 80, it would appear that *Da* had at least fourteen leaves ($\langle 66$–$79\rangle$), eight more than yet accounted for at *Bc* (and one more than final *Ec* inscribed). Certainly these were added either by *Bb, Bc,* or *D.* Turning to the topics involved, one sees that the Dansker material (Leaves 107–16), omitting Leaf 115, which was brought in by an addition at *G,* amounts to about eight leaves in a distinguishable unit, while the remaining leaves at the beginning (Leaves 104–7) belong to the basic story situation. From this, one may hypothesize that the Dansker material was an addition. Whether it was added at *Bb,* or *Bc,* or at *Da,* or piecemeal at all three, cannot be determined from this context alone. But the later passages involving the Dansker, which are interdependent with this one, all belong to *Bc* (Leaves 117, 120, 121, [121b], 122–23) and to *Cb* (167–70). The conclusion therefore seems warranted that the Dansker material in this chapter also belongs substantially to *Bc,* as part of the same dramatization phase at *Bc[C].*

Leaf	Topic	Ba	Bb	Bc[C]	Da	Eb	Ec	Others
[Ch. 10]								
117	In lurch of ship / B spills soup.			31², 31⁵	80	125	125²	
118	C about to pass, / sees who did it.			31³, 31⁶	81	126		
119	"Handsomely done."					127		
[119a]	B is tickled, / joins in laugh.			Bcp / Lf Is				
120	B joins in laugh.					128		
121	C canes drummer.					129		
					[End of D foliation]			

The soup-spilling may have been referred to in *Ba* (see clip on Leaf 145), but the dramatized episode as such belongs to *Bc[C]*, since its surviving first two leaves belong there, as do the introduction to it on the preceding leaf and the later interdependent leaves listed in the above discussion. Although *Da* and also *Eb*, which inscribed the last three leaves (*Eb* 127–29), must have included revisions and perhaps some additions, the matter itself, as an integral part of the episode, had already to be present in some form at *Bc[C]*.

Note that the *D* foliation ends here at its intersection with the beginning of the *C* foliation.

Leaf	Topic	Ba	Bb	[Bc]Ca	Eb	Ec	Ed	Ee/F	G	p
[Ch. 11]										
[121a]	Some portrait of / C—labyrinth.		{ S / Bb⁺p / Lf Is							
[121b]	Why was J. Legs / down on Billy?			S / *2						
[121c]	What was matter?				S / *130 / E/G					
122	What was matter?			⟨1⟩	130				*	
123	Why down on B? / But he was.			⟨2⟩	E/G / 131					
124	No cause in prior / knowledge.				E/G / 132				*	
125	A spontaneous / antipathy.				E/G / 133					
126	C a peculiar human / creature.							134		
127	X——'s labyrinth.							135		
128	Knowing the world,							136		
129	not human nature.							137		
130	Holy Writ; Plato.							138		
131	Calvin's dogma.							139		

Leaf	Topic	B		C	E				G	p
		Ba	Bb	[Bc]Ca	Eb	Ec	Ed	Ee/F		
[131a]	No wine-bibber; pride guards.				S 136	S 141[3]				
[131b]	Never speaks ill; What signalizes....				S 138	S 141[5]				
132	Pride; speaks no ill; signalizes....							140		
133	Exempt from law of reason.				139	141[6]	144	141		†
134	True madmen, seem rational.							* [142]		Lf Is
135	Dark sayings.			*			145	143		†
[Ch. 12]										
[135a]	Lawyers, Experts, Clergy.			S [9]						
[135b]	"			S 10						
[135c]	C's figure vs. B's heroic form.			S 142						
[135d]	C's antipathy, due to B's beauty.			S [143]						
[135e]	Envy universally shameful.			S 144						
[135f]	Spenser and Milton on envy.			S 145						
136	C's figure vs. B's.							146[1]		
137	C's antipathy.							146[2]		
138	Envy shameful.							147		
139	C's envy not vulgar passion.					Is	?*	Lf 148		
140	It struck deeper.			*	146			149		
141	Disdains innocence.				147			150		
142	No power to annul.				148			151		
[Ch. 13]										
143	Spilled soup....			⎰Cb⎱ 16[3]	149					

[End of E foliation]

```
        C                    F
   Cb      Cc
```

Leaf	Topic	B		C	E				G	p
		Ba	Bb	[Bc]Ca	Eb	Ec	Ed	Ee/F		
144	C feels contempt.			17						
145	Squeak's reports.	*		18						
146	"	*		19						
147	Perverts B's innocent frolics.	*45, 45[p1]		18, 20						
148	Hate needs no purveyor.	45, 45[p2]		21	21[1]					
149	But how about C's conscience?	Is		*	Lf 21[2]					
150	Soup-spilling justified revenge.			22						
151	C welcomed it— new experiments.			23						

The analysis of Claggart now in Ch. 11, 12, and part of 13 (Leaves 122–47) was developed by Melville, through several painstaking revisions, from thirteen original *B* leaves 32–45.

At *Bc*[*C*] he incorporated a radical expansion of his treatment of Claggart (in Ch. 9–17). For foliation of some of this expansion he still used the *B* number-set (Ch. 9, 10, 17). But for the central analysis, beginning here (Ch. 11) he made a completely new fair-copy sequence, in the same ink as *Bc*, incorporating the material which had stood on the thirteen (or more) *B* leaves and on the draft leaves of his expanded analysis, and foliated them with the new number-set *C*. By this process he superseded and destroyed all the original *B* leaves here, so that we cannot tell just what materials were on them. For what became Ch. 11, 12, and the beginning of 13, where *B* had had thirteen leaves, this *Ca* fair copy had some twenty-two (*Ca* ⟨1⟩–20, with two leaves added to 16), thus including a substantial nine-page expansion of the analysis of Claggart. However, Melville's subsequent complex revisions at *Eb*, *Ec*, *Ee/F*, and *E/G* necessitated new fair-copy leaves that superseded the first eighteen *Ca* leaves, ⟨1–16²⟩, most of which did not survive. For this reason, as in the case of the superseded and destroyed *B* leaves, we cannot tell just what material was on the *Ca* leaves and what was carried over from them to the final version.

Nevertheless, not quite all the *Ca* draft and fair-copy leaves here were destroyed. Two leaves, a pencil-draft fragment, a leaf fragment, and two clips survived, all with valuable genetic clues.

For the opening passages of Ch. 11, several successive versions survived. First, the fragmentary pencil draft [121a]247†v is the beginning, just prior to *Bc*[*C*], of Melville's earliest analysis of Claggart's "inner personality." Here we see Melville first hesitantly entering that "murky labyrinth." By the time he had the analysis in final form at *Ee/F* he had expanded the passage (around the seed word "labyrinth") into the fictional colloquy with the "honest scholar" and moved it further along in the chapter (Leaves 126–29). The subsequent chapter-opening at *Ca* is missing, but a fragment of its *Eb* counterpart survives, [121c]207†v, and this in turn corresponds to the matter on *E/G* 130. Next, a fragment survives from *Ca* 2 which asks "why should Jemmy Leggs . . . be down on Billy Budd?" and suggests the answer "antipathy." In *Eb* this matter was expanded to occupy three leaves, *Eb* ⟨131⟩, ⟨132⟩, ⟨133⟩, and finally it stands on four leaves, *E/G* 131–33, *Ee/F* 134.

The two later segments of Ch. 11 (Leaves 126–29, 130–35) were also heavily revised in successive *E* stages. *Eb* had here leaves ⟨134–41⟩. These were worked over and partially renumbered in pencil at the purely local Stage *Ec*. *Ec* must have expanded the single leaf *Eb* ⟨135⟩ into eight pencil-draft leaves *Ec* ⟨135–41²⟩—evidence being that *Eb* 136 was kept and renumbered 141³ and that other leaves also got numbers in that series. The material of this *Ec* "bulge" was the colloquy with the "honest scholar," which stood on fewer leaves as fair-copied into *Ee/F* 134–37. The last *Eb* leaves (136–⟨41⟩) in the chapter also underwent heavy pencil revisions at *Ec* and were renumbered

Ec 141³–⟨*141*⁸⟩. At *E/G* two of these were superseded (Leaves [131a, 131b]); one was retained (Leaf 133). At *Ee/F*, fair-copy leaves 134–40 were also supplied. Late pencil revisions heavily affected the last three leaves of the chapter (Leaves 133–35). Leaf 135 is particularly problematical.

The two surviving leaves *Ca* ⟨*9*⟩–10 are the superseded leaves mistakenly included by Weaver (in his Ch. 10) and by Freeman (as Ch. 12, "Lawyers, Experts, Clergy / An Episode"). The evidence of their supersession is clear. Their only foliation is the *Ca* number 10 on the second leaf. (The preceding leaf originally had pinned to its top a clip, later removed, presumably foliated "9," since the ink and matter are continuous from it to 10.) That the leaves were superseded at *Eb* is established by the fact that neither carries *E* foliation, and that there was never a place for them in the *E* number series. Nor is there any authority for restoring them, near their genetic site, where Weaver and Freeman printed them. After Melville's death his wife found the leaves, labeled them "For Billy Budd", and—not realizing they had been superseded—added "Find proper place for insertion". Evidently it was Weaver, misled by her notations, who inserted them, for he allowed but did not write numbers 124 and 125 for them in his [*W*] foliation. To do so, he ignored Mrs. Melville's other, and correct, notation on Leaf 135, "146 *red* follows".

These two superseded *Ca* leaves offer most valuable evidence on the genesis of the trial scene and the whole expansion stage, *X*, that followed upon *C*. (See pp. 36–37.)

What Melville had in Ch. 12 at *B* we cannot tell. Since there were seventeen *Ca* leaves, ⟨*1–16*²⟩, it is probable that this discussion of Claggart's envy was largely an innovation at *Ca*. Evidently Melville revised these *Ca* leaves considerably, for he had to supersede them all with *Eb* fair-copy leaves, though with no increase in number. For *Eb* 146 he kept a substantial clip from *Ca*. These *Eb* leaves too, in turn, he revised thoroughly in pencil before *Ee/F*. Then he made fair-copy leaves *Ee/F* 146¹, 146², 147, of the first three, 142–44, while retaining the last four, 145–48. By chance he preserved *Eb* 142–45 when he used their versos (along with the versos of *Eb* 136, 138, above) in drafting his late pencil reworking of the passage about the surgeon and Vere. As it happens, therefore, all the *Eb* leaves in Ch. 12, along with those surviving in Ch. 11, remain to provide an extended example of Melville's meticulous process of revising and recasting. In this chapter, three stages are visible: the *Eb* version, the pencil revision, and the final fair copy. Consistently he revises the elaborative pencil revision as he makes the fair copy; and for the final version he is working toward directness—pruning qualifications, compressing metaphors, and eliminating the allusions to Milton and Spenser.

Original *Ba* material survives in Ch. 13 from *Ba* ⟨*44*⟩–45 (as clips on Leaves 145–47, and Leaf 148), indicating that this early layer of Melville's treatment of the Claggart-Billy relationship involved Claggart's use of his corporals to foment trouble for Billy. At *Ca* Melville expanded somewhat his treatment of Claggart's reactions and his conscience, at the beginning and end of the chapter.

Leaf	Topic	B		C			F	G	p
		Ba	Bb	[Bc]	Cb	Cc			
[Ch. 14]									
152	Another incident:				24				
153	B asleep on deck.				25				
154	Waked by intruder.				26				
155	Goes to chains.				27				
156	Is offered coins.					28^1			
157	Will he help?					28^2			
158	B drives him off.					28^3			
159	An afterguardsman.					*29			
160	Veterans bigoted.				30				
[Ch. 15]									
161	Incident puzzles B.				31				
162	Instinct recoils.				32				
163	Sees fellow;					33^1			
164	but is uncertain.					33^2			
165	Fellow nods.					33^3			
166	Billy confused.					33^4			
167	Consults Dansker.				34				
168	"Jemmy Legs...."					*35			
169	D falls silent.					*36			

The episode of Billy's temptation by the afterguardsman, Claggart's *agent provocateur*, was not present at all in *Ca* or earlier. Melville added it, and Billy's consequent second consultation with the Dansker, on *Cb* leaves 24–36, inserting them between *Ca* leaves 23 and 24. Still later, at *Cc*, he elaborated the material at two points. First between *Cb* 27 and 30 he dramatized Billy's reaction; then between *Cb* 32 and 34 he built up Billy's later deck encounters with the emissary afterguardsman.

Leaf	Topic	B		C			F	G	p
		Ba	Bb	[Bc]Ca	Cb	Cc			
[Ch. 16]									
170	B can't blame C.			*	37				
171	B's simpleness.			*24^2	38^1				
172	Knows man little.					38^2			
173	Sailors are a			Is	Lf				
	juvenile race.			*†	38^3				
174	No distrustfulness.					39^1			
175	Unlike men of the					39^2			
	world.								

It seems possible (but only a guess) that the material of this chapter, Melville's commentary on Billy's innocent simplicity, may stem from the two *Ba* leaves, ⟨46–47⟩, which were all that originally stood in the position now occupied by Leaves 149–77. At *Ca* he had only two leaves here, *Ca* ⟨24–25⟩. At *Cb* also he had two, *Cb* 38–⟨39⟩. On *Cc* 38–39 (with added leaves) Melville developed further the relation of Billy's attitude to general sailor psychology.

Leaf	Topic	B		C			F	G	p
		Ba	Bb	[Bc]Ca	Cb	Cc			
[Ch. 17]									
176	No more troubles,			26	40				
177	but C's smile &			Is	Lf				
	glance			*27	41				
				[End of C foliation]					
				Bc/Ca	Bc/Cb				
178	would follow B.	48		†					
179	Ambiguous smile &	Is		Lf					
	red light from	*49I		49¹					
	C's eyes.								
180	B saw these	*49II		49²					
	but misconstrued.								
181	B had no mistrust.	50		50¹					
182	Innocence blinded.	*[51]I	50²						
	C's messmates.								
183	Their odd glances.		*	50³					
184	B unconcerned.			50⁴					
185	Afterguardsman.				50⁵				
186	B evades him,				50⁶				
187	seeking no ex-				**				
	planations.				50⁷				
188	Something must	{ *[51]		{ Lf					
	come of C's			{ 50⁹,					
	monomania.	{ ... II	*50⁵	{ 51					

The core of this chapter, the respective attitudes of Claggart and Billy, stems from *Ba*, whose leaves, or part-leaves, 48, 49, 50, ⟨*51*⟩, survive in it, taking up at Leaf 178, where Melville's *C* foliation ended. Also at the *C* stages, but employing the *B* number-set, Melville elaborated the material on each of the *Ba* leaves. He made his most extensive elaborations on the topic of Claggart's messmates and emissary (Leaves 183–88). He did so in two stages: first, at *Bb* by cutting *Ba* leaf ⟨*51*⟩ in two (with about two lines cut away) and inserting *Bb* leaves 50³ and 50⁴ between its two parts numbered 50² and 50⁵; then later at *Cb*, bringing in reference to the afterguardsman he had meanwhile introduced above at the same stage, *Cb*. Here, at *Cb* 50⁵ he stated that "when the two did happen to meet, invariably came the fellow's off-hand cheerful recognition, sometimes accompanied by a passing word or two." But later when he added *Cc* 33¹–33⁴ above, on Billy's deck encounters, he ended by saying on *Cc* 33⁴, "After that, there was no more recognition on either side." Later he noticed the inconsistency and in a pencil revision he canceled the contradictory sentence last quoted; elsewhere in the story, however, he failed to notice other inconsistencies standing in fair copy.

The first major segment of the manuscript (Leaves 2–188, including the "bridge" leaves 178–88) ends with Ch. 17. Its copy Stages *C*, *D*, *E* did not affect the second segment, which begins here with Ch. 18. This second major segment (Leaves 189–351) is made up of leaves of the two copy sequences *G* and *F*, with some substages, late revision sequences, and a few leaves retained from *B* stages. The *G* and *F* copy sequences represent expansions in part from *B* leaves 52–75, and in larger part from the pencil-draft Stage *X* which in genetic chronology came between *D* and *E*. Some of the leaves and clips which Melville carried over from *B* (53–66) occur near the beginning, dealing with Claggart's accusation and confrontation of Billy. Further *B* leaves (75–⟨85⟩) which he also retained stand at the end, carrying the news account and the ballad. In the long story sequence between *Bb* 66 (the confrontation) and *Bc* 75 (the news account), however, no *B* leaves or clips survive. Just what was included within this sequence as it stood in the *B* stages is therefore conjectural. Billy's killing of Claggart was certainly there; and his condemnation, the chaplain's visit, and the hanging must have been reported, but in quite summary fashion. There is no evidence of extensive *B* expansion, such as that offered all through the first segment of the manuscript by fair-copy leaves retained into later copy sequences. Clearly the present lengthy episodes subsequent to the confrontation scene were developments during the phase we have designated *X*, with little *B* material behind them. From what must have been the numerous pencil-draft leaves of *X* itself, only a few draft fragments of Vere's speech to the court survive. The ensuing analysis therefore must be confined mostly to developments within and revisions following the fair-copy Stages *G* and *F*.

| Leaf | Topic | B | | | X | F | G | | p |
		Ba	Bb	Bc[C]			Ga	Gb	
[Ch. 18]									
189	Some time passed.						1		
190	Ship & captain							2¹	
191	are suited for						2	2²	
	detached service.							†	
[191a]	Master-at-arms		S						
	appears at main-		*53						
	mast after chase.		I						
192	French ship seen;		*[53]						
	she escapes.		...II				3		
193	C appears at mast.		54				4		
194	V sees him.						5		
195	Feels distaste.						6		
196	C speaks up.		*				7		
197	"Say *impressed*...."						8¹		
198	C's suspicions.		57	56²			8†	8²	
199	Refers to mutinies.						9		
200	Vere offended						10		
201	by C's allusion.						11	11¹	
202	V's intuition.							11²	
203	V not disturbed.						12		
204	Finds C vague.						13		

Leaf	Topic	B			X	F	G		P
		Ba	Bb	Bc[C]			Ga	Gb	
205	C's manner breeds distrust in him.		{ * Bb/?E 59¹						
206	"Who is he?" "William Budd."						14 15		
207	A deep adroit one.	*62	*60² *				Lf 16		†
208	Lt. R had told of B's adieu.		{ *I 61¹	Lf			17		†
209	Capt. had good opinion of B as a "sailor-man."		{ ...*II Bb/Ga 61²				18		
210	"King's bargain."						19		
211	Demands proof.						20		
212	C states charges.						21		
213	V's eyes; C's eyes.						22		
214	Considers course.						23		
215	To summon proof?						24		
216	Wants privacy.						25		
217	Summons Albert						26		
218	to fetch B.						27		
219	Bids C to cabin.		64	65¹			28	28¹	

The central material here of Ch. 18, Claggart's interview with Vere at the mast, was already present in the *B* stages. Leaves and clips which Melville retained from *Ba* and *Bb* testify to this fact and suggest that, as in the earlier portions of the story, at *Bb* and *Bc* he slightly dramatized the expository narration of *Ba*. For the most part the chapter is carried by fair-copy leaves of *Ga*, with clips from the *B* stages and some incidental *Gab* and *Gb* revisions and expansions. Notably, some *Gb* redrafting took place on *Ga* 1 and *Ga* 2 when *Gb* 2¹ was inserted between them, an addition mostly to the effect that Vere's character especially adapted him for any duty calling for initiative, knowledge, and ability (for such "unforeseen difficulties" as do in fact arise). Similarly, on the top of *Ga* 5, as Melville copied from his revision at the foot of the preceding leaf, he added the detail that Vere had no personal knowledge of Claggart before this voyage, an addition that for one thing exonerated Vere of responsibility for Claggart's presence aboard and for another thing supported the ensuing statement inserted on *Gb* 11² as to the *intuitive* quality of Vere's distaste for Claggart. The addition of *Gab* 8¹, with Vere's command "Be direct . . . ," dramatizes the interchange. Further interesting alterations were made by Melville in pencil revisions. On Leaf 207, for example, his reworking in pencil left the second sentence incoherent and changed Claggart's metaphor "red clover" to "ruddy-tipped daisies," thus introducing an unnoticed inconsistency with the allusion to "pitfal[l] under the clover" on *Ga* 20. Another pencil revision on Leaf 208 changed Vere's metaphor for Billy from "a flower scarce yet fully released from the bud" to "who in the nude might have posed for a statue of young Adam before the Fall".

Leaf	Topic	B Ba	B Bb	B Bc[C]	X	F	G Ga	G Gb	p
[Ch. 19]									
220	B not afraid.							28^2	
221	B and C confront; C's accusation.	*	*66				29 Ga^{+}†		†
222	B's expression.						30		
223	His tongue-tie.						31		
224	V divines it.						32		
225	"Take your time."						33		
226	B fells C.						34		
227	C is dead.						35		
228	V turns official.						36		
229	Summons surgeon.						37		
[229a]	Surgeon infers C is dead.						S 38		
[229b]	V informs him. Time is the worst.						S 39		
[229c]	The thoughtful surgeon agrees.						S 40		

		Fa	Fb	Ga
[229d]	The year 1797 a crisis for Christendom.		S F/Ga 1	41
[229e]	Revolution became wrongdoer: none foresaw advance.		S F/Ga 2	42
[229f]	Nore Mutiny too prompted reforms in navy.		S F/Ga 3^1	43
230	Surgeon sees C is dead.			G^{+}p 38
231	Divine judgment on Ananias.			G^{+}p 39
232	Struck by angel; angel must hang.			G^{+}p 40
233	Desire for secrecy unaccountable.			G^{+}p 41

Here, too, the major topic, Claggart's confrontation of Billy in Vere's cabin, was present in *Ba*, and on *Bb* 66, by evidence of the clips on Leaf 221. That a treatment of the killing was also present seems certainly entailed. The chapter was carried mostly by fair-copy leaves of *Ga* probably stemming largely from the *B* stages, up to the point where Vere summons the surgeon (Leaf 229). Melville's *Gb* and pencil revisions up to this point were slight though interesting. At *Gb* 28^2, for example, he added Billy's thoughts upon finding himself in the captain's cabin. In a pencil-revision patch on Leaf 221 he added the comparison of Claggart to an asylum physician mesmerically eyeing a patient. And on the next leaf he struggled to improve his description of Claggart's eyes fixed upon Billy's; he changed their color from violet to black and then back to violet, and labored to introduce a comparison to creatures of the deep, succeeding with the metaphor of the "paralyzing lurch of the torpedo-fish."

At the point where the surgeon catches sight of Claggart's body, Melville made major pencil revisions and additions to his *Ga* fair copy. In an extensive revision sequence, he supplanted *Ga* leaves 38–40, which covered the surgeon's part in the cabin scene and his reaction to Vere's behavior, with post-*Ga* pencil-draft leaves 38–41 which substituted a new version of the scene, radically altering the reaction assigned the surgeon at *Ga*.

At the same time, Melville went directly on to supplant also *Ga* leaves 41–43 (hitherto printed as the "Preface") with new post-*Ga* pencil-draft leaves 42–43 and 44–45, the first two comprising an altogether new brief chap_ ter (20) and all four dealing with the surgeon's now reversed reaction—one of misgiving—as to Vere's behavior and the mental state that prompted it. (The revisions are discussed in the Introduction, pp. 9–11, 34–39.)

It should be noted that the *Fa* fair-copy sequence and foliation had begun at the point where the *Ga* chapter on the era ("Preface") later stood (at *Ga* 41). In his *Ga* copy sequence, however, Melville kept on copying when he reached this point, putting *Fa* ⟨1–6⟩ into *Ga* fair copy and, as he did so, keeping a clip from *Fa* on *Ga* 45 (Leaf 239). On *Fa* leaves 7–15, which he retained, he merely added numbers in the *Ga* set (49–56). He also placed *Fa* numbers 1–3 on his *Ga* leaves 41–43 ("Preface").

Leaf	Topic	B			X	F		G	p
		Ba	Bb	Bc[C]		Fa	Fb	Ga	
[Ch. 20] 234	Surgeon full of disquietude.							G^+p 42	
235	Suspects V not quite sound.							G^+p 43	

The two leaves of Ch. 20, together with the opening two leaves of the next, were added in pencil revision subsequent to *Ga*, as explained just above. (See Introduction, pp. 11, 34–37.) Leaves 234, 235, 236 were drafted on the versos of discarded *Eb* leaves 142, 144, 138, which carry analysis of Claggart that had been recently superseded by *Ee/F* leaves.

Note that here Melville further dramatized the situation by now projecting into the surgeon as his own thoughts a course that had already (at *Fa* 7) been attributed to Vere as the one he would "fain" follow but rejected for stern military reasons.

Leaf	Topic	B			X	F		G	p
		Ba	Bb	Bc[C]		Fa	Fb	Ga	
[Ch. 21] 236	Line between sanity and insanity.							G^+p 44	
237	As to V, everyone must determine.							G^+p 45	

Leaf	Topic	Ba	Bb	Bc[C]	X	Fa	Fb	Ga	p
238	V's words true.							44	
[238a]	V's difficulties.				Lf Is				
239	Jugglery of events.					*		45	
240	Circumspectness.							46	
241	V criticized later.							47	
242	Temporary secrecy.							48	
243	Would have delayed.					7		49	
244	Action necessary.					8		50	
245	Court convened.					9		51^1	
246	Marine officer.					10		51^2	
247	Other members.					11		52	†
248	Captain's cabin.					12		53	
249	V testifies.					13		54	
250	"I am true to King."					14		55	
251	"No malice. . . ."					15		56	
252	Did B suspect. . . ?					16			
253	Reply lingered.					17			
254	Why should C lie?					18			
255	B can't answer.					19			
256	V: it's irrelevant.					20			
257	B looks to V.					21			
258	Mystery of iniquity.					22			
259	Not for court.					23			
260	"I have said all."					24			
[260a]	V speech to court.				Lf Is				
[260b]	"				7				
[260c]	"				$10,9^2$				
261	Officers troubled.					25			
262	V gazes at sea.					*[26]	26		
263	Faces officers.					27			
264	Begins to speak.					28			
265	V speech to court.					29			
266	"					30			
267	"					31			
268	"						32		
269	"					33			
270	"					34			
271	"					35			
272	"					36			
273	"					37			
274	"					38			
275	"					39			
276	"					40			
277	"					41			
278	V speech ends.					42			
279	Court sits silent.					43			
280	Officer-instinct.					44			
281	Like Somers.					45			
282	Easy after battle. . . .					46			
283	B sentenced.					47			
284	Mortal punishment.					48			

The material of Ch. 21, the longest one, is carried for the most part by fair-copy leaves of *Fa*. Little, if any, of it was present in the *B* stages or at any time through *D*, since Melville composed the trial scene at Stage *X* as a radical expansion between *D* and *E*.

From Stage *X*, four passages survive, all of them in pencil draft. The first,

Leaf [238a] 1v, speaks in exculpatory vein of the effect of the era on the professional and moral difficulties of Captain Vere, emphasizing how inadequately even sea officers—much less landsmen—of a later day could understand them. The other three passages from X, [260a]83†v, [260b]87†v, [260c]20v, carry portions of Vere's speech to the court. All are obviously early drafts since, though similar in purport to the final Fa form, they do not closely approximate its wording and since, moreover, the final form shows considerable expansion over their material. From them it is clear that Melville must have carried on much revision and expansion within Stage X, while from the fact that he kept and brought forward from X no ink fair-copy leaves it is evident that he never made any such before F and G.

In this chapter two inconsistencies arose during the course of revisions, one from revisions before and during Fa, the other from the major late pencil revision. Both remained, unreconciled, in the final version.

The first inconsistency arose within X stages prior to Fa fair copy and was transcribed over into it. The inconsistency concerns the number and personnel of the court—whether it was made up of four or of three officers, and whether or not "a lieutenant of minor grade" was one of them or had in revision been supplanted by the "officer of marines." (In the X draft fragment [260a]83†v the number is twice given as "four officers" but they are not identified.) In the Fa fair copy Melville writes on Leaf 245 that Vere elected three officers: "the First Lieutenant, a lieutenant of minor grade, and the Sailing Master." But on Leaf 246, in the very next sentence, inscribed in the same ink and apparently in immediate sequence with the preceding leaf, he goes on to explain Vere's appointing "an officer of marines" and to characterize him carefully in preparation for his ensuing role in the trial scene. This "thoughtful" marine captain—making a fourth member of the court—plays (on Leaves 254, 257, 258, 272) the role dramatized from "Lawyers, Experts, Clergy" of the juror (as it were) who, "puzzled" by the "phenomenon" of Claggart's apparently unmotivated malice, raises the question about it that leads to Vere's ruling it out of naval court as "a 'mystery of iniquity', a matter for psychologic theologians to discuss." Although the marine captain makes a fourth member, the number three is reiterated on Leaf 247 (the marine officer and "the other two") and in four passages during the ensuing scenes (Leaves 257, 261, 263, 271). Later Melville evidently noticed the inconsistency, for in a pencil revision canceled "a lieutenant of minor grade" (on Leaf 245) and inserted instead "the captain of marines," thus reducing the number to three by substituting the marine captain for the minor lieutenant. But even so, the inconsistency remained, for Melville overlooked the fact that on Leaf 275 the junior lieutenant still appears and even speaks! So inadvertently he left in his final version the inconsistency as to both the number and personnel of the court. The explanation of the discrepancy is clear in general though not in detail: it arose in the X drafts, or possibly in the course of Fa inscription from them, during the incompletely executed revisions which involved development of the officer of marines and reduction of the court from four to three members. Then in making his *Fa* fair copy Melville transcribed the inconsistent passages including the minor lieutenant, without being aware of their discrepancy. Later he mistakenly supposed that by substituting the officer of marines for the minor lieutenant on Leaf 245 he had corrected it.

[The anomaly in the *Ga* foliation at Leaves 245–46, which might seem related to the above revisions, is in fact not so. The *Ga* foliation 51^1, 51^2, suggests that leaf 51^2 was added later, but since the inscription on both leaves is continuous in the brown *Fa* ink, and since the *Fa* foliation is uninterrupted, it seems clear that the number 51^2 was merely Melville's way of later correcting his inadvertently having numbered two leaves as 51.]

The other inconsistency in the chapter was introduced later when Melville substituted the two opening leaves (236–37) as part of the late pencil revision of *Ga*, in which he opened Vere's behavior to question by changing the reaction he had assigned the surgeon. The change introduces an inconsistency in whether Vere's course was or was not according to usage. Compare the *Fa* passage on Leaf 245, ". . . [Vere] was glad it would not be at variance with usage . . . ," with the *G+p* passages, written later of course, on Leaves 234 and 236, where both the surgeon and the officers consider his course contrary to usage. (See note to Leaf 233, *a drumhead court*.)

Aside from these inconsistencies, another point of interest attaches to Leaf 237, supplied in the pencil revision, where in the course of his remarks on the difficulty of drawing the line between sanity and insanity, Melville recurred to the topic of professional "experts" testifying—a topic which he had included in the by now long-since superseded "Lawyers, Experts, Clergy" episode. Thus, in effect, he salvaged and reused the topic of "experts" from that episode as he had already used its other materials (the jury puzzled by the question of motivation) at *X* in constituting the trial scene which ensues.

One final point attracts comment. Melville was doing more than his usual amount of revising and composing even while transcribing from the *X* draft to his *Fa* fair copy—that is, he was copying even less directly than usual from his earlier version. At least, the *Fa* leaves show more cancellations and false starts made at the time of inscription or immediately thereafter. One example is at Leaf 262, where Melville recast the description of Vere gazing at the sea. Another example is at Leaf 268, which Melville inserted after inscribing, revising, and canceling its substance on Leaf 269. The revision results in one of Vere's passages of high eloquence.

Leaf	Topic	B			X	F		G	p
		Ba	Bb	Bc[C]		Fa	Fb	Ga	
Ch. 22]									
285	V and B closeted.					49			
286	"					50			
287	"					51			
288	"					52			
289	V's agony seen.					53			

The materials of Ch. 22 stem from X, and stand on Fa fair-copy leaves betraying no evidence of their form earlier than Fa.

Leaf	Topic	B			X	F		G	p
		Ba	Bb	Bc[C]		Fa	Fb	Ga	
[Ch. 23]									
290	Incidents brief.					54	†		
291	Hour and half.					55			
292	All hands called.					56			
293	V informs them.					57			
294	Listen dumbly.					58			
295	Crew murmur.					59			
296	C buried—usage.					60			
297	B in irons—also						F/G		
	usage.					61	61^1		
298	Communicate only						F/G		
	with chaplain.						61^2		

In Ch. 23 too the materials stem from X, and betray nothing of their form earlier than Fa. However, Melville was obviously recasting and composing while he copied, as numerous false starts and cancellations show. The later running pencil revisions are also fairly heavy at points. Twice he made notations for revisions in substance which he did not complete. One, on Leaf 294, suggests that he may have intended to work in an allusion to Jonathan Edwards in connection with "the clergyman's announcement of his Calvinistic text." The other notation, on Leaf 295, calls for "Another order to be given here in place of this one"; and the substitute order is added at the top: "the word was given to about ship". At the end, Ga added another leaf, the substance of which prepared briefly for the chaplain's visit in the next chapter.

Leaf	Topic	B			X	F	G		p
		Ba	Bb	Bc[C]		Fa	F/G	Ga	
[Ch. 24]									
299	Various decks.					62			
300	B prone in irons.					63			
301	The scene.					64			
302	Scene. His looks.					65			
303	"					66			
304	B slumbering.					7			
	Adolescent look.					67			
305	Chaplain comes,					8			
	comes again.					68			
306	B welcomes him.					9			
	No idea of death.					69			
307	No fear of it.					70			
308	Barbarian; Angles.					71			
309	No idea of Savior.					72			
310	Like Tahitians.					73			
311	Chaplain kisses B.					74			
312	Couldn't intervene.					*75	75		

Except for its concluding leaf Ch. 24 also stands entirely in *Fa* fair-copy leaves; yet some speculation is possible concerning its origins. Both of its main narrative elements, a description of the scene of Billy's imprisonment and an account of the chaplain's visit, must have been present in some form not only at the earliest *B* stage but also from the earliest *A* stage as well, for the ballad, which the headnote was written to introduce, has Billy as its imprisoned speaker and refers to the chaplain's visit. It seems very likely that the passages describing Billy in the present tense (on Leaves 300, 301, 302) stem directly from the original headnote, the surviving leaf of which (like Melville's similar headnotes for other late poems) is also in the present tense. Both the description and the chaplain's visit must have been treated very briefly, however, up through the earliest *B* stage, since as noted above, the *B* number-series has a gap only from 66 to 72 between the confrontation and the first ballad leaf, though, undoubtedly, later *B* stages added leaves.

At *F/G*, Melville revised (on *F/G* 75) and evidently omitted some of his remarks involving the anomaly of a chaplain in a warship, as indicated by his notation "76 omitted." See note to Leaf 311, *the young sailor's essential innocence.*

The incomplete revision on Leaf 312, concerning the "musket on the altar at Christmas," has caused earlier editors some difficulty. It must be treated as incomplete, however. See note to Leaf 312, *a musket . . . on the altar.*

| Leaf | Topic | B | | | X | F | G | | p |
		Ba	Bb	Bc[C]		Fa	F/G	Ga	
[Ch. 25]									
313	Dawn comes.					77			
314	All hands summoned.					78			
315	The scene.					79			
316	Billy brought up.					80			
317	"God bless. . . ."					81			
318	Crew echo B.					82			
319	Final signal.					83			
320	B hanged.					84			

Ch. 25, on the hanging, stands altogether in fair-copy *Fa* leaves giving no indication of its earlier state. The *B* stages must have included some account of the hanging, but the dramatization cannot have been carried very far, judging from the few leaves that stood between *B* 66 and 72, and from the slight degree of dramatization generally present in *Ba* and *Bb*. Billy's blessing of Captain Vere certainly belongs to *X*, that is, to the phase following the build-up of Vere in *X* and in what are now Ch. 6 and 7.

The chapter at first ended with *Fa* leaves ⟨85–86⟩, which (with 84) carried the interchange between the purser and the surgeon, beginning in the same paragraph in which Billy's motionless hanging is told. This passage Melville heavily revised and expanded in pencil, as seen on Fa 84, and at the beginning of his G copy stage transcribed it, no doubt with further revisions, as a new chapter on the four F/G leaves 85, $86^{1\text{-}3}$.

Leaf	Topic	B			X	F	G		p
		Ba	Bb	Bc[C]		Fa	F/G	Ga	
[Ch. 26]									
321	Purser & surgeon.					85			
322	"					86^1			
323	"					86^2			
324	"					86^3			

The genesis of Ch. 26 has been discussed just above. Like his Nelson "divergence" and his "irruption" on the chaplain, the chapter grew out of a brief passage on a subject long a pregnant one for Melville. Unlike the other two examples, this was dramatized, not editorialized, and that fact may be one reason he allowed it rather than suppressed it as he did his irruption on the chaplain and wavered about doing with his divergence on Nelson. Here the pregnant subject was the limitations of the "man of science," which he had touched on with "the medical experts" in "Lawyers, Experts, Clergy," Leaf 353, and on notable occasions throughout his earlier works.

Leaf	Topic	B			X	F	G		p
		Ba	Bb	Bc[C]		Fa	F/G	Ga	
[Ch. 27]									
325	Sound from crew.					87			
326	A murmur.					88			
327	Whistles					89			
328	and commands.					90			
329	B readied for burial.					Lf Is			
						91	(Is)		
330	Buried in sea.						92		
331	Seafowl; discipline.						93		
332	At quarters.						94		
333	Vere on "forms."						95		
334	Now full day. . . .						96		

In Ch. 27, four leaves and half of a fifth (Leaf 329), on the crew's reactions to the hanging, are of Fa fair copy and in its brown ink. In the middle of Leaf 329 the fair copy continues, with the burial, but now in blue-gray ink of G, while the F number-set is still employed. There is nothing to indicate the original composition stage or any earlier form of the materials, though in all likelihood it belongs to X. Again, Melville was freely revising and perhaps at points even composing as he copied. Concerning the passage on Vere as a "martinet" and his view of "forms," see the discussion above of Leaves 81–87, Ch. 7.

Leaf	Topic	B			X	F	G		p
		Ba	Bb	Bc[C]		Fa	F/G	Ga	
[Ch. 28]									
[334a]	Notes for fight & history of spar.				*				
335	Sequel needed—						97		
336	three chapters.						98		
337	Fight.						99		
338	Death of Vere.						100		
339	His dying words.						101		

Some chance preserved (in a folder of miscellaneous scraps) a fragment of Melville's pencil-draft notes for what became Ch. 28, on the engagement with the French ship, and for what became Ch. 30, on the subsequent history of the yard from which Billy was hanged—[334a]361, Plate VIII.

Three points of discrepancy between the draft and the final F/G and B/X versions show that it was drafted before them, and also, therefore, before the stage in X from which they were copied. That is, it belongs relatively early within the X stage. One discrepancy is in the time scheme. According to the notes the chase took place "the previous morning," whereas on Ga 2 the chase began "in the latter part of an afternoon watch." A second discrepancy occurs in the ship names. In his notes the French ship is the *Directory*, not the *Athéiste* of F/G 98, 99 (see discussion of this name below). A final discrepancy concerns the yard from which Billy was hanged. In the notes it is broken off in the engagement and taken to Gibraltar, whereas in the final B/X draft nothing is said of either of these points. In the final version what is left at Gibraltar is Captain Vere, not the yard. Though Vere is not mentioned in the notes it seems most likely that Melville already had his death in mind (in the "&c &c &c"), since the engagement serves no other function than as the occasion of his mortal wounding. Had these notes been drafted *after* composition of the corresponding final passages, or of their sources in X, the discrepancies noticed above would not have occurred; they are assigned, therefore, to early X.

The chapter itself stands entirely on F/G leaves which conclude the fair-copy sequence derived from X. It is the first of three brief chapters by way of sequel. These chapters comprise, evidently, the "Supplement" mentioned in the notations, since they deal with matters that occurred after Billy's life ended.

The most interesting genetic point is Melville's treatment of the ship names. He changed both names: the earlier *Directory* of the notes became here the *Athéiste;* and the *Indomitable* itself, as he reconsidered directly the naming of fighting ships, he changed to the *Bellipotent*. (For discussion of the latter change see pp. 20–21, 199. The name *Athéiste* he did not actually write in his ink fair copy at F/G but left a space for it on each of its two occurrences and in pencil wrote it in the margin. Mrs. Melville later inserted the name in pencil in each space. The explanation of Melville's so writing the name may be that he wished to use the French word for "atheist" as the ship's name but was not certain that "athéiste" was the correct form and so penciled it in the margin intending to verify it. Had he done so, he would have found that the French word in 1797, as now, was "athée," while "athéiste" was an obsolete form, never standard. (Leyris [1937], pp. 188–89, retains l'*Athéiste*.)

| Leaf | Topic | B | | | X | F | G | | p |
		Ba	Bb	Bc[C]	B/X	Fa	F/G	Ga	
[Ch. 29]									
340	News report.			{ 75^2 { p75					
341	"		76	† / p 76^{p1}					
342	"		*77	†77					
343	"		*	78^1					
344	["Here ends. . . ."]	78		78^2					
[Ch. 30]									
345	Spar remembered.				79				
346	And Billy.				80				
347	Ballad by sailor.				81				
348	The ballad.		72		82				
349	"		73	†	83				
350	"		74^1		84				
351	"		{ 75 { 75^2 { 74^2						

With the two final chapters, which contain the news account and the ballad, the manuscript reverts to leaves largely from the *B* stages. In the story as it stood through the *B* stages and *D*, the ballad (now in Ch. 30) preceded the news account (now in Ch. 29), which then ended the story. This fact is made evident by the original foliation of the ballad leaves, *Bb* 72, 73, 74, 75, and by that of the continuating leaves of the news account, *Bb* and *Bc* 75^2, 76, 77, 78, 78^2. It is confirmed, moreover, by the notations Melville made on the last leaf of the news account, 78^2. There, at some point after the *B* stages, or by *D*, he wrote in pencil, "End"; but later canceled the word and added the coda, "Here ends a story. . . ."

The stage at which Melville reversed the order, placing the news account before the ballad, was during *X*, before *F* and *G*. This is shown by the pencil notation at the top of *Bc* 75^2, the first leaf of the news account: "P 25 (pencil) precedes". When this notation was made, in other words, what stood just before this first leaf (75) of the news account was not still the last ballad leaf (74), and not yet the last *F/G* leaf (101), but leaf 25 of an *X* pencil-draft sequence.

At the point in *X* when Melville reversed the order of news account and ballad thus, he deprived the ballad of whatever introduction had led up to it, though the immediately preceding leaf, *B* 71, survived as Leaf 20v, thrice used: for *B* 71; for *X* 10, 9^2; and finally for *Eab* 18^1. At the same time, in placing the ballad after the news account, he had to draft a new introduction, Leaves 345, 346, 347. That he did draft these leaves at this stage of *X*, though he foliated them in the *B* series (the only series available) is clear from the fact that their numbers, 79, 80, 81, take up from the last news-account leaf, 78^2, and that the ballad is refoliated with the continuating numbers 82, 83, 84. The new (or redrafted) introduction to the ballad, in its reference to the subsequent history of the spar from which Billy was hanged, stems from the *X* draft notes "For the Supplement." (See discussion of Leaves [334a] ff.)

One point of genetic interest deserves comment. The news account, since it was written in the *B* stages, before Captain Vere's role was developed during *X*, makes no mention of his part in the affair of "the tenth of the last month," or of the engagement with the French ship (which would have been very soon after), or of his mortal wound, or his death—although all of these would have had to be known to anyone in a position to originate the report from which the account stemmed. As a matter of fact, since everybody aboard, as the later development had it, knew at least the "outside" story of the case and sympathized with Billy, no imaginable informant could have given "in good faith" a report subject to such diametric distortion as that displayed in the news account. These matters that were developed later than the composition of the account make its last sentence, particularly, anachronistic: "Nothing amiss is now apprehended aboard. . . ." That Melville was aware of something of the sort seems implied in his pencil notation at the head of the first leaf (Leaf 340), "Speak of the fight & death of Captain Vere". He never went on to do so by revising the account, but canceled the notation. (It must be said that no critic has noted the omission.)

(For discussion of the development of the ballad from the earliest surviving leaves, see pp. 3–6.)

The Genetic Text: Transcription

EXPLANATION AND KEY

The Genetic Text is a literal transcription of the *Billy Budd* manuscript, leaf by leaf including superseded leaves, in a form that incorporates our analysis of it. It is designed to show the growth of the text, insofar as that can be seen from the surviving leaves. To do so, we present as the running text the earliest version that Melville inscribed on each leaf. At the same time we report all of his revisions as bracketed interruptions, at the points where he made them in the running text. In the centered headings we label each leaf by its original copy stage and by the later stages in which it stood, by means of our stage letters attached to Melville's own successive foliations. We also label each passage on the leaf by means of our stage letters at the left margin of the text. In addition, we label each revision by the stage at which Melville made it. Thus a reader can begin with the *earliest surviving* version of each passage of the text and follow Melville's revisions of it through to the final version. Furthermore, by inferences from the stage labels and successive foliations a reader can learn much about the growth of the narrative as a whole. (For this purpose, our table and discussion of Foliations are essential. See pp. 241–69.)

But a warning is necessary. It is not possible to follow the entire growth of the text *verbatim*, from the beginning; or to find the "earliest version" of the story; or even to recover the story intact as it stood at any intermediate stage. The reason it is not possible to do so lies in the composing and copying procedures by which Melville constituted the manuscript as it finally stands. Ordinarily he composed in pencil, with many false starts and running revisions; then he copied a group of leaves so drafted (which were often already the product of several pencil-revision stages) into an ink fair-copy sequence. As a rule, whenever he copied, he destroyed his original or intermediate draft leaves; only a few of them were inadvertently preserved, when he re-used their versos. Having completed a fair-copy sequence in ink, he then made further revisions in pencil, once more recopying in ink those leaves most heavily revised. Normally he destroyed the superseded leaves, though several of these too were by chance preserved. Therefore, few of the leaves in the final manuscript are the draft leaves of original composing; most belong to various fair-copy sequences which Melville inscribed at stages over a period of some five years, 1886–91. For this reason, to repeat, what a reader can now follow *verbatim* in the Genetic Text is the growth of the text only from the *earliest surviving version* of a given passage, not, in most passages, from its original composition.

A second warning: the leaves as they stand here in order do not carry a text that existed as a whole at any one stage previous to the final state—the state which includes all the revisions on them.

Our only departure from literal transcription of Melville's text is in the case of words he wrote in pencil draft so imperfectly that we have thought it futile to attempt to decide the actual letters present; such words we have reported in standard spelling. (See, for such words, Plate VIII.) We have given Melville's misspellings literally; they are so frequent that we have not called attention to them by the use of *"sic."*

To read the earliest version Melville inscribed on each leaf, follow the running text by skipping over the matter in square brackets.

To read the revisions, read inside the brackets.

Stages of Inscription

The following letters designate the copy stages. The stages, as well as the substages given in parentheses, refer to the time of *inscription*, not that of *composition*. (In the body of the text these stage letters are in italics, as here; in the centered heads and marginal labels they are in boldface roman and italics.)

A
B　(*Ba, Bb, Bbb, Bc, Bca, Bcb*)
C　(*Ca, Caa, Cab, Cb, Cba, Cbb, Cc, Cca*)
D　(*Da, Daa, Dab, Db*)
X
E　(*Ea, Eaa, Eab, Eb, Ec, Ed, Ee*)
F　(*Fa, Fb*)
G　(*Ga, Gb*)
late pencil　(also designated by *p*)
　　+　stage later than that designated by stage letter to which it is attached (e.g., *Bb*+)
　　x　substage uncertain (e.g., *Bx*)
　F/G　leaf numbered as of first stage designated, but actually inscribed at second stage designated

Media of Inscription

Since most of the inscription is in ink, the above stage letters also signify that the medium employed is ink, unless otherwise indicated, as follows:

　p　in pencil
　i　in ink (of indeterminate stage)
　Dap　in pencil of stage designated
　p Ca　in pencil, then in ink of stage designated
　p i　in pencil, then in ink of indeterminate stage

Most of the inscription is in Melville's hand. In the body of the Genetic Text, all words reported in roman are Melville's unless otherwise labeled. All words in italics are those of the editors.

HM inscription by Herman Melville
ESM inscription by Elizabeth Shaw Melville (his wife)
W inscription by Raymond Weaver (the first editor)

Revisions

The Genetic Text reports all revisions, bracketed, directly following the word(s) revised.

→ . . . → enclosed revision was made at time leaf was first being inscribed
  [. . .] enclosed revision was made later than initial inscription of leaf
[. . . {. . .} . . . {. . .} . . .] enclosed revision underwent secondary revisions (enclosed in braces)
[*Bb* . . . {*Ca* . . .}] enclosed revisions were made at stages designated
    Note: When revision was made soon after initial inscription, in indistinguishable medium, no stage is designated.
  > insert, above and with caret, the word(s) following
  ⊁ insert, above but without caret, the word(s) following
  < cancel the word(s) following (by lining out)
  ⊀ erase the word(s) following
  ≫ restore the word(s) following (by underlining or by erasing line-out mark)
  add add, on same line, the word(s) following
  w.o. write over (superimpose) the word(s) following
  x } undeciphered letter(s) (number of x's approximates number of letters in-
  xxx} volved)
  - - two hyphens are employed at ends of lines to distinguish Melville's hyphenations from those incidental to the present edition
  v verso of a leaf

For example, revisions of a passage on Leaf *2*, with marginal label *Da*, are reported thus:

. . . some one signal [*p* < some one < signal ⊁ a superior {*Ea* ⊀ a superior ≫ some > superior}] figure . . .

This is to be read thus:

The passage was inscribed at *Da*, reading ". . . some one signal figure. . . ." Later, in pencil, cancel "some one" and also cancel "signal"; insert above, without caret, "a superior". Later, at Stage *Ea*, erase "a superior" and restore "some"; also insert, above and with caret, "superior".

In other words, the passage successively stood:

At *Da:* some one signal figure
In pencil revision between *Da* and *Ea:* a superior figure
At *Ea:* some superior figure

Foliation

In the Genetic Text each leaf carries one or more numbers centered at the head: first, in boldface italics, the Houghton Library leaf number; then, with our stage letters, in boldface roman, the number(s) Melville gave it; finally, the number in the series put on by some later hand, almost certainly that of Raymond Weaver, which we designate W, in brackets.

Example: *3:* **Da 2, Db 2^1, Ea 2.** **[W 2]**

The manuscript has recently (May, 1961) been foliated with the Houghton Library series. Each leaf in the manuscript proper (1–365) now carries a penciled number from this series on the lower left corner.

1–351   leaves in the final manuscript sequence
352–61   superseded leaves
362–65   associated folder leaves (see Extra-Textual Leaves, pp. 426–29)
[*135a*]*353*   superseded leaves are also assigned bracketed numbers, thus, indicating their genetic position; they are printed in the Genetic Text in that position
[*347a*] "Daniel Orme" *17v*   superseded leaf re-used (recto) and now standing in another work

Melville's process of foliation is discussed above, pp. 226 ff. In the Genetic Text his numbers on each leaf are given with the stage designations, as listed above. Although these are Melville's numbers, we have not reported the literal form of erasures, revisions, and media, but have presented them in interpreted form. For example, what we report as **Da 2, Db 2^1** appears on the leaf as the number "2" followed by a circled "1", on the upper left corner, in green crayon. Our analysis shows that Melville wrote the "2" at *Da* and later added the circled "1" at *Db*.

Stage Labels

Stage letters, as listed above, have been inserted at the left margin to label the stage at which the text below them was *inscribed* (not the stage at which it was *composed*).

Ba   text was inscribed at stage designated
*Ba   text is *on an attached clip* from a leaf inscribed at the stage designated (when number of leaf is known it is also given: e.g., **Eb 94;* when inferred, it is given in brackets)
*Eb 95(I) ⎫   text is on two clips—labeled (*I*) and (*II*)—from the stage and leaf designated, and edges of clips originally joined; i.e., text on them was originally continuous on the same leaf. When the edges did not join (i.e., when part of leaf was cut off between them), the form (. . . *II*) is used
*Eb 95(II) ⎭   for the second clip
†*Eaa*   text is *on an attached patch* inscribed at the later stage designated

Stage *A* Leaves

We have designated as "Stage *A*" all the writing Melville did on *Billy Budd* from the time he first put pencil to paper up to the time he began making the fair copy which he numbered at midtop-leaf in green crayon and which we have designated "Stage *B*." Within Stage *A* he must have developed the story through many waystages, as he did all his late manuscripts. But what these waystages were, he left us no means of knowing, for he destroyed all his worksheets for Stage *A* except four pencil-draft leaves. (Two associated conjunct leaves he used as folders also survive from this stage. See pp. 426–27.) Aside from these four leaves, then, we have none of the dozens Melville must have used during Stage *A* in developing the work from its inception up to the fair copy we designate Stage *B*. It is therefore, as we have said, impossible to document the whole growth of *Billy Budd*. Even so, these four leaves, taken along with the manuscripts of Melville's other late writings, allow us to make dependable inferences about when and how he started the work and what he had in it at first. (See Introduction, pp. 3–6, and Plates I–IV.)

These four leaves from Stage *A* were not kept by Melville as part of the final *Billy Budd* manuscript itself but were preserved among the leaves of the manuscript sketch called "Daniel Orme." The preservation was fortuitous: when Melville had copied what he had drafted on them he crossed it out and later thriftily used the backs of the leaves in drafting "Daniel Orme." Thus merely by chance he preserved the crossed-out *Billy Budd* matter on their verso sides.

We can date these four draft leaves from Stage *A* with some certainty. Melville inscribed the leaves in or just before the early months of 1886, certainly no later. For this dating, the major evidence is their association with the "Daniel Orme" leaves. As stated above, Melville used their backs in drafting that sketch. Along with them, similarly, he also used backs of other second-hand leaves, including two whose fronts he had first used in drafting two letters. One of these letters he had drafted in January, the other in April or May, 1886. Evidently, then, Melville was drafting "Daniel Orme" shortly after he wrote the letters, that is in the early months of 1886. And since he had by then already copied the four *Billy Budd* leaves, and discarded them, it is obvious that at that time—early 1886—he had already carried his work on *Billy Budd* beyond the point they represented. Therefore, these four draft leaves have to be dated no later than early 1886. From this dating it follows that the inception of *Billy Budd* was somewhat earlier—that is, that Melville began it possibly in 1885, or even before.

[*344a*]: "Daniel Orme" 3v.

[*From Stage* A *a single unfoliated leaf of the prose part of* Billy Budd *survives. It was evidently the opening leaf of Melville's original pencil draft of a headnote to the ballad. Evidence that it was the original draft is that Melville did not inscribe it straight off (as he did the ballad draft leaves), but made false starts, erasures, and revisions while he wrote. The matter on it corresponds to what ended up several years later on Leaves 38 and 39 of the final manuscript.*]

A: pencil

Billy B →*w.o.* Budd→ [≯a rollicking seaman { <a rollicking seaman}] yet more familiarly →≮yet more familiarly *w.o.* sometimes→ known as →*alter* as *to* among→ his shipmates as Handsome →≮as Handsome *w.o.* under the knicknames→ Handsome, [*underlined*] [<Handsome ≯"Beauty"] xx xx → ≮xx xx *w.o.* and J ≮J *w.o.* The Jewel, [*underlined*]→ he being a man [?] in [?] his xx →≮a man in his xx *w.o.* in person→ [>(*at top, to follow* he being) not only →<not only→ goo →<goo→ goodnatured →<he being <goodnatured→ >(*still above, circled, with guide-line to caret*) he being not only sparklingly →<sparklingly→ pleasant in temper, →<pleasant in temper ≯genial,→ {<genial ≯(*above*) genial in temper, and sparklingly so;} ≯but (*before* in person) >(*after* person) also] a goodly object [<goodly *add* brilliant {<a brilliant object ≫goodly}] to behold; [*passage finally reads* he being not only genial in temper, and sparklingly so, but in person also goodly to behold;] his features, ear, foot, and in a less degree even his sailor hands all indicating n →<indicating n→ together →<together <all→ but more particularly [<particularly ≯strikingly] his [>whole {<whole} frame and] natural bearing [<bearing >(*with guide-line and caret*) carriage] all →<all→ indicating no ignoble lineage →<no *add* some <ignoble lineage→ superior and noble stock →< some . . . stock→ exceptional and superior stock →<exceptional . . . stock→ a lineage contradicting his lot; he, [*alter semicolon to period and alter* he *to* He] in war time, Captain of a gun's crew in a seventy- - four, is summarily condemned [>at sea] to be hung as the ringleader of an incipient mutiny [>(*below, circled*) the spread of which was apprehended] [≯a mutiny] projected under the [*orange crayon cancel whole leaf*]

[*347a*]: "Daniel Orme" 17v.

[*The earliest of the three surviving ballad draft leaves, which is not foliated, carries a six-line version of the opening. Although Melville inscribed the lines in pencil, he was evidently not composing them but copying them from an earlier draft in order to get a clear working copy on which to do further revising. His intention is revealed by the fact that he began with his usual ornamented rule at the top, and further that he inscribed the lines*]

without false starts—as he could rarely compose. Still another indication
that this is not the earliest draft of these lines is that they occupy only the
top half of the leaf, and that to continue them Melville pinned below
them a clip (or clips)—now gone—from an earlier draft.]

A: pencil

———◆———

Very good of him, Ay, so long to stay
And down [<down] on his marrow bone here to pray
For the likes of me. Nor bad [<Nor bad ≯I like { <I like ≯ (*below*) I bless}]
   his story,
The Good Being hung and gone to glory.—
What's this? only the sun's last ray → ⊀ 's last ray *w.o.* taking leave→
Raying [<Raying ≯Crimson] through the gun-port. My last eve.
[*clip was pinned on below*]

[347b]: 2, "Daniel Orme" 4v.

[*The second surviving ballad draft leaf begins with a later, seven-line*
version of the above lines, followed by eight additional trial lines. Again
copying from an earlier draft, Melville wrote this leaf straight off, in pen-
cil, and then revised it. In the process he canceled everything following line
six and pinned over the canceled segment a patch (now gone) that evi-
dently carried a fuller version of the draft lines it covered up.

Melville numbered this leaf "2" in blue crayon, an indication that by
then at least one leaf preceded it—probably, since the ballad itself opens
here, a prose headnote. But we know from the surviving initial leaf of the
headnote draft which we have that one or more leaves of prose once fol-
lowed. Perhaps when Melville numbered the ballad draft leaf he had not
yet written his headnote, which he expected to occupy only a single leaf, or
perhaps the headnote existed either in draft or in fair copy on but one
leaf.]

A: pencil
Very good [<Very good ≯Kind] of him, Ay, to come my way [<come >xx
   →<xx→ *add* sail { <sail my way ≯(*above*) enter Lone Bay}]
And down on his marrowbones here & pray
For the like of me. I bless [<bless ≯hail { <hail ≫bless}] his [<I bless his
   >He told of a { <He told of a *add* (*with guide-line to caret*) And good his}]
   story—
[*add* Of] The good boy hung and gone to glory,
And all [<And all ≯Hung] for the likes of me. But, look,
That light [⊀That light *w.o.* What light { <What light >How light} { ⊀How
   light *w.o.* How bright} { <How bright *add* Plays}] on the cannon! [*add*

comma] the sun's last →[⟨sun's last *w.o.* day taking leave [⟩sun (*without canceling* day)]→
Peering [⟨Peering ⟩Burning] thru the port there [⟨there ⟩here] —Billy's last eve.
[*interline* And there goes Tidds our mess's privy cook]
A jewel block——
[*single rule* { ⟨*rule*}]
A pearl——
[*single rule*]
O, its me.
[*single rule*] [⟨*the lines* A pearl *and* O, its me. (*including rules*)]
Sh → *w.o.* Messmates→ —
Shipmates—
No song to those halyards, they'll hoist away
Sorry for ye, boys, but ye needs obey
[*orange and blue crayons cancel lower segment of leaf* Burning . . . obey *and pin on a clip* (*now gone*) {*orange and blue crayons cancel top segment of leaf*}]

[*347c*]: "Daniel Orme" 16v.

[*The third, and last surviving, ballad draft leaf opens with the last two lines of the above leaf, but in a later version. Its being unfoliated is further indication that this leaf does not belong to the same stage and sequence in which the above leaf was foliated "2". (Possibly some of its lines overlap with those that were on the patch later pinned on the above leaf.)*
Melville inscribed this leaf, like the other two, as a pencil trial copy of lines already composed, and then he revised it. A clip or patch (now gone) was at one time pinned on below these lines, continuing their matter—an indication that at this stage the ballad already extended beyond them.]

A: pencil
So be, so be, [⟨so be ⟩—well, well— { ⟨well, well *add* let rip—}] no malice
  bear they [⟨let rip ⟨no . . . they ⟩(*above*) all's up and I must up to. (*sic*)]
[*add line at right side* All →⟨All→ Early in the morning they →⟨they→ the
  deed they will do]
Since the game is up [⟨Since ⟩Yes { ⟨Yes ⟨the ⟩The little *alter* game is *to*
  game's} { ⟨The *add* (*before* little) My} { ⟨My →Our} (*finally reads* Our
  little game's up)] they must needs obey.
And [⟨And ⟩Well,] to these and many another crew [*add dash*] [*interline*
Since who was my mother I could say { ⟨mother ⟩(*below*) m →⟨m→}
  { ⟨Since . . . say *add* (*at foot of leaf, circled, with guide-line to caret*) Since
  who was my mammy I never could say}]
In a queerish [⟨a queerish ⟩my last queer] dream here I bid adieu [*add dash*]

A queerish [<A queerish ⊁For most part a] dream of days [<days ⊁ships]
no more. [*add dash*]

A general-muster [<general ⊁a >(*after* muster) of men] from every shore
[*add dash*]

[*interline* Hail to ye, fellows, and is it you? {<Hail . . . you?}]

Countrymen, yes, and Moor & Swede [*add comma*]

Christian Pagan Cannibal breed

[*clip was pinned on below*]

[*blue crayon cancel all writing on leaf*]

Final Leaves

1:

[X⁺p (*probably late-pencil*) *draft of dedication. Verso of leaf was inscribed earlier; see p. 430.*]

X⁺p

Dedicated
to
Jack Chace
Englishman
Wherever he [<he > (*above, circled, with guide-line*
to caret) *that great heart*] may now be
Here on earth or [>harbored] in Paradise
Captain of the Main-top [*capitalize* top]
[>(*below, circled, with guide-line to caret*) in the year 1843]
in [>(*circled*) historic { <historic}] the U.S. Frigate
"United States" [*ESM p notation* for Billy Budd]

[1a] 352:

[*Superseded pencil-draft title slip, of uncertain stage* (C?), *mounted on leaf. Verso of slip was inscribed earlier; see p. 432.*]

C?: pencil on slip

Billy Budd [*underlined*]
Foretopman [*underlined*]
What befell him
in the year of the
Great Mutiny
&c

[*p* <(*underlined*) Billy Budd / Foretopman]
[*ESM p* ⪢ (*above canceled underlined* Billy Budd) Billy Budd {*ESM* ⪡ (*her own insertion*) Billy Budd *and trace over HM's cancellation, thus* Billy Budd / Foretop-man}]

Editor's note: This superseded pencil-draft title slip is approximately the bottom third of a leaf whose verso was earlier inscribed (at right angles to title draft) with pencil draft of a passage finally on *Eb 128* (Leaf 120).

Melville must have inscribed this title draft at a stage later, of course, than the stage at which he copied forward the pencil passage on its verso; and that copy stage was probably *Bc*[*C*]. So the draft may date from any stage between *Bc*[*C*] and *Eb*—most likely from late *C*, or *D*. One consideration pointing to late *C* or *D* is that Melville at that point, just prior to *X*, supposed the story was finished, was preparing a fair copy, *D*, and might then have drafted a title page for it. Another consideration pointing to the stage prior to *X* concerns the adequacy of the title. In the story Melville twice approximates the phrase in the draft subtitle, "What befell him," first on *Ec 121* (Leaf 111), and again on *F/G 97* (Leaf 335). Both of these passages were probably copied from earlier stages since they stand in ink fair copy deriving ultimately from *B* or *C*. Now, in the *F/G* passage Melville comments directly on the fact that the final three chapters go beyond "what befell him," and the fact that he felt it necessary so to comment would seem to imply that he would not have considered the subtitle adequate by then—therefore, that he had drafted the title at a stage preceding the *X* expansion that necessitated those final chapters.

In any case, Melville canceled this title, though sparing the subtitle, and supplanted it by the late-pencil title which he added on the opening leaf of the story (*Da 1:* Leaf 2). (For some of the late pieces, contemporary with *Billy Budd*, numerous draft titles survive.)

It is most doubtful that Melville left this semi-canceled draft title in title-page position at the head of the manuscript—followed by his later title on the opening page of the story. Our hypothesis, suggested by Mrs. Melville's penciled restoration of the canceled title, and supported by her similar practice elsewhere in the late manuscripts, is that she found the superseded draft slip after her husband's death when she was engaged in sorting all his late manuscripts, and that she then mounted the slip on a leaf and placed it at the front of the *Billy Budd* manuscript. Her so placing it gives it no authority, since she made various other errors in her attempted placing of leaves—in *Billy Budd*, notably in the conjectured "Preface."

2: Da 1; Ea 1.

Da

[p (*on top left corner, circled*) Billy Budd / Sailor / (An inside narrative.)]
[*Dap notation* (*boxed, on top right corner*) Friday Nov. 16. 1888. / Began.]
[*X? Eap? notation* (*boxed below first notation, with fist*) Revise—began / March
2d 1889]

———◆———

In the time before steamships, and [*p Ea* <and >or then] more frequently
than now [*p Ea add comma*] a stroller along the docks of any considerable
sea-port would occasionally have his attention arrested by a group of bronzed
mariners, man-of-war's men or merchant-sailors in holiday attire ashore
on liberty. In certain instances [*p* <In certain instances ≯Sometimes xx
{ ≮Sometimes xx (*thus restoring canceled* In certain instances)}] they would
flank, or, like a body-guard quite surround some one signal [*p* <some one
<signal ≯a superior {*Ea* ≮a superior ≫some >superior}] figure of their
own class but signalized [*p* <but signalized (*as part of first revision on next
leaf*)]

3: Da 2, Db 2¹; Ea 2. [W 2]

* Da 2

by its preeminence, [*p* <preeminence ≯bright { ≮bright *add* superior-
ity} {*Ea* <but signalized by its superiority}] moving along with [*p* >lumi-
nousness { ≮luminousness}] them like [*p* >signalized { ≮signalized}] Aldebaran [*p* >superior { ≮superior}] among the lesser [*p* ≯(*over* lesser) twinkling (?) { ≮twinkling ≫lesser}] lights of his constellation. That signal figure
[*Ea* <signal figure >shining object { <shining >signal}] was the "Handsome Sailor" of the picturesque [*Eap* <picturesque >less prosaic] time
[*Eap* <time >era { ≮era ≫time}] [*p* >alike] of the military and merchant
navies. [*p* <navies >marine. { ≮marine. ≫navies.}] With no perceptable
[*p correct to* perceptible] trace of vanity or vainglory rather [*p* <vanity or
vainglory rather ≯the vainglorious {*Ea* ≮the vainglorious *add* the ≫vain-
glory rather *altering* y *to* ious *and* >about him, (*before* rather)}] with the off- -
hand unaffectedness of natural → <natural→ innate [*p Ea* <innate ≫natural]
regality, he seemed to accept the spontanious [*p correct to* spontaneous] homage of his shipmates. [*Da⁺p notation* Insert *add* A somewhat remarkable instance recurs to me. {*Ea* ≮*notation and add on leaf*}]

Ea

A somewhat remarkable instance recurs to me. In Liverpool, now half a century ago I saw under the shadow of the great dingy street-wall of Prince's
Dock

4: Ea 3.

[*Verso of leaf was inscribed earlier; see p. 430.*]

Eaa

(an obstruction long since removed) a common sailor, a son of Ham [*p* <a son of Ham] so intensely black that he must needs have been a native born [*p* <born] African. [*p* <*period* >of the best { <best >(*above, circled*) unadulterate} blood of Ham.] A symmetric [*p* ⊁barbaric { <barbaric}] figure much above the average height. The two ends of a gay silk handerchief thrown loose about the neck danced upon the displayed ebony of his chest; in his ears were big hoops of gold, and a Scotch [*p* >(*below* Scotch) Highland] bonnet [*Eab* >(*below, circled*) with a tartan band] set off his shapely head. [*Eab add* It was a rather {*p* <rather} hot noon in July; and his handsome {*p* <handsome} face, lustrious with perspiration, beamed with {*p* >barbaric} good humor.]

5: Eab 3².

Eab

In jovial sallies right and left, [*p* >his white teeth flashing into view,] he rollicked along, the centre of a company of his shipmates. These were made up of such an assortment of tribes and complexions

* Db

as would have well fitted them to be marched up by the eccentric [*p* <the eccentric] Anacharsis Cloots before the bar of the first French Assembly as Representatives of the Human Race.

Eab

In the [*p* <In the ⊁At each] spontanious [*p* *correct to* spontaneous] tribute rendered by nearly every [*p* <nearly every ⊁any { <any ⊁the}] wayfarer [*p alter to* wayfarers] at [*p* <at ⊁to] this black pagod of a jolly [*p* <jolly] fellow—the tribute of a pause and stare, and less frequent an exclamation, [*p add dash*] the motley retinue showed that [*p add* (*on next line*) they took that]

6: Ea 4.

Ea

sort of pride in their mighty [>black] sailor [*p* <their mighty black sailor >the evoker of it] which the Assryian priests doubtless showed for their [>carved and] deified [*p* <carved and deified >grand sculptured] Bull when the faithful prostrated themselves.

7: Db 2⁴; Ea 5.

Db

[*p add at top* To return]

If in some cases a bit of a nautical Murat in setting forth his person ashore, the white forecastle-magnate [*p Eaa* <white forecastle-magnate *add* handsome sailor] of the period in question evinced nothing of that spurious sea-fop [*p Eaa* <that spurious sea-fop >the dandified] Billy-be-Dam, an amusing character still →<still→ all but extinct now, but occasionally to be encountered [≯in form yet more amusing {*Eaa* ≮in form yet more amusing, *add comma and add* (*at bottom of leaf, circled, with guide-line to caret*) and in a form yet more amusing than the original,}] at the tiller of the boats on the tempestuous Erie Canal or, more likely, vaporing in the groggeries along the tow-path.

8: Da 3; Ea 6.

Da

in this forecastle hero. [*p* >magnate. {≮magnate.}] [*p Db* <in this forecastle hero] Invariably a proficient in his perilous calling, he was also more or less of a mighty boxer or wrestler. [*Ea add* (*at bottom of leaf, circled, with guide-line to caret*) It was strength and beauty. Tales of his prowess were recited.] Ashore he was the champion; afloat the spokesman; [*p* >*two words, later erased* (*undeciphered*) { >whatever →<whatever→ on every suitable occasion}] Always foremost. Close-reefing topsails in a gale, there he was, astride the weather yard-arm-end, foot [*p* >the Flemish horse as] in "stirrup," both [*p* >brown {≮brown}] hands tugging at the "ear-ring" as at a bridle, [*p Ea* ≯in very much] the attitude [*p* <the attitude {≫the attitude}] of the [*p* <the] young Alexander curbing the fiery Bucephalus. [*p* <Bucephalus ≯steed {<steed ≯(*above, after* curbing) an xxxxx xxxx} {≮an xxxxx xxxx ≫Bucephalus}] A supurb figure, [*p* <figure ≯outline, {<A supurb outline, >A figure} {≮A figure ≫A supurb figure, *correcting* supurb *to* superb}] tossed up as by the horns of Taurus against the thunderous

9: Da 4; Ea 7.

Da

[*p* >black {≮black}] sky, cheerily hallooing to the strenuous file along the spar.

The moral nature was seldom out of keeping with the physical make. Indeed, except as toned by the former, the comeliness and power, always attractive in masculine conjunction, could hardly [<could >(*after* hardly) could] have drawn the sort of honest admiration [<honest admiration {≫honest} ≯homage] the Handsome Sailor in some examples received from his less gifted associates.

10: Da 5; Ea 8.

Da

Such a cynosure, at least in aspect, and something such too in his [p <his] nature, though with very [p <very] important variations that will evolve themselves [p <that will evolve themselves ⯈ to become apparent { <to become *add* made}] as the story proceds, was welkin-eyed Billy Budd, [p > (*at top, with guide-line to caret*) or Baby Budd as yet →<yet→ more familiarly →> (*at side, circled, with guide-line to caret*) under circumstances hereafter to be given→ he came to be calld at last { <calld at last > (*below he circled*) at last}] aged twenty-two [p <two ⯈ one] a tar [p <tar ⯈ foretopman] of the British [<British {p ≫ British}] fleet toward the close of the last decade of the eighteenth century. Not [<Not >It was not] very long prior to the time of the narration that follows he had [<he had] that he had entered the fleet, [p <fleet ⯈ King's service] having been impressed on the Narrow Seas

11: Da 6; Ea 9.

Da

from a homeward-bound English merchantman into a seventy-four outward-bound, H.M.S. Indomitable. [*underlined*] [*alter period to semicolon*] That king's-ship, [p <That king's- ⯈ which] as was not unusual in those hurried days having been obliged to put to sea short of her proper complement of men. Plump upon Billy at first sight [>in the gangway] the boarding Lieutenant [p >officer (*before* Lieutenant) >Ratcliffe (*after* Lieutenant)] pounced, even before the merchantman's crew was [p >formally] mustered on the quarter- - deck for his [p > (*below, circled, with guide-line to caret*) more deliberate { <more}] inspection. [*add* And] Him only he elected. For whether it was because the other men [*add* when] ranged before him showed to

12: Da 7; Ea 10.

Da

ill advantage after Billy, or whether he had some scruples in view of the merchantman being rather short-handed, however it might be, the officer contented himself with his first spontanious [*correct to* spontaneous] choice. To the surprise of the ship's company, though much to the Lieutenant's satisfaction Billy made no demur to his capture. [p <to his capture *add period* (*after* demur)] But, indeed, any demur would have been [>as] idle as the protest of a goldfinch popped into a [p ⯈ wire { <wire}] cage.

13: Da 8, Db 8¹; Ea 11.

* Da 8
[*Dap notation (at top)* Saturday Nov 17 {*p* <*notation*}]
   Noting this uncomplaining acquiescence, all but cheerful one might say, the shipmaster cast [<cast >turned] a surprised glance of silent reproach at the sailor.

Db
Now he [*p alter* he *to* the ⋗sea-captain { <Now the ⋖sea-captain > (*below, with guide-line to caret*) The shipmaster}] was one of those worthy mortals found in every p →<p→ vocation however humble [*p* <however ⋗even the *alter to* humbler >ones] —the sort of person whom everybody agrees in calling "a respectable man." And—nor so strange to report as [>it] may appear to be—though a ploughman of the troubled waters, and a life-long contender [<and a *alter* contender *to* contending] with the intractable elements, alike in nature [*capitalize* nature] and man [<alike in Nature and man] there was nothing the [*alter to* this] honest fellow [*p* <fellow *add* soul]

14: Db 8²; Ea 12.

Db
at heart loved better than the [<the] simple peace and quietness. [*alter to* quiet] For the rest, he was fifty or thereabouts, a little inclined to corpulence perhaps, [*p* <perhaps] a preposessing [*add* full { <full}] face, unwhiskered, and of an agreeable color, [*p add dash*] a rather full face, kindly and [<kindly and] humanely intelligent in expression. On a fair day with a fair wind and all going well, a certain musical chime in his voice seemed to be the veritable unobstructed outcome of the inmost [*p Eaa* <in *from* inmost >inner (*before* most)] man. But there were t →<t→ occasions when his extreme conscientiousness was his torment. [*Dbp* <But . . . torment *add* (*at bottom of leaf*) He was very { <was very ⋗had so much prudence much (?)} conscientious {*add* ness (?)} and there { >were} occasions when these virtues (*several word-beginnings and words canceled and erased*) {*Eaa re-cancel* But . . . torment ⋖*entire pencil draft and supplant it by the following* He had much prudence, much conscientiousness, and there were occasions when these virtues were the cause of overmuch disquietude in him.}]

15: Db 8³; Ea 13.

Db
On a passage, so long as his craft was in any proximity to land, no sleep for G →<G→ Captain Graveling. He took to heart those serious responsibilities not so heavily borne by some shipmasters.
   Now while Billy Budd was down in the forecastle getting his kit together,

the Indomitable's [*underlined*] lieutenant, burly and bluff, nowise disconcerted by Captain Graveling's omitting to profer the customary hospitalities
on an occasion so unwelcome to him, an omission simply the resu →<resu→
caused by preoccupation of thought, uncerimonously invited himself into the
cabin, and also to a flask from the spirit-locker,

16: Db 8⁴; Ea 14.

Db

a receptacle which his experiend eye instantly discovered. In fact he was one
of those sea-dogs in whom all the hardship and peril of naval life in the great
prolonged wars of his time never kille →<kille→ impaired the natural instinct for sensuous enjoyment. His duty he always faithfully did; but duty is
sometimes a dry obligation, and he was for irrigating the aridity of it, [*p* <the
⹊its <of it] whensoever possible, with a fertilizing decoction of strong waters.

* Da

For the cabin's proprietor there was nothing left but to play the part of the
inforced host with whatever grace and alacrity [*p* <alacrity >(*below*) good
will {<good will ≫alacrity}] were practicable.

17: Eaa 15.

Eaa

As necessary adjuncts to the flask, he silently placed tumbler and water-jug
before the irrepressable guest. But excusing himself from partaking just then,
dismally watched the unembarrased officer deliberatly diluting his grog a
little, then tossing it off in three swallows, pushing the empty tumbler away,
yet not so far as to be beyond easy reach, at the same settling himself in his
seat and smacking his lips with high satisfaction, looking straight at his [<his
>the] host.

These proceedings over, the Master spoke →<spoke→ broke the silence;

18: Eaa 16.

Eaa

and there lurked a rueful reproach in the tone of his voice: "Lieutenant, you
are going to take my best man from me, the jewel of 'em."

"Yes, I know" rejoined the other, immediatly drawing back the tumbler
to him [*p* <to him]

19: Da 12; Ea 17.

Da

preliminry to the refilling of it; [*p* →(*above* it) pretty soon {⹊pretty soon}]
[<the refilling of it >a replenishing;] "Yes; I know. Sorry" [*no period*]

"Beg pardon, but you do'nt understand, Lieutenant. See here now. Before I shipped that young fellow, my forecastle was a very [*p* <very] rat-pit of quarrels. It was black times [>, I tell you,] aboard the Rights [*underlined*] [*p add quotation marks* (*around underlined* Rights)] here. It [<It *add* I >was] worried to that degree that [<that] my pipe had no comfort [>for] me. But Billy came; and it was like a Catholic priest striking peace in an Irish shindy. Not that he preached to them or said or did anything in particular; but a virtue went out of him, sugaring the sour ones. They took to him like hornets to treacle; all but the buffer

20: Da 13, D/Ea 13¹; Ea 18, Eab 18¹.

[Verso of leaf was inscribed earlier: see p. 430.]

* Da 13 on Ea leaf
of the gang, the big shaggy chap with the fire-red whiskers. He indeed out of envy, perhaps, of the new-comer, and thinking such a sweet and pleasant fellow, [*p add quotation marks* (*around* sweet and pleasant fellow,)] as he mockingly called him to his face [*p* <called him to his face ⊁ (*below*) designated him to the others,] could hardly have the spirit of a game-cock, must needs bestir himself in trying to get up an ugly row with him.

21: Eab 18².

Eab
Billy forebore with him and a sort of [*p* <a sort of] reasoned with him in a quiet [*p* <quiet ⊁ pleasant] way— [*p add quotation mark*] he is something like myself, lieutenant, to whom aught like a quarrel is hateful [*p add quotation mark*] —but nothing served. So, in the second dog-watch one day the Big [<Big ⊁ Red] Whiskers in prescence of the others, under pretence of showing Billy [>just] whence a sirloin steak was cut—for the fellow had once been a butcher—insultingly gave him a dig under the ribs. Quick as lightning Billy let fly. [*ESM p* ⊁ (*over an erasure*) his arm.] I dare say he never meant to do quite as much as he did, but anyhow he gave the burly [*p* >xx (*below* burly)] fool a terrible drubbing.

22: Da 14; Ea 19.

Da
It took about half a minute, I should say. [*p* <say ⊁ think] And, lord bless you, the lubber was astonished at the celerity.

* Bc?
And will you believe it, Lieutenant, the Red Whiskers now really loves Billy— loves him, or is the biggest hypocrite that ever I heard of. But they all love him [*p add period*]

23: Bb? 7³; Da 15; Ea 20.

Bb?
Some of 'em wash and [>(*after* 'em) do his *alter* wash *to* washing, <and] darn his [p B⁺ <his >the seat of his {p <the seat of his ≫his}] old trowsers for him; the carpenter is at odd times making a pretty little chest of drawers for him. Anybody will do anything for him; [p <him *add* Billy Budd] and it's the happy family here. But now [p <But *capitalize* now ≯, Lieutenant {≫But}] if that young fellow goes—I know how it will be aboard the "Rights" [*underlined*] here. [<here *add period (after underlined* "Rights")] Not again very soon, I think, [<I think] shall I, coming up from dinner, lean over the capstain smoking a quiet pipe—no, not very soon again, I think. Ay, Lieutenant, you are going to take away the jewel of 'em; you are going to take away my peacemaker." [p *alter period to exclamation mark*] [p *add draft (at bottom of leaf)* And with that he {>the good soul} had {>really} some ado to check a sob. →<sob. *add* rising sob.→ {>(*before* rising) sort of} {B⁺ *cancel this pencil draft and add* And with that the good soul had really some ado in checking a rising sob.}]

24: Da 16; Ea 21.

* Bc?
"Well," said the lieutenant [<lieutenant ≯(*below*) officer {p <officer (*leaving no subject*)}] who had listened with amused interest to all this, and now waxing merry with his tipple; "Well, blessed are the peacemakers; [<*semicolon*] especially the fighting ones! [<ones >peacemakers {p *add period*}] And such are

Da
the seventy-four beauties poking their →<poking their→ some →<some→ the upper tier [<the upper tier >some] of which you see poking their noses out of the port-holes of yonder war-ship. [p <*period* >lying-to for me. *also* >(*below, circled, with guide-line to caret*) pointing her out thro the cabin window {Ea ≮lying-to . . . window >(*at bottom of leaf, circled, with guide-line to caret*) lying-to for me" pointing thro' the cabin window at the Indomitable. (*underlined*)}] But courage! do'nt look so downhearted, man. I p →<I p→ Why, I pledge you in advance the King's [<King's >royal] approbation. Rest assured that his [*capitalize* his] Magesty [p *alter to* Majesty] will be delighted

25: Da 17; Ea 22.

Da
to know [p <know >learn {<learn ≫know}] that in a time when [p *begin then cancel* xx] the King's [p Ea <the King's >his] hard tack is not sought for [>by sailors] with such alacrity [p Ea <alacrity ≯avidity] as should be;

[[*288*]]

and some [<and some >a time also when some] shipmasters secretly [*p Ea* <secretly >privily] resent the [*p* >King's {<King's}] borrowing of →<of→ from them of [*p Ea* <of] a tar or two for a →<a→ a short cruise; [*p* <a short cruise >the King {*Ea* <the King >the service;}] His Magesty, I say, will be delighted to know [*p Ea* <know >learn] that one at least of →<one at least of→ one [*underlined*] shipmaster at least cheerfully surrenders to the service, [<service ⊁King] the very [*p Ea* <very] flower of his flock, in →<in→ [>a sailor] who with equal cheerfulness assents. [*p* ⊁ (*after equal*) glad →<glad→ loyalty *alter* cheerfulness *to* cheerfully {*Ea* <loyalty cheerfully assents >(*below, circled, with guide-line to caret*) loyalty makes no dissent.}] —But where's my [*p* >our { <our}] beauty? Ah," looking through the cabin's open door
[*Dap notation (in right margin)* Nov 18 { ⊀*notation*}]

26: Ea 23.

―――――――――

Ea
"Here he comes; and, by Jove—look at him [*p* <look at him ⊁lugging along his chest] —Apollo with his portmanteau! —My man," stepping out to him, "you can't take that lumbering chest [*p* <lumbering chest ⊁big box] aboard a war-ship. The chests [*p* <chests ⊁boxes] there are mostly shot-boxes. Put your duds in a bag. [*p alter period to comma and add* lad.] Boot and saddle

*** Bb**
saddle [*Ea* <saddle] for the cavalryman, bag and hammock for the blue-jacket." [*p Ea* <blue-jacket." >man-of-war's-man."]
    The transfer [*ESM Bb+ mend* er] [*p* ⊁of duds {*Bc* <of duds >(*below, circled, with guide-line to caret*) of duds from chest to bag} {*p* <of duds}] was made. And, after seeing his man into the cutter and then following him down, the lieutenant [*Bbp* ⊁(*below*) boarding-officer {*ESM Bb+* ⊀lieutenant <boarding-officer *and add* boarding-officer} {*HM Ea* <boarding-officer ≫lieutenant}]

27: Bb 7⁵, Bc 7⁷; Da 19; Ea 24.

―――――――――

Bb
pushed off from the Rights-of-Man. [*underlined*] That was the merchant-ship's name; [*Bbp* >in sailor fashion abbreviated by Captain & crew into the "Rights" {*Bc* <in . . . "Rights" >(*below, circled, with guide-line to caret*) tho' by her master and crew abbreviated in sailor fashion into The Rights. (*underlined*)}] its [*Bc* <its *add* The] hard-headed Dundee owner being [*Bc* <being *add* was] a staunch admirer of Thomas Paine

*** Ba (I)**
whose book by that title [*Bc* <by that title] in rejoinder to Burke's arraign-ment of the French Revolution had then been published for some time and had gone everywhere.

Bb

In christening his vessel [*Bc* >(*in left margin, circled, with guide-line to caret*) after the title of Paine's volume] the man of Dundee was something like his contemporary shipowner, Stephen Girard of Philadelphia, whose sympathies, alike with his native land and its liberal philosophers, were [*Bc* <were >he { <he >were} { <were ≫he}] evined [*ESM Bb+p i* <evined ⊁evinced] by nameing [*p i correct to* naming] his ships [*Bcp* >(*below, circled, with guide-line to caret*) respectively { ⊀respectively}] after Voltaire, and the Encyclopedists [*Bcp* <and the Encyclopedists >Diderot &c {*Bc* ⊀Diderot &c >, Diderot, and so forth.}]

28: [**Bbp** notation follows 7⁵ green], Bc 7⁸; Da 20; Ea 25.

---

* Ba (II) on Bb leaf

Now, [*Bbp add* But (*before* Now) {*ESM Bb+* ⊀But *w.o.* But *alter* Now *to* now}] when the boat swept under the merchantman's [*ESM Bb+* <(*poorly-shaped*) man's >-man's] stern, and officer and oarsmen read [<read >were noteing >(*below, circled, with guide-line to caret*) , —some bitterly and others with a grin, {*p add dash*} {*i* <were noteing *and add below* (*before* —some bitterly*) were →<were→ were noteing} {*correct to* noting}] the name emblazoned there; just then it was that

29: Ba 7⁶, Bc 7⁹; Da 21; Ea 26.

Ba

the captive [*Ba+p* <captive >new recruit { <new *add* enforced} { <enforced ≫new} {*Bc w.o.* new recruit}] jumped up from the bow where he had been directed to sit →<where . . . sit→ where the coxswain had directed him to sit, and waveing [*Ba+p i alter to* waving] his tattered [<his tattered] hat to his silent shipmates sorrowfully looking over at him from the taffrail, bade the lads [*Ba+p i* >a genial] good-bye. [*alter period to comma* >(*below, circled, with guide-line to caret*) particularly Red Whiskers {*p* <particularly Red Whiskers}] Then, [*alter* Then *to* then] making a salutation as to the ship herself, "And good bye to you [*p Bc* >too, old] Rights of Man." [*underlined*] "Down, Sir [*p* >*exclamation mark*]," roared the [*Bb* >kidnapping {*p Bc* <kidnapping}] lieutenant, instantly assuming all the rigor of his rank, tho [*ESM Bb+ alter to* though] with difficulty repressing a smile.

30: [Ba ?7⁷, Bc ?8¹]; Da 22; Ea 27.

[Ba *foliation mostly trimmed off after* E.]

Ba

To be sure Billy's action was a terrible breach of naval decorum. [*p* <decorum. ⊁discipline. { <discipline. ≫decorum.}] But in that [>decorum

{*p* <decorum *add* discipline} { ⫷discipline ≫decorum}] he had never been
instructed; in consideration of which the lieutenant would have passed it over
had it not been [*Ba+p* <passed it over > (*below, circled*) thought nothing more
of it {*Bb* ⫷thought . . . it > (*before* have) hardly > (*after* have) been so energetic <had it not been ⫸in reproof}] but for the concluding farewell to the
ship. This he [>rather] took as meant to convey a sly [*p Bc* <sly >covert]
sally on Billy →<Billy→ the captive's [*p Bc* <captive's >new recruit's]
part [*p add comma*] against [*p* <against ⫸a sly sally →<sally→ slur as to
{*Bc* ⫷a sly slur as to *add* a sly slur at}] impressment in general, and that of
himself in especial. [*Bb add* And yet,]

Bb

[*Bb addition pasted on as bottom of leaf*] more likely, if satire it was in effect, it
was hardly so by intention, for Billy tho' happily endowed with the gayety
[*mend*] [*ESM Bb+* <gayety ⫸gayety] of high health, youth, [*ESM Bb+*
<youth >youth {*HM p* ⫸& <& *add comma* (*after* youth)}] and a free
heart, was yet by no means of a satirical [*p* <satirical ⫸caustic {*Bc w.o.*
cau →<cau→ ≫satirical}] turn. The will to it and the mental [*Bb+p* <men-
tal ⫸sinister {*Bc* ⫷sinister > (*circled, with guide-line to caret*) sinister}] dexterity were alike wanting. And to [*p* <And *capitalize* to] deal in double meanings
and serpentine [*p Bc* <serpentine] insinuations of any sort were equally
[*Bb+p alter* were *to* was <was equally ⫸absolutely {*Bc* ⫷(*again*) was equally ⫸was quite foreign →<foreign→}] foreign to his nature. [*Bc* <nature
>xx {*scratch out* xx ≫nature}]

31: Ba 7[8], Bc 8[2]; Da 23; Ea 28.

Ba

insinuations. The will to it and the dexterity were alike wanting. [*Bb* <insinu-
ations . . . wanting]

As to his capture [*p* <capture ⫸impressment {*Bc* ⫷impressment ⫸en-
forced enlistment,}] that he seemed to take pretty much as he had always
taken any [*Bb+p* <had . . . any > (*circled, with guide-line to caret*) was wont
to take *add* the →<the→ any {*Bc* ⫷was . . . any *add* he was wont to ≫taken
any (*altering* taken *to* take)}] vicissitude of weather. Like the animals, tho'
[*ESM Bb+ alter to* though] no philosopher [*p add comma*] he was yet a
f →<yet a f→ practically [*Bb+p* > (*at bottom of leaf, circled, with guide-line
to caret*) and without knowing it {*Bc* ⫷*pencil addition and add* (*before* practically) without knowing it,}] a fatalist. And, [*p* >indeed { ⫷indeed}] it
may be, that he rather liked this adventurous turn in his affairs, which promised an opening into novel scenes and martial excitements.

Aboard the Indomitable [*underlined*] [*ESM Bb+ mend ship's name*] the
new recruit [*p Bc* <the new recruit >our merchant-sailor] was forthwith
rated as an able [*p add hyphen*] seaman and assigned to the starboard watch
of the fore-top.

⟦ *291* ⟧

32: Ea 29.

Ea

He was soon at home in the service, not at all disliked for his [>unpretentious] good looks and a sort of genial happy-go-lucky in his [p <in his] air. No merrier man in his mess: in marked contrast to certain other individuals included like himself among [mend] the impressed portion of the ship's company; for these when not activly employed were sometimes, and more particularly in the [>last] dog-watch when the drawing near of night [<night >twilight] induced revery, apt to fall into a saddish mood which in some partook of sullenness. But they were not so young [mend] as our foretopman, and no few of them must

33: Ea 30.

Ea

have known a hearth of some sort, while [<while] others may have had wives and children left, too probably, in uncertain circumstances, and hardly any but must have had acknowledged kith and kin, while for Billy, as will shortly be seen, his entire family was practically confined to [ESM p <to >invested in] himself.
[p chapter-ending mark ———◇———]

34: Eab 31.

Eab
[p chapter-beginning mark ———◇———]
  Though our new-made foretopman was well recieved in the top and on the gun-decks, hardly here was he that cynosure he previously had [p transpose previously to follow had] been among those minor ship's companies of the merchant marine, with which companies only had he p →<p→ hitherto consorted.
  He was young; and despite his all but fully developed frame in aspect looked even younger than he really was, oweing to a lingering adolescent expression in the as yet smooth face all but feminine in the [<the] purity of natural complexion

35: Eab 32¹.

Eab

but where, thanks to his seagoing, the rose had m →<rose had m→ lily was quite suppressed and the rose had much [p <much ≯ (below) some] ado [> (at top of leaf, circled, with guide-line to caret) visably] to flush through the tan.
  To one essentially such a novice in the wrinkled [p <wrinkled] complexities of factitious life, the abrupt transition from his former and simpler sphere

to the ampler and more knowing world of a great war-ship; this might well have abashed him had there been any conciet or vanity in his composition. [mend] Among her miscellanious multitude, the Indomitable [underlined] mustered

36: Bb or Bc 8⁵; Da 26; Ea 32, Eab 32². [W 33]

* ***Ba [8ˣ]***
company [Eab <company] several individuals who however inferior in grade were of no common natural stamp, sailors more signally susceptive of that [p >nobler { <nobler}] air which continuous martial discipline and repeated prescence in battle can in some degree impart even to the average

Bb or Bc
man. As the handsome sailor [handsome sailor *underlined*] Billy Budd's position aboard the seventy-four was something analagous to that of a rustic belle transplanted into the circle of the court. [p <into the circle of the court ≯(after rustic) beauty >(after transplanted) from the provinces to a court →<to a court→ and brought into competition with the high dames of the court. {Da ≮rustic . . . court add rustic beauty transplanted from the provinces and brought into competition with the high dames of the court.} {p ≯ (after high) born}]

37: Da 27; Ea 33. [W 34]

Da
But this [p >alteration { <alteration *add* change of circumstances}]   he scarce noted. As little did he observe that something about him provoked an ambiguous amused [p <amused] smile in one or two harder faces. [<*period* >among the blue-jackets. {p <blue-jackets *add* petty officers} { <petty officers ≫blue-jackets}] Nor less unaware was he of the peculiar favorable effect his person and demeanor had upon the more intelligent officers of the quarter-deck. [<of the *and with line transpose* quarter-deck *to precede* officers *add colon after* officers] [p <officers ≯gentlemen of the (*before* quarter-deck)] Nor could this well have been otherwise.

38: Da 28; Ea 34. [W 35]

Da
Cast in a mould peculiar to the finest physical examples of [>those] Englishmen in whom the Saxon strain would seem not at all to partake of any Norman or foreign [p <foreign ≯other] admixture, he showed in face that mild [<mild] humane look of reposeful good nature which the Greek sculptor [Ea >in some instances] gave to his heroic strong man, the Farnese [Ea <the Farnese] Hercules. But this again was subtly modified by another and pervasive element in his composition. [p <in his composition *add period* (*after* element) {Ea <element. >quality}] The ear, small and shapely, the arch of

[[*293*]]

the foot, the curve in mouth and nostril, even the indurated dyed →<dyed→ hand dyed to the orange-tawny of the toucan's bill, a hand telling alike of the halyards

39: Da 29, Db 29¹; Ea 35, Eab 35¹. [W 36]

Da

and tar-bucket; but, in →<in *w.o.* above→ all, something in the mobile expression, and every chance attitude and movement, something suggestive of a mother eminently favored by Love and the Graces; all this mysteriously [<mysteriously >strangely] indicated a lineage in direct contradition to the [*p* <the *add* his] lot. The mysteriousness here, however, [*p* <however] became less mysterious through a matter-of-fact elicited during the scene of Bi →<during the scene of Bi→ when Billy [*p* >at the capstan] was being formally mustered into the service. Asked by the officer, [> (*at bottom of leaf, circled, with guide-line to caret*) a small brisk little gentleman as it chanced] among other questions, his place of birth, he replyed, "Please, Sir, I do'nt know."

"Do'nt know where you were born?—Who was your father? [*no quotation mark*]

[*39*]: Superseded Db 29²; Ea 36.

[*Same leaf as present* Eab 36, *Leaf 39, upside down, with these superseded numbers and this writing covered at bottom by clip.*]

Db

"God knows, Sir, but I do'nt. [*p* <, but I do'nt *add period* (*after* Sir)] I was found, but where I do'nt know." [*the clip from Da (now on Eab 36) followed at this Db stage*]
[*Eab red crayon cancel passage and replace it by inserting 35² which incorporates its substance*]

40: Eab 35². [W 37]

Eab

"God knows, Sir."
Struck by the straightforward simplicity of these replies, the officer next asked "Do you know anything about your beginning?"

"No, Sir. But I have heard that I was found in a basket of oakum [*p* <of oakum >pretty silk-lined (*before* basket)] hanging one morning from the knocker of a good man's door in Bristol"

41: [Db 29²]; Eab 36. [W 38]

*** Da on Db leaf**

"Found [*underlined*] say you? Well," his →<his→ throwing back his head and looking up and down the new recruit; [*p* <new recruit >noble stature

{ <noble stature ≫new recruit}] "Well it turns out to have been a prettey good find. Hope they'll find some more like you for the fleet." [*p* <for the fleet *add* the fleet sadly ne →<ne→ needs them {*Eaa* ⊰the fleet sadly needs them >(*after* you), my man.} { <my man *add* my man; the fleet sadly needs them." *add bracket to confirm paragraph before next sentence.*} {*p* <man ⊱foundling.} { <foundling. ≫man}]

Yes, Billy Budd was a foundling, a presumable [*p* <foundling, a presumable {≫foundling, a presumable}] bye-blow, and, evidently, no ignoble one. [*Da+p* >(*at bottom of leaf, circled, with guide-line to caret*) High →<High ⊱Fair→ descent was as evident in him, as in a blood horse. For the rest, with little or none {*Eaa* ⊰Fair . . . none *add* Fair →<Fair *add* Noble→ descent was as evident in him as in a blood horse.

For the rest, with little or no sharpness of faculty or any trace of the wisdom of the serpent, nor yet}]

42: Bb 3ᵖ⁷, Bc 8⁸; Da 30; Ea 37. [W 39]

Bb
Without the wisdom of the serpent or any sharpness of faculty nor yet [*D+p add bracket for new paragraph* (*before* Without) <Without ⊱With no trace of (*before* the wisdom) <any sharpness ⊱his acuteness { <With no <his *and revise to read* Without acuteness of faculty or any trace of the wisdom of the serpent} {*Eaa* <Without . . . nor yet (*leaving sentence incomplete*)}] quite a dove, he possessed that kind and degree of intelligence going along with the unconventional rectitude of a sound [*p* <sound ⊱pristine { ⊰pristine ≫sound}] human creature [*Bb+p add* , one {*ESM Bb+* ⊰one *w.o.* one}] to whom has not yet [*p* <has >has {*i w.o.* has}] been proffered the [*Bb+p* >questionable {*ESM Bb+* ⊰questionable *w.o.* questionable}] apple of knowledge. He was

* Ba
illiterate; he could not read, but he could sing, and like the illiterate

* Ba
nightingale was sometimes the composer of his own song.

Of self-consciousness he seemed to have [>little or] none, or about as much of it [*p Bc* <of it] as we may reasonably [*p Bc add* impute to the animal creation. {*p* <the animal creation ⊱(*over an erased earlier phrase*) an intelligent mastiff} {*p* <an intelligent mastiff >(*below*) a dog of Saint Bernard's breed}]

43: Ea 38. [W 40]

Eaa
Habitually living with the elements and knowing little more of the land than as a beach, or, rather, that portion of the terraqueous globe providentially

[[*295*]]

set apart for dance-houses doxies and tapsters, in short what sailors call a fidlers' green, [p add quotation marks (around fidlers' green,)] his simple nature remained unsophisticated by that maze of [<that maze of >those guarded {p <guarded}] moral obliquties which are not in every case incompatible with that manufacturable thing known as respectability. But are sailors without v →<without v→ , frequenters of fiddlers'-green, [p add quotation marks (around fiddlers'-green,) alter green to greens] without vices? No; but less often than with landsmen do they partake of viciousness [<viciousness ⊁crookedness] of heart. These same vices, so called, [p <they <These same alter period to comma ⊁(below) their (before vices) and transpose the resulting phrase their vices, so called, to precede partake (with circling and guideline to caret)] seeming

44: Da 31, Db 31²; Ea 39. [W 41]

Da

They are but [D⁺p <They are but ⊁Most of them →<them→ of these "vices" are the] frank manifestations of the [<the] untutored man, [D⁺p ⊁or] manifestations in accordance with natural law. [Eaa crayon <Most . . . law and continue on revision-patch]

† *Eaa*

to proceed less [p transpose less to precede to] from mere [p <mere] viciousness than from [p <from] exuberance of vitality after long constraint; or [p alter to colon <or] frank manifestations in accordance with natural law.

Da

By his original constitution aided by the cooperating influnces of his lot, Billy in many respects [add was] little more than a sort of [>unassuming {p <unassuming}] upright barbarian, much such perhaps as Adam presumably might have been ere the urbane Serpent glided [D⁺p <glided ⊁insinuated himself] upon the scene. [D⁺p <insinuated . . . scene add bowed himself into his company.]

And here be it submitted, that [D⁺p >apparently] helping to corroborate the [D⁺p >(at bottom of leaf, circled, with guide-line to caret) spirit that underlies the {<spirit that underlies the}] now unpopular [D⁺p <now unpopular ⊁ridiculed {<ridiculed}] dogma of Man's Fall, [D⁺p >a dogma now popularly ignored] it is observable that where simpler unsophisticated [Eaa crayon <bowed . . . sophisticated and replace by revision-patch]

† *Eaa*

bowed [ESM p <bowed >wriggled] himself into his company.

And here be it submitted that apparently going to corroborate the doctrine of man's fall, a doctrine now popularly ignored, it is observable that where the simpler unsophisticated virtues [p add (below unsophisticated) unadulterated {≮the . . . virtues add certain virtues pristine and unadulterate}]

45: Da 32; Ea 40. [W 42]

* Da 32

virtues eminently [*Eaa* <virtues eminently >peculiarly] characterise [characterize?] anybody in the external uniform of civilization, such virtues [*Eaa* <such virtues >they] will upon scrutiny seem not to be derived from custom or convention, [*D*⁺*p* >(*between lines*) but rather →⸦to be alien qualities→ out of keeping with these &c— {*Eaa* ⸦but rather . . . &c—}]

Db

but rather to be alien →<alien→ out of keeping with these, as if indeed exceptionally transmitted from a period prior to cities [*p* <cities ⸦Cain's fr →<fr→ city] and citified man. The character pi →<pi→ marked by such virtues [<virtues >qualities] has to an unvitiated taste an untampered-with flavor like that of berries, while the man thoroughly civilized [civilised?] [*p* >even in a fair specimen of the breed] has to the same moral palet [*p alter to* pallet] a questionable smack as of some [*p* <some *add* a] compounded wine. In [*Db*⁺ <In >(*at bottom of leaf, circled, with guide-line to caret*) To any stray inheritor of pristine virtue [<pristine virtue >of these primitive qualities] found, like Caspar Hauser, wandering dazed in] the nominally [*Db*⁺ <the nominally {*p add* any}] Christian capitals [*p alter to* capital] of our day [<day >time]

46: Da 33; Ea 41. [W 43]

Da

The [*alter* The *to* the] [*p* ⸦old {<old *add* good-natured}] poet's famous invocation, near two thousand years ago, of the good rustic out of his latitude in pagan Rome, [*p* <pagan ⸦Ces <Ces *add* the *and* >(*after* Rome) of the Cesars] still appropriatly holds:—

    [*p add* Honest and poor, {*p* <Honest and poor,} {*p* ≫
    Honest and poor,}] "Faithful in word and thought
    What has Thee, Fabian, to the city brought."

Though our handsome sailor [*p alter to* Handsome Sailor] had as much of masculine beauty as one can expect anywhere to see; neverthless, like the beautiful woman in one of Hawthorne's minor tales, there was just one thing amiss in him. No visable [*p alter to* visible *by dotting for two i's*] blemish indeed, like →<like→ as with the lady; no, but a [*alter* a *to* an >occasional] liability to an →<an→ a vocal defect. Though in the hour

47: Ea 42, E/Gp 42¹. [W 44]

* Eaa 42 on G leaf

of elemental uproar or peril, he was everything that a sailor should be, yet under sudden provocation of strong heart-feeling his voice would [*Ea*⁺*p*

⤳sometimes { <sometimes >nearly always}] [G <and ⫸nearly always <would >(*on patch on leaf, below, circled, with guide-line to caret*) *as follows*]
† *G*
otherwise a →<a→ singularly musical, as the organ →<as the organ→ as if expressive of the harmony within, was apt to

* *Eaa on G leaf*
develop an organic hesitancy, [*Ea⁺p* ⤳or worse, { ⫸or worse,}] in fact more or less of a stutter. [*p* ⤳stammer { <stammer *add* or even worse}]
[*Ea⁺p chapter-ending mark* ——◇—— {*G blue crayon cancel chapter-ending mark*}] [*p guide-line to corner of leaf*]

48: E/Gp 42². [W 45]

G
In this particular Billy was a striking instance that the arch interferer, the envious marplot of Eden still has more or less to do with every human consignment to this planet of earth. In every case, one way or another he is sure to slip in his little card, as much as to remind us—I too have a hand here.
† *G*
[*continuing, originally, from* a stutter.]
    The avowal of such an imperfection should be evidence not alone that the Handsome Sailor [*with circling and guide-line to caret transpose* the Handsome Sailor *to follow inserted* in (*after* imperfection) *and* >he (*after* that)] is not presented as a conventional hero, but also that the story in which he is the main figure is no romance.
[*p chapter-ending mark* ——◇——]

49: Eb 43, Ec 43¹. [W 46]

* *Eb 43 (I)*
[*p notation* { ⫸*notation (undeciphered)*}]
[*p chapter-beginning mark* ——◇——]
    At the time of Billy Budd's arbitrary enlistment into the Indomitable [*underlined* that ship on her way to join the Mediterranean fleet. Not many days [*Ec* <Not many days >No long time] elapsed before the junction was

Ec
effected. As one of that fleet the Indomitable [*underlined*] [<(*underlined*) Indomitable >seventy-four] participated in its movements, tho' at times on account of her superior sailing qualities, in the abscence of frigates, despatched on separate duty as a scout or otherwise. [<or otherwise >or on more prolonged service. {*p* <or <more prolonged *and with insertions revise to read* and at times on less temporary service.}] But with all this the story has little

concernment, restricted as it [⊁is,] mainly [p <mainly] to the inner life of one particular ship and the career of one →<one→ an individual man. [p <man >(*below*) sailor]

50: Ec 43². [W 47]

Eb 43 (II) on Ec leaf
[*Ec new paragraph*] It was the summer of 1797. In the April of the same [p <same *alter* the *to* that] year had occurred the commotion among the men--of-war's men [p <among . . . men ⊁in the fleet lying {p <in the fleet lying}] at Spithead followed in May by a second and yet more serious outbreak [p >in the fleet] at the Nore. The latter is know, [p *alter to* known] and without exaggeration in the epithet, as the Great Mutiny. It was indeed

51: Eb 44. [W 48]

Eb
a demonstration more menacing to England than the contemporary manifestoes and conquering and prosyliting armies of the French Directory.

Bx
To the [p ⊁(*below*) British { <British} {≫British}] Empire the Nore Mutiny was what a strike in the [p <the ⊁her { <her}] fire-brigade would be to London threatened with [p <with >by] general arson. In a time [<time >crisis] when the [p <the {≫the}] country [p i <country >kingdom] might well have

Bx
anticipated the famous signal that [i *add* a few >years later {p <a few ⊁(*below*) some}] published along the winged [p i <winged >naval] line of battle what it was that upon occasion England expected of Englishmen; then it was that [p <then it was that >(*below*) that (*underlined*) was the time when {i ⊰that (*underlined*) . . . when >(*below*) that (*underlined*) was the time}]

52: Bx 12; Da 38; Eb 45. [W 49]

Bx
[i *add* when] at the mast-heads of the three-deckers [i <three-deckers >first-rates {p <first-rates ≫three-deckers}] and seventy-fours moored in her own waters [p i <waters >roadstead,] —a fleet, the right [<right >puissant {p i <puissant ≫right}] arm of what was at that period the one [p i <of what . . . one >*word undeciphered because later scratched out* {i *add* of a >(*below*) Power then all but the sole}] free conservative power [i (*as part of preceding revision*) <power >(*below*) one] of the Old World, the blue-jackets, to be numbered by thousands ran up with huzzahs [i *alter to* huzzas] the British

colors with the union wiped out [*i* >and the cross; { <and the cross >(*after* union) and cross >(*after* out) *semicolon*}] by that cancellation converting [*p i* <converting >transmuting]

[*the rest of the original Bx writing on this leaf itself is covered by three patches, but it is possible to read the heavy revisions as the passage on the leaf stood in three stages:*]

[*a*] *Bx*

the flag of organic law and right into the enemy's red rag of [<rag of >meteor of] revolt and universal revolution. [<revolt and universal revolution *alter to* universal revolution and convulsion,] reasonable discontent growing out of practical grievances in the fleet had been ignited into irrational combustion, and

[*b*] *Bx*⁺

the flag of [>(*single word, later erased*) founded(?)] law and right into the enemy's red meteor of universal revolution and convulsion, as by live cinders blown across the Channel from France in flames, reasonable discontent . . . [*as above*]

[*c*] *Bx*⁺*p*

the flag of founded [?] law and right into the enemy's red meteor of regicidal crusade indefinite classes [?] & immeasurable revolt as by . . . [*as above*] [*Bx*⁺ *red crayon cancel whole passage and affix three revision-patches over it*]

† *Bx*⁺

the flag of founded law and freedom defined, into the enemy's red meteor

† *Bx*⁺

of unbridled and unbounded revolt.
Reasonable

† *Bx*⁺

discontent growing out of practical grievances in the fleet had been ignited

53: Bbb 13; Da 39; Eb 46. [W 50]

* *Bb 13*

into irrational combustion as by live cinders blown across the Channel from France in flames. [*Bb*⁺*p* >of the time →<of the time→ in this →<this→ ⫸that terrific →<in that terrific ⫸(*below*) at that momentous→ conjuncture it conv {*cancel and erase all*}]

The event converted into

Bbb

into [<into] irony [>for a time] those spirited strains of Dibdin—as a song- - writer at that [<that >the {*p*≫that}] European conjuncture no mean auxiliary to the English Government [*p circle* at that European conjuncture *and* (*with caret*) *transpose to follow* Government] —strains celebrating, among other

things, the devotion of the British tar, to the throne, that is, to the state, to his country:— [*Bb*⁺ <that is . . . country:— ⫸*comma (after* throne) *add colon and dash* {*p* <to the throne ≫that is, to the state, to his country *then* <to the state (*reading is* the devotion of the British tar, that is, to his country:—)} {*p* >patriotic (*before* devotion) *without canceling* that is, to his country}]
"And as for my life, t'is the King's!" [*verse underlined*]

* Bb?

Such an episode in the Island's [*p i* >grand] naval story no wonder that [*p* <no wonder that] her [>naval] historians [*p* >naturally] abridge; one of them [*Bb*⁺*p* >(James) {*ESM Bb*⁺*i erase and w.o.* (James)} {*p* >(before James) G.P.R}] candidly acknowledging that fain would he pass it over did not "impartiality forbid fastidiousness."

54: Bbb? 13², 14; Da 40; Eb 47. [W 51]

* Bb

And yet his mention of the →<of the→ is less a narration than a reference, hardly →<hardly→ having to do hardly at all with details. Nor are these [*p i* >readily] to be found in the libraries. Like some other events befalling

Bbb?

states everywhere and in every age [*p* <and >including America <in every age {≫in every age *and circle and insert it after* events}] the Great Mutiny was of such character that national pride along with views of policy would fain shade it off into the historical background. Such events can not be ignored, but there is a considerate way of historically treating them. If a well-constituted individual refrains from blazoning aught [*p* >amiss or] calamitous in his history; [*p* <history >family] a nation in the like circumstance may without reproach be equally discreet.
[*p notation (circled, at bottom) for an insertion not made* Do we publish no medicines pass the lines &c]

55: Bb 13, 13¹, 13³, 15; Da 41; Eb 48. [W 52]

* Ba on Bb leaf

Though after parleyings between Goverment and the ring-leaders, and concessions by the former as to some incontestable [*p* <incontestable ⫸glaring] abuses, the first outbrea →<outbrea→ uprising [*p i* (*below, circled on leaf, with guide-line to caret*) —that at Spithead—] with great [*p* <great] difficulty was [*p* <was] put down [*add comma*] or pacified →<pacified→ matters [*p* ⫸for the time] pacified; yet [*p i* >at the Nore] the unforseen [*ESM Bb*⁺ *correct to* unforeseen] renewal of insurrection [>, and {<, and}] [*p* <insurrection *add* revolt {⫸revolt ≫insurrection}] on a yet larger scale [*p add comma*]

56: Bbb? 16¹; Da 42; Eb 49. [W 53]

Bbb?

and emphasised [emphasized?] in the conferences [p *mend* f] that ensued by demands deemed by the authorities not only inadmissable [*ESM? correct to* inadmissible] but [p i >aggressivly] insolent, evinced— [p <evinced ≯indicated] if the Red Flag did not sufficiently signify it— [p <signify it *add (before dash)* do so,]

* Ba? * Bb?

what was [p <what was {≫what was (*vestige of earlier revision*)}] the spirit animating the men. Final suppression, however, there was; [p *notation (above, with caret)* Insert { ≮Insert}] but only made possible perhaps by [p *addition (at bottom of leaf, circled, with guide-line to caret)* the steady →<steady >unswerving→ loyalty of the marine corps] a voluntary resumption of loyalty among

Bbb?

influential sections of the crews. [*Bbb*⁺*p caret and fist and the word* Insert { <Insert} *to indicate insertion of above clip*] [p *large bracket for new paragraph*] To some extent the Nore Mutiny may be regarded as somewhat [p i <somewhat] analagous to the

57: Bb 16²; Da 43; Eb 50. [W 54]

Bb

distempering irruption of contagious [p *alter to* contageous] fever in a frame constitutionally sound. [*alter period to comma and add* and which anon throws it off.]

At all events, of these thousands of mutineers were some of the tars who not so very long afterwards— [p *circled query* the Aggamenon?] whether [>wholly] prompted [p >thereto] by patriotism, or [p *begin then cancel word (above line)*] pugnacious instinct, or by both, —helped to win for →<for→ a coronet for Nelson at the Nile, and, →<and,→ and then a [p <then a ≯the naval] crown of crowns [p *Bc* >for him] at Trafalgar. To the insurrectionists of the Nore, [<insurrectionists of the Nore >mutineers] those [p >superb { <superb}] battles [p ≯and especially Trafalgar] were a plenary [>and splendid { <and splendid}] absolution; [p *Bc* >and a grand one;] since for [p <since *capitalize* for] all that goes to make up [>scenic {p *Bc* >(*circled, with line to caret*) naval} display, and {p <and}] heroic magnificence in arms, Trafalgar stands alone in human annals. [p *revise to read* Trafalgar stands unmatched in naval annals. {p <naval ≫human} {*then cut off bottom of leaf and mount remainder on whole-leaf*}]

† *late pencil*

chapter-ending mark ———◇——— →*add notation* End of chapter.→ [◁*chapter-ending mark* ◁ *notation* End of chapter. <*(above, on leaf)* Trafalgar . . . annals >*(on new leaf)* those battles stand →<stand→ especially Trafalgar stand unmatched in human annals. And very probably Old Ocean will never behold the like again. {*p* <And . . . again.}]

[*p chapter-ending mark (at bottom of leaf)* ———◇———]

58: Nelson–chapter 1.

G

[*p (in upper right corner)* Concerning "the greatest sailor since the world began." {*ESM p notation query* Tennyson?}]

[*p chapter-beginning mark* ———◇———]

In this matter of writing, purpose [*p* <purpose ≯resolve] as one may to keep to the main road, some [>branching {*p* <branching}] by-paths have an allurement [*p* <allurement ≯enticement] not readily [*p* ≯to be] withstood. Beckoned by the genius of Nelson [*p* <Beckoned . . . Nelson >Knowingly {*p* <Knowingly}] I am going to err into such a by-path. If the reader will keep me company I shall be glad. At the least we can promise ourselves that pleasure which is wickedly said to be in sinning, for a literary sin it →<it→ the [*p add* brief { <brief}] divergence will be. [*p add bracket for new paragraph*] Very likely it is no new remark that the inventions of our time have at last brought

[58a] 233v: Superseded Bb 16⁵.

[*The matter on this leaf corresponds to matter finally on Leaves 59 and 60; probably the matter on the missing clips also corresponded to matter now on those leaves.*]

Bb

[*space at top from which clip was removed*]
now, [<now *add (in margin)* to-day {*Bb+p* <to-day ≯at sea}] tho [*ESM Bb+ alter to* though] [*Bb+p* ≯now] in sea-encounters [*p* <sea ≯modern (*before* encounters) <modern ≯(*below*) latter { <latter}] >there (*after* encounters)] a certain kind of displayed gallantry be fallen out of date as no longer [<no longer >hardly now { <now *add* now, (*after* appliable)}] applyable, [*alter to* appliable] [*p* <now *add* now (*before* hardly)] did the valor of [*p* <valor of ≯knighthood signalized in] the old navies [*p add* by such characters] [*G blue crayon cancel whole passage, copying its matter forward*]
[*space from which clip was removed*]
would be jeered at for pigmies →<pigmies→ toys. [*ESM? p add (below)* popguns] [*p* <*whole line*] [*p add* and American naval captains of the war of 1812 {*G blue crayon* <would . . . 1812}]

〚 *303* 〛

59: Nelson–chapter 2.

G

about a change in sea-warfare in degree corresponding to the revolution in all warfare effected by the original introduction of →<of→ from China into Europe of gunpowder. The first European fire-arm, a clumsy contrivance [*p add comma*] was, as is well known, scouted by no few of the knights as an [*p* <an ⟩a base] implement basely cumbersome and cowardly, [*p* <basely . . . cowardly ⟩xx] good enough peradventure for varlets [*p* <varlets ⟩peasants { <peasants ⟩(*below*) weavers}] too craven to stand up crossing steel with steel in frank fight. But as ashore knightly valor tho' shorn of its blazonry did not cease with the knights, neither at [<at >on the] seas

60: Nelson–chapter 3.

G

though nowadays in encounters there a certain kind of displayed gallantry be fallen out of date as hardly applicable to [<to >under] changed circumstanes, did the nobler qualities of such naval magnates as Don John of Austria, Doria, Van Tromp, Jean Bart, and [<and] the long line of British Admirals [>(*below, circled, with guide-line to caret*) and the American Decaturs of 1812] become obsolete with their wooden walls.

61: Bb 16⁵, 16⁶; Nelson–chapter 4.

Bb

Nevertheless, to one [*p* <one ⟩anybody] who can hold the Present at its worth without being inappreciative of the Past, it may be forgiven [*p add comma*] if to him [*p* <him ⟩(*below*) such an one,] the memorable [*p i* <memorable >solitary] old hulk at Portsmouth, Nelson's Victory, [*underlined*] seems to float there, not [*ESM mend t*] alone as the decaying monument of a fame incorruptable, [*ESM mend in and correct to* incorruptible] but also as a [*p* >poetic] reproach, softened by its picturesqueness, to the Monitors [*underlined*] and iron →<iron→ [*p* >(*below*) yet] mightier [>hulls of the {*p add* European}] iron-clads. [*alter* clads *to* clad { <*period add* clan.} {*p* <clan *alter* clad *to* clads}] And this not altogether because they [*p* <they ⟩these monsters { <these monsters *add* such craft}] are unsightly, [*p* >ugly { <ugly}] totally lacking in →<totally lacking in→ unavoidably lacking in [*p* <in] the symmetry [*p* >magesty, loftiness & { <magesty, loftiness &}] and grand lines of the old battle-ships, but equally for other reasons. [*p notation (bracketed, at bottom of leaf)* xx the mark on the deck where he fell { ⟨notation}]

62: Bb 16⁷; Nelson-chapter 5.

Bb

[*Bb⁺p* ⫸ (*above line*) the sentiment { ⫷ the sentiment}]

There are those, [<those >some] perhaps, who while not altogether inaccessable [*ESM? correct to* inaccessible] to that [*p* ⫸poetic] reproach, [*p* ⫸just alluded to,] may yet [>as utilitarians and { <as utilitarians and}] on behalf of the new order, be disposed to parry it; and this to the extent of iconoclasm, [*mend* a] if need be. [*p* ⫸For example,] Prompted by the sight of the star inserted in the Victory's [*underlined*] [⫸quarter-] deck designating the spot where the Great Sailor [*p* <Great Sailor ⫸unique hero {*p* <unique hero ≫Great Sailor}] fell, they may s →< they may s→ these Positivists [<Positivists >utilitarians {*p* >martial (*before* utilitarians)}] of war [*p* <of war] may suggest considerations implying that

* Ba

Nelson's ornate publication of his prescence [*p i* <prescence >person] in battle was [*p* ⫸not only] unnecessary, [*p add* but] not military, nay savored of foolhardiness and vanity.

[*p guide-line to next leaf*]

63: Bb 16⁸; Nelson-chapter 6.

[*Verso of leaf was inscribed earlier; see p. 430.*]

Bb

[*G remove clip and add Gp guide-line to where writing begins*] They may add, too, that under the circumstances [*p* <under the circumstances ⫸at Trafalgar] it was in effect nothing less than a courting of [*p* <courting of ⫸challenge and →<and→ to] death; and it [*p* <it *add* death] came; and that but for his bravado Nelson [*p* <Nelson ⫸the victorious Admiral] might possibly have survived the battle, and so, instead of having his sagatious [*ESM? correct to* sagacious]

64: Bb 16⁷, 16⁹; Nelson-chapter 7.

* Bb 16⁷, 16⁹

dying injunctions injudiciously [*p* <injudiciously] overruled by his immediate successor in command he himsef when the battle [<battle ⫸contest] was decided might have brought the [*p i* <the *add* his] battered [*p* <battered >xx →<xx→ shattered { ⫷shattered ≫battered *altering it to* shattered}] fleet to anchor, a proceeding which would [*p i* <would >might] have averted the deplorable loss of life by shipwrck [*p* ⫸in the tempest {*i* ⫷in the tempest *add* in the}]

[[*305*]]

G

elemental tempest that followed the martial tornado. [p <tornado >one.]

Well, should we set aside the more than disputable point whether oweing →<oweing→ the weather →<the weather→ →*add* for→ various reasons it was possible to anchor the fleet, then plausibly enough the Bethamites of war may urge the above.

65: Nelson–chapter 8.

* ***Bb***

But the might-have-been [*underlined*] is but boggy ground to build on. And [>, certainly, in tr →<tr→ foresight as] with respect [<with respect] to the large [p *alter to* larger] issue of an encounter, and anxious preparations for it—sounding and [p <sounding and] buoying the perilous [*Bb*+*p* <perilous >deadly {p <deadly} {≫deadly} {*ESM w.o.* deadly}] way and mapping it out, as at Copenhagen—few commanders have been so painstakingly circumspect [*ESM mend*] as this [p ≯same] re →<re→ unrecking [*Bb*+*p* <unrecking >reckless {*ESM w.o.* reckless}] declarer of his person in battle. [*G* <battle *add* x →<x→ in fight.]

G

Personal prudence even when dictated by [≯quite] other than selfish considerations surely is no special virtue in a military man; while an excessive love of glory, [p >such as was Nelson's {p <such as was Nelson's}] energizing to the uttermost the heart-felt [p <the ≯his *add* honest <heart-felt ≯English {p <his English} {*G revise to read* impassioning a less vital →<vital→ burning impulse the honest}] sense of duty, is the first. If the name of [<of] Wellington [*underlined*] is not so [*add* much] of a trumpet to the blood as the simpler

66: Nelson–chapter 9.

G

name Nelson, [*underlined*] the reason for this may perhaps be inferred from the above. Alfred in his ode →<ode→ funeral ode on the victor of Waterloo ventures not to call him the greatest soldier of all time, tho' in the same ode he invokes Nelson as "the greatest sailor since the world began."

If, as is not improbable, x →<x→ with the mysterious pres →<If . . . pres→

At Trafalgar Nelson on the brink of recei →<recei→ of opening the fight sat down and wrote his w →<w→ last brief will and testament. If under a [*w.o.* the] presentiment of a [<a ≯the most] magnificent [*add* of all] victory [*alter* victory *to* victories] to be crowned by his own glorious death, a sort of priestly motive led him to dress his

[[*306*]]

67: Nelson-chapter 10.

G

person in the jewelled vouchers of his own shining deeds; if thus to have
adorned himself for the altar and the sacrifice [>were indeed vainglory,] then
affectation and fustian is each [>more] heroic line in the great epics and
dramas, since in such verse →<verse→ lines the poet but embodies in verse
those exaltations and sublimities [<and sublimities] of sentiment that a
nature like Nelson, the opportunity being given, vitalizes into acts.
[*p chapter-ending mark* ———◇———]

68: Bb 17²; Da 44, 44ᵖ², 44; Eb 60. [W 55]

Bb

[*p chapter-beginning mark* ———◇———]
[*p* >Yes, {<Yes,} {≫Yes,}] The uprising [*p* <uprising ⊁outbreak] at
the Nore was put down. But not every grievance was redressed. If the contractors, for example, were no longer permitted to ply their immemorial iniqui-
ties and cheat in the rations, and by so doing help famish the men; [*Bb⁺p*
>*(between lines) revision at once erased and incorporated in ink* some practises
peculiar to their tribe, {*p* >*(above, circled, with guide-line to caret before comma)*
everywhere} such as providing shoddy cloth, rations not sound, or false in
the measure; <their immemorial . . . men] not the less impressment, for one
thing, went on. By custom sanctioned for centuries, and judicially maintained
by a Lord Chancellor as late as Mansfield, that mode of manning the fleet, a
mode at present →<at present→ now fallen into a sort of abeyance but never
formally renounced, it was not practicable to give up in those years.

69: Ba? 17, Bb 17³, Bxp 16; Da 45; Eb 70. [W 56]

Ba

it was not practicable to [*Ba⁺p* >suspend or {<suspend or}] do away with
in those years. [*Bb green crayon then ink* <it was . . . years. *(adding same
matter at bottom of leaf before this one)*] Its abrogation would have been perilously crippling to [*Ba⁺p* <been perilously *alter* crippling *to* crippled <to
{*ESM w.o.* ed}] the indispensable fleet, one wholly [>under] canvas, no
steam-power, its innumerable sails and thousands of cannon, everything in
short, worked by muscle alone; a fleet the more insatiate in demand for men,
because then multiplying its ship of all grades against contingencies present
and to come of a [*p i* <a >the] convulsed continent. [*capitalize* continent]
Lurking discontent survived the [>two {*p* <two}] suppressed mutinies.
[*Ba⁺p* <mutinies >outbreaks] [*Ba⁺p* >In *(incomplete revision)*] Hence it
was not altogether unreasonable to apprehend, or at least be prepared for
[*Ba⁺p* <be prepared for] [*Bbp i* <Lurking . . . prepared for] [*Bbp notation (above)* Insert {⊀notation}]

[[*307*]]

70: Bb 17⁴; Da 46; Eb 80. [W 57]

=========

* Bb 17⁴ (I) on Bc leaf
Discontent foreran the Two Mutinies, and more or less it lurkingly sur-
vived them. Hence it was not unreasonable to apprehend some return of
trouble sporadic or general. An →<An→ One instance of such apprehensions:
Bc
In the latter part of the [<latter part of the] same year with this or there-
abouts, [<or thereabouts, >story,] Nelson, then V →<V→ Vice Admiral
Sir Horatio, being with the fleet off the Spanish coast, was directed by the
Admiral in command to shift his pennant from the Captain to the Theseus;
[*ship names underlined*] and for this reason: that the latter ship having newly

71: [Bcp notation follows 17⁴ green]; Da 47; Eb 90. [W 58]

=========

* Bb 17⁴ (II) on Bc leaf
arrived on the station from home where it had taken part in the naval insurrection, [*p* <naval insurrection ⫸Great Mutiny] danger was suspected
→<suspected→ apprehended from the temper
[*p guide-line to next leaf*]

72: Bb 17⁵; Da 48; Eb 91. [W 59]

=========

Bb.
of the men; and [*p Bc* >it] was thought that an officer like Nelson was the
one, not [*p* >indeed] to terrorise [terrorize?] →<terrorise→ flog [*p Bc*
<flog ≫terrorise] the crew into base subjection, but win them, by magnetic
[*p Bc* <magnetic] force of his [*p* >mere prescence & magnetic { ≪magnetic}]
heroic [*mend*] personality [*p Bc* <personality >prescence. {*p* <prescence}
the final intention apparently was of his mere prescence & heroic personality
(*although* personality *was not restored, it is required by the insertion of ampersand before uncanceled* heroic)] back to thorough allegiance. [*p Bc revise to
read* allegiance as devoted as his own. {*Bc revise to read* to an allegiance if not
as enthusiastic as his own, yet as true.}]
So it was that for an interval, [*p Bc* <an interval *add* a time] on more
than one quarter-deck anxiety did exist. At sea precautionary vigilance was
strained against relapse. At short notice an engagement might come on. When
it did, in some extreme instances [*p* <extreme] the lieutenats assigned to
batteries felt it incumbent on them [*p Bc* >in some instances (*from above, by
circling and caret, canceling and re-writing* instances) {*ESM w.o.* instances} {*p
add comma after* them)}] to stand with drawn swords behind the men working the guns.
[*p notation* End of chapter ———◇——— { ≪*notation and add chapter-ending
mark* ———◇———}]

73: Eb 92, Ec 92. [W 60]

* Eb 92
[*ESM* p notation 49 follows 48 green {green *underlined*}] [p *chapter-beginning mark* ——◇——]
But on board the seventy-four in which Billy now swung his hammock, [*Ec* >very] little in the conduct [<conduct >manner] of the men and nothing [p ⊁obvious] in the demeanor of the officers would have suggested to an ordinary observer that the Great Mutiny was a recent [*Ec* <recent {≫recent}]

Ec
event. In their general bearing and conduct the commissined officers of a war- - ship naturally take their tone from the commander, that is if he have that ascendency of character that ought to be his.

74: Eb 93. [W 61]

Eb
[p >The "Indomitable's" Commander { <The "Indomitable's" Commander}] Captain the Honorable Edward Fairfax Vere, to give his full title, was a man [p <man >confirmed bachelor { <confirmed}] of forty or thereabouts, a sailor of distinction even in a time prolific of naval heroes. [p <naval heroes ⊁great ones { <great ones ⊁ (*below*) renowned seamen.} { <renowned seamen} {≫renowned seamen}]] Though allied to the highest [p *alter* highest *to* higher] nobility his advancement had not been altogether oweing to influences connected with that circumstance. He had seen much service, been in many [p <many {≫many} {*Ec* <many >various}]] engagements, always acquitting himself as an officer of sound judgement and cool intrepidity [*Ec* <of . . . intrepidity >(*interlined*) just to {p <just to >(*interlined, circled, with guide-line to caret*) but mindful of the welfare of his men} {*Ec* ⋖but . . . men >(*below*) mindful of the wellfare of} his men, but never tolerating an infraction of discipline;] [*Ec add* thoroughly versed in the science of his profession, {p i >and} intrepid to the verge of temerity,]

75: Eb 94, Ec 94¹. [W 62]

* Eb 94
but [*Ec* <but >though] never injudiciously so. [p *Ec* <so. >daring. {p <daring. ≫so.}] For his gallantry in the West Indian waters as flag-lieutenant under Rodney in that Admiral's crowning victory over De Grasse, he was made a post-captain.

Ec
Ashore dressed as a →<dressed as a→ in the garb of a civilian scarce anybody [*ESM?* p >one *to replace* body] would have taken him for a sailor, more

especially that his →<his→ he never intr →<intr→ garnished his [*p* <his] unprofessional talk with nautical terms, and grave in his bearing, evinced little appreciation of mere humor. It was not out of keeping with these traits that
[*p guide-line to next leaf*]

76: Ec 94². [W 63]

* Eb 94 on Ec leaf
[*p guide-line continued (from upper left corner to clip)*]
On a passage when nothing demanded his paramount action, he was the most undemonstrative of men. Any landsman observing this gentleman not conspicuous by his stature and wearing no pronounced insignia, emerging from his retreat [*p* ⊁cabin (*without canceling* retreat)] to the open deck, and noting the silent deference of the officers retiring to leeward, might have taken him for the King's honored [<honored]

77: Eb 95, Ec 95¹. [W 64]

* Eb 95 (I)
guest, a civilian aboard the King's-ship some highly honorable discreet envoy on his way to an important post.

Ec
But in fact this unobtrusivness of demeanor [>may have] proceeded from a certain unaffected modesty of manhood [*mend* d] [*add* sometimes] accompanying a resolute nature, a modesty evinced at all times not calling for pronounced action, and which shown in any rank of life suggests a virtue aristocratic in kind. [*p guide-line to next leaf*]

[77a] 84†v.

[*Superseded* Ea or Eb *patch. Black-ink fair-copy, matter corresponding to passage now on Leaves 78–79.*]
† Ea or Eb
sometimes he would stand on the weather-side of the quarter-deck holding by the mizzen rigging and [*Ebp* >long] gazeing [*correct to* gazing] off at the blank sea. At the presentation to him then of some minor matter interrupting the current of his revery, he would
[*Eb orange crayon cancel whole passage*]

78: Ec 95². [W 65]

* Eb 95 (II)
As with some others engaged in various departments of the world's more heroic activities, Captain Vere tho [*ESM p cross* t *alter* tho *to* though] practical

enough upon occasion would at times betray a certain dreaminess of mood. Standing alone on the weather-side of the quarter deck, and [<and] one hand holding by the rigging he would absently gaze off at the blank sea. At the presentation to him

79: Eb 96. [W 66]

[*Verso of patch was inscribed earlier; see p. 430.*]

Eb
then of some minor matter interrupting the current of his thoughts he would show more or less irascibility; but all but [*p* <all but] instantly he would control it.

Among naval →<Among naval→ In the navy he was popularly known by the appelation—Starry Vere. How such a designation happened to fall to him [*p* <him (*by error leaving* to *uncanceled*) *add* (*on hinged addition-patch with notation* Insert P 96 red.)]

† *late pencil*
upon one who whatever his sterling qualities was possessed of no brilliancy →<no brilliancy→ none →<was . . . none→ could hardly be said to have →<could . . . have→ was without brilliancy →<brilliancy→ any brilliant ones

Eb
was in this wise: A favorite kinsman, one →<one→ Lord Denton, [*p* ⤳a free-hearted fellow,] had been the first to meet and congratulate him upon his return to England from his West Indian cruise; and but the day previous turning over a copy [>of] Andrew Marvell's poems had lighted, not for the first time however, upon the lines entitled Appleton House, [*title underlined*] [*p* ⤳the name of] one of the seats of their

80: Eb 97. [W 67]

Eb
[*p notation* 100 red (*underlined*) follows]
common ancestor, a hero in the German wars of the seventeeth century, in which poem occur the lines,
> "This 'tis to have been from the first
> In a domestic heaven nursed,
> Under the discipline severe
> Of Faixfax and the starry Vere" [*no period*]

And so, upon embracing [*mend* b] his gallant [<gallant] cousin fresh from Rodney's great →<great→ gallant →<gallant ≫great→ victory wherein he had played so gallant a part, [>full of { <full of *add* brimming over with} just family pride in the sailor of their house,] he exuberantly exclaimed, "Give you →<you ⤳ye→ joy, Ed; give ye joy, my starry Vere!" This got currency, and the novel prefix serving in familiar parlance readily to distinguish him [*p* <him

[[*311*]]

>the Indomitable's captain] from another Vere his senior, [p ≯a distant relative] an officer of like rank in the navy, it remained permanently attached to his [p <his >the] surname.

[p chapter-ending mark ———◇———]

81: Vere–chapter 1. [W 69]

Eb ink

[ESM p notation (at top right) copied from HM's notation on Leaf 363 Capt Vere—— to be inserted after first account of him]

[p chapter-beginning mark ———◇———]

In view of the part that the Commander of the Indomitable [underlined] plays in a →<a→ scenes shortly to follow, it may be well to fill out a little [p <a little] that passing [p <passing ≯running {<running}] sketch of him outlined in a [ESM p <a >the] previous chapter.

In certain respects [p <In certain respects >Aside {add Quite (before Aside) <Quite} from his good {<good} qualities as a sea-officer] Captain Vere was an exceptional sea-officer. [p <sea-officer ≯man. {<man ≯ (below) character.}] Unlike no few of England's renowned sailors, long and arduous service and great [p <and great ≯with signal] devotion to it, had not resulted in absorbing and salting [p underline salting] the entire man. He had a marked [p add leaning]

82: Vere–chapter 1², 2. [W 70]

Eb ink

toward everything intellectual. He loved books, never going to sea without a newly replenished library, compact but of the best. The isolated leisure, in some cases so wearisome [p add comma] falling at intervals to commanders even during a war-cruise, never was tedious to Captain Vere. With nothing of that literary taste which less heeds the matter [p <matter >thing conveyed] than the style, [p <style ≯vehicle] his bias was toward those books to which every mind at once serious and broad and occupying [p <at once ≯seriously {≫at once <seriously add superior} {<mind ≰superior ≯ (over erasure) serious mind of superior order} {<serious and broad and occupying ≫occupying (for clarity recancel of broad and)}] a [<a >any active] post of au →<au→ authority in the world, naturally takes to; [p <takes to ≯inclines:] books treating of a →<a→ real [p <real add actual] men and events no matter of what era—history, biography and

83: Vere–chapter 3. [W 71]

[Verso of patch was inscribed earlier; see p. 430.]

Eb ink

[p >unconventional] writers that, [p <that] like Montaigne, frankly [p <frankly ≯who, honestly {<who add (before honestly) who, free} from cant

[[312]]

& convention,] and in the spirit of common sense [*p* >penetratingly { <penetratingly}] philosophise [philosophize?] upon those greatest of all mysteries, facts. [*p* <those . . . facts >realities.]

In this line of reading he found that which he had vainly sought in the [<the] miscellanious converse [*ink and green crayon* <In . . . converse (*and rest of leaf?*) *then cut off rest of leaf, paste on three-quarters of new leaf as patch, and continue*]

† *late pencil*
In this line of reading he found confirmation of his own more reserved thoughts —confirmation which he had vainly sought in social converse, so that as touching every fundamental topic, [<every >most *alter* topic *to* topics] there was [<was >had got to be] established in him some positive convictions, which he forefelt would unalterably abide in him [<unalterably >(*after* him) essentially unmodified] [>proof to all sophistries { <proof to all sophistries}] so long as his intelligent part remained unimpaired. Cons → <Cons→ In view of the troubled period in which he lived, [<he lived ⟩his (*mend*) lot was cast] this was well for him. His [<His ⟩Those { <Those ≫His}] [⟩settled] convictions were as a dyke against those

84: Vere-chapter 4¹, 4. [W 72]

[*Verso of patch was inscribed earlier; see p. 430.*]

Eb ink
It was [*p* <It was >The said convictions were as] a dyke serving to resist those angry [*p* <angry ⟩impetuous >invading (*below*)] [*p* (*at time of pencil revision-patch on previous leaf*) <The . . . those] waters of new-fangled [*p* <new-fangled >novel] opinion social and political [*p* <and >(*after* political) and otherwise,] which carried away as in a torrent [*p* <torrent ⟩deluge { <deluge ≫torrent}] no few minds in those days, minds by nature not inferior to his own. While other members of that aristocracy to which [*p* >by birth] he belonged were incensed at the innovators mainly because the theories advocated [*p alter* the *to* their <advocated] were inimical [*mend* l] to their interests as a class, [*p alter* their *to* the <interests as a ⟩privileged *alter* class *to* classes] Captain Vere intellectually [*p* >(*below*) disinterestedly *also* >(*above*) disinterestedly] opposed them not alone as [*p* >(*below, circled, with guide-line*) in great part] impracticable but so far partaking of the unsound as to border on the insane. [*p* <insane >(*below*) cracked.] It was France that was → <that was ⟩from (*before* France)→ came the tempest then sweeping the greater part of Christendom; [*p* <not alone . . . Christendom; *add hinged patch*]

† *late pencil*
them [>(*above, on original leaf, with guide-line to caret*) not alone] because they seemed to him to be [<to be] not susceptible [⟩in (*before* susceptible)

〚 *313* 〛

then <not in *and alter* susceptible *to* insusceptible] of being embodied [<being *alter* embodied *to* embodiment] in permanent [<permanent *add* lasting] institutions, but even where pr →<even where pr→ at war with the true welfa →<true welfa→ peace of the world and the true welfare of mankind. Not that he was a [<Not that he was a >No] bigot for monarchal forms, but [<but] he regarded the [<No . . . the]

85: Vere-chapter 5. [W 73]

[*At late-pencil revision stage this leaf replaced original Vere-leaf 5 when its top was cut off and its bottom was mounted on this leaf. This leaf was used first one end up, then the other, and it was numbered 5 each time, in pencil. Verso of leaf was inscribed earlier; see p. 430.*]

late pencil
[*probably continuing incomplete sentence on patch on Leaf 84 (if one supplies the word* ideas) as to political liberty which prompted the American Revolution [*p* <as to . . . Revolution *and turn leaf other end up*]

late pencil
[*p bracket for new paragraph*] With minds less stored than his & far →<far→ less earnest,

* Vere 5
[*top has been cut off 5 and the bottom placed on this leaf as a clip*] some officers of his rank, with whom at times he would necessarily consort, found him lacking in the social [<social >convivial {*p* <convivial *add* companionable}] quality, [*p* >a] dry and bookish, [*p* >gentleman] as they deemed. Upon his [*p* <his ⊁any] chance withdrawal from their company one would be [*Ebp* (*prior to above pencil revisions*) *had added here at bottom of leaf a circled phrase involved in the insertion referring to the American Revolution which was later cut out (see above)* Hampdens of our Revolu →<our Revolu ⊁(*below*) 1776→ {*p and green crayon* <those . . . 1776}]

86: Vere-chapter 6. [W 74]

Eb ink
apt to say to another, Ve →<Ve→ something like this: "Vere is a noble fellow, Starry Vere. [*p* <Starry Vere {≫Starry Vere}] Spite the gazzette, [*p alter to* gazzettes,] Sir Horatio [*p* ⊁meaning him who became Lord Nelson] is at bottom scarse a better seaman or fighter. But between you and me now do'nt you think there is a queer streak of the [*p* >martinet- <martinet-] pedantic in [*p* <in >running thro'] him? Yes, like the King's yarn in a coil of navy-rope. [*p alter period to question mark*]
    [*p add* In fact] This sort of confidential criticism was doubtless provoked by the circumstance [*p* <circumstance ⊁fact] that [*p* ⊰In fact >(*before*

[[*314*]]

This) Some apparent ground there was for *add semicolon* (*after* criticism) <was doubtless provoked by the fact that >since (*so that passage finally reads* Some apparent ground there was for This sort of confidential criticism; since)] not only did the Captain's discourse never fall into the familiar or →<familiar or→ jocosely familiar, but he was apt [*p* <he was apt] in illustrating [*p* >of] any point touching the stirring personages

87: Vere–chapter 7. [W 75]

[*Verso of patch was inscribed earlier; see p. 430.*]

Eb ink
and events of the period [*p* <the period ≯the world] to drop [*p* <drop ≯cite] some allusion to Plutarch, say, or Livy, [*p* >(*after* allusion) the ancients, say (*further words undeciphered*) {*p* ≮the ancients, say *and undeciphered words* <allusion . . . Livy >(*between lines*) historic character or incident of antiquity as freely →<as freely→ quite as freely as} {*orange crayon* <and events . . . as freely as *and p recast whole passage on patch*}]

† *late pencil*
and events of the time he would [*p* ≯(*below*) be as apt to] cite some historic character or incident of antiquity with the same easy [<with the same easy (*sentence left incoherent*)] air that he would cite from the moderns. He seemed

Eb ink
unmindful of the circumstance that to his bluff company such [*p* >remote] allusions however pertinent they might [*p* >really] be were too [*p* <too ≯altogether] alien and remote. [*p* <and remote ≯to men whose reading was mainly confined to the journals.] But consideratness in such matters is not easy to minds [*p* <minds ≯natures] constituted like Captain Vere's. Their honesty prescribes to them a [*p* <a >directness, sometimes] far-reaching directness [*p* <directness] like that of a migratory fowl in its →<in its→ that in its flight takes no note [*p* <takes no note >never heeds] when it crosses a frontier.
    It may help to show how he himself regarded his "little weakness" as some of his friends [*p* <It . . . friends *and discard following page(s), leaving the chapter to end at* frontier. *but with no chapter-ending mark.*]

88: E/p 100 [p notation (follows 97 red {red *underlined*})]. [W 77]

[*Verso of leaf was inscribed earlier; see p. 430.*]

———◇———

late pencil
    Of the →<Of *capitalize* the→ lieutenants, marine officers →<marine ≯and (*before* officers)→ of marines →<and . . . marines→ and other off →<off→

[[*315*]]

commissioned officers →<officers >gentlemen→ forming the Captain's →<the >(*above*) Vere→ staff it is not necessary here parti →<parti→ to particularise, [particularize?] not →<not→ nor →≯is it <is it→ specially to mention →<specially to mention→ needs it to specialize the warra →<specialize the warra→ make special →<special→ any mention of any of the warrant-officers. But among the petty →>-officers→ was one who can not be passed →<who can not be passed→ →*alter* who *to* whom→ it as well →<it as well→ →<whom→ who having much to do with the story, claims attention →<claims attention→ may as well be forthwith introduced. His portrait we →<we >I→ essay, without presuming to hit it.→<without . . . it ≯but shall never hit it.→ This was John [*p* <was John *add* was]

*Bb [18⁴]

[*p add* John] Claggart, the Master-at-arms. But the titl →<the titl→ that [>sea-] title may to some [*p* <some *add* most {<most}] landsman seem somewhat equivocal. Originally x →<x→ doubtless

89: Bb 18⁵; Da 53; Eb 101. [W 78]

Bb

the function of the officer so entitled [*p* <the (*before* function) >this →*alter* this *to* that→ petty-officer's <of the officer so entitled] was the instruction of the men in the use of arms, sword and cutlas. [*p* <sword and cutlas *add* *period* (*after* arms) {*p* ≫sword and cutlas >or (*above* and)}] But very long ago, owing to the advance in gunnerey making hand-to-hand- encounters xxx →<xxx→ less frequent and giving to nitre and sulpher the preeminence over steel, that function ceased; the Master-at-arms of a great war-ship becoming a sort of Chief of Police charged [*p* >(*below, with circling and guideline to caret*) among other matters] with the duty of preserving order on the populous lower [*p* <lower ≫lower] gun-decks.

Claggat [*p alter to* Claggart] was a man about forty years of age. [*p* <forty years of age *add* five and thirty,]

90: Bb 18⁶; Da 54; Eb 102. [W 79]

*Ba 18

[*B⁺p* (*at top*) *incomplete revision* ≯the eyes (*circled*) {≮the eyes}] somewhat spare and tallish, [*p alter to* tall] yet of no ill figure upon the whole. His hand was too small and shapely to have been accustomed to hard toil. The face [*B⁺p* <The face >His contenance {≮His contenance ≫The face}] was a notable one; the features [*p* >all except the chin] cleanly cut as those on a fine [<fine] Greek [*p* <Greek {≫Greek}] medallion;

Bb

yet the chin, beardless as Tecumsah's, had something [*p* >of strange protuberant broadness] in its make that [>strangely {*p* <strangely}] recalled

the prints of [*p* >the Rev^d] Dr. Titus Oates, the historic [>veracious {*p* <veracious}] clergyman and [*p* ⊁drawling] witness [*p* >(*below*) deponant <clergyman →*transpose* deponant *to follow* historic→ and {*Bc* ≮historic deponant and drawling <clergyman and witness >historic deponant with the drawl →<drawl→ clerical drawl}] in the time of Charles II and the [*p* >infamous {<infamous} fraud of the] alleged Popish Plot. It served Claggart in his function [*p* <function ⊁office] that his eye could cast a tutoring glance. His brow was of the sort phrenologically associated with more than average intellect; [>(*with circling and guide-line to caret*) thinish {*p* <thinish}] silken bla →<bla→ jet curls partly

91: **Bb 19^1; Da 55; Eb 103. [W 80]**

Bb
falling [<falling >clustering] over it, making a foil to the palor [*p* *alter to* pallor] below, a palor [*p* *alter to* pallor] tinged with a faint shade of amber akin to the hue of some [*p* <some] time-tinted [*p* *Bc* >white {*p* <white}] marbles of antiquity. [*p* <of antiquity *add* of old. {*p* <of old *add period* (*after* marbles)} {*p* ≫of old.}] This complexion, one →<one→ in a marked way [<in a marked way >so {*p* <so} singularly] contrasting with the tanned [*p* *Bc* <tanned >bronzed {*p* *revise to* the red or deeply bronzed}] visages of the sailors, and in part the result of his official seclusion from the sunlight, tho it was not exactly displeasing, neverthless seemd to hint of something defective or unwholesome in the blood. His aspect [*p* *Bc* <or unwholesome . . . aspect >or abnormal in the constitution and blood. But his general aspect] and manner [*p* *add* , these {<these}] were so suggestive

* Bab
of an education and career incongruous with his position →<position→ function [>naval (*before* function)] [*p* <function ⊁position {*p* <position ≫function}] that when

92: **Bb 19^2; Da 56; Eb 104. [W 81]**

* Ba 19 (I)
not actively engaged in it he looked to be some person of →<to be some person of→ like a man of high quality, [>social and moral,] who for reasons of his own was going [*p* <going {*ESM p* >keeping}] incog. [*p* >or made up for a disguise. {*p* <or made up for a disguise.}] [*Ba*^+*p add* Tho >(*above, circled, with guide-line to caret*) he was an Englishman {*Bb* ≮Tho . . . Englishman}] Nothing was known of his former life. But [<But]

Bb
It might be that he was an Englishman; and yet there was →<was→ lurked a bit of accent in his speech suggesting that possibly he was not such by birth but through naturalization in [*p* >early] childhood.

⟦ *317* ⟧

93: Bb 19³; Da 57; Eb 105. [W 82]

* Ba 19 (II)

among [*Bb capitalize* among] certain grizzled sea-gossips of the [*p Bb* >gun--
decks and] forecastle went a rumor perdue that this gentlemanly [*p Bb* <this
gentlemanly >the] master-at-arms was a chevalier [*underlined*] who had
volunteered into His Magesty's service [<His Magesty's service >the King's
navy] by way of compounding for some sort of [*p Bb* <sort of {*B+p* <some
add a} {≪a ≫some}] mysterious polite [*p Bb* <polite] swindle whereof
[*Ba+p* >not long previous {≪not long previous}] he had been convicted in
London. [*Ba+p notation for addition* King's Bench {*Bb* ≪notation then revise
and add as follows*}] [*Bb* <convicted <in London. >(*after* been) arraigned
add at the King's Bench. Though { <Though >That >(*before* That) The fact
alter That *to* that} nobody, of course, { <of course} could substantiate this,
→<*comma*→ report { <report}

94: Bb 20¹; Da 58; Eb 106. [W 83]

* Ba 20

{*add* report, >(*before* report) vague} {*p* <vague} was {*p* > , of course,} nothing against its secret currency.] [*Ba+p notation* (*underlined, with large caret in
left margin*) New chapter { ≪*underlined notation*}] Such a rumor once started
on the gun-decks agan →<agan→ in reference to almost anyone below the
rank of a commissioned

Bb

officer would, during the period [*p* <period ≯era { <era ≫period}] assigned
to this narrative, have seemed not altogether defi →<defi→ wanting in plausability [*p alter to* plausibility { <plausibility >credibility}] [*p* >at least { <at
least}] to the tarry old wiseacres of a man-of-war crew. And indeed a man of
Claggart's accomplishments, without any [*p* <any ≯prior] nautical experience entering the navy at mature life, as he did, and neccessarily alloted to
→<to→ at the start to the lowest grade in it; this was something which in the
dearth of all [*Ebp* <all ≯exact] knowledge as to his real [*Ebp* <real] anticedents, [*Ebp correct to* antecedents] opened [*Eb* >to the invidious] a somewhat mysterious field for invidious doubt and surmise. [*Eb* <a somewhat . . .
surmise *add* a wide field, however vague, for unfavorable doubt and surmise.
{*Ebp* <unfavorable doubt and ≯invidious} { <invidious ≫unfavorable}]
[*B+p chapter-ending mark* ——————◇—————— {*Eb* <chapter-ending mark}] [*Ebp add*
(*circled, in left margin*) *notation for addition-patch* A man who never alluded to
his prior life ashore; these circumstances &c {*Eb* <notation and add patch
below} orange crayon cancel this was something . . . surmise. *and place revision-
atch over those lines*|

† *Eb*

a man →>too→ who never made allusion to his previous life ashore; these were circumstances which in the dearth of exact knowledge as to his true anticedents opened to the invidious a vague field for unfavorable surmise.

95: Da 59; Eb 107. [W 84]

Da

In reference to the privy gossip as to Claggart's prior [*D⁺p* <prior ⟩pre-vious] career as a landsman →<as a landsman→ ashore, and as tending to show that it was not so verry absurd after all, it should be remembered that [*Eb red crayon cancel whole passage, and Eb* >(*at top of leaf, with blue crayon guide-line*) But the sailors' {>dog-watch} gossip concerning him derived a vague plausability from the fact that] now for some period the British Navy could so little afford to be squeamish in the matter of keeping up as far as possible [<as far as possible] its [*p* <its *add* the] muster-roll, [*p alter to* -rolls] that not only were the [<the] press-gangs notoriously abroad [*add* both] afloat and ashore, but there was little or no secret about the fact [*Eb* <the fact >another matter, namely] that the London police were encouraged →<encouraged→ at liberty to capture

96: Da 60; Eb 107². [W 85]

Da

any able-bodied suspect [*underlined* {*p* <*underlining*}] and [*p* <and *add* , any] questionable fellows [*p alter to* fellow] at large and summarily ship them [*p* <them >him] to the dock-yard or fleet. Furthermore, even among voluntary enlistments there were instances where the motive to it →<to it→ thereto partook neither of patriotic impulse nor yet of a random desire to experice a bit of sea-life and martial adventure. Insolvent debtors of the [<the] minor grade, together with the promiscuous lame ducks of morality found in the Navy a convenient and secure refuge. Secure, because once enlisted aboard a King's-Ship, they were in sanctuary, as it were. [*Eb* <were <it were *and revise to read* were as much in sanctuary, as the transgressor of the Middle Ages harboring himself under the shadow of the altar.]

97: Da 61¹; Eb 108. [W 86]

Da

These facts [*Ec* <These facts >Such sanctioned irregularities] which for obvious reasons the Goverment would hardly think to parade at the time and which consequently, and as affecting the least influential class of mankind, have all but dropped into oblivion, would seem to lend color to x →<x→ a [>strange {strange}] thing which I heard in my youth [<which . . . youth] from an old American negro who had [*add* years before] served in the British

navy: namely →<namely→ It was this: [*revise to* to this effect:] In the case of a ship [*add* or] squadron [<or squadron] short of hands and whose [<whose {≫whose}] speedy [<speedy {≫speedy}] despatch was →<despatch was→ sailing was imperative, the deficient quota would sometimes be made up [<made up ⊁eked out] by draughts culled direct from the jails. [*Ec blue crayon* <to lend . . . jails {*Ec* <would seem} *and place revision-patch over those lines*]

† *Ec*
lends color to something for the truth whereof I do not vouch, and hence have some scruple in stateing; something I remember having seen in print though the book I can not recall; but the same thing was personally communicated to me now more than forty years ago by an old pensioner in a cocked hat with I →<I→ whom I had a most interesting talk on the terrace at Greenwich, a Baltimore negro, a Trafalgar man.

98: Eb 109. [W 87]

† *Ec*
it [*capitalize* it] was to this effect: in [*capitalize* in] the case of a [>war-] ship short of hands and [<and] whose speedy sailing was imperative, the deficient quota [>(*below, circled, with guide-line to caret*) in lack of any other way of making it good,] would be eked out by draughts culled direct from the jails.

Eb
For reasons previously suggested it would not perhaps be easy at the present day directly to prove or disprove the allegation. But allowed as a verity, how significant would it be of England's straits at the time confronted by those momentous [<momentous >terrible { <terrible >horrible} {*p* <horrible}] wars which like a flight of harpies rose [>(*below, circled, with guide-line to caret*) shrieking] from the din and dust of the fallen Bastile.
[*p guide-line to next leaf*]

99: Eb 110. [W 88]

Eb
That era, now long past, [<now long past] appears measurably clear to us who wh →<wh→ look back at it, and but read of it. But to our grandfathers, [*p* <our ⊁the ⊁(*after* grandfathers) of us graybeards] the more thoughful of them, [>the genius of] it presented an aspect like that of Camoen's Spirit of the Cape, an eclipsing menace mysterious and prodigious. Not America was exempt from apprehension. After [*p* <After >At the height of] Napoleon's un-exampled conquests, when he bowled down kings and states like ninepins, [*p* <when he . . . ninepins] there were some [*p* <some >Americans] who had fought at Bunker Hill who looked forward to the possibility that the Atlantic might prove no effectual [*p* <effectual] barrier against the [*p* >world-wide

{ <world-wide >ultimate}] schemes of the upstart Corsican. So I had it from venerable men know to me in my youth. [*p chapter-ending mark* ——————◇——————]
[*p* <the upstart . . . my youth. >(*interlined*) this french { >portentous} upstart from the revolutionary chaos who seemed the →<the→ in act of fulfilling the direful →<the direful→ judgment proclaimed →<proclaimed→ prefigured in the Apocalyse.]

100: Eb 111. [W 89]

Eb
[*p chapter-beginning mark* ——————◇—————— { <*mark*}]
But the less credence was to be given to the gun-deck talk touching Claggart, seeing that no man holding his office in a man-of-war can ever hope to be popular with the crew. Besides, in derogatory comments upon anybody [*ESM? p* <body ⊁one] against whom they have a grudge, or for any reason or no reason mislike, sailors in some degree [*p* <in some degree] are [*p* >much] like landsmen, they are apt to exaggerate or romance. [*p add* about him. { <about him. *add* it.}]
About as much was really known to the Indomitable's [*underlined*] tars of the master-at-arms' career before entering the service as an astronomer knows

101: Eb 112. [W 89 {*sic*}]

Eb
about a comet's travels previous [*p* <previous >prior] to its first observable appearance in the sky. The babble [*p* >of the sea quid-nuncs] [*ESM p* <babble ⊁verdict] has been cited only by way of showing what sort of moral impression the man made upon rude uncultivated natures whose conceptions of human wickedness were necessarily of the narrowest, limited to ideas of vulgar rascality, [*p add dash*] a thief among the swinging hammocks during a night-watch, or the man-brokers and land-sharks of the sea-ports.

102: Bb 27; Da 64; Eb 113. [W 90]

Bb
It was no gossip, however, but fact, that tho, [*ESM? p alter to* though] as before hinted, Claggart upon his entrance into the navy was, as a novice, assigned to the least honorable section of a man-of-war's crew, the drudges, [*p* >waisters (*to replace* drudges) { <waisters}] [*p* >embracing (*before* the drudges) *and alter* drudges *to* drudgery] he did not long remain there.

* Ba
The superior capacity he immediatly [*p* <he immediatly >*a revision now undeciphered because erased* { ⊀*revision* ≫he immediatly}] evinced, his constitutional sobriety, flatte →<flatte→ ingratiating deference to superiors, to-

gether with a peculiar ferreting genius manifested on a singular occasion, all this capped by a certain austere patriotism [p >which { <which}] he developed [p <developed *add* evinced { <he evinced}] had [Bb⁺ <had] [Ba⁺p >rapidly { ⟨rapidly >abruptly} {Bb⁺ ⟨abruptly *w.o.* abruptly}] advanced him rapidly [Bb⁺ <rapidly] to the influential [<influential] position he now occupied in the seventy-four. [p Bb⁺ <he . . . seventy-four. >of master-at-arms.]

103: Eb 114. [W 91]

Eb

Of this maratime Chief of Police the ship's-corporals, so called, were the immediate subordinates, and compliant ones; and this, as is to be noted in some business departments ashore, all →<all→ almost in →*alter to* to→ a degree inconsistent with entire moral volition. His place

***Ba**

put various converging wires of underground action into [p *i* <action into ⋗influence under] the chief's control, capable when astutely worked thro' his understrappers of operating to the mysterious discomfort if nothing worse, of any of the sea-commonalty.

Eb leaf

[p *chapter-ending mark* ——◇——]

104: Ec 115¹. [W 92]

Ec

[p *chapter-beginning mark* ——◇——]

The life of [*alter to* Life in] the fore-top well agreed with Billy Budd. There, when not actually engaged on the yards aloft →<aloft→ yet higher aloft, the topmen, who as such had each [p <each] been selected [p <selected ⋗chose { <chose >(*below*) picked out}] for their [p <their >alert { ⟨alert ≫their} { <their}] youth [p >activity] and agility [p <agility >alertness { <alertness *transpose* activity *to follow* and} {*add comma*}] constituted an aerial club lounging at ease against the smaller stun'sails rolled up into cushions, spinning yarns [*mend*] like the lazy gods, and frequent [p *alter to* frequently] jesting on [p <jesting on ⋗amused with] what was going on in the busy world of the decks below. No wonder then that a young fellow of Billy's disposition was well content in that [p ⋗ (*without canceling* that) such] society; [p *alter semicolon to period*] giving [p *alter* giving *to* Giving] no cause of offence, and [p <and ⋗to anybody, he was] always [p *add* alert at a call.]

105: Ec 115². [W 93]

Ec

true to duty. [p <true to duty] So in the merchant service it had always [p <always] been with him. But now such a punctilousness [p ⋗in duty] [>was]

[[*322*]]

shown that his topmates would sometimes good-naturedly laugh at him for it. This heightened alacrity had its cause, namely, the impression made upon him by the first formal gangway-punishment he had ever witnessed, which befell the day following his impressment. It had been incurred by [*p* >by a little fellow, young, and much →<and much→ a novice] an after-guardsman absent from his assigned post when the ship was being put about, [*p alter comma to semicolon*] →>a deriliction→ resulting in a rather serious hitch in [*p* <in *add to*] that maneu →<maneu→ manoeuvre, [*mend*] one demanding instantanious [*p mend to* instantaneous] prop →<prop→ promptitude in letting go and making fast.

106: Ec 116. [W 94]

Ec
When Billy saw the culprit's naked back under the scourge gridironed with na →<na→ red welts, and worse; when he marked the [*p* >dire] expression in the liberated man's face as with his woolen shirt flung over him [*p* >(*two lines above, circled, with guide-line to caret*) by the executioner] he rushed forward from the spot, [*p* >to bury himself in the crowd,] Billy was horrified. He resolved that never though remissness would he make himself liable to such a visitation or do or omit aught that might merit even verbal reproof. What then was his surprise and concern when ultimatly he found himself getting into [>petty] trouble occasionally about such matters as the stowage of his bag or something amiss in his hammock, matters under the police

107: Ec 117. [W 95]

Ec
oversight of the ship's-corporals of the lower decks, and which brought down on him a vague threat from one of them.

So heedful in all things [>as he was,] how could this be? He could not understand it, and it more than vexed him. When he spoke to his [*Ecp Ec* >young] topmates about it—young fellows like himself— [*Ecp* <—young fellows like himself—] either they were [*Ecp* <either >either] incredulous or quizzed [*Ecp* ⪢lightly jested at { ⪡lightly jested at}] him for his anxiety. [*Ec* <it . . . anxiety *add* it *and continue, incorporating above pencil revisions*] they were either lightly incredulous or found something comical in his unconcealed anxiety. "Is it your bag, Billy? [> " said one "] well, sew yourself up in it, bully boy, and then you'll be sure to know if anybody meddles with it."

Now there was a veteran aboard who because his years began to disqualify him for more active work

108: Ec 118. [W 96]

Ec

had been recently assigned duty as main-mast-man in his watch, looking to the gear belayed at the rail roundabout that great spar near the deck. [>At off- - times] The foretopman had picked up some acquaintance with him, and now in his trouble it occurred to him that he might be the sort of person to go to for wise council. He was an old Dansker long anglicised [anglicized?] in the service, of few words, many wrinkles and some honorable scars. His wizzened face, colored like an →<an→ [*p* <colored like >(*below, circled, with guide-line to caret*) time-tinted and weather-stained to the complexion of] an antique parchment, exhumed from some dilapidated →<exhumed . . . dilapidated→ was here and there peppered blue by the chance premature →<chance premature→ chance explosion of a gun-cartridge in action.

109: Ec 119. [W 97]

Ec

[>He was an Agamemnon-man; {*p underline* Agamemnon}] Some two years prior to the time of this story he had [<had *alter* he *to* having] served under Nelson when but Sir Horatio in the old Agamemnon, [*underlined*] a [*alter* the *to* that <old Agamemnon, (*underlined*) a (*inserting new clause at beginning of sentence*)] ship immortal in navy →*alter to* naval→ memory, and which dismantled and in part broken up to her [*p* ≯bare] ribs is seen a grand skeleton in Hayden's etching. As one of a boarding-party from the Agamemnon [*underlined*] he had received a cut slantwise along one temple and cheek leaving a long pale scar like a flash of [<flash of >streak of dawn's {*p begin then cancel another word*}] light across [*p* <across ≯(*below*) falling athwart] the gunpowder visage. →<gunpowder *add* dark→ It was on account of that scar and the [>desperate {<desperate}] affair in which it was known that he had recieved it, [>(*below, circled, with guide-line to caret*) as well as from his blue-peppered complexion] that he [*p* <he >the Dansker] went among the Indomitable's crew by the name of Board-her-in-the smoke. [*p add quotation marks around* Board-her-in-the smoke.]

110: Ec 120. [W 98]

Ec

Now the first time that his small weazel-eyes happened to light on Billy Budd, a certain grim internal merriment set all his ancient wrinkles into antic play. Was it that his eccentric unsentimental old sapience not fooled by books [*p* <not fooled by books ≯primitive in its kind] saw or thought it saw something which in contrast with the present [*p* <present ≯war-ship's] environment looked oddly incongruous in the handsome sailor? But after slyly study-

ing him at intervals, the old Merlin's equivocal merriment was modified. When [>by chance] the twain would meet, [*p alter period (after* modified) *to semicolon* >For now *alter* When *to* when <by chance <would meet ≫would meet] it would start on [*alter to* in] his face a quizzing xxx →<xxx→ sort of look, but it would be but momentary

111: Ec 121. [W 99]

Ec
and sometimes replaced by an expression of speculative foresight [*p* <foresight ≯query] as to what might eventually befall a nature like that, dropt [*ESM? p alter to* dropped] into a world not without some man-traps and against whose subtleties simple courage lacking experience and address and without any touch of defensive ugliness [*p add comma*] is of little avail, [*p alter comma to semicolon*] and where such innocense as man is capable of does yet in a moral emergency neither [<neither ≯not always] sharpen the faculties nor [<nor *add* or] fortify [*p* <fortify ≯enlighten] the will.

However it was the Dansker in his ascetic undemonstrative [*p* <ascetic <undemonstrative {*p*≫ascetic}] way rather took to Billy. Nor was this only because of a ce →<a ce→ the [*p* <the ≯a certain] philosophic interest awakened in him. [*p* <awakened in him. *add* in such a character. There was another cause.]

112: Ec 122. [W 100]

[*Verso of patch was inscribed earlier; see p. 430.*]
Ec
While the old man's eccentricities, sometimes bordering on the ursine, repelled the juniors, Billy, undeterred thereby, [*p addition (on top margin, circled, but not marked for place of insertion) probably belongs here* revering him as a salt hero] would make advances, never passing the venerable [<venerable ≯brave old {*p* <brave}] Agammenon-man without a salutation marked b →<b→ by that respect which is seldom lost on the aged however crabbed [*mend first* b] at times or whatever their station in life.

There was a fantastic [*p* <fantastic] vien of dry humor, or what not, in the mast-man; and, weather in freak of patriarchal hum →<hum→ irony touching Billy's [*p* ≯youth and] athletic frame, or for some other [*p* >and more recondite] reason, invariably [*p* <invariably ≯from the first] in addressing him he [*p* >always] substituted Baby for Billy.

† *late pencil*
[*on hinge-patch placed on leaf with notation* Add bottom of page 122] This it was →<This it was→ Thus it was [*add* And *(before* Thus) ≯ *(above)* by the name { <by the name}] that the foretopman came to be →<And thus . . . to be→ The Mastman [<Mastman ≯Dansker] in fact being the originator

[[*325*]]

of the name [<name ⟩knickname prefix { <knickname prefix (*without restoring* name)}] by which the foretopman eventually became known aboardship.

113: Ec 123. [W 101]

Ec

Well then, in his mysterious little difficulty going in quest of this strange mentor, [*p* <this strange mentor ⟩the wrinkled one] Billy found [>him] off [*mend*] duty in a dog-watch ruminating by himself seated on a shot-box of the upper gun-deck [>now and then] surveying with a somewhat cynical regard certain of the [>more swaggering] promenaders there. Billy recounted his trouble, again wondering how it all happened. The salt seer attentively listened, accompanying the [*p* >foretopman's] recital with queer twitchings of his wrinkles and problematical little sparkles of his jet-black [*p* <jet-black ⟩small ferret] eyes. Making an end of his story, B →<B→ the foretopman asked, "And now, do tell [*p* <(*by error?*) do tell >, Dansker,] me what you think of it."

114: Ec 124, Ec/G 124¹. [W 102]

* *Ec 124*
The old Dansker, [*p* <Dansker ⟩man] shoving up the front of his tarpaulin and slo →<slo→ deliberatly rubbing the scar there →<scar there→ upper part of →<upper part of→ [*p* >long slant] scar where →<where→ at the point where it entered the thin hair, laconically said, Baby Budd →<Baby Budd→ "Baby Budd" (meaning the Ma →<"Baby Budd (meaning the Ma→ "Baby Budd, Jimmy Legs" [*G underline* Jimmy Legs {*p mend to* Jemmy}] (meaning the master-at-arms) "is down on you"

G

"Jimmy Legs!" [*underlined*] ejaculated Billy his welkin eyes expanding; "what for? Why he calls me the sweet and pleasant young fellow, [the sweet and pleasant young fellow *underlined*] they tell me."

"Does he so?" grimly [<grimly] grinned the grizzled one; then said [*p* >Ay >(*above*) Baby lad] "A sweet voice has Jimmy Legs" [Jimmy Legs *underlined*]

115: Ec/G 124². [W 103]

G

"No, not always. But to me [>he] has. I n →<n→ seldom pass him but there comes a pleasant word."

"And that's because he's down upon you, Baby Budd."

Such reiteration along with the manner of it, incomprehensible to a novice, disturbed Billy almost as much as the mystery for which he had sought some [<some] explanation. Something less unpleasingly oracular he tried to extract; but the old sea-Chiron thinking perhaps that for the nonce he had

⟦ *326* ⟧

116: Ec 125¹. [104]

Ec

sufficiently instructed his young Achilles, pursed his lips, gathered all his wrinkles together and would commit himself to nothing [*mend*] further. [*p chapter-ending mark* ————◇———— {*add notation* Billy young and innocent (?) and a little xxx &c} { ≮Billy . . . &c ≮*chapter-ending mark and add notation* (*circled, above*) The experience (?) prudence &c} {*G* ≮The experience . . . &c and add (after further.)* Years, and those experiences which befall certain →>shrewder→men subordinated life-long to the will of superiors, all this had developed in the Dansker the pithy guarded cynicism that was his leading chracteristic.}] [*p* >(*before* Years) *large bracket for new paragraph*] [*p chapter-division mark* ————◇————]

Ec

The next day a little [*G* <little *alter* a *to* an] incident served to confirm Billy Budd in his incredulity as to the main-mast-man's [*p* <main-mast-- man's ≯Dansker's] strange summing up of the case submitted to him. [*p* <to him *add period (after* submitted)] [*p guide-line to next leaf*]

117: Bca 31², Bcb 31⁵; Da 80; Eb 125, Ec 125². [W 105]

Bca

true. [*p* <true >That was so { <so ≫true} { <That was true}] And not very long afterwards a little [*p* ≯apparent { <apparent}] incident confirmed it. [*p* <it ≯Billy's word. { <Billy's word ≫it}] [*p* <And . . . it] The ship at noon going large before the wind was rolling on her course, and the foretopman [*p capitalize* foretopman] being [*p* <the Foretopman being ≯he] below at dinner and engaged in some sportful talk with the members of his mess, chanced in a sudden lurch to spill the entire contents of his soup-pan upon the [*p* >new] scrubbed deck. [*p* >Claggart,] The Master-at-arms, official rattan in hand, happened to be passing along the battery there [<there] in a bay of which the mess was lodged, and the greasy liquid streamed just across his path. He →<He→ Stepping over it, he was proceeding

118: Bca 31³, Bcb 31⁶; Da 81; Eb 126. [W 106]

Bca

on his way without comment, since the matter was nothing to take notice of under the circumstances, when he happened to observe who it was that had done the spilling. His countenance changed.

119: Eb 127. [W 107]

Eb

Pausing, he was about to ejaculate something hasty at the sailor, but checked himself, and pointing down to to the streaming soup, playfully tapped him from behind with his rattan, [p >equivocally { <equivocally}] saying [p >in a low musical voice peculiar to him at times] "Handsomely done, my lad! And handsome is as handsome does too!" [p <does too!" ⊁did it too] And with that passed on. Not noted by Billy as not coming within his view was the involuntary smile, or rather grimace, that accompanied the [<the >Claggart's] [p ⊁equivocal] words. Aridly it drew down [p ⊁and distorted { <and distorted}] the thin corners of his shapely [p ⊁-curved { <-curved}] mouth. But everybody taking his remark as intended →<intended→

[*119a*] *352v:*

[*Superseded pencil draft of passage now on Leaf 120. On verso of draft-title slip.*]

Bc pencil

superior they had to laugh, [*several words missing where leaf is cut off*] accordingly. In this laugh, Billy of course joined; not displeased →⟨not displeased→ and very likely was [<Billy . . . was *add* Billy] a bit tickled [>it may be] by the allusion to his being the handsome sailor, >triumphantly →<triumphantly→ addressing &c →<addressing &c→ merrily joined, and addressing his messmates triumphantly →<triumphantly→ exclaimed [*orange crayon cancel entire leaf including this passage*]

120: Eb 128. [W 108]

Eb

meant for humorous, and at which therefore as coming from a superior they were bound to laugh, [*ESM* p ⊁"with countefeid {countefied?} glee"] acted accordingly; and Billy with no reason →<with no reason→ tickled, it may be, by the allusion to his being the handsome sailor, merrily joind in; then addressing his messmates exclaimed "There now, who says that Jimmy Legs is down on [*mend*] me!" "And who said he was, Beauty?" demanded one [p *add comma* { <comma} >Donald] with some surprise. Whereat the foretop-man looked a little foolish recalling that it was only one person, Board-her-in- - the-smoke who had suggested what to him was the smoky idea that this pleasant [p <pleasant]

121: Eb 129. [W 109]

Eb

Master-at-arms was in [*caret here by error*] any [*p* >special {*p* <special *add* peculiar}] way hostile to him. Meantime that off → <off→ functionary resuming his path must have momentarily worn some expression less guarded than that of the bitter [*p* <bitter ⊁dry {<dry ≫bitter}] smile, [*p* >(*below, circled, with guide-line to caret*) and invading {<invading ⊁usurping} the face from the heart, some distorting expression perhaps,] for a drummer-boy heedlessly frolicking along from the opposite direction and chancing to come into light collision with his person was strangely disconcerted by his aspect. Nor was the impression lessened when the official [*p* >impetuously] giving him a sharp cut with the rattan, vehemently exclaimed "Look where you go!" [*p chapter-ending mark* ———◇———]

[121a] 247†v:

[*Superseded pencil draft, from expansion stage between* B *and* C. *Probably this was the original opening of the chapter now beginning on Leaf 122. Its matter now appears (cf. "labyrinth") on Leaf 127.*]

Bb⁺pencil

Some portraiture of Claggart → <Claggart→ the outward Claggart has already been given. But → <But→ As to his inner personality, one does not care to hazard getting lost in a murky [<murky ⊁dark] labyrinth [*leaf cut off here but two words visible at end of next line* that. Yet] [*E orange crayon cancel leaf*]

[121b] 208†v:

[*Superseded passage from* Ca 2. *Later this was expanded into matter now on Leaves 123, 125.*]

* Ca 2

why should Jimmy Legs [*underlined*] —to use the words here of the elderly messmate [*C⁺p* <here . . . messmate ⊁here (*before* to use) ⊁Dansker's (*before* words)] —be secretly down [down *underlined*] on Billy Budd? In the absence of direct motive assignable, could it be an instance of inimicality beginning in a spontanious antipathy [<antipathy ⊁aversion {*p* <aversion *add* repugnance} {*p* ≫antipathy}] [*E orange crayon cancel passage*]

[121c] 207†v:

―――――――――――

[Superseded passage from Eb 130, replaced by Leaf 122.]
* Eb 130
[Eb⁺p chapter-beginning mark ―――◇―――]
What [p >then { <then}] was the matter with the master-at-arms? [p >And]
Whatever it might be [p <might be >was >(above, circled, with guide-line to
caret) that disturbed him] [p >how] could it [p >altogether { <altogether
add directly}] have to do with Billy Budd [p <Billy Budd add (circled, at top
of leaf, with guide-line to a point now cut off, but probably this passage) him could
it →<could it→ could the trouble have to do]
[brown crayon cancel all] [remainder of leaf cut off, not preserved]

122: E/G 130. [W 110]
―――――――――――

G
[p chapter-beginning mark ―――◇―――]
    What was the matter with the master-at-arms? And, be the matter what
it might, how could it have direct relation to Billy Budd with whom prior to
the affair of the spilled soup the master-at-arms [p <the master-at-arms ≯he]
had never come into any special contact official or otherwise? Yes, what
[<Yes, capitalize what] [p >indeed] could the trouble have to do with the
[p ≯inoffensive →<inoffensive→ ≯x →<x→ ≯(before the) one so little
inclined to give offence as] the merchant-ship's peacemaker, [underlined]
[p add even] him [p ≯too { ≪too}] who in Claggart's own phrase was "the
sweet and pleasant young

123: E/G 131. [W 111]
―――――――――――

G
fellow? Yes, why should Jemmy Legs, [underlined] to borrow the Dansker's
expression, be down [underlined] on the good-natured [p <good-natured]
Handsome Sailor?
* G
But, at heart and not for nothing, as the late chance encounter may indicate,
[p >to the discerning] down on him, secretly down on him [p add comma]
he assuredly was.
    Now to invent something in [<in >as to { <as to add touching}] the
more private career of Claggart, something involving involving →<involv-
ing→ the youthful sailor, [<the youthful sailor {p ≯the foretopman <the
foretopman ≯Billy Budd} {G ≪Billy Budd >(after involving) Billy Budd,}]
some romantic incident →<some . . . incident→ of which something he himself [alter he to the <himself >latter] should be wholly ignorant, some romantic incident implying

124: E/G 132. [W 112]

G

least [*p* <least]   that Claggart's knowledge of the young sailo →<sailo→
blue-jacket began at some period prior [*p* <prior ≯anterior] to catching sight
of him on board the seventy-four—   [>all]   this, would →<would→ not
[*p* ≯so]   difficult to do, might avail in an interesting way [*p* <an <way
>(*after* in) a way more or less] to account for whatever of enigma may ap-
pear to lurk in the [*p* *add* case.]

G

But in fact there was nothing of the sort. And yet the cause, one very probable however unprovable, [*p* <one . . . unprovable] necessarily to be assumed as the sole one assignable, is [*p* >even { <even}] in its [*p* >very]
realism as much charged with that romantic [*p* <romantic]

125: E/G 133. [W 113]

G

prime element of Radclifian romance, [>the mysterious, (*underlined*)]   as
any that the ingenuity of the author of the Mysteries of Udolpho [*title underlined*] [*mend* U] could devise, since [*p delete comma and insert period* <since
≯For]   what can more partake of the mysterious than an antipathy spontanious and profound such as [≯is] evoked in certain exceptional mortals by
the mere aspect of their contrary in [<their contrary in] some other mortal,
however harmless he may be? [*p add* if not called forth by this very harmlessness itself.]

   Now there can be [*p* <be ≯exist] no irritating juxtaposition of dissimilar
personalities comparable to that [*p* >which is possible] abord a p →<p→
great war-ship fully manned and at sea.

126: Ee/F 134. [W 114]

G

[*G on leaf replaces earlier clip*] There, every day [>among all ranks] almost
every man comes into more or less of contact with almost every other man.
Wholly there to avoid [*p* >even] the sight of an aggravating object one must
needs give it Jonah's toss or jump overboard himself. Imagine how [*p* ≯all]
this abnormal proximity and attrition [*p alter to* abnormally recurring proximity or rubbing against his contrary { <abnormally . . . contrary}]   might
eventually operate on some peculiar human creature the direct reverse of a
saint?

Ee/F

   But for the [*p* >adequate] comprehending of Claggart [*p* >by a normal
nature] these hints are insufficient. To pass from Budd to him [*p* <Budd to

him >a normal nature ≫to him] one must cross "the deadly space between."
And this is best done by indirection.

127: Ee/F 135. [W 115]

Ee/F

Long ago an honest scholar my senior, said to me in reference to a man
[*p i* <a man >one] now →<now→ who like himself is now no [*mend*] more,
[>(*below, circled, with guide-line to caret*) a man so unimpeachably respectable
that against him nothing was ever openly said tho' among the few much
{*p* <much >something} was whispered, "Yes X—— is a nut not to be
cracked by the tap of a lady's fan.] [*p add then delete quotation marks* (*before*
You)] You are aware that I am the adherent of no organised [organized?]
religion much less of any philosophy built into a systim. Well, for all that,
[*add yet*] there is no getting into X——'s [<yet there is no getting into
X——'s *and add* I think that to try and get into X——, enter his] labyrinth
[>and get out again,] without a clue derived from some source other than
what is is →<is→ known as knowledge of the world [knowledge of the world
underlined] I should get →<I should get *add dash* (*after* world)→ that is
[*p* <is ≯were] hardly possible, at least for me. [*p add quotation mark*]

128: Ee/F 136. [W 116]

Ee/F

"Why" said I, "X—— however singular a study to some, is yet human,
and knowledge of the world assuredly implies the knowledge of human nature,
and in most of its varieties."

"Yes, but a superficial knowledge of it, serving ordinary purposes. But for
anything deeper, I am not certain whether to know the world and to know
human nature be not two distinct branches of knowledge, which while they
may coexist in the same heart, yet either may be [*p* <be ≯exist] with little
or nothing of the other. Nay, in an average man of the world, his constant
rubbing with it blunts

129: Ee/F 137. [W 117]

Ee/F

that finer spiritual insight indispensable to the essential [*p* <essential] understanding of [*p* ≯the essential in] certain exceptional characters, whether
evil ones or good. [>In a matter of some importance] I have seen a girl wind
an old lawyer about her little finger. Nor was it the dotage of senile love.
Nothing of the sort. But he knew law better than he knew the girl's heart.
Coke and Blackstone hardly shed so much light into [*p* ≯certain { <certain}]
obscure [*p* >mystic human heart { ◁mystic human heart *add* spiritual}]
places as the Hebrew prophets. And who were they? Mostly recluses."

At the time [*p* >my inexperience was such that] I did not quite see the force [*p* <force ⊁drift] of all this. [*p* ⊁It may be that] I see it now. And, indeed, if that lexicon which

130: Ee/F 138. [W 118]

Ee/F
is based on Holy Writ were any longer popular, one might with less difficulty define and denominate a nature like Claggart's. [*p* <a nature like Claggart's ⊁ (*below*) certain phenomenal men.] As it is, one must turn to some authority not liable to the charge of being tinctured with the Biblical element.

In a list of definitions included in the authentic translation of Plato, a list attributed to him, occurs this: "Natural Depravity: a depravity according to nature." A definition which so [<so >tho'] savoring of Calvinism, by no means involves

131: Ee/F 139. [W 119]

Ee/F
Calvin's dogma as to total mankind. Evidently its intent makes it applicable but to individuals. Not many are the examples of this depravity which the gallows and jail supply. At any rate for notable instances, since these have no vulgar alloy of the brute in them, but invariably are dominated by intellectuality, one must go elsewhere. Civilization, especially if of the austerer sort, highly favors it →<highly favors it→ is auspicious to it. It folds itself in the mantle of respectability. It has its petty [*p* <petty >certain negative] virtues serving as silent auxiliaries. It never allows wine to get within in its guard.

[*131a*] *232v:* Superseded Eb 136, Ec 141³.

[*Corresponds to matter now on Leaves 131, 132.*]

Eb
[*Ecp* >For example] Hardly ever is he a wine-bibber. If he have no [>aver →<aver→ natural] distaste for the grape [*Ecp* >(as is possible) { <(as is possible)}] such as some [*Ecp* >people] have even for the peach, he at any rate is inclined to [*Ecp* <is inclined to ⊁sincerely] despise [*Ecp alter to* despises] that over-genial influence which may lead even a temperate drinker at a holiday table [*Ecp* <even ... table ⊁one] imprudently [>sometimes { <sometimes}] to open his heart. There is a tall [<tall >singular {*Ecp add* ascetic} { <ascetic}] pride in the spiritually depraved [*Ecp* <the spiritually depraved ⊁him { >(*without canceling* him) Plato's depraved one}] operating as a safe-guard against [*Ecp* ⊁most of] the vulgarizing [<vulgarizing ⊁physical] vices. And against some of the moral →<moral→ graver moral [*Ecp* <graver moral >more spiritual →<spiritual→ spiritual { <spiritual

≫moral}] vices as well. Seldom [*Ecp* <Seldom ≯Not frequently] is the man [*Ecp guide-line to corner of leaf*] [*Ee/F brown crayon cancel whole leaf*]

At Eb this leaf read:

Hardly ever is he a wine-bibber. If he have no natural distaste for the grape such as some have even for the peach, he at any rate is inclined to despise that over-genial influence which may lead even a temperate drinker at a holiday table imprudently to open his heart. There is a singular pride in the spiritually depraved operating as a safe-guard against the physical vices. And against some of the graver moral vices as well. Seldom is the man

At Ee it read:

For example Hardly ever is he a wine-bibber. If he have no natural distaste for the grape such as some people have even for the peach, he at any rate sincerely despises that over-genial influence which may lead one imprudently to open his heart. There is a singular pride in Plato's depraved one operating as a safe-guard against most of the physical vices. And against some of the more moral vices as well. Not frequently is the man

[*131b*] 236v: Superseded Eb 138, Ec 141⁵.

[*Corresponds to matter now on Leaf 132.*]

Eb

assumed by the depraved one, serving as it does among other things to conciliate or neutralize as blindfold persons who should be the natural helpers of any individuals →<s→ the object of his [*Ecp* <his] subtler machinations. Yes, he is altogether free of →<Yes . . . of→ But not →<But *capitalize* not→ only is he free from acerbity, but [*Ecp* >is apt to be {*add (before* is) upon →>fit→ occasion}] a great [*Ecp* <great] denouncer of cynics, [*Ecp* ≯in short a professed optimist] invariably speaking well of the world and its denizens. [*Ecp revise to* cynics. Never does he speak ill of the world, much less of human nature. Take →<Take→ Analyzing anything he says you will find nothing of the Pessimist. { <Analyzing . . . Pessimist}] [*Ee brown crayon cancel the passage from* machinations *to here and place a revision-patch (now gone) over it*]

But the thing which in eminent instances signalizes this phenominal creature [*Ecp* <creature ≯man, for man he is,] almost setting him apart from humanity [*Ecp* <almost . . . humanity >(*circled, with guide-line to caret*) masquerading under the garb of respectability { >(*below, before* under) among those (?) →<those→ truthful (?) citizens} { <truthful citizens *re-cancel* among . . . citizens} { <masquerading . . . respectability}] is this: Though his bearing himself →<bearing himself→ even temper and discreet bearing would [≯appa (*incomplete word*)] seem to intimate a mind peculiarly subject to the law

⟦ *334* ⟧

132: Ee/F 140. [W 120]

Ee/F

It is not going too far to say that it is without vices or small sins. There is a phenominal [*ESM p correct to* phenomenal] pride in it that scornfully [*p* <scornfully] excludes them. Never mercenary or avaricious and so forth. [*ESM p* <and so forth >(*after* them *apparently to replace* Never *and make a complete sentence*) *from* anything (*insertion does not make coherent sense*)] In short the depravity here meant partakes nothing of the sordid or sensual. It is serious, but free from acerbity. Though no flatterer of mankind it never speaks ill of it. [*p* <it *add* mankind. { ≪mankind. ≫it}] [*pencil draft for foregoing sentence occurs on Leaf 133 on pencil patch, canceled* It is serious but free from acerbity. No flatterer of mankind it never speaks ill of it.]

But the thing which in eminent instances signalizes this [<this >so] exceptional [>a] nature is this: though the man's even temper and discreet bearing would seem to intimate a mind peculiarly subject to the law

133: Eb 139, Ec 141⁶, Ed 144, Ee/F 141. [W {121}]

[*Verso of patch was inscribed earlier; see p. 430.*]

Eb

of reason, not the less in his soul's recesses [*p* <his soul's recesses ≫heart] he would seem to riot in complete exemption from that law having apparently little to do with it [<it >reason] further [*mend*] →>than→ to employ it as an ambidexter implement for effecting the irrational. That is to say: Toward the accomplishment of an aim which in wantonness of atrocity [*p* <atrocity ≫malignity {≫atrocity (*without canceling* malignity)}] partakes [*alter* partakes *to* partake *and insert* may (*before* partake) {*p* <may *add* would seem to}] of the insane, he will [*p* >(*below, circled, with guide-line to caret*) sometimes (*?*) { ≪sometimes}] direct a cool judgement sagatious and sound.

[*Ee/F add* Such men are madmen, and of the most dangerous sort; for {*p* <and . . . for ≫secretive ones} their lunacy {*continue on pencil-addition patch*}]

† *late pencil*

but →<but→ not continuous [>& persisting (*?*)] but occasional, evoked by some special object →<evoked . . . object ≫and special→ is not to be di →<is . . . di→ in the outward proceding [>not] to be distinguished from sanity →<sanity→ their sound →<sound→ sanity, for whatever the aims [*?*] →<whatever the aims→ they are →<they are→ for they →<for they→ it is yet more secretive →≫(*before* it) indeed→ →<for indeed . . . secretive *add period* (*after* sanity)→

Leaf finally reads:
of reason, not the less in heart he would seem to riot in complete exemption from that law having apparently little to do with reason further than to employ it as an ambidexter implement for effecting the irrational. That is to say: Toward the accomplishment of an aim which in wantonness of atrocity/malignity would seem to partake of the insane, he will direct a cool judgement sagatious and sound.

Such men are madmen, secretive ones their lunacy not continuous & persisting [?] but occasional, and special in the outward proceding not to be distinguished from their sanity.

134: Ee/F⁺p 142. [W 122]

[Pencil revision on leaf supersedes passage on Leaf 133 and its pencil-revision patch. Verso of leaf was inscribed earlier; see p. 430.]

late pencil
These men are [>true] [<These men are true >Charity pronounces these men {<Charity . . . men ≫These men are}] madmen, and [<and >but {<but ≫and}] of the most dangerous sort, for their lunacy pervades [?] not →<pervades not→ is not continuous, but occasional →<but occasional ≫but occasional→ evoked by some special object; it is [≯watchfully {<watchfully >(*circled, with guide-line to caret*) protectively}] secretive and self-contained →*revise to read successively* as it is self-contained→ →, and hence self-contained→ →, which is as much to say it is self-contained,→ nor [<nor ≯so that] when [≯moreover,] most active is it [<is it ≯it is] to the normal →<normal→ average mind [>not] distinguishable from sanity, and for the reason above stated [<stated ≯suggested] that whatever its aims may be, [>(*below, circled, with guide-line to caret*) and the {>xx <xx} {≯mad} {<mad} aim is {<is >(*below*) be →<be→} always →<always→ never divulged →<divulged→ declared—] this →<this→ the method [>and →<and→ the outward action {<action >proceding} are] is [*not canceled*] always perfectly rational.
[*add* Now] Something such an one was Claggart

* Ee/F [142]
[*p bracket whole sentence on clip, with notation (circled, in right margin, with fist)* to come in afterwards] And of these was [*p* <And of these was] Claggart, in whom was [*p* >the mania of] an evil nature, not engendered by vicious training or corrupting books or licentious living, but self-subsisting [*p* <self-subsisting >born with him] and innate, in short "a depravity according to nature." [*p closing bracket*]

Leaf finally reads:
These men are madmen, and of the most dangerous sort, for their lunacy is not continuous, but occasional evoked by some special object; it is protectively

⟦ *336* ⟧

secretive, which is as much to say it is self-contained, so that when moreover, most active it is to the average mind not distinguishable from sanity, and for the reason above suggested that whatever its aims may be, and the aim never declared—the method the outward proceding is/are always perfectly rational.

Now Something such an one was Claggart Claggart, in whom was the mania of an evil nature, not engendered by vicious training or corrupting books or licentious living, but born with him and innate, in short "a depravity according to nature."

135: Ed 145, Ee/F⁺p 143. [W 123]

[Versos of both leaf and patch were inscribed earlier; see p. 431.]
late pencil
[*ESM p notation at top* 146 red {red *underlined*} follows]
Dark sayings are these, some will say. But why? Is it because they somewhat savor of of Holy Writ in its phrase "mystery of iniquity"? [*p insertion on patch below for placement here*]

† **late pencil**
If they do, it was unintended, but rather sought to be avoided →<sought to be avoided→ sought to be →<sought to be→ →<it was unintended but rather→ →>(*above*) such savor→ was not →<not→ far enough from being intended, but was unavoidable →<but was unavoidable→ for little will it commend them →<them→ the →<the→ these pages to many a reader of to-day.

late pencil
The →<The→ The point of this →<this >(*above*) the present→ story turning on the hidden of the →<of the→ nature of the Master at Arms has necessitated [?] this →<this ≫this→ chapter, and now with an →<and now with an <*comma and add period* (*after* chapter)→ and the character of it as well. [<and . . . well.]

* *Ca*
[*p* >With an] added hint or two in connection with the little incident at the mess, [*p* <the little incident at the mess >what { <in . . . what (*adding guide-line from* two *to* the)} {≫in connection with the little incident at the mess} {<little}] the resumed narrative must [*p* >now { ≮now}] be left to justify →<to justify→ to establish [*p Ca*⁺ <establish >vindicate,] as it may, its own credibility.
[*p marginal notation* xx Chapter { ≮*notation*}]

Leaf finally reads:
Dark sayings are these, some will say. But why? Is it because they some-what savor of of Holy Writ in its phrase "mystery of iniquity"? If they do, such savor was far enough from being intended, for little will it commend these pages to many a reader of to-day.

⟦ 337 ⟧

The point of the present story turning on the hidden nature of the Master at Arms has necessitated [?] this chapter. With an added hint or two in connection with the incident at the mess, the resumed narrative must be left to vindicate, as it may, its own credibility.

[135a] 353: Superseded Ca [9].

[*Top half of leaf had a clip pinned on (now gone) which probably had the foliation. Not foliated after* C—*i.e., superseded at or before* E *stage.*]

Ca

[*Cap (part way down, at right) chapter-title* An Episode *and notation (circled)* New Chapter *(written over chapter-beginning mark* ———◇——— *)*]
[*C⁺p remove clip and add chapter-title (in mid-leaf)* Lawyers, Experts, Clergy *above chapter-beginning mark* ———◇———]
[*ESM p notation (at top)* For Billy Budd / Find *proper place for insertion (fist beneath)*]

[*C⁺p add* This it is that makes the most perilous of God's creatures. { <This . . . creatures}] [*C⁺p add (circled)* by the way] Can it be this [*C⁺p* <this ≯the] phenomenon, [*C⁺p* ≯upon wh <upon wh] disowned or [*C⁺p* ≯at least] not acknowledged, [*C⁺p* >conceded (*without canceling* acknowledged)] that in some criminal cases puzzles the courts? And for →<And for→ For this cause have our juries in →<in→ at times not only to endure the prolonged contentions of the lawyers [*C⁺p* <the ≯feed { <feed ≯(*after* lawyers) with their fees}] but also the yet more perplexing strife of the [*C⁺p* >feed { <feed}] medical experts? [*C⁺p* ≯with theirs] —But why leave all [<all *add* it] to the laity →<laity→ laymen? [<laymen *alter the to* them?] why not subpoena [*C⁺p* ≯summon { ≮summon}] [*ESM? p question mark (in parentheses) in right margin (beside erasure over* subpoena) { ≮*question mark*}] [*add* as well] the clerical proficients? Their vocation [*C⁺p* <But why . . . vocation {*cut off this sentence*} {*C⁺p add notation (below)* Restore *and mount the two segments of cut leaf on another blank leaf*}]

[135b] 354: Superseded Ca 10.

Ca

bringing them into peculiar contact with so many human beings, and sometimes in their least guarded hour, in interviews very much more confidential than those of physcian and patient; this would seem to qualify them to know something about those intricacies involved in the question of moral responsibility; whether in a given case, say, [>the] crime proceeded from mania in the brain or rabbies [*C⁺p correct to* rabies] of the heart. As to any differences among themselves these clerical proficients might develop on the witness- - stand, [*C⁺p* <witness] these could hardly be greater than the direct [*C⁺p* >professional { <professional *add* practical} { <practical}] contradictions

exchanged between the [C+p >remunerated] medical experts as, essentially, advocates for and against. [C+p <as . . . against *add period* (*after* experts)] [C+p *check-mark* (*in left margin opposite* experts . . . against)]

[135c] 234v: Superseded Eb 142.

Eb

[Eb+ *orange crayon notation* New Chapter {*blue crayon fist* (*at left*) *and box* (*around* New Chapter)}]

Claggart's figure was not amiss. His brow, as before said, was shapely, and the entire face, excepting the [Eb+p >Titus Oates {<Titus Oates}] chin, classically fine; and there were indications that he was [Eb+p *cancel much of the foregoing and revise to read* That Claggart's figure was not amiss, and his face, in →<in→ save one feature, intellectually handsome has already been said. It is now to be added that at times he seemed to be →<to be→] not insensible of such →<such→ these [Eb+p <these *add* his {<his *add* his} {< his ≫such}] favorable [Eb+p >physical {<physical}] points [Eb+p *add comma* (*after* points) {<favorable points}] [Eb+p >as were his] serving as they did obviously [Eb+p <obviously] to signalize him in the crowd. But the form of Billy Budd was animally [Eb+p <animally >physically {<physically}] heroic, [Eb+p ≯tho but animally so, {<tho but animally so,}] and his face tho [Eb+p *add apostrophe*] without [Eb+p >aught {<aught *add* aught of}] the intellectual look [Eb+p *alter to* intellectuality <look] of Claggart's was [Eb+p >yet] exempt from the draw-back of any imperfect feature.

In the →<In the→ Under the adaptive form in whi [<Under . . . in whi] [Eb+p *add* (*at top of leaf, circled, with guide-line to caret after* feature) Besides, it was often irradiated by {<it . . . by} the hidden sun of {<of ≯in} his cheerful {<cheerful} heart threw out →<threw out *add* rayed forth→ a cheery aureola around him. {*cancel this addition and add its revised substance at bottom of leaf* Besides, the sun in his heart, threw →<threw→ rayed forth a light that beautified him the more.}]
[Eb+ *orange crayon cancel bottom half of leaf* (*a clip, now gone, was pinned on top of the canceled portion*)]

[135d] 231v: Superseded Eb [143].

[*Space on top half of leaf where a clip* (*from* B *or* C) *was pinned on; foliation was probably on clip; the leaf itself was not foliated.*]

Eb

an [Eb+p >indirect] inkling as to what it was that had presented the first palpable point to his antipathy, Billy's personal beauty. [p *add* (*after* antipathy) *dash* {<—Billy's personal beauty *add* (*after* antipathy) *period*} {<(*by error?*) antipathy ≫antipathy ≯at sight—envy.} {<—envy.}] In Claggart, envy [*Eb⁺p* <Claggart, envy] and antipathy, passions apparently incompatible [*Eb⁺p* <incompatible ≯irreconcilable] were nevertheless born [*Eb⁺p* <born] conjoined like Chang and Eng in one birth.

But what is envy [Eb⁺p <But what is envy]
[*Ee/F brown crayon cancel whole passage*]

[135e] 235v: Superseded Eb 144.

Eb

But is envy [*Eb⁺p* ≯really] such a very dreadful thing? [*Eb⁺p* <very dreadful thing ≯monster as the poets have painted it] That depends upon [*Eb⁺p* >(*above, circled, with guide-line to caret*) its degree and] the →>sort of→ nature affected by it, and other circumstances. But what [*Eb⁺p* <and other circumstances. But *add period* (*after* it) *capitalize* what] essentially it is [*Eb⁺p* <it >envy >(*after* is) that] may be inferred from the fact, the f →<the f→ that though in repeated instances [*Eb⁺p* <What . . . instances ≯Well, tho] men had →*w.o.* have→ pleaded guilty to murder, arson, [*Eb⁺p transpose* murder, arson,] and kindred enormities no mortal has ever [*Eb⁺p* <no . . . ever *add* , did ever any one] seriously confessed to envy; [*Eb⁺p alter* confessed *to* confesse *alter semicolon to question mark*] for something [*Eb⁺p* <for *capitalize* something] there is in that vice that →<that→ [*Eb⁺p* <that vice ≯it] universally felt to be more shameful →<shameful→ [≫shameful >to the individual *add* and more] derogatory to human nature [>at large {*Eb⁺p* <at large}] than even felonious crime, whereof when intense it has not seldom been the parent. [*Eb⁺p* <whereof ≯whereto *alter* intense (*by adding* sified) *to* intensesified {<when intenseified ≯(*after* whereto), when excessive} {<parent ≯instigator.} {<*whole clause* whereto . . . instigator. <*comma* (*after* crime) *and add period.*}] In his personification of envy, Spencer [*Eb⁺p* <In . . . Spencer] [*blue crayon cancel whole leaf*]

Leaf finally reads:
Well, tho men have pleaded guilty to arson, murder, and kindred enormities, did ever any one confess to envy? Something there is in it universally felt to be more shameful than even felonious crime.

[135f] 230v: Superseded Eb 145.

Eb

depicts her as [*Eb⁺p* <depicts her as ≯Envy in extreme is {<Envy . . . is *add* Spencer ≫depicts ≯envy (*before* as)}] a ghastly hag forever chewing a [*Eb⁺p* >poisonous] toad. "Pale ire, envy, and despair" [*Eb⁺p* ≯this {<this}] is Miltonic. Behind [*Eb⁺p* ≯these] frescoed walls [*Eb⁺p* ≯of flesh] it is the closeted skeleton. But → <But→ Yet [*Eb⁺p* <Yet ≯But] not [*Eb⁺p* <"Pale . . . skeleton]
[*Eb⁺p then blue crayon cancel whole passage*]
[*rest of leaf blank; originally a clip was pinned on*]

136: Ee/F 146¹. [W 126]

Ee/F
[*p chapter-title* Pale ire, envy and despair]
[*ESM p* queries (*circled, with arrow pointing to HM's chapter-title above*) *undeciphered because erased; still legible is her erased notation p.* 144]

————◆————

That Claggart's figure was not amiss, and his face, save the chin, well moulded, has already been said. Of these favorable points he seemed not insensible, for he was not only neat but careful in his dress. But the form of Billy Budd was heroic; and if his face was without the intellectual look of the pallid Claggart's, not the less was it illuminated, [<illuminated *add* lit] like his, from within, though from a different source. The bonfire in his heart made luminous the ruddiness [<ruddiness ≯rose-tan] in his cheek.

137: Ee/Fp 146². [W 127]

Ee/F
In view of the marked contrast between the persons of the twain, it is more than probable that [>when] the Master-at-arms in the scene last given applied to the sailor the proverb Handsome is as handsome does; [Handsome ... does *underlined*] he there let escape an [>ironic] inkling xx →<xx→ not observed at the time, [<observed at the time >caught by the young sailors who heard it] as to what it was that had first [*mend*] moved him against Billy, namely, his striking [*p* <striking ≯significant] personal beauty.
    Now envy and antipathy passions irreconcilable in reason, neverthless in fact [*p* >may] spring conjoined like Chang and Eng in one birth. Is Envy then such a monster? Well, though many an

138: Ee/F 147. [W 128]

Ee/F
arraigned mortal has in hopes of mitigated penalty pleaded guilty to horrible actions, did ever anybody seriously confess to envy? Something there is in it universally felt to be even [<even] more shameful than even felonious crime. And does →<does→ not only does everybody disown it

139: Ee/F 148. [W 129]

* Ec? on Ee/F leaf
but the better sort of men [<of men] are inclined to incredulity when it is seriously [*p* <seriously ≯earnestly {<earnestly >in earnest}] imputed to any [*p* <any ≯an] intelligent man. But since its lodgement is in the heart

not the brain, no degree of intelligence [*p* <intelligence ≯intellect] supplies a guarantee against it, Inly it so self-humiliates a man that it is sought to be locked up [*no period*] [*p i* <Inly . . . locked up] But Claggart's was no vulgar form of the passion. Nor, as directed toward Billy Budd

140: Eb 146, Ee/F 149. [W 130]

Eb

did it partake of that streak of apprehensive jealousy that marred Saul's visage perturbidly brooding on the comely young David. Claggart's envy struck deeper. At bottom [<deeper. At bottom]

* Ca

deeper. If askance he eyed the good looks, cheery health and frank enjoyment of his [*p* <his] young life in Billy Budd, it was because these happened to go [*p* <happened to go ≯went] along with [*p* <went along with ≯were the outward expression of {<were ≯seemed to be} {<seemed to be the outward expression of ≫along with (*intention must have been to restore also* went)}] a nature that as Claggart magnetically felt, had in its simplicity never willed malice or felt unavailing remore. [<or felt unavailing remore. >or experienced the reacting bite of the {*p alter to* that} serpent in it. {*p* <reacting >(*above, with guide-line to caret*) reactionary pang in the secret sessions of thought.} {<reactionary pang >(*before* in the) or knew the pxx (*undeciphered*)} {*i* ≮or knew . . . thought. >reactionary (*before* bite *with guide-line to caret*) <in it *add period* (*after* serpent)} (*clause finally reads* or experienced the reactionary bite of that serpent.)] To Claggart, →<To Claggart→ To him, the spirit lodged within Billy,

Eb

and looking out from his blue [<blue ≯azure {*p* <azure ≯ (*below*) welkin}] eyes as from windows, that [*p* >(*below, circled*) ineffability] it was which

141: Eb 147, Ee/F 150. [W 131]

Eb

made the dimple in his rich [*p* <rich ≯dyed] cheek, suppled his joints, and dancing in his yellow curls made him [*p* >preeminently] the handsome sailor. [*p alter to* Handsome Sailor.] One person excepted the master-at-arms was perhaps the only man in the ship [>intellectualy] capable of of [*p* >fully {<fully >(*above, circled, with guide-line to caret*) adequately}] appreciating the moral phenomenon [>presented] in Billy Budd. He recognized in →*w.o.* his *add* In him (*before* He) *alter* He *to* he <his→ his own direct opposite →<In him . . . opposite→ And the insight but intensifed his passion, which assuming various [*p* ≯secret] forms within him, [*p* <him ≯his secret selfhood {<his secret selfhood *add* him}] at times assumed that of [>cynic] disdain—disdain of innocence. [*p alter period to dash*] To be m →<m→ nothing more than in-nocent! Yet in an æsthetic [*add* way] he saw the charm of it, the [>cou-rageous] free-and-esay →esay→ -easy temper of it, and fain would have shared it, but he despaired of it.

142: Eb 148, Ee/F 151. [W 132]

Eb

With no power to annul the elemental evil in him, tho readily enough he could disguise [*p* <disguise ⊁hide] it; apprehending the good, but powerless to be it; a nature like Claggart's surcharged with energy as such natures almost invariably are, what recourse is left to it but to recoil upon itself and like the scorpion for which the Creator is alone [<is >is (*after* alone)] responsible, live [*p* <live ⊁act] out to the end the nature [*p* <nature >stage-part { <stage}] alloted it.
[*p chapter-ending mark* ———◇———]

143: Cb 16³; Eb 149. [W 133]

Cb

[*ESM p notation* Follows 151 red (red *underlined*)]
[*p notation* New chp (*underlined*) and chapter-beginning mark ———◇———]

Passion, and passion in its profoundest, is not a thing demanding a lofty [*p* <lofty >scenic { <scenic >a palatial}] stage whereon to play its part. Away [*p* <Away] down upon [<upon >among] the groundlings, among the beggars and rakers of the garbage, it [*p Cb⁺* <it >profound passion] is enacted. And the circumstances that provoke it, however trivial or contempt-able, [<contemptable >mean,] are no measure of its power. In the present instance the stage is a [*Cb⁺p* ⊁ship's { ⊰ship's}] scrubbed deck, [<deck >gun-deck,] and the matter [*p* <the matter > (*below*) one of the { >outward} { <outward >external} provocations] a sailor's [<sailor's >man-of-war's- - man's] spilled soup.

Now when the Master-at-arms noticed whence came that greasy fluid [*Cb⁺p underline* greasy *and write query* (*under* fluid) liquid? { ⊰*underlining and* liq-uid?}] streaming before his feet, he must have taken it—to some extent wil-fully, perhaps— [<perhaps—] and welcoming it [*p* <and welcoming it] [*p notation* (*underlined, with fist below*) xx →<xx→ Insert afterwards]

144: 3; Ca 17. [W 134]

Ca

perhaps—not for the coincidence [*p* <coincidence >mere accident] it all but [*p* <all but] certainly [*p* <certainly ⊁assuredly] was, but for the sly escape of an →<an→ a spontanious [*p correct to* spontaneous] feeling on Billy's part

more or less answering to the antipathy on his own part. [p <part *add period* (*after* own)] In effect a foolish demonstration and very harmless, he must have thought, [p (*with circling and guide-line to caret*) *transpose* he must have thought *to follow* demonstration] which yet [<which yet] like the futile kick of a cow, [p <cow ⋗heifer] which yet were the cow [p <the cow ⋗heifer {<heifer *add* xx} {<xx ≫heifer}] a shod stallion, would not be so harmless. Even so was it that into the gall of his impulsive hate [<impulsive hate {Ca^+p >(*below*) envy} {Cb^+ ⦉envy >envy}] Claggart [p <his ⋗Claggart's *and* <Claggart ⋗he] infused the vitriol of deliberate [p Cb <deliberate >his] contempt.

145: Ca 18. [W 135]

---

* Ba

[p *add* But] The incident confirmed to him [*written over erased pencil catch-phrase* The incident confirmed to him] certain tell-tale reports purveyed to his ear by Squeak, [Squeak *underlined*] one of his more cunning Corporals, a little [p <little >a grizzled little] man, [p <*comma*] short and spare, [p <short and spare] so nicknamed

Ca

by the sailors on account of his squeaky voice, and sharp grizzled [p <grizzled] visage mousing [<mousing >ferreting] about the dark corners of the lower decks after interlopers, satirically suggesting to them the idea of a whiskered [<whiskered] rat in a cellar.

146: Ca 19. [W 136]

---

* Ba

From his master [p *alter to* master's {<master's ⋗Chief's} {Ca ⦉Chief's ⋗(*below, with guide-line to caret*) Chief's}] employing him as an implicit tool in laying little traps for the worriment of the Foretopman, [Ca >(*on leaf, below, circled, with guide-line to caret*)—for it was from the Master-at-arms that those per →<those per→ the {p >petty} persecutions heretofore mentioned {Cb <mentioned *add* adverted to} had proceeded—] this [p Ca <this >the] Corporal having naturally enough surmised →<surmised→ concluded that his →<his→ his [p Ca >master] could have no love for him →<him→ the sailor, made it his business, like a [p Ca <like a] faithful understrapper, [p Ca ⋗that he was,] to foment the animosity [p Ca <animosity >(*below*) ill blood] by perverting to his Chief

147: Ba 45, 45ᵖˡ; Ca 18, 20. [W 137]

---

* Ba 45

certain innocent frolics of the [p Ca >good natured] Foretopman, [Ba^+p <Foretopman ⋗sailor {⦉sailor ≫Foretopman}] besides inventing for him

[p <him ⸓his mouth] sundry contumelious epithets he claimed to have overheard from his mouth. [p Ca <from his mouth *add period (after* overheard) {p >him let fall.}] The Master-at-arms never suspected the veracity of these reports, more especially as to the epithets, for he well knew how [p >secretly] unpopular [Ba+p ⸓from the nature of his office { ⸘from . . . office *and incorporate substance in revision on leaf*}]

Ca

, and for no special →<and for no special→ may become a master-at-arms [p >(*below, circled, with guide-line to caret*) at least a master-at-arms of those days] zealous in his function, and how the blue-jackets shoot at him in private their raillery and wit; the nickname by which he goes among them (Jimmy Legs) [*name underlined*] implying under the form of merriment their [>cherished] disrespect and dislike. Besides, did not Squeak's tale secretly [p Cb <Besides . . . secretly] [p *guide-line to next leaf*]

148: Bab 45, 45ᵖ²; Ca 21, Cb 21¹. [W 138]

Bab
[p *guide-line continued, from upper left corner to first word to cancel original paragraph-break here*]
But indeed [p <indeed >in view of the greediness of hate for pabulum] it hardly needs [*alter* needs *to* needed] a purveyor to feed the perverse [p <the perverse >any ill { <ill *add* bad} { <any <bad *add* Claggart's}] passion. Profound [<Profound >Consider. An uncommon {p <Consider *and insert bracket for new paragraph (before* An uncommon)}] prudence is natural to the [p Cb <natural to the >habitual with the] subtler depravity, for it has everything to hide. And in case of a᾿ suspected →<suspected *alter* a *to* an→ injury but suspected, its secretiveness voluntarily cuts off proof, [Ba+p >it (*before* off) <proof >(*at foot of leaf, with guide-line to caret after* off) from enlightenment or disillusion] and [Ca <it <off . . . and ⸘from . . . disillusion >(*at foot of leaf, circled, with guide-line to caret before* action) it off from enlightenment or disillusion; and, not unreluctantly,] action is taken upon surmise as upon certainty. And the retaliation is apt to be in extreme [p <extreme ⸓monstrous] disproportion to the [>supposed] offence; for when in anybody was revenge in its exactions aught else but an [p >(*below, circled*) inordinate {Ca ⸘inordinate >inordinate}] usurer.

149: Cb 21². [W 139]

* Ca?
But how with his [p Cb <his >(*on leaf, with circling and guide-line to caret*) Claggart's] conscince? for those →<those >tho'→ consciences are unlike as brows [<brows >(*circled*) foreheads] and noses, [<and noses] every intelli-

gence has one →<has one *add comma (after* intelligence)→ including the [*p* >*(circled)* Scriptural { ⊀Scriptural <including the *i*>(*on leaf, below, circled, with guide-line to caret)* not excluding the Scriptural}] devils who "believe and tremble," has one. But Claggart's conscience being but the lawyer to his

150: Ca 22. [W 140]

Ca

will, made monsters [*p* ⊁ogres] of trifles, probably arguing that Billy's →<Billy's→ the motive its client [<its client] imputed to Billy in spilling his [<his *add* the] soup just [>then & there { <then & there <*caret*}] when he did, together with the epithets alleged, these, if nothing more [*p add comma*] made a good [*p* <good ⊁strong] case, [*p* ⊁against him *alter comma to semicolon*] nay [*p add comma*] justified animosity into a sort of retributive rightiousness. [*p correct to* righteousness] The Pharisee is [*p* <is ⊁being { <being *(without restoring* is)}] the Guy Fawks prowling in the hid chambers underlying some natures like [*p* <some natures like ⊁the] Claggart's. [*p alter to* Claggart] And they can [>really] form no conception of an unreciprocated malice.

151: Ca 23. [W 141]

Ca

Probably, the master-at-arms' clandestine persecution of Billy were started to try the temper of the man; but they [<they >it] had not su →<su→ developed any trait →<trait→ quality in him that enmity could make [*p* >official] use of or pervert into even plausable [*p correct to* plausible] justification of itself; [*p* >even *(before* pervert) *without canceling* even *(before* plausible) <of itself *add* self- *(before* justification) *and add semicolon (after* justification)] so that the incident [*p* <incident ⊁occurrence] at the mess, petty tho' it was, [<tho' it was ⊁if it were,] was a welcome one to that so →<so→ kind →<kind→ peculiar conscience that has been attributed to Claggart. →<that has been attributed to Claggart→ we have xxxx →<xxxx→ inadequately descri →<descri→ discribed →<discribed >*(below)* touched upon.→ [*p* <we have inadequately touched upon. ⊁assigned as →<as→ to be the private mentor { <private mentor *(leaving hiatus)*}] of Claggart; and, { ⊁for the rest,} not improbably he p →<he p→ it put him upon new experiments.]

152: Cb 24. [W 142]

Cb

———◇——-

Not many days after the last incident narrated something befell [>Billy] Budd that more gravelled him that aught that had previously occurred.

⟦ *346* ⟧

It was a warm night [>for the latitude;] and the Foretopman, whose watch it was below, should ha →<it was below, should ha→ at the time was properly below, was, with →<with→ dozing on the [<the >the uppermost] deck whither he had ascended from his hot hammock one of hundreds swinging so closely suspended [<swinging so closely >(*after* suspended) so closely {*p* >(*circled*) wedged} together] over the [*p* <over the ≯over a] lower gun-deck [*p* gun- {≫gun-}] that there was little or no swing to them. He lay [*add* as] in the shadow as [*p* <as] of a hill, [*p* <*comma and add* -side] stretched under the lee of the booms, [booms *underlined*]

153: Cb 25. [W 143]

Cb

a long pile [*p* <long pile >(*circled*) piled ridge] of spare spars where [*p* <where >amidships between foremast & mainmast and among which] the ship's largest boat, the launch, was stowed, temporarily inverted for repairs, its broad bottom looming up in the night like a vague dome. [*p add period* (*after* stowed) <temporarily . . . dome] He [<He *add* (*at bottom of leaf, circled, with guide-line to caret*) Alongside of three other slumberes from below, he] lay near the foreward end of the booms [<of the booms >booms' (*before* foreward end)] not far from [*p* <not far from >which →<which→ not far from →<not far→ >(*above, after* near) that {<that ≯one} {<one ≫that} end of . . . which approaches (*passage finally reads* lay near that end of the booms' which approaches) (from *and apostrophe are left*)] the foremast; his station [*add* aloft] on duty as a foretopman being right [*p* <right ≯just] over the deck-quarte →<quarte→ station of the forecastlemen, entitled [*p* <entitled ≯entitling] him according to usage to make himself more or less [<more or less >more especially {*p* <more especially ≫more or less}] at home in that neighborhood.

154: Cb 26. [W 144]

Cb

Presently he was stirred into semi-consciousness by sombody, who must have previously sounded the sleep of the others, touching his shoulder, and then as Billy [<Billy >the Foretopman] raised his head, breathing into his ear in a quick whisper, "Slip into the weather [<weather >lee] fore-chains, Billy; there is something in the wind. Quick →<Quick→ D'ont speak. Quick, I will meet you there"; and disappeared.

Now Billy like sundry other [*p* >essentially] goodnatured fellows [*p* <fellows ≯ones] had [*p* ≯some of] the weaknesses that pertain to [*p* <that pertain to >inseparable from essential] good nature; and among these was [*p* >a reluctance, or rather →<or rather→ almost] an incapacity of plumply [*p* <plumply >repellingly {<repellingly *add* curtly} {<curtly ≫plumply}] saying no [no *underlined*] to an abrupt proposition not obviously absurd or iniquitous nor made in any unfriendly way. [*p* <obviously {≫obviously} *and*

alter or *to* nor { <nor made . . . way ≯ on the face of it, nor obviously unfriendly nor →<nor ≫nor→ *add period* (*after* iniquitous)} (*passage finally reads* not obviously absurd, on the face of it, nor obviously unfriendly, nor iniquitous.)] As little did he have [*p* <As . . . have ≯ And being of warm blood, had →<had→ > (*above, circled*) he had ≯ not] the [>cold {*p* <cold}] phlegm [*p* ≯ silen →<silen → tacitly to] to negative it [*p* <it > (*below*) any proposition] by silent →<silent→ unresponsive inaction.

155: Cb 27. [W 145]

Cb

Like his sense of fear, his apprehension [*p* >as to aught out { <out > (*circled*) outside} of the common { <common ≯ honest & natural}] was seldom very quick. Besides, upon the present occasion, he was →<he was→ the drouse from his sleep still hung upon him.

However it was, he mechanically rose, and lazily [*p* <lazily ≯ sleepily] wondering what could be in the wind, [in the wind *underlined*] [*p* <*underlining*] betook himself to the designated place. The →<. The *add comma*→ a narrow platform [>, one of six,] outside of the high bulwarks and screened by the great dead-eyes and multiple columned lanyards of the [*p* ≯ fore- - { <fore-}] shrouds and back-stays; and, in a great war-ship of that time, a spot so →<a spot so→ of dimensions corresponding to the ample hull; [*p* <corresponding to the ample ≯ commensurate *add* 's *to* hull ≯ magnitude (*revision leaves syntactical gap; intention obviously was to read* commensurate to the hull's magnitude)] a tarry little [*p* <little] balcony in short overhanging the sea, and so secluded that one seaman [*p* <seaman ≯ (*below*) mariner]

156: Cc 28¹. [W 146]

Cc

of the Indomitable, [*underlined*] made it even in daytime →<made it even in daytime→ a non-conformist forecastleman [*p* <forecastleman ≯ old tar] of a serious turn, made it even it →<it→ in daytime his private oratory.

In this retired nook the stranger soon joined Billy Budd. There was no moon as yet; the ha →<the ha→ a haze obscured the star-light. He could not distinctly see the stranger's face. Yet from something in the outline and carriage, Billy kn →<kn→ took him to be, and correctly, for a →<a→ one of the afterguard.

"Hist! Billy", said the man; [*p* > (*below, circled, with guide-line to caret*) in the same rapid { <rapid > (*below*) quick cautionary} whisper as before] "You were impressed, were't you? Well, so was I;" and he paused, as to mark the effect. But Billy not knowing [>exactly] what to mak [*p correct to* make] of this

[[*348*]]

157: Cc 28². [W 147]

Cc

said nothing. Then the other: "We are not the only impressed ones, Billy. There's a gang of us. —Could'nt you [*p add dash*] help—at a pinch? [*no quotation mark*]

"What do you mean? [*no quotation mark*] demanded Billy now [*p* <now ⤲here] thoroughly awakened [<thoroughly awakened {*p* ≫thoroughly} {*p* <thoroughly}] shaking off the drousy feeling. [*p* <the >his *delete* y *from* drousy <feeling]

"Hist, hist! [*p* >in a husky {<in a husky *add* the hurried} whisper now growing husky, with th →<with→] see here;" and the man held up two small objects faintly twinkling in the nightlight; [*p add quotation mark*] see, they are yours, Billy, if you'll only—"

But Billy broke in, and in his [*p* ⤲hot →<hot→ resentful] eagerness to deliver himself his vocal infirmity [*p* >somewhat] intruded; "[*p* >D—D Damme,] I do'nt know what you are [*p* >d—] d—driving

158: Cc 28³. [W 148]

Cc

at, [*p* >afterguardsman {<afterguardsman}] or wh— [*p* <wh—] what you mean, but you had better g—g—go where you belong." [*p alter period to exclamation mark*] For the moment the fellow [>, as confounded,] did not stir; and Billy springing to his feet, said "If you d—d—dont [*delete first* d—] start, I'll t—t—toss you back over the [>r—] rail!" There was no mistaking this and the mysterious emissary decamped disappearing toward →<toward→ in the direction of the mainmast in the shadow of the booms.

"Hallo, what's the matter?" here came [*p* >growling] from a forecastleman awakened from his deck-dose [doze?] by Billy's raised voice. And as the foretopman reappeared and was recognised [recognized?] by him; "Ah, Beauty, [*underlined*]

159: Cc 29. [W 149]

* Cca

is it you? Well, something must have been the matter for you st—st—stuttered."

"O," [*comma mended and replaced?*] rejoined Billy, now all right again and [<all right again and] mastering the impediment; "I found an afterguardsman sneaking [<sneaking {≫sneaking} {*p* <sneaking}] in our part of the ship here and I bid him be off where he belongs."

Cc

"And is that all you did about it?" →*delete question mark and quotation mark and add comma*→ foretopman?" gruffly demanded another, an irasciable old fellow of brick-colored visage and hair, and who was known to his associates [*alter* associates *to* associate >(*below, circled*) forecastlemen] as Red Pepper; [*name underlined*] "Such sneaks sho →<sho→ I should like to marry to the gunner's daughter!" by that expression meaning that he would like to subject them to disciplinary castigation over a gun.

160: Cb 30. [W 150]

Cb

However, the foretopman's [*p* <foretopman's ⊁Billy's] rendering of the matter satisfactorily explained →<explained→ accounted for the brief commotion to these inquirers, [*p transpose* (*circled*) to these inquirers, *to follow* accounted] since of all the sections of a ship's company the forecastlemen, old [*p* <old] veterans for the most part and bigoted in their [>sea-] prejudices, are the most jealous in resenting territorial encroachments, especially on the part of any of the afterguard, of whom they they have but a sorry opinion, chiefly landsmen, never going aloft except to reef or furl the mainsail, and incapable of handling [*p* <incapable of ⊁(*below*) not →<not→ in no wise competent to *alter* handling *to* handle] a marlinspike. [*p* <*period and* >(*below, with guide-line*) and →<and→ or turning in a dead-eye, (*underlined*) say.]

161: Cb 31. [W 151]

Cb

[*p chapter-beginning mark* ———◇———]
   This incident sorely puzzled Billy Budd. It was an entirely new experience; the first time in his life that he had even been personally apprached in underhand intrigueing fashion. Prior to this encounter he had known nothing of the afterguardsman, the two men being stationed wide apart, one foreward and aloft during his watch, the other on deck and aft. [*add bracket for new paragraph*] What could it mean? And could they really be guineas, those two glittering objects the interloper had held up to his [>(Billy's)] eyes?

162: Cb 32. [W 152]

Cb

Where could the fellow get guineas? Hardly so plentiful [>as buttons] are they with sailors [*p* <Hardly so plentiful as *add* (*before* buttons) Why even s →<s→ <are they with sailors >(*after* buttons) are not so plentiful {*p* >(*above, circled, after, and without canceling,* buttons) spare buttons}] at sea. [*p* >(*below*) and even buttons sometimes are scarce { <and even . . . scarce}] The more he turned the matter over, the more he was non-plussed, and made uneasy and discomforted. In his instinctive recoil →<instinctive recoil *add* disgustful→ recoil from an overture which tho' he but ill comprehended he

instinctivly knew x →<x→ must involve evil of some sort, Billy Budd was like a young horse fresh from the pasture suddenly inhaling a vile whiff from some chemical factory and by repeated snortings tries to get it out of his nostrils and lungs. In this [*p* <In *alter* this *to* This] frame [*p* >of mind barred] all desire of holding further

163: Cc 33¹. [W 153]

Cc

parley with the fellow, even were it but to →<to→ for the purpose of gaining some enlightenment as to his real [*p* <real] design in clandestinely [*p* <in clandestinely {≫in}] approaching him. And yet he was not without natural curiosity to see how such a visitor in the dark would look in broad day.

He espied him the following afternoon in his [*p* ≯first] dog-watch below one of the smokers on that foreward part of the upper gun deck allotted to the pipe. He recognised [recognized?] him by his general look [*p* <look ≯cut] and build, more than by his round freckled face →<face ≫face→ and fugitive eyes of watery blue, [*p add (after* and*)* p →<p→ <watery ≯glassy <glassy >pale <fugitive ≯m →<m→ *add* glassy (*passage finally reads* face and glassy eyes of pale blue,)] shaded [*ESM p* <shaded ≯veiled] with lashes all but white.

164: Cc 33². [W 154]

Cc

And yet Billy was a bit uncertain whether indeed it were he—the young [<the young >yonder] fellow [*p* <fellow ≯ (*above canceled* young) chap] about his own age chatting and laughing in free-hearted way, leaning against a gun; a genial young fellow enough to look at, and something of a rattle-brain, to all appearance. Rather chubby too for a sailor even an afterguardsman. In short the last man in the world, one would think, to be overburthened with thoughts, especially those perilous thoughts that must needs belong to a con- spirator in any serious project, or [*p* >even] to the confident [*p* <confident ≯underling] of one. [*p* <one. > (*below*) such a conspirator.]

165: Cc 33³. [W 155]

Cc

For all that, [>in some sort] he must needs have been a sly one. [*p* <one ≯dog. { <dog *add* fox}] [*p* <For . . . fox.] For altho' [*p* <For *capitalize* altho'] Billy was not aware of it, the fellow, with a sidelong [>watchful] glance had perceived Billy first, and then noting that he [*p* <he ≯Billy] was looking at him, [*p* >thereupon] nodded a familar sort of friendly recognition as to an old acquaitance, without interrupting the talk he was engaged in with the group of smokers. A day or two afterwards chancing to →<to→ in the dog-watch [*p* <dog-watch ⸴evening] promenade on a gun deck, to pass Billy, he offered a flying word of good-fellowship as it were, which by its unexpectedness, and equivocalness under the circumstances

166: Cc 33⁴. [W 156]

Cc

so embarrased Billy that he knew not how to respond to it, and let it go unnoticed. After that there was no more recognition on either side. [*p* <After . . . side. (*after canceling this sentence,* HM *marked* After that there *for restoration but then again canceled the entire sentence*)]

Billy was now left more at sea [*p* <sea ⸴at a loss] than x →<x→ before. [*written over beginning of another word*] The ineffectual speculations into which he was led was so disturbingly alien to him that he did his best to smother them. It never entered his mind that here was a matter which from its suspiciousness, [*p* <suspiciousness ⸴questionableness *add* (*before* questionableness) extreme] it was his duty as a loyal tar →<tar→ blue-jacket to report in the proper quarter. And, probably, had such a course →<course→ step been suggested to him, he would have been deterred from taking it by the thought,

167: Cb 34. [W 157]

Cb

one of novice-magnanimity, that it would savor overmuch of the dirty work of a tell-tale. He kept the thing to himself. Yet upon one occasion, tempted →<tempted→ he could not forbear a little disburthening himself to the old Dansker, tempted [*p* (*above* tempted) *start but neither finish nor cancel a substitute word*] thereto perhaps by the influence of a fine balmy night, [*p* <fine >(*after* night) when the ship lay becalmed *alter comma* (*after* night) *to semicolon*] the twain, silent for the most part, sitting together on deck, their heads propped against the bulwarks. But it was only a partial and annoyemous [*sic?*] account that Billy gave, the unfounded scruples above referred to preventing full disclosure to anybody. Upon hearing Billy's version, the old [*p* <old ⸴(*below*) sage] Merlin of the sea [<Merlin of the sea >(*below*) Dansker] seemed to

168: Cb 35. [W 158]

* *Cba* 35

divine more than he was told; and after a little meditation during which his wrinkles [>were] pursed them [<them] as into a point, quite effacing for the time that quizzing expression they [*p* <they >his face] sometimes wore, —"Did'nt I say so, Baby Budd?" [*add bracket for new paragraph*] "Say what?" demanded Billy.

"Why, Jemmy Legs [*name underlined*] is down [*underlined*] on you."

"And what" rejoined Billy in amazement, "has Jemmy Legs [*name underlined*] to do with that cracked afterguardsman?"

Cbb

"Ho, it was an afterguardsman then. A cat's-paw, a catsp → < catsp → cat's-paw!" And with that exclamation, which, whether it had reference to a light puff of air [*p marginal notation (circled, at right) flaw?*] just then coming over the calm sea, or subtler relation to the afterguardsman, there is no telling, the old Merlin gave a twisting wrench with his

169: Cb 36. [W 159]

* Cba 36

black teeth at his plug of tobacco, vouchsafing no reply to Billy's impetuous question, tho' now repeated, for it was his wont to relapse into grim silence when interrogated in skeptical sort

Cbb

as to any of his sententious oracles, not always very clear ones, rather partaking of that tenebrific [*p* < tenebrific > obscurity] which invests most Delphic deliverances from any quarter.

[*p chapter-ending mark* ———◇———]

late pencil

In → < In→ Long experience had very likely brought this old man to the conclusion that never to give advice → < the . . . advice→ that [>bitter] prudence which never interferes in aught and never gives advice.

170: Cb 37 [*at first* 38?]. [W 160]

Cb

[*p chapter-beginning mark* ———◇———]

Yes, despite the Dansker's pithy insistence as to the Master-at-arms being at the bottom of these strange experiences of Billy on board the Indomitable, [*underlined*] the young sailor was ready to ascribe them to almost anybody but the man who, to use Billy's own word → < word→ expression, "always had a pleasant word for him." Well may this [*p* < Well may *capitalize* this >is to] be wondered at. Yet not so much to be wondered at. In certain matters, some [*p* <some] some sailors even in mature life remain

* Ca

unsophisticated enough. But a young seafarer of the disposition of the foretopman, [*p* < the >our athletic *capitalize* foretopman] is much of a child-man. And yet a child's utter [*p* < a child's utter >for the child its { ≺for the child its ≫a child's} {≫utter}] innocence is but its blank [*p* <blank ≯utter {≫blank (*without canceling* utter)}] ignorance, and the former [*p* <former ≯innocence]

[[*353*]]

171: Cb 38¹. [W 161]

***

* Caa 24² on Cb leaf
inevitably [p <inevitably >naturally { <naturally ⊁ (below) more or less} wanes as intelligence waxes. But in Billy Budd intelligence, such as it was, had advanced [p add comma] while yet his simplicity [alter simplicity to simple-mindedness] remained for the most part unaffected. [p mend] Experience [mend] is a teacher indeed; yet did Billy's years make his experience small; [Ca⁺p notation Insert (fragmentary))]
* Cab
He [<He > (below) Besides] He had none of that intuitive knowledge of the bad which in natures not good [(> below, on leaf, circled, with guide-line to caret) or incompletely so] foreruns experience, and therefore may pertain, as in some instances it too clearly pertains, [>does (before pertains) alter to pertain] even to youth.

172: Cc 38². [W 162]

***

Cc
And what could Billy know of man except of man as a [p >mere] sailor? And the old-fashioned sailor, the veritable man-before-the-mast, the sailor from boyhood up, he, tho' indeed of the same species as landsmen [>a (before landsmen) and alter to landsman] is in some respects almost as [p <almost as >very { <very >singularly}] distinct from him as a man is from a woman. [p <as a man is from a woman] The sailor is frank force, [p i alter to frankness <force] the landsman is finesse. Life is not a game with the sailor, demanding the long head; no [>intricate] game of chess where nothing is to be achieved by [<nothing is >seldom is anything { <seldom is anything to be achieved by > (below, circled, with guide-line to caret) few moves are made in}] straight-forwardness, but more often [<but more often >and ends are attained] by indirection; an oblique, tedious, intricate [<intricate >barren] game hardly worth that poor candle burnt out in playing it.

173: Cc 38³. [W 163]

***

* Ca on Cc leaf
[vestigial insertion, circled, the property of (?) { ⊀insertion}]
[p add Yes,] As a class, sailors are in character a juvenile race. And [<And >Even] their deviations are marked by juvenility. And this more especially holding true
† Cab
[add with the] sailors of Billy's time. Then, too, certain things which apply to all sailors, do more pointedly apply to the younger [p <apply to the younger ⊁ operate {add here & there,} upon the →<the→ junior] one. He has been [p <has been add is {Cc green crayon <He is}]

174: Cc 39¹. [W 164]

Cc

he [*p alter* he *to* He { <He >Every sailor, too}] is accustomed to obey orders without debating them; his life afloat is externally ruled for him; he is not brought into that promiscuous commerce with mankind where [>unobstructed free agency on] equal terms—equal superficially, at least—soon teach [*alter* teach *to* teaches { <teaches >teaches}] one that unless upon occasion he exercise a distrust keen in proportion to the fairness of the appearance, some foul turn may be served him. A ruled undemonstrative distrustfulness is so xx →<xx→ habitual, not with business-men so much [*p add comma*] as with men who know their kind in less shallow relations than business, namely, [*p* >certain] men-of-the-world, that they

175: Cc 39². [W 165]

Cc

come at last to employ it all but unconsciously; and some of them would very likely feel real surprise at being charged with it as one of their general characteristics.

176: Ca 26, Cb 40. [W 166]

Ca

[*p notation* New Chapter]
[*p chapter-beginning mark* ———✧———]
  But after the little matter at the mess Billy Budd no more found himself in mysterious [*p Cb* <mysterious >strange] trouble at times about his hammock or his clothes-bag or what not. While, as to that smile that deluded him [*p Cb* <deluded him >occasionally suned →<suned→ sunned him,] and [>the] pleasant passing word, these were if →<if→ if not more frequent, yet if anything more pronounced than before. [*p add bracket for new paragraph*] But for all that, there were certain other demonstrations now. When Claggart's unobserved glance happened to

177: Cab 27, Cb 41. [W 167]

* Caa? 27 on Cb leaf

[*p notation* (*on leaf*) 48 green (green *underlined*) follows]
light on belted Billy rolling along the →<the→ the upper gun-deck in the leisure of the last [<last >second] dog-watch exchanging passing broadsides of fun with ga →<ga→ other young promenaders in the crowd; that evil eye [<evil eye >glance] would follow the cheerful sea-Hyperion with

178: Ba 48. [W 168]

Ba

would follow the unconscious sailor with [B+p > (at top) cheerfully (?) tarrying (?) handsome good-fellow { <cheerfully . . . good-fellow >cheerfully tarrying young} { <cheerfully tarrying young >cheerful sea Hyperion} {Ca ◁cheerful sea Hyperion (incorporating its substance in passage now on preceding leaf) <would follow . . . with}] a settled meditative and melancholly [p correct to melancholy] expression, the [p (over the) write his] dark hazel [<dark hazel] eye [p add s {◁s}] strangely [p <strangely ▷mysteriously {by erasing <mysteriously ≫strangely}] suffused with incipient feverish tears. Then would Claggart look like the man of sorrows. And [B+p >And yes, {Ca ◁And yes, add Yes, and}] sometimes the melancholly [p delete one l] look [p Ca <look >expression] would have in [>it] a touch of [p Ca ▷soft] yearning and softness, [p Ca <and softness] as if he [p Ca <he >Claggart] could even have loved Billy but for fate. [B+p >forbidding { <forbidding add & ban}] It was [B+p <It was ▷But this was] an evanescence, and quickly replaced [B+p <replaced >repented of, as it were] by an immitigable look pinching and dwarfing [B+p <pinching and dwarfing ▷shrinking & pinching { <shrinking add (after pinching) & shrinking}] the whole intellectual head [B+p ▷of the man] as by incantation [B+p <as by incantation] into the semblance of a wrinkled walnut. Various were these invountary caprices. [B+p >(below, circled) of passion] [Cap and green crayon <for fate . . . of passion and incorporate substance in revision on patch]

† **Ca**

for fate and ban. But this was an evanescence, and quickly repented of, as it were, by an immitigable look, pinching and shrivelling the visage into the momentary semblence of a wrinkled walnut.

179: Ba 49, Bc 49¹. [W 169]

*** Ba 49 (I)**

[p >But] Sometimes catching sight along the vistaed batteries [p <the <batteries add a (before vistaed) ▷lower deck (after vistaed) {Ca <along . . . batteries >in advance}] of the foretopman advancing [Ca <advancing >coming] in his direction, he would, [p <he would ▷Claggart { <Claggart ≫he would}] upon their nearing, [p >would { <would}] step aside a little to let him pass, dwelling upon him [p Ca <him ▷Billy] for the moment [spelling elided] with an ambiguous smile. [p Ca <an ambiguous >the glittering dental (before smile) >of a Guise. (after smile)] [p <smile ▷satire] But [p >invariably { <invariably}] upon any abrupt unforseen encounter a red light would forth from his eye like a spark from a struck [Ca green crayon <struck {p also <struck alter a to an}] anvil in a dusk smithy. [p two large check marks (in left margin beside last sentence)]

[[*356*]]

180: Bc/Ca 49². [W 170]

Bc/Ca

That quick fierce light was a strange one, darted from orbs which in repose were of a color nearest approaching a deeper violet, the softist →*correct to* softest <softest→ softest of shades.

* Ba 49 (II)

Tho' some of these peculiar emanations [*p Ca* <peculiar emanations >(*circled, with guide-line to caret*) caprices of the pit] could not but be observed by Bi →<Bi→ their object, yet were they beyond the construeing [*Ca add as revision of canceled first line on next leaf* of such a nature.]

181: Ba 50, Bc/Ca 50¹. [W 171]

Ba

of so simple and untutored a nature. [*B⁺p* <so simple and untutored a >the (*incomplete revision*) {*Ca* <of . . . nature *add substance to last sentence on preceding leaf*}] And the thews [*ESM p underline* thews *and* ⸖ *question mark as query*] of Billy were incompatible [*p* <in ⸖ not {<not *add* hardly (*before* compatible)}] with that sort of sensitive spiritual organization [organisation?] which in some cases instinctivly [*p* ⸖ which in less vigorous souls {⟨which . . . souls}] conveys to ignorant innocense a waring →*correct to* warning→ [*p* <warning >admonition] of the proximity of the malign. He thought the Master-at-arms acted in a manner rather queer at tims. That was all. But the occasional [*p* <occasional {≫occasional}] frank air and pleasant word [*p* ⸖ when those {<when those}] went for what they purported to be, for the [*p* <the (*in error for* for?)] young sailor [*p* >athlete {⟨athlete}] was not yet of those who distrust [*p* ⸖ not being (?) aware (?) of {*i* ⟨not . . . of ⸖ not →<not *add* never→ having heard as yet of}] the "too fair-spoken man."

182: Bb 50². [W 172]

[*Top clip is from same Ba leaf (Ba* ⟨51⟩) *as that on Leaf 188.*]

* Ba (I)

Had the foretopman been conscious of having done or said anything to provoke the ill will of the official, it would have been different with him, and his sight would [*p Bb* <would >might] have been [*p* >x →⟨x→ purged {*Bb* ⟨purged >purged if not}] sharpened. As it was innocense was [<was >(*below*) *a revision later cut off* {≫was}] his blinder.

Bb

So was it with him in yet another matter. Certain [*p Bc/Ca* <Certain >Two] minor officers— [*p* >and among them {⟨and among them}] the

armorer, →*capitalize* armorer→ [>and] [Bb^+p ⪢ship's yeoman, apothecary
<Armorer { ⪡ship's yeoman, apothecary ⪢Armorer}] Captain of the Hold,
and others [<and others {Bb^+p ⪢Apothecary &c for bo} { ⪡Apothecary &c
for bo}] with whom he had never exchanged a word, [p ⪢neither his needs
nor { ⪡neither his needs nor}] his position in the ship not [p <not ⪢not]
bringing him into contact with them; these men began →<began→ now for
the first began to cast upon Billy when they chanced to see [p <see ⪢meet
(?) {Bb/Ca ⪡meet >encounter}] him, that peculiar glance unmistakable to
the experienced [Bb^+p ⪢(*below*) to him upon it falls if { ⪢a person of some}
experience { ⪡to him . . . experience}] [Bc/Ca <glance . . . experienced *and
incorporate substance on following leaf*]

183: Bc/Ca 50³. [W 173]

Bc/Ca
glance which evidences that the man casting →<casting→ from whom it
comes has been some way tampered with and to the prejudice of him upon
whom the glance lights. Never

* Bb
did it occur to Billy as a thing to be noted or a thing suspicious, tho' he well
knew the fact, that the Armorer [Bb^+p <Armorer ⪢ship's-yeoman { ⪡ship's- -
yeoman ⪢Armorer}] and Captain of the hold, [*capitalize* hold] [Bb^+p >&
others →<& others→ c { ⪡& others c} >(*below, circled, with guide-line to
caret*) with other men →<men→ officers of that grade {Bc/Ca ⪡with . . .
grade *and incorporate substance in same space* with the ship's-yeoman, apothecary, and others of that grade,}] were by naval usage, messmates of the master- -
at-arms, men [Bc/Ca <men {*add* men}] with ears convenient to his [Bc/Ca
>confidential] tongue. [Bb^+p *alter period* (*after* tongue) *to semicolon and add*
(*below*) and more →<more→ further that the master-at-arms what he did not
know—was in →<in→ the man ascendant in that exclusive mess. {Bc/Ca
⪡and further . . . mess *and incorporate substance in addition on* Bc/Ca *leaf*}]

Bc/Ca
and, moreover—which he did not know—that in this exclusive mess the Master-at-arms was the ascendant man. [p <and . . . man *and re-alter semicolon*
(*after* tongue) *to period*]

184: Bc/Ca 50⁴. [W 174]

Bc/Ca
But the general popularity that our Handsome Sailor's [*underlined*] exemption from all vanity, [<exemption from all vanity] manly forewardness upon
occasion, and irresisable good nature indicating no mental superiority, however, to →<, however, to→ tending to excite an invidious feeling in any fellow
sailor; [<in any fellow sailor *add semicolon* (*after* feeling)] this pop →<pop→

good will on the part of [*add* most of] his shipmates made him the less to concern himself about such mute aspects toward him as those to →<to→ whereto allusion has just been made. [*p* >(*at bottom but not marked for insertion*) aspects he could not →⋟so→ fathom as to take in then what →<take in then what→ infer their whole import]

185: Cb 50⁵. [W 175]

Cb

As to that conundrum [*Cb+p* <conundrum >problem] of the dark, [*Cc* <As to that ⋖problem <of the dark *add* As to] the afterguardsman, tho' Billy [>(*below, circled, with guide-line to caret*) for reasons already given] necessarily saw little of him, yet when the two did happen to meet, invariably came the fellow's off-hand cheerful recognition, which but lacked the pleasant passing word of the master-at-arms to make it equally →<which . . . equally→ sometimes accompanied by a passing [>pleasant] word or two. Whatever that man →<man→ equivocal young fellow's [*p* <fellow ⋟man's { <man's ⋟person (*before uncanceled* 's)}] original design may really have been, [*p* >(*below, circled, with guide-line to caret*) or the design dep →<dep→ of which he might have been but →<but→ the deputy] it seemed evident [*p* <it seemed evident *add* certain it was] from his manner upon these occasions, that he had wholly dropped that design. [*p* <that design. *add* it.]

186: Cb 50⁶. [W 176]

Cb

It was as if his precocity of crookedness (and every vulgar villian is precocious in his villainy) [<in his villainy) *add close-parenthesis* (*after* precocious)] had for once deceived him, and the man he had sought to play upon [*p* <play upon ⋟entrap] as a simpleton, [>had] through his very simplicity [*p* >ignominiously { <ignominiously} {≫ignominiously}] baffled him.

Any shrewd one would think [*p revise to* But shrewd ones may opine] that it would be →<would be→ was [*p mend* was] hardly possible for Billy to restrain from →<restrain from→ refrain from bluntly →<bluntly→ going up to the afterguardsman and bluntly demanding to know his purpose in the initial interview. [*p* <*period* >(*below, with guide-line to caret*) so abruptly closed in the fore-chains] The shrewd one would [*p* <The *alter to* Shrewd ones <would ⋟may] also think it likely that →<likely that→ but natural in Billy to set about

187: Cb 50⁷. [W 177]

* Cb

sounding some of the [*ESM? p* >other] impressed men of the ship in order to discover what basis, if any, there was for the emissary's obscure suggestions as to lurking [<lurking >plotting] disaffection aboard. Yes, any shrewd one would [p <any <one would >may so (*leaving incomplete revision*)] so think.

* Cba

But something more, and [<and >or, rather,] something else than mere shrewdness is perhaps needful for the due understanding of such a character as Billy Budd's.

[p *chapter-ending mark* ———◈——— { ⊀*chapter-ending mark*}]

188: Bb 50⁵, Cb 50⁹ [Cb notation 50⁸ green omitted], Bc/Cab 51. [W 178]

188: **Bb 50^5, Cb 50^9 [Cb notation 50^8 green omitted], Bc/Cab 51. [W 178]**

[*Bottom clip is from same* Ba *leaf as clip on top of Leaf 182, with about two lines missing between them.*]

* Bb

As to Claggart, the monomania of [*i* <of >in] the man—if that indeed it were—as involuntarily disclosed by starts in the manifestations detailed, yet in general

* Ba (. . . II)

covered over by his self-contained and rational demeanor; this, [p ⋟pent frenzy { ⊀pent frenzy}] like a subterranean fire was eating its way deeper and deeper in him. Something positive [<positive >decisive] must come of it.

[p *chapter-ending mark* ———◈——— {G *blue crayon w.o. similar chapter-ending mark*}]

189: **Ga 1. [W 179]**

Ga

[p *notation (with fist, and underlined) follows 51 green*]

[p *notation (boxed, at top of leaf)* See side for Number of Page {*ESM* p >right hand (*before* side)}]

[p *chapter-beginning mark* ———◈———]

Some time passed after the abruptly ended interview in the fore-chains and [Gb <Some . . . and ⋟ (*above, with guide-line*) After the mysterious interview in the fore-chains, the one so abruptly ended there by Billy,] nothing especially german to the story occurred until the events now about to [p >be] narrated.

Elsewhere it has been said that in the lack of frigates (of course better sailers than line-of-battle ships) in the English fleet of that period →<fleet of that period→ squadron up the Straits at that period, the Bellipotent 74 [*ship name underlined*] on account of her sailing qualities not common in a ship of her rate [Ga⁺p <on account of . . . rate >perhaps quite as much { ⊀perhaps quite as much} {Gb <on account of . . . rate *and incorporate substance of revision on added leaf Gb* 2¹}]

⟦ *360* ⟧

190: Gb 2¹. [W 180]

Gb

was occasionally employed not only as an available substitute for a scout, but at times on detached service of more important kind. This was not alone because of her sailing qualities, not common in a ship of her rate, but quite as much, probably, that the character of her commander, [>it was thought,] specially adapted him for any duty where under unforseen difficulties a prompt initiative might have to be taken in some matter calling for → <calling for→ demanding knowledge and ability in addition to those [>qualities] implyed in good seamanship and so forth. [*p* <and so forth *add period (after* seaman-ship)]

191: Ga 2, Gb 2². [W 181]

Ga

was occasionly employed on detached service, as a sort of [*Ga⁺p* <sort of ⫸substitute for a] scout or otherwise [*Ga⁺p* <on (*before* detached service) ⫸not only as a substitute for a scout but {*add* even} {<even} at times on <(*after* service) as . . . otherwise ⫸of {⫸quite} another sort.] and sometimes on more or less distant expeditions. It was on seperate duty of the latter sort [*Gb* <was occasionly . . . latter sort (*also* <*revision at bottom of Ga 1) and incorporate substance on added leaf Gb 2¹ and on revision patch placed over the above canceled passage*]

† Gb

It was on an expedition of the latter sort, a somewhat distant one, and when the Bellipotent [*underlined*] was almost at her furthest remove from the fleet

Ga

that in the latter part of an afternoon-watch she [*p* >unexpectedly] came in sight of a ship of the enemy. It proved to be a frigate. The latter percieving thro' the glass that the weight of men and metal would be heavily against her, invoking her light heels crowded sail to get away. After a chace urged almost against hope and lasting until about the middle of the first dog-watch [*p add comma*]

[*191a*] 222†*v:*

[*Superseded top segment of* Bb 53. *Matter corresponds to that now on Leaf 192, top. With perhaps one line missing it joins the clip at the bottom of Leaf 192.*]

* Bb 53 (I)

of the chace [*Bb⁺p* <of the chace >accompanying it] had altogether waned down, the master-at-arms cap in hand appeared at the place of official interview → <the place of official interview→ an allotted by the mainmast → <an

allotted by the mainmast→ the mainmast →<cap in hand appeared at *add guide-line (from after* master-at-arms) *and continue*→ ascending from below to the upper deck, appeared [*p* <below . . . deck >(*after* from) his { >subterranean} sphere] by the →<by the *add period (after* appeared)→
[*Ga ut leaf off here and mount bottom segment as clip on Ga 3, canceling the above passage by green crayon*]

192: Ga 3. [W 182]

Ga

[*ESM p notation 54* green follows]
she signally succeeded in effecting her escape.

Not long after the pursuit had been given up, and ere the excit →<excit→ interest [<interest >excitement incident thereto] had altogether waned away, the Master-at-Arms ascending from his cavernous sphere made his appearance cap in hand by the mainmast [<mainmast >mainmast]

* Bb [53] (. . . II)
respectfully [*Bb*⁺*p* >requesting { ≪requesting}] waiting the notice of Captain Vere then walking [*p Ga* <walking >solitary paceing { <paceing ≫walking}] the after-deck, [*p Ga* <after >weather-side of the quarter- (*before* -deck)] evidently [*p Ga* <evidently >doubtless somewhat] chafed at the failure of the [*p* >recent { ≪recent}] pursuit. [*p* <pursuit >(*below*) chace. { ≪chace. ≫pursuit}] The spot where Claggart stood was the place alloted to men of the [*p Ga* <the] lesser grades seeking some more particular interview either [*p undeciphered erasure along bottom of clip* . . . that he should obtain (?) permission of . . .]

193: Bb 54; Ga 4. [W 183]

Bb

with the officer-of-the-deck or the captain. [*p* >himself.] But from the latter it was not often that a sailor or petty- [*mend* y] officer [>of those days] would seek a hearing; only some exceptional cause, would, according to established custom, have warranted that.

Presently, just as Captain Vere [*p* <Captain Vere ≯the Commander] worried by [*p* <worried by ≯absorbed in] his reflections was on the point of turning aft in his promenade, he became sensible of Claggart's prescence, [*p correct to* presence] and seeing the doffed cap held in deferential expectancy, [*p notation* (Insert) { ≪(Insert)}] knew what that →<that *add* it→ meant. [<seeing ≯saw <knew what it meant <*comma and add period (after* expectancy)] On the instant [*B*⁺*p* >(*below, circled for insertion, with guide-line to caret*) No sooner did Captain Vere observe who it was that stood awaiting him, than { ≪No sooner . . . than}] that expression that flits across the face of most men sud →<sud→ at unawares encountering a person [*Ga* <On . . . person *and draw guide-line to next leaf, which incorporates substance of above revisions in its second paragraph (and on Ga 6)*]

194: Ga 5. [W 184]

Ga

Here be it said that Captain Vere personal knowledge of this petty-officer had only begun at the time of the ship's [>last] sailing from home, Claggart then for the first, in transfer from a ship detained for repairs, [*mend*] supplying on →<on→ in [*p* <in >on board] the Bellipotent the place of a previous Master-at-arms [*p* ⊁now {<now}] disabled from duty [*p* <from duty] and in hospital [*p* <in hospital] ashore.

No sooner did the Commander observe who it was that now so [*p* <so] deferentially stood awaiting [>his] notice, than a peculiar expression came over his face. [*p* <his face ⊁him.] It was not unlike that which uncontrolably will flit across the

195: Ga 6. [W 185]

Ga

countenance of one at unawares encoutering a person who tho' [*ESM p alter to* though] known to him indeed has hardly been long enough known for thorough knowledge, but whose →<whose→ something in whose aspect nevertheless now for the first operates upon him with a r →<operates >>operates <operates on him with a r→ provokes a vaguely repellant distaste. But coming to a stand, and resuming much of his wonted official manner, save that a sort of impatience lurked in the intonation of the opening word, he said "Well? what is it, Master-at-Arms?" [*add bracket for new paragraph*] With the air of a subordinate grieved at the necessity of being a messenger of ill tidings and [*Gb add comma (after* tidings) *add* while] conscientiously determined to be frank but to shun [*Gb (after* frank) *add* , yet <but to >(*below, circled, with guide-line to caret*) equally resolved upon *alter* shun *to* shunning] overstatement,

196: Ga 7. [W 186]

Ga

Claggart at this invitation or rather summons to disburthen, spoke up. What he said, conveyed in the language of no uneducated man, was to this [*Gab* <this *add* the] effect [*Gab* >(*at bottom of leaf, circled, with guide-line to caret*) following if not altogether in these words, namely, that →<that →]

* Bb

that during the chace and preparations for the possible encounter he had seen enough to convince him that at least one sailor aboard [*p* >one {<one}] not a volunteer [*p* <not a volunteer] was a [*p* >rather {<rather}] dangerous character in a ship mustering

Gab

some who not only had taken a guilty part in the late serious troubles, but
others also who, like the man in question, had been →<been→ entered His
Magesty's service inder another form than enlistment.

197: Gab 8¹. [W 187]

[Inserted after constitution of 8².]

Gab

At this point Captain Vere with some impatience interrupted him: "Be
direct, man; say impressed men."

Claggart made a gesture of subservience, and proceeded.

198: Bb 57, Bc 56²; Ga 8, Gb 8². [W 188]

Bb

Quite lately [*p* ⊁ (*above* lately) Wherof (*not marked by caret for insertion and
not canceled*)] he (Claggart) had begun to suspect that [*p* >on the gun-decks]
some sort of movement [*p* >prompted by the sailor in question] was covertly
going on, but he had not thought himself warranted in reporting the suspicion
so long as it [>vaguely] remained nothing more than that. [*p* <vaguely
<nothing more than that. ⊁a vague one. {*p* <a vague one ⊁ (*below*) indis-
tinct.}] But from what he had that afternoon observed in the individual in
question [*p* <individual in question ⊁sailor { <sailor *add* man referred to}]
the suspicion [*p* >of something ominous { <ominous >(*circled, above*) clan-
destine} going on] had advanced to a point less removed from certainty. Nor
could the general opinion he had →<Nor . . . had→ Nor could his impression
as to the man's character be altogether illusory since he could su →<su→
summon two or three good men who would testify that they in part shared
it. He well knew [*p then green crayon* <Nor . . . knew *and supplant by Gab
revision-patch*]

† Gab

He deeply felt, he added, the serious responsibility assumed in making a
report involving such possible consequences to the individual mainly concerned, besides tending to augment those natural anxieties which every naval
commander

199: Gab 9. [W 189]

Gab

must feel in view of lamentable [<lamentable >extraordinary] outbreaks so
recent as those which, he sorrowfully said [>it,] it needed not to name.

Now at the first broaching of the matter Captain Vere taken by surprise
could not wholly dissemble his disquietude. But as the testifier [<the testifier

>Claggart] went on, his [<his ≯the former's] aspect changed into restiveness under something in the testifyer's [*correct to* testifier's] [*ESM p* ≯a witness'] manner in giving his testimony. However, he refrained from interrupting him. And Claggart, continuing, concluded with this:

200: Ga 10. [W 190]

Ga

Claggart continuing [*p add comma*] concluded thus: [*Gab* <Claggart . . . thus:] God forbid, Sir, [*p* <Sir ≯Your honor,] that the Bellipotent's [*underlined*] should be the experience of the ——"

"Never mind that!" [*p* ≯here] peremptoraly broke in the superior, his face paling [*p* <paling >altering] with anger, [*p* >instinctively] divining the ship that the other was about to name, one in which the Nore Mutiny had assumed a [*p* >singularly] tragical character that for a time singularly [*p* <singularly] jeopardised [jeopardized?] the life of its commander. Under the circumstances Captain Vere [*p* <Captain Vere >he] was indignant at the purposed allusion. When the commissioned officers themselves

201: Ga 11, Gb 11¹. [W 191]

Ga

were on all occasions very heedful how they referred to recent deplorable events, [*p* <deplorable events ≯(*before* recent) the >(*after* recent) Great Mutiny of →<of→ in the fle →<in the fle→ ≯the Fleet *then* >(*after* recent) events <Great <Mutiny (*passage finally reads* the recent events the Fleet)] for a petty-officer unnecessarily to allude to them in the prescence [*p alter to* presence] of his Captain, [>this struck him] as a most immodest presumption. Besides, to his quick sense of personal honor, [*p* <personal honor ≯self-respect] it [*p* >even] looked [*p* >(*above, circled, with guide-line to caret*) under the circumstances] [*p* ≯something] like an attempt to alarm him. Nor [*p* >at first] was he without some surprise that a man →<a man→ one who so far as he had [*p* >hitherto] come under his notice had hitherto [*p* <hitherto] shown considerable tact in his difficult [<difficult] function should in this case [*p* <case ≯particular] be →<be→ xx →<xx→ evince such lack of it. So at least it did seem to him. [*Gb* <So . . . him.] [*add then delete comma (after* it)] [*p add notation* Insert]

202: Gb 11². [W 192]

Gb

But these thoughts [*mend*] and kindred [>dubious] ones rapidly passing [<rapidly passing ≯flitting] through [<through ≯across] his mind were suddenly replaced by an intuitional surmise which though now →<now→ at first →<at first→ as yet obscure in form served practically to affect his reception of the ill-tidings. Certain it is, that long versed in

203: Ga 12. [W 193]

Ga

For the rest, long [p <For the rest ≯So that { <So that *capitalize* long}]
versed in the [*Gb* <Long versed in the *and insert Gb 11²*] ins-and-outs of
[*Gb* <ins-and-outs of >everything pertaining to] the complicated life→<life→
gun-deck life, and x →<and x→ which like every other form of life, has its
darker [p <darker >secret mines and dubious] side, which is ever [*Gb*
<which is ever ≯so often {p <so often}] the side [p >popularly] disclaimed,
Captain Vere did not permit himself to be unduly disturbed by the general
tenor of his subordinate's report.

[p >Furthermore,] If in view of recent events prompt action should be
taken at the first palpable sign of recurring insubordination, [p ≯for all that,]
not judicious was it →<was it→ would it be, he thought, to keep the idea
of lingering disaffection alive by undue forwardness in crediting a vague [*alter
a to an* <vague]

204: Ga 13. [W 194]

Ga

informer even if his own subordinate and charged [p >among other things]
with police [*leave space for word* {p *add* surveilance}] of the crew

205: Bb/?E 59¹, 59; Ga 14. [W 195]

Bb/?E

This feeling would not perhaps have so prevailed with the Commander [p
<the Commander ≯him] were it not that upon a [p <a ≯one { ≪one ≫a}]
former [<former >prior] occasion the official patriotic zeal of [p <official
<of ≯ *(after* zeal) officially evinced by] Claggart had [p >somewhat] irritated
his instinctive sense [p <his ≯ *(over an erasure)* the former's { <the former's
instinctive sense ≯him}] as appearing [p ≯somewhat { <somewhat *add*
rather}] supersenseable and strained. Besides, [p <Besides ≯Furthermore]
something even in the official's

* Bb

unexceptionable [p <unexceptionable >self-possessed { >and decorous}
{ <and decorous >*(circled, with guide-line to caret)* and somewhat ostenta-
tious}] →>manner→ in making his specifications strangely [p >& painfully
{ <& painfully}] reminded the Captain [p <the Captain ≯his critic { <his
critic ≯Vere} { <Vere *add* him}] of a bandsman, a perjured [p ≯ *(below,
without canceling* perjured) perjurous] witness in a capital case before a court- -
martial [p >ashore] of which when a lieutenant he [p > *(without canceling*
he) Captain Vere] had been a member.

206: Ga 15. [W 196]

[*Gab added much of the writing on this leaf to replace substance of a clip* (*probably from* B) *originally pinned on leaf.*]

Ga

[*p add* Now] The peremptory check given to the Master-at-arms [<the Master-at-arms ⪢ Claggart] in the matter of the arrested allusion was quickly followed up by his question [<question *alter his to* this *add colon* (*after* this)] "You say that there is at least one man who is d → <man who is d→ [<"You say . . . one {≫"You say . . . one}] dangerous character [<character >man] aboard. Who is he?" [*p* <Who is he >Name him.]

"A foretopman, your honor—by name William Budd." [*p* <by name *and* (*with guide-line and caret*) *transpose* A foretopman, your honor *to follow* William Budd.]

"William Budd" repeated Captain Vere with surprise; [*p* <surprise ⪢ un- feigned astonishment] "and was it not he [*p* <was it not he ⪢ mean you the man] that Lieutenat Ratcliff took from the merchantman not very long ago— yes, [*p* <yes] the young fellow who seems to be so popular with the men— Billy, the Handsome Sailor, as they call him?

207: Ga 16. [W 197]

[*Two clips pasted on* Ga *leaf:* (1) *from* Bb; (2) *from* Ba 62, Bb 60^2. *Verso of patch on lower clip was inscribed earlier; see p. 431.*]

* Bb

"The same, Sir; [*p* <Sir ⪢ Your honor] but for all his youth and good looks, a deep one. [Bb$^+$*p notation* (*bracketed, with guide-line to an added leaf, now gone, which bore a revision later incorporated here in ink*) Insert] [Bb$^+$ >Not for nothing does he insinuate himself into the good will of his shipmates, since at the least they will at a pinch say a good word for him. {*p* >(*below, after* say) all hands will} {*p* >(*below, after* him *changing period to comma*) and all hazards.} (*revision leaves the sentence incoherent*)]

* Ba 62, Bb 60^2

Did Lieutenant Ratcliffe happen to tell you, Sir, [*p* <Sir *alter* you *to* your ⪢ honor] of that adroit fling of his [*p* <his ⪢ Budd's,] jumping up in the cutter's bow under the merchantman's stern when xx → <xx→ he was being taken off? It is even under [*p* <under ⪢ masqued by] that sort of merry [*p* Ga <merry >(*over erasure*) good humored] air that vindictivly [Ga <vindic- tivly >at heart] he resents his impressment." [*p* Ga <quotation mark and add Your honor, {*p* >(*below, circled, with guide-line to caret*) I am greatly mistaken or} there is a pitfall under his ruddy {*p* <ruddy≫ ruddy} clover." {*p* <Your honor . . . clover." *add revision-patch*}]

† *late pencil*

His cheek is →<is→ it is ruddy, Your honor. →<Your honor→ →⧸Your hon <Your hon→ →<His cheek it is ruddy→ You think he is goodly to see, but he is as →<You ... as→ You have but noted [?] his ruddy →<ruddy >fair→ cheek. Beware the man-trap under the red clover →<Beware ... clover→ A man-trap may be under red clover →<red clover→ the ruddy-- tipped daisies. [*sentence finally reads* You have but noted {?} his fair cheek. A man-trap may be under the ruddy-tipped daisies.]

208: Bb 61¹; Ga 17. [W 198]

[*Verso of patch was inscribed earlier; see p. 431.*]

* Bb 61¹ (I) on Bc leaf

Now the Handsome Sailor [*underlined*] as a signal figure among the crew had naturally enough attracted the Captain's attention from the beginning. [*p* <beginning ⧸first.]

Ga

[*Ga* (*on leaf, replacing a clip that earlier covered this space*)] Lieutenant Ratcliffe on his →<on his→ upon his good fortune in lighting on such a fine [<fine] specimen [<specimen ⧸flower { <flower ≫specimen} {*p* <specimen ≫flower}] of masculine strength and beauty, a flower scarce yet fully [<fully {≫fully}] released from the bud. [*p* <of masculine ... bud ⧸the genus homo] [*p cancel whole Ga passage and add notation* (*in left margin*) Insert *and incorporate substance on revision-patch*]

† *late pencil*

Tho' not →<not→ not to ve →<to ve→ not a very →<not a very→ in general a →<a ⧸not→ very demonst [*sic* (*for* demonstrative?)] man →<man→ to his officers, he had congratulated Lieutenant Ratclife upon his good fortune in lighting on such a fine specimen of the genus homo, whose cheek →<whose cheek→ who in the nude might have posed for a statue of Adam →<Adam→ young Adam before the Fall.

Bc

As to Billy's adieu to the ship Rights-of-Man, [*underlined*] which the boarding lieutenant had indeed reported to the Captain, [*Ga* <the Captain *add* him] but [*p* >, in a deferential way] more as a good story than aught else, he [*Ga* <he ⧸Captain Vere] [*add* (*with guide-line and caret*) tho mistakenly understanding it as a satiric sally,] had but thought so much the better of Billy [<Billy >the impressed man] for it; as a military sailor, [*p alter* sailor *to* sailor's *add* xx { ⧸'s xx}] admiring the spirit that could take an ab →<ab→ arbitrary enlistment so merrily [*p mend to* merrily] [*p* ⧸(*below*) wittily (?) { ⧸wittily}] and sensibly.

[[*368*]]

209: Bb/Ga 61²; Ga 18. [W 199]

[*Leaf was evidently constituted at* Ga *to mount* Bb *clip from same leaf (with intervening lines missing) as clip on Leaf 208.*]

* Bb (. . . II)
[*add* And] Billy's [*p* <And Billy's ⪢the latter's { ≺the latter's ⪢ (*above, on leaf*) The foretopman's}] conduct, too, so far as it had fallen under the Captain's [*p* <the Captain's ⪢his { ≺his ≫the Captain's}] notice had confirmed the first happy opinion of him, [*p* <opinion of him ⪢augury,] while the new recruit's qualities as a sailor-man [*underlined*]

Ga
seemed to be such that he had thought of reccommending [*p correct to* recommending] him to the executive officer for promotion to a place that would more frequently bring him under his own observation, namely, the captaincy of the mizzen-top, replacing there in the starboard watch a man not so young whom partly for that reason he deemed less

210: Ga 19. [W 200]

Ga
fitted for the post. Be it added [*p* <added ⪢said { <said *add* parenthesized here}] that since the mizzen-top-men having not to handle such breadths of heavy canvas as the [>lower] sails on the main-mast and fore-mast, a young man if of the right stuff not only seems best adapted to duty there, but in fact is generally selected for it →<it→ the captaincy of that top, and the company he commands →<he commands→ is often composed →<is often composed→ under him are light hands and often but striplings. In sum, Captain Vere had from the beginning deemed Billy Budd to be what in the naval parlance of the time was called a "King's bargain" [*underlined*] that is to say, for His

211: Ga 20. [W 201]

Ga
Brittanic Magesty's [*p mend to* Majesty's] navy a capital investment at small outlay. [*p add* or none at all.]
After a brief pause during which the reminiscences abovementioned passed vividly through his mind and he weighed the import of Claggart's last suggestion conveyed in the phrase "pitfal under the clover," and the more he weighed it the less reliance he felt in the informer's good faith, suddenly he turned upon him: [*p* ⪢and in a low voice] "Do you come to me, Master-at- -arms with so foggy a tale? Let the rest go. [*p* <Let the rest go.] But [*add* , as to Budd, {*p* <But}] cite me an act or spoken word [*add* at all { <at all} {*p* ⪢of his}] confirmatory of what you charge [*p* <charge ⪢insinuate *add*

(*before* insinuate *with line to indicate connection*) in general { <insinuate ≫charge}] against him. Stay, [>(*below, circled, with guide-line to caret*) drawing nearer to him and speaking yet lower {*p* <and speaking yet lower} *also add quotation marks (after* Stay *and before* heed)] heed what

212: Ga 21. [W 202]

Ga

you speak. In [<In >(*circled*) Just now, and in] a case, →<*comma*→ like this, there is a yard-arm-end for the false-witness."

"Ah, your honor," [*add exclamation mark (after* honor)] sighed Claggart mildly shaking his shapely head as in sad deprecation of such unmerited severity of tone. Then, bridling—erecting himself as in virtuous self-assertion, he circumstantially alleged certain things, [<things] words and acts, which [>collectivly,] if credited, led to presumptions mortally inculpating Budd. [>And] For some of these thxx →<thxx→ averments, he added, substantiating proof was not far.

213: Ga 22. [W 203]

Ga

With gray eyes impatient and distrustful essaying to fathom to the bottom the →<the→ Claggart's calm violet ones, Captain Vere again heard him out. The perplexity →<The perplexity *alter period (after* out) *to semicolon*→ then for the moment stood ruminating. The mood he evinced, Claggart—himself for the time liberated from [>the other's] scrutiny—steadily regarded with a look difficult to render, [*p add dash*] a look curious of the operation of his tactics, a look such as might have been that of the spokesman of the envious children of Jacob deceptivly imposing upon the troubled patirarch the blood- - dyed coat of young Joseph.

214: Ga 23. [W 204]

Ga

Now though [*p* <Now *capitalize* though] something exceptional in the moral quality of Captain Vere made him, in earnest encounter with a fellow- - man, a veritable touch-stone of that man's essential nature, yet now as to the →<the→ Claggart and what was [*p* >really] going on in him his feeling partook less of [>intuitional] conviction than of strong suspicion clogged by strange dubieties. That [<That ≯The] perplexity he evinced proceeded less from aught touching the man informed against—as Claggard doutless opined—than from considerations how best to act in regard to the informer. At first indeed he was naturally for

215: Ga 24. [W 205]

Ga

summoning that substantiating proff [<proff *alter* substantiating *to* substantiation] of his allegations which Claggart said was at hand, →<*comma add period*→ But such a proceeding would result in the matter at once getting abroad, which in the present stage of it might, he thought, m →<might <m→ might undesirably affect the ship's company. If Claggart was a false witness, [*p add dash*] that closed the affair. And therefore before trying the accusation, he would first practically test the accuser; and he thought this could be done in a private →<private→ quiet undemonstrative way.

The measure he determined upon involved a shifting of the

216: Ga 25. [W 206]

Ga

scene, or [<or >a] transfer to a place less exposed [>to observation] than the broad quarter-deck. [*add* For] Although the few gun-room officers there at the time had, in due observance of naval etiquette, withdrawn to leeward the moment Captain Vere had begun prom →<prom→ his promenade on the ship's [<ship's >deck's] weather-side; and tho' during the colloquy with Claggart they of course ventured not to diminish the distance; and though throughout the interview Captain Vere's voice was far [>from] high, and Claggart's voice was yet lower; [<voice was yet lower >silvery and low;] and the wind in the cordage and the wash of the sea helped the more to put them beyond ear-shot;

217: Ga 26. [W 207]

Ga

nevertheless, the interview's continuance already had attracted some [<some] observation from [>some] topmen aloft and some [<some] others [*alter* others *to* other >sailors] in the waist or further forward.

Having settled upon h →<h→ the cou →<the cou→ his →<his <Having . . . upon→ Having determined upon the course to adopt, [*p* <the course to adopt ≫the (*altering* the *to* his) ≯measures] Captain Vere forthwith took action. Turning [>Abruptly (*before* Turning) *alter* Turning *to* turning] to Claggart he asked "Master-at-arms, is it now Budd's watch aloft?" [*add bracket for new paragraph*] "No, your honor," →*delete comma add period*→ Whereupon, "Mr. Wilkes," [*p add exclamation mark (before quotation mark)*] summoning the nearest midshipman, "tell Albert to come to me." Albert was his [*p* <his >the Captain] hammock-boy, a sort of sea-valet in whose discretion and fidelity his master had much

218: Ga 27. [W 208]

Ga

confidence. The lad appeared. "You know Budd the foretopman?"

  "I do, Sir" [*no period*]

"Go find him. It is his watch off. Manage to tell him out of ear-shot that he is wanted aft. Contrive it that he speaks
[*guide-line to next leaf*]

219: Bb 64, Bc 65¹; Ga 28, Gb 28¹. [W 209]

[*Leaf has writing of three stages on it. Evidently clip(s) at first covered top three-quarters of leaf, being later removed and the leaf inscribed under where clip(s) had been. A canceled irrelevant phrase is at the top:* Ascribed to the entire class in .]
[*space, at first covered by clip(s) later removed*]

Bc

to nobody. Keep him in talk yourself. [*p* <yourself *add period (after* talk) {≫yourself}] And not till you get well aft here, let →<let→ not till then let him know that the place where he is wanted is my cabin. You understand. [*p alter period to comma* ≻Albert: {<Albert}] Go.—Master- -
[*Ga remove clip that followed, then add on leaf:*]

Ga

at-Arms show yourself on the decks below, and when you think it time for Albert to be coming with his man, stand by quietly to

Bb

follow the sailor in. [*p add quotation mark*] [*p notation (with marginal pointers for space-out)* Chapter {*brown crayon add chapter-ending mark* ———◇———}]

  [*p add* Now] When the foretopman found himself [*p* ≻(*below*) in the cabin,] closeted, [*p* ≻there] as it were, with the Captain and Claggart, he was surprised enough. But it

220: Gb 28². [W 210]

Gb

was a surprise unaccompanied by apprehension or distrust. To a nature essentially honest and humane, immature [*p transpose* immature (*with circling and caret) to precede* nature *and alter* a *to* an] and inexperienced, [*p* <and inexperienced] [>forewarning] intimations of subtler danger from one's kind are [<are *add* come] tardily or not [<or not ≻if] at all. The only thing that took shape in the young sailor's mind was this: Yes, the Captain, I have always thought, looks kindly upon me. Wonder if he's going to make me his coxswain. I should like that. And may be now he is going to ask the master-at-arms about me.

* Bb 66

"Shut the door there, sentry [*add quotation mark and comma* (*after* sentry)
> (*with guide-line to caret*) said the commander; *add quotation mark* (*before*
stand)] stand without, and let nobody come in.—Now, master-at-arms

* Ba

, tell this man to his face exactly [*p* <exactly] what you told [*p* >of him to]
me"; and stood prepared to scrutinize the two [*p i* <two >mutually] confronting visages.

Ga

Claggart hesitated not an instant. [*Ga^{+}p revise to read* Without hesitation]
Deliberatly advancing within short range of the sailor, he spoke. Without
emphasis and in a tone more musical than ever, briefly cir → <cir→ he delivered the accusation point-blank into his eyes. [*Ga^{+} brown crayon* <Without
. . . eyes. *incorporate substance on revision patch*]

† Ga^{+}

With the measured step and calm collected visage [<visage >air] of an
asylum-physician approaching in the public hall some patient beginning to
show indications of a coming parox → <parox→ paroxysm, Claggart deliberatly advanced within short range of Billy, and mesmerically looking him in the
eye, briefly recapitulated the accusation.

[*Verso of patch was inscribed earlier; see p. 431.*]

Ga

Not at first did the accused one [*p* <the accused one ≯Billy] take it in.
When he did, the rose-tan of his cheek looked struck as by white leprosy. He
stood speechless [*p* <speechless] like one impaled and gagged. Meanwhile
the accuser' violet [*p* <violet] eyes removing not as yet from the blue [*p*
<blue ≯welkin { ≮welkin ≫blue}] dilated ones, underwent a phenominal
[*p correct to* phenomenal] change, their wonted dark rich [*p* <dark ≯ (*after*
rich) violet { ≮violet *add* black} { ≮black *add* violet}] color blurring into a
muddy purple. Those lights of human [*p* <human >Adam's { ≮Adam's
≫human}] intelligence losing human expression, gelidly protruding like the
alien eyes of certain unspeakable [*p Ga* <unspeakable >uncatalogued] creatures of the deep. [*p* <the deep *and make trial revisions with concurrent erasures and a final erasure restoring* the deep *and leaving revision only partly
decipherable* tropic parts of that elemental host . . . Not the → <Not the→ Not
only their first human expression . . . mesmeric experts . . . hungry . . . {*p after
erasure incorporate substance of revision on patch*} {*ESM p notation add*}]

† *late pencil*

The →⧸first→ mesmeristic [?] glance was one of fascin →<fascin→ serpent
fascination; the last was →<was→ threw up a stone wall →<was ... wall→
was as the strong →<strong ⧸paralyzing→ lurch of the torpedo-fish [*ESM?
p notation (in left margin)* add p 30]

223: Ga 31. [W 213]

Ga

[*p notation (in right margin, circled and canceled)* 27 follows]

"Speak, man!" said Captain Vere to the transfixed one struck by his aspect
[*p* >even] more than by Claggart's, "Speak! defend yourself." Which appeal
caused but an ineffectual [*p* <an ineffectual ⧸a strange] dumb gesturing and
gurgling in Billy; amazement at such an accusation so suddenly sprung upon
[<upon >on] him, [*p* <him ⧸inexperienced nonage; this, { <nonage ⧸good-
ness} { <goodness ⧸virtue} { <virtue ⧸youth} { <youth ≫nonage} (*passage finally reads* on inexperienced nonage; this),] and, it may be, spiritual [*p*
<spiritual ⧸spontanious { <spontanious}] horror of [*p* <of ⧸at { <at}]
the accuser [*p* ⧸unearthly glance { <unearthly glance *add* eyes,}] serving to
bring out his ever-lurking [*p* <ever-] defect and in this instance [*p* >for
the time] intensifing [*mend to* intensifying] it into a [*p* ⧸convulsed] tounge--
tie, [*p mend* tounge *to* tongue *and alter comma to semicolon*] while the intent
head

224: Ga 32. [W 214]

Ga

and entire body →<body→ form straining forward in an agony of ineffectual
eagerness to obey the injunction to speak and defend himself, gave an expression to the face like that of a condemned vestal [*p capitalize* vestal ⧸priestess]
in the moment of being secretly [*p* <secretly] buried alive, and in the first
struggle against suffocation.

Though at the time Captain Vere was quite ignonrant of Billy's liability
to vocal impediment, he now immediatly divined it, since vividly it [<it
>Billy's aspect] recalled to him that of a bright young schoolmate of his whom
he had once seen struck by [*p* >(*below*) much] the same

225: Ga 33. [W 215]

Ga

startling impotence in the act of eagerly rising in the class to be foremost in
responce to a testing question put to it by the master. Going close up to the
young sailor, and laying a soothing hand on his shoulder, he deliberatly [*p*
<deliberatly] said "There is no hurry, my boy. Take your time, take your
time." Contrary to the effect intended, these words so fatherly in tone, doubt-

less touching Billy's heart to the quick, prompted yet more violent efforts at utterance—efforts soon ending for the time in confirming the paralysis, and bringing to his face an expression which was as a crucifixion to behold. The next

226: Ga 34. [W 216]

Ga

instant, quick as the flame from a [*p* ⊁discharged] cannon's mouth, [*p* <'s mouth ⊁at night] his right arm shot out, and Claggart dropt [*p alter to* dropped] to the deck. Whether intentionally or but owing to the young athlete's [*p cross* t] superior height, the blow had taken effect full upon the forhead, so shapely and intellectual-looking a feature in the Master-at-arms; so that he [*p alter* he *to* the >body] fell over backward →<backward→ lengthwise, like a heavy plank tilted from erectness. A gasp or two, and he lay motionless.

"Fated boy," breathed Captain Vere in tones [*alter to* tone] so low as to be almost a whisper, "what have you done! But here, help me."

227: Ga 35. [W 217]

Ga

The twain raised the felled one from the loins up into a sitting position. The lean [<lean >spare] form flexibly acquiesed, but inertly. It was like handling a dead snake. They lowered it back. Regaining erectness Captain Vere with one hand covering his face stood [>to all appearance] as impassive as the object at his feet. Was he absorbed in taking in all the bearings of the event and what was best not only now at once to be done, but also in the sequel? Slowly he uncovered his face; and the effect was as if the moon emerging from clipse should reappear with quite anot her

228: Ga 36. [W 218]

Ga

aspect than that which had gone into hiding. The father in him, manifested towards Billy thus far in the scene, was replaced by the [*p* ⊁military] disciplinarian. In an [*p* <an ⊁his] official tone he bade the foretopman retire to a state-room aft, pointing it out, [*p add parentheses (around* pointing it out,)] and there remain till thence summoned. [*p* >(*below, circled, with guide-line to caret*) And →≪And→ The →*alter* The *to* This→ order Billy in silence mechanically obeyed] Then going to the cabin-door where it opened on the quarter-deck, he [*p* <he >Captain Vere] said to the sentry without, "Tell somebody to send Albert here." When the lad appeared his master so contrived [*add* it] that he should not catch sight of the fallen man [<fallen man ⊁prone one.] " →*delete quotation mark*→ "Albert," he said to him,

[[*375*]]

229: Ga 37. [W 219]

Ga

"tell the Surgeon I wish to see him. You need not come back till called."
When the Surgeon entered—a self-poised man [*p* ⪢character (*above, without canceling*, man)] of that grave sense and experience that hardly anything could surprise, [*p* ⪢take him aback (*above, without canceling*, surprise)] —Captain Vere advanced to meet him, [*p* ⪢thus unconsciously intercepting his view of Claggart] and checking [*p* <checking ⪢and interrupting] the other's [*p* >wonted] cerimonious salutation, said, "Nay. Look, [*p* <Look] tell me how it is with yonder man," pointing [*p* <pointing ⪢directing his attention] to the prostrate one. [*p* >The surgeon turned, and] At catching sight of the dark blood now oozing from nostril and ear, and strikingly in contrast with Claggart's always bleached complexion, the Surgeon [*p* <the Surgeon ⪢ (*below*) he] [*p* <The Surgeon turned, and At catching ... complexion, he]

[229a] 355: Superseded Ga 38. [W 220a]

Ga

from this as well as other indications at once inferred what it was that lay plank-like before him. Yes, the young mute's blow, an athlete's, a blow elecrically [>con →<con→ energised x →<x→ by] the inmost [<inmost] spasm of his heart, unintentionally had had upon its object the [*p add* all but] [>instantanious] operation of the divine judgement on Annannias.

Captain Vere intently watching the Surgeon's face, asked, "Is it so then? I thought it. But verify it." And the customary tests were made, confirming the Surgeon's first glance.
[*G+p cancel whole leaf*]

[229b] 356: Superseded Ga 39. [W 221a]

Ga

At Captain Vere's motion, the Surgeon assisted him in removing the body to the compartment aft opposite to that where the foretopman remained for the time self-immured. This being done, the officer was in brief terms [*mend*] enlightened as to the circumstances which had resulted in the trajedy.

"Go now" said Captain Vere in conclusion; "before taking action I must have [*p* >have yet (*without canceling* have)] a few moments to mature the line of conduct I shall adopt. The case is without precident and it [*p* <without precident and it ⪢no wonted one, nor] could not [*p* <not] have happened at a worse time [*p* <worse ⪢(*after* time) worse {<worse *add* more trying.}] for →<for→ either for me or the [*p* <either for me or the >(*below*) worse for the man mainly concerned. It was then w →<was then w→ is worse →<It ... worse *add* —or for me.→ → <worse ... me. *add* for everybody→

→ <for everybody ≫ (*original*) worse *and* > (*above, circled, with guide-line to caret after* time) every way and for everybody→ →*then* <before taking . . . adopt > (*at foot of leaf*) Go. I need→ → <Go. I need *add* (*after* trying.) A few moments of→ → <of > (*above, circled, with guide-line to caret*) for further→ thought and I shall act. (*passage finally reads* The case is no wonted one, nor could have happened at a worse time every way and for everybody more trying. A few moments for further thought and I shall act.)]
[*G+ blue crayon cancel whole leaf*]

[229c] 357: Superseded Ga 40. [W 221b]

Ga
striker of the blow." [*p* <striker of the blow] Too well the thoughf → <thoughf→ thoughtful officer knew what his superior meant. [*p* <Too well . . . meant] As the former [*p* <the former *add* he { <he ≯Surgeon}] withdrew he could not help thinking how worse [*p* <worse ≯ (*below*) more] than futile [>the utmost discretion] sometimes proves in a world [*p* <a world ≯this human sphere] subject [*p* >as it is] to unforseeable fatalities; the prudent method adopted by Captain Vere to obviate publicity and trouble having resulted in an event that necessitated the former, and, under existing circumstances in the navy indefinitly magnified the latter.
[*p chapter-ending mark* ———◇——] [*G+ blue crayon draw a box around last eight lines* unforseeable fatalities . . . the latter.]

[229d] 358: Superseded F/Ga 1; Ga 41. [W 1]

Ga
[*ESM p query* Preface for / Billy Budd?]
[*p chapter-beginning mark* ———◇——]
    The year 1797, the year of this narrative, belongs to a period which as everybody [<body >thinker] now feels, involved a crisis for Christendom not exceeded in its undetermined momentousness at the time by any other recorded event. → <event→ era. [*p* <recorded > (*after* era) whereof there is record.] The opening proposition made by the Spirit of that Age, was one hailed by the noblest men of it. Even the dry tinder of a Wordsworth took fire. The Old World's [<was one . . . took fire <The Old World's > (*after* Age) involved]

[229e] 359: Superseded F/Ga 2; Ga 42. [W 2]

Ga
the rectification of the Old World's hereditary wrongs. To [> (*before* To) In France *alter* To *to* to] some extent this was [>bloodily] effected. But what then? Straightway the Revolution [*p* <Revolution ≯regency as assuming to

be →<assuming to be→ that →<that→ righter of wrongs ≫Revolution
(*passage reads* the Revolution regency as righter of wrongs)] itself became a
wrongdoer, [*p* ≯one] more oppressive than the Kings. Under Napoleon it
enthroned upstart kings, and initiated that prolonged agony of [>general {*p*
<general >(*circled, with guide-line to caret*) Continental}] warfare [<fare
>and massacre {<and massacre}] that ended in [*p* <that ended ≯whose
last →<last >(*above, circled, with guide-line to caret*) final→ throes →<s→ was
in →<in→ at →<at→ →≫at→] Waterloo. Nor during [*p* <Nor *capitalize*
during] those years could [*p* <could >not] the wisest [*p* ≯could] have
forseen that the outcome of all would be what apparently [*p* <apparently
>(*below, circled, with guide-line to caret*) to some thinkers] it has [*p* ≯since]
turned [*p* <it has turned (*leaving sentence incoherent*)] out to be, an [*alter
an to* a >political] advance along [>nearly] the whole line for man. [<man.
add Europeans.]

[229f] 360: Superseded F/Ga 3¹; Ga 43. [W 3]

Ga

Now as elsewhere hinted, it was a contagion [<a contagion >something
caught] from the Revolutionary Spirit that that →<that→ at the Nore in-
spired [<the Nore <inspired ≯Spithead ≯emboldened] the sailors of the
British fleet in the first place [<the sailors . . . place >the man-of-war's men]
to rise against real abuses, [*p* ≯long-standing ones,] and afterwards at the Nore
to make inordinate [*p* >and] aggressive demands, successful resistance to
which was confirmed only when the ringleaders were hung for an admonitory
spectacle to the [>anchored] fleet. Yet in a way analagous to the operation
of the Revolution at large the Nore [<Nore >Great] Mutiny, tho' naturally
deemed by →<by >(*after* tho') by Englishmen→ monstrous at the time,
doubtless gave the first latent prompting to those progressive reforms in the
British navy which for its sailors makes it a service [*ESM p add* to be faithful
to. {*ESM* ≮to be faithful to <those progressive >most important *add period*
(*after* navy) <which for . . . service} (*passage finally reads* the first latent
prompting to most important reforms in the British navy.)]

230: G⁺p 38. [W 220]

[*Verso of leaf was inscribed earlier; see p. 431.*]

G⁺ pencil

The Surgeon turned, [<turned ≯looked,] and for all his self-possessed
→*alter to* possession→ of character, [<possession of character ≯command]
[>somewhat] started at the the spe →<spe→ spectacle. [<the spectacle
≯abrupt revelation.] On Claggart's always bleached [<bleached ≯pallid]
complexion, the d →<the d→ thick black blood was now oozing from nostril
and ear. To the gazer's professional eye death was patent →<death was

patent→ it was unmistakably a corpse [<a corpse ≯no living man] that he saw.

"Is it so then? [*no end quotation marks*] said Captain Vere intently watching him. [*p alter period to comma*] "I thought it." But verify it." Whereupon the customary tests confirmed the Surgeon's first glance. Captain Vere stood motionless. The other [<Captain Vere . . . other (*alter period to comma after motionless*)] who now looking up in unfeined concern, cast an inqu →<cast an inq→ cast a look of intense inquisitiveness upon his superior.

231: G⁺p 39. [W 221]

[Verso of leaf was inscribed earlier; see p. 431.]

G⁺ pencil
But Captain Vere, with one hand to his brow, was standing motionless. Suddenly, seizing [<seizing ≯catching the] the Surgeon's xx →<xx→ arm convulsively, he exclaimed, pointing down to the body— [≯Look { <Look}] "It is the divine judgment on Ananias!" [<*quotation mark add* Look!]

"But how, how? [≮*question mark add dash*]

"Thus it was," said Captain Vere [<"But . . . Vere]

Di →<Di→ Disturbed by his [<his ≯the { <the ≯an} { <an ≯the}] excited manner so unwonted in the speaker →<so unwonted in the speaker→ he had never before observed in the "Indomitables" Captain, and as yet wholly ignorant of the affair, the [>prudent] Surgeon nevertheless held his peace, only casting →<casting→ [>again] looking an earnest interrogatory as to what it was that →<it was that→ it was that had resulted in such a tragedy.

232: G⁺p 40. [W 222]

[Verso of leaf was inscribed earlier; see p. 431.]

G⁺ pencil
But Captain Vere was [>now] again motionless and [<and] standing absorbed in thought. But again starting, he exc →<exc→ vehemently exclaimed—Billy Budd was the angel of God →<Billy . . . God→ Righteously →<Righteously→ He was →<He was→ "Struck [>dead as { <as}] by the [<the ≯an] angel of God! Y →<Y→ Yet the angel must hang! [*no quotation mark*]

At these interjections, [<interjections ≯passionate ≫interjections] mere incoherences to the S →<the S→ the listener as yet unapprised of the antecedents, the Surgeon was profoundly discomposed. "Sir" said he →<"Sir" said he→ But becoming now less xx →<xx→ passionate, →<becoming . . . passionate→ Captain Vere →<Captain Vere→ and →<and→ [≯now] as reccolecting himself, the →<the→ Captain Vere in less passionate tone briefly related the circumstances leading up to the event.

233: G⁺p 41. [W 223]

[Verso of leaf was inscribed earlier; see p. 431.]

G⁺ pencil

But come; we must despatch" he added. Help me to remove him [>mea
→<mea→ (meaning the body)] to yonder compartment, designating the
→<the→ one opposite that where the foretopman remained immured. Anew
disturbed by a p →<a p→ a request that seemed so →<seemed so→ under
the →<under the→ seemed so strange →<seemed so strange→ as implying
a desire for secrecy, seemed unaccountably strange to him, there was nothing
for the subordinate to do but comply.——"Go now" said Captain Vere with
something *[erasure of earlier addition (undeciphered) shows here, circled for
insertion above]* of his wonted manner—Go now. I →<I→ I [≯presently]
shall call a drum-head court. Tell the lieutenants what has happened, and tell
the Captain →<the Captain→ Mr *[no period]* Mordant," meaning the captain of marines", and charge them

234: G⁺p 42. [W 224]

[Verso of leaf was inscribed earlier; see p. 431.]

G⁺ pencil

[ESM p query Page 43 missing? { ≮query}]
to keep the matter to themselves."

———◆———

Full of disquietude [>and misgiving] the prudent [<prudent] Surgeon
left the cabin. Was Captain Vere suddenly affected in his mind? →*delete question mark and add comma*→ or was it but a pas →<pas→ transient condition,
[<condition ≯excitement] brought about by so extraordinary [<extraor-
dinary >unusual { <unusual >unexpected} { <unexpected >strange & ≫ex-
traordinary}] a tragedy? As to →<As to→ Where the →<Where the→ As
to the drum-head court, it struck the Surgeon as impolitic, if nothing more.
The thing to do, he thought, was to confine Bill →<confine Bill→ place Billy
Budd in confinement and in a way dictated by usage, and postpone further
action in so extraordinary a case, to such time as they should rejoin the
squadron, and then refer it to the Admiral. Again →<Again→ *[add He recalled the unwonted agitation of Captain Vere and his excited exclamations
(addition continued on next leaf)]*

[[380]]

235: G⁺p 43. [W 225]

[Verso of leaf was inscribed earlier; see p. 431.]

G⁺ pencil

[*addition continued from last leaf* so at variance with his normal manner. Was
he unhinged?]

But much as he demurred, [<much ... demurred ≯assuming that he is,
it is not so susceptible of proof] what could he →*write* the *over* he→ Surgeon
[<what ... Surgeon ≯What can →*write* then (?) *over* can→ can he] do? No
more trying situation is conceivable than that of a subordinate officer acting
under a →<acting under a→ at the orders of [*alter* a *to* an <subordinate
≯(*after* officer) subordinate <at the orders of ≫under] a Captain whom he
suspects to be not quite sound [<quite sound *add* (*after* be) , if →<if→ not
mad indeed, but yet ≫quite >(*below, after* not quite) unaffected] in his intellects. T →<T→ Then [?] res →<Then res→ To resist is perilous. →<To
resist is perilous→ To resist is mutiny. →<resist is mutiny→ argue with his
→<his→ [<with >(*above*) his order to] him would be insolence. To resist
him would be mutiny.

Accordingly, he →<he→ in obedience to Captain Vere, →<Accordingly
... Vere ≫(*capitalizing* in) in obedience to Captain Vere,→ he [>briefly
{ <briefly >(*above, circled, with guide-line to caret*) without comment} { <with-
out comment}] communicated the facts to the lieutenants as to →<the facts
... as to ≫(*but then re-cancel*) to the lieutenants→ what had happened to the
lieutenants & captain of marines; and →<and→ con →<con ≫and→ waited
how they would receive it. [<and ... receive it ≯saying nothing as to the
Captain's state.] His own →<His own→ They fully shared his own surprise
and concern. [*passage finally reads* In obedience to Captain Vere, he communicated what had happened to the lieutenants & captain of marines; saying
nothing as to the Captain's state. They fully shared his own surprise and
concern.]

236: G⁺p 44. [W 226]

[Verso of leaf was inscribed earlier; see p. 431.]

G⁺ pencil

Like him too they seemed to think that such a matter should be referred to
the Admiral.

———◇———

[≯(*above*) In the rainbow,] Who [<In the rainbow ≯in the rainbow] can
draw the line where the violet [≯tint] begins or →<begins or→ ends and
the orange [*add* tint] begins? Each hue is distinct →<Each ... distinct→
As different →<As different→ Equally impossible is it, in the beginnings of
the hues →<in the ... hues→ to draw the line between the first aberrations

→<to draw ... aberrations→ →<Equally ... it→ The two tints →<The two tints→ Wee →<Wee→ [≯Distinctly] We see the absolute [<absolute ≯distinct {<distinct}] difference of the colors, but where exactly does the one [>first blendingly] enter into the other? Between san →<san→ [<Between ≯So with] sanity and insanity. In pronounced cases they are evident enough →<they are evident enough→ there is no question about them. [*add* But] In [>some supposed] cases, in various [>degrees, supposedly] less pronounced, to draw the exact line between is →<between is→ separating →<separating→ of demarcation few will undertake. [<.*add in margin (at top of chapter, circled, with guide-line to caret)* tho for a fee {>becoming considerate} the →<the→ some exp →<exp→ professional experts will undertake it →<undertake it *add period (after* will)→] [*add (at other side of chapter-space, probably for insertion here, though not so indicated)* There is nothing namable but that some men will {>*(below, circled, with caret)* or undertake to} do it for pay.]

237: G⁺p 45. [W 227]

G⁺ pencil

[≯*(above)* In {<In}] Whether Captain Vere was →<was→ had suddenly become the victim of aberration, and whether the proceedings →<proceedings→ part he took in the events shortly to be given, confirm it, this →<it, this→ the supposition, I for one, decline to determine [<*whole sentence* Whether ... determine]

In other words, there are instances where it is next to impossible justly [<justly ≯positively] to determine whether a man is of sound or unsound mind →<of <or unsound mind→ in his mind or beginning to be otherwise. [<*whole sentence* In other ... otherwise.]

Whether Captain Vere, as the Surgeon [≯professionally &] privately [?] surmised, was [>really] the [>sudden] victim of any degree of aberration, the rea →<the rea→ every one must determine [≯for himself] by the light of the →<by the light of the→ by such light as this narrative af →<af→ may afford.

238: Ga 44. [W 228]

Ga

so much more humane than it was in the time [<time ≯days] of Nelson. [*p* <Nelson *add* Collingwood {≫Nelson ≯*(after* Nelson) and *add (after* Collingwood) , two characters essentially humane.} {<Nelson and Collingwood, two characters essentially humane. ≯*(after* of) this story.}] [*p* <*whole passage* so much ... this story.]

Now as elsewhere →<Now as elsewhere→

Now [*p* <Now] Captain Vere's words to the Surgeon to the effect that the [*p* <Captain Vere's ... effect that *capitalize* the] unhappy event in the cabin [*p* <in the cabin ≯which has been narrated] could not have happened at a

worse juncture, was but [*p* >too] true. For it was close on the heel of the suppressed insurections of the fleet, [*p* <of the fleet] an after-time so [*p* <so ⊁very] critical to naval authority, demanding from every English sea-commander two qualities not readily interfusable—prudence and rigor. And [*p* <And >Moreover] there was something [>in the case] yet more trying. [*p* <yet more trying ⊁(*after* something) crucial] In the [<In the]

[*238a*] *1v:*

[*Superseded pencil-draft fragment from Stage* X, *no foliation, on verso of dedication draft leaf (Leaf 1). Corresponds to matter now on Leaf 238.*]

X pencil
[*top half of leaf blank where clip was removed*]
   Alike [<Alike ⊁Indi { <Indi *add* Both} { <Both *add* Both}] directly and indirectly the era lent a →<a→ emphasis to the difficulties professional and moral falling on Captain Vere by reason of the tragic event just recounted; difficulties inadequa →<inadequa→ not adequately to be estimated by a lan →<a lan→ landsmen of our time, →<landsmen . . . time→ every sailor [<sailor ⊁sea-officer] of our time, and still less so →<so→ by most landsmen. Look at it. →<Look at it.→
[*X*+ *brown crayon* <*whole passage*]

239: Ga 45. [W 229]

---

* F
   In the juglery of circumstances preceeding and attending the event [*p* >on board the Indomitable] and in the light of that martial code whereby it was formally to be judged, innocense and guilt personified in Claggart and Budd x →<x→ in effect changed places.

Ga
The palpable [*p* <The palpable >Legally { ≪Legally >In a legal view the apparent}] victim of the tragedy, the man killed, [*p* <the man killed] was he who had sought to victimise [victimize?] another, →<another *add* a→ man blameless; and the [*p* >indisputable] deed of the blameless one, [*p* <blameless one ⊁man { <man ⊁latter}] navally regarded, constituted the most heinous of martial [*p* <martial ⊁military] crimes. Yet more. The essential right and wrong [>involved] in the matter, the clearer that might be, so much the

240: Ga 46. [W 230]

Ga
worse for the responsibility of a loyal [>sea-] commander inasmuch as he was not authorised [authorized?] to determine the case [<case >matter]

on that primitive basis, not seldom an impractical [*p* ⊁ (*above* impractical) *a new suffix* cable] abstraction even in civil life [>and] under the most liberal form of it. [*p add period* (*after* basis) <not seldom . . . of it]

Small wonder then that the Indomitable's [*not underlined*] captain though in general a man of [>rapid] decision, felt the necessity of →<of→ of →*alter* the *to* that <necessity of→ circumspectness not less than promptitude was demanded →<demanded→ necessary. Until his →<his *add* he→ could decide upon his course, and in each detail; and not only so, but until the last result →< last result→

241: Ga 47. [W 231]

Ga

concluding measure was upon the point of being enacted, he deemed it advisable, in view of the →<the→ all the circumstances to guard as much as possible against publicity. Here he may or may not have erred. Certain it is however that subsequently in the confidential talk of more than one or two gun-rooms [>and cabins] he was not a little criticised [criticized?] by some officers, a circum →<circum→ fact imputed by his friends and vehemently by his cousin Jack Denton to professional jealousy of Starry Vere. [*underlined*] Some imaginative ground for invidious comment there was. The maintenance

242: Ga 48. [W 232]

Ga

of temporary [<temporary] secresy in the matter, the confining all knowledge of it for a time to the place where the homocide occurred, the quarter-deck cabin; in these particulars lurked some resemblance to similar [<similar ⊁ the] policy adopted in those revolutionary [*p* <revolutionary] trajedies [*p alter to* tragedies] of the palace which have [>occurred] more than once in the capital founded by Peter the Barbarian. [*p add* Tartar. { <Barbarian Tartar *add* Great, chiefly great by his crimes} { <Great . . . crimes >(*after* Peter the) Barbarian.}]

243: Fa 7; Ga 49. [W 233]

Fa

The case indeed was such that fain would the Indomitable's [*underlined*] captain have [>deferred] taking any action whatever respecting it further than to keep the foretopman a close prisoner till the ship [*p* ⊁ re- (*with question mark in margin*)] joined the squadron and then submitting the matter to the judgement of his Admiral at the same time apprising him how far was the foretopman at heart from being either a mutineer or murderer. [*p Fb* <at the same . . . murderer *add period* (*after* Admiral)]

But a true military officer is in one particular like a true monk. Not with more of self-abnegation will the latter keep his vows of monastic obediance than the former his vows of allegiance to military [p <military ⇗(below) martial] duty.

244: Fa 8; Ga 50. [W 234]

Fa

Feeling that unless quick action was taken on it the deed of the foretopman [p add commas (after it and after foretopman)] so soon as it should be known to them [<to them ⇗on the gun-decks] would tend to awaken any slumbering embers of disaffection [p <disaffection ⇗the Nore] among the crew, a sense of the urgency of the case overruled [p >in Captain Vere] every other consideration. But tho' a conscientious disiplinarian he was no lover of authority for mere authority's sake. Very far was he from embracing opportunities for monopolising [monopolizing?] to himself the perils of moral responsibility none at least that could properly be referred to [>an official] superior in rank [<in rank]

245: Fa 9; Ga 51¹. [W 235]

Fa

or shared with him by his official →<official→ official equals or even subordinates. So thinking he was glad it would not be at variance with usage to turn the matter over to a summary court of his own officers, reserving to himself as the one on whom the ultimate accountability would rest, the right of maintaining the →<the→ a supervision of it, or [p >formally or] informally interposing at need. Accordingly a drum-head court was summarily convened, he electing the individuals composing it, the First Lieutenant, a lieutenant of minor grade, [p <a lieutenant of minor grade ⇗the captain of marines] and the Sailing Master.

246: Fa 10; Ga 51². [W 236]

Fa

In associating an officer of marines with the sea-lieutenants in a case having to do with a sailor the Commander perhaps deviated from general custom. The sele →< The sele→ He was prompted to →<to→ thereto by the circumstance that he took that soldier to be a rather [p <rather] judicious person, a man of some reading, [p <a man of some reading] thoughtful, and not wholly [p <wholly >intellectually { <intellectually add altogether}] unfitted →<unfitted→ incapable of grappling with a difficult case one [<one] unprecedented in his prior experience. Yet even as to him he was not without some latent misgiving, for [>(below, circled, with guide-line to caret) withall] he was an extremely good-natured man, an

247: Fa 11; Ga 52. [W 237]

[Verso of patch was inscribed earlier; see p. 431.)

Fa

enjoyer of his dinner [>a sound sleeper] and inclined to obesity. [*p notation* Insert]

† *late pencil*

the sort of [<the sort of ⫸in some respects an easy-going { <in some respects an easy-going} (*left incoherent*)] man who tho' he would never shrink in →<in→ from →<would ... from→ might →<might *add* (*after* he) would→ always maintain [?] his manhood in fight [<fight ⫸battle] might not prove altogether reliable in a moral dilemma affecting →<affecting→ involv →< involv→ involving aught of the tragic.

Fa

For the other two →<For ... two→ As for →<for→ to the First Lieutenant and· [⫸the] Sailing Master Captain Vere could not but be aware that though honest natures, of approved gallantry upon occasion their intelligence was mostly confined to the matter of active seamanship and the fighting demands of their profession—men in short to whom in no instance perhaps could life →*add period* (*after* profession) <—men ... life→ The court was held in the same cabin where the unfortunate affair had taken place. This cabin, the Commander's, was →<was→ embraced the entire area under the poop-deck. Aft, and lining a portion of [<lining a portion of >on] either side

248: Fa 12; Ga 53. [W 238]

Fa

was a small state-room [*p* >the one now { >temporarily} a dea →<dea→ jail & the other a dead-house] and a yet smaller compartment leaving a space between which, forward, →<which, forward→ expanding foreward into a goodly oblong of length coinciding with the ship's beam. A sky-light of moderate dimension was overhead and on [<on ⫸at] each side [<side ⫸end of] the oblong space were [>two] sashed port-hole windows readily [<readily >easily] convertable back into embrasures for the [*p* <the] short carronades belonging to them. [*p add period* (*after* carronades) <belonging to them]

All being quickly in readiness, Billy Budd was arraigned, Captain Vere necessarily appearing as the sole witness in the case, and as such temporarily sinking his rank, though singularly maintaining it in a

249: **Fa 13; Ga 54. [W 238 {sic}]**

Fa

matter apparently trivial, namely, that he testified from the [*p* >ship's]
weather-side with that object having caused the court to sit on the lee-side.
Concisely he narrated all that had led up to the catastrophe, omitting nothing
in Claggart's accusation and deposing as to the manner in which the prisoner
had received it. At this testimony the three officers glanced with no little
surprise at Billy Budd, the last man they would have suspected either of the
mutinous design alleged by Claggart or the undeniable deed he himself had
done.

250: **Fa 14; Ga 55. [W 239]**

Fa

The First Lieutenant taking judicial primacy and turing toward the prisoner,
said, "Captain Vere has spoken. Is it or is it not as Captain Vere says?" In
responce came syllables not so much impeded in the utterance as might have
been anticipated. They were these: "Captain Vere tells the truth. It is just
as Captain Vere says, but it is not as the Master-at-Arms said. I have eaten
the King's bread. [*p* <*period* >and] I am true to the King."

"I beleive you, my man" said the sole [*p* <sole] witness in →<in→ his
voice indicating a suppressed emotion not otherwise betrayed.

251: **Fa 15; Ga 56. [W 240]**

Fa

[*ESM p notation (with fist)* 16 on left side of page follows]
"God will bless you for that, Your Honor!" not without stammering said
Billy, and all but broke down. But immediatly was recalled to self-control by
another question, to which with increased [*p* <increased >the same emotion-
al] difficulty of utterance he said "No, there was no malice between us. I never
bore malice against the Master-at-arms. I am sorry that he is dead. I did not
mean to kill him. Could I have used my tongue I would not have struck him.
But he fouly lied to my face and in prescence of my Captain, and I had to
say something, and I

252: **Fa 16. [W 241]**

Fa

[*ESM p notation (with fist)* 56 on right side of page {<*notation*}]
could only say it with a blow, God help me!"
In the impulsive [>above-board] manner of the frank one the court saw
confirmed all that was implied in words that just previously had perplexed

them coming as they did from the testifier to the trajedy [*p correct to* tragedy] and promptly following Billy's [>impassioned] disclaimer of mutinous intent —Captain Vere's words, "I believe you, my man".

Next it was demanded of him →<demanded of him→ asked [>of him] whether he knew of or suspected aught savoring of incipient trouble (meaning mutiny, tho' the explicit term was avoided) going on in any section of the ship's company.

253: Fa 17. [W 242]

Fa

The reply lingered. This was naturally imputed by the court to the same vocal embarrassment which had retarded or obstructed previous answers. But in main it was perhaps [<perhaps] otherwise here; the question immediatly recalling to Billy's mind the interview with the Afterguardsman in the fore- - chains. But an innate repugnance to playing the →<the→ a part at all approaching that of an informer against one's own shipmates—the same erring sense of uninstructed honor which had stood in the way of his reporting the matter at the time though as a loyal man-of-war-man it [*p* <it >this {<this ≫it}] was incumbent [*p add* on him and failure so to do if charged against him and proven, would have subjected him to the heaviest of penalities;]

254: Fa 18. [W 243]

Fa

on him [*p* >(*at top of leaf*) and not {<not >failure} so to do {>(*below, circled*) if proven} made him liable to the heaviest of penalities; {*erase revisions and transfer substance to foot of preceding leaf*}] so to do; [*p* <on him ⟨*addition* <so to do] this, with the blind feeling now his, that nothing really was being hatched, prevailed with him. When the answer came it was a negative.

"One question more," said the officer of marines now first speaking and with a troubled earnestness, "You tell us that what the Master-at-Arms said against you was a lie. Now why should he have so lied, so desperately [<desperatly >maliciously] lied, since you declare there was no malice between you?"

At that question [>unintentionally] touching on a spiritual sphere wholly

255: Fa 19. [W 244]

Fa

obscure to Billy's thoughts, he was nonplussed, evincing a confusion indeed that some observers, such as can readily [*ESM p* >be] imagined, would have construed into involuntary evidence of mysterious [*ESM p* <mysterious ⟩hidden] guilt. Nevertheless he strove some way to answer, but all at once relinquished the vain endeavor, at the same time turning an appealing glance towards Captain Vere as deeming him his best helper and friend. The Com-

mander [*p* <The Commander >Captain Vere] who had been seated for a time rose to his feet, addressing the soldier. [*p* <soldier ⊁questioner {*ESM p* <questioner ⊁(*below*) interrogator}] "The question you put to him, Sir, [*p* <Sir] comes naturally

256: Fa 20. [W 245]

Fa

enough. But how can he rightly answer it? or anybody else? unless indeed it be he who lies within there" designating the compartment where lay the corpse. "But he [*p* <he >the prone one tho →<tho→ there will →≮will→] will not rise to our summons. In effect [*p* ⊁tho', as] it seems to me, that your [*p* <that your *add* the] point [*p* ⊁you make] though attesting your [*p* ≮your] thoughtfulness [*p* <though ... thoughtfulness] is not →<not→ hardly material. Quite aside from any conceivable motive actuating the Master-at-arms, and irrespective of the provocation to the blow, and [<and ⊁or] even the blow itself, [*p* <or ... itself] a martial court should [*p* <should >must needs {*p* >(*below, circled, with guide-line to caret*) in the present case}] confine its attention to the [*p* >blow's] consequce, which [*p* >consequence ⊁(*below*) justly] is to be deemed not otherwise than as the prisoner's [*p* <prisoner's ⊁(*below*) striker's] deed."

257: Fa 21. [W 246]

Fa

This utterance the full significance of which it was not at all likely that Billy took in, nevertheless caused him to cast [<cast >turn] a wistful interrogative look at →<at→ toward the speaker, a look not unlike that of →<of→ which in its dumb expressiveness → *transpose, circled, with caret* in its dumb expressiveness *to follow* look → a dog of generous breed might turn upon his master seeking in his face some elucidation of a previous gesture ambiguous to its [<its >the canine] intelligence. Nor was the same utterance without marked effect upon the three officers, more especially the soldier. Couched in it seemed to them a meaning unanticipated, involving a

258: Fa 22. [W 247]

Fa

prejudgement as it were [<as it were] on the speaker's part. It served to augment a mental disturbance previously evident enough.

The soldier once more spoke; in a tone of suggestive dubiety addressing at once Captain Vere and →<Captain Vere and→ his associates and Captain Vere: "Nobody is present—none of the ship's company, I mean, who might

shed lateral light, if any is to be had, upon what remains mysterious in this matter."

"That is thoughtfully put" said Captain Vere; "and →<"and→ "I see your drift. Ay, there is a mystery; but, to use a Scriptural phrase, it is "a mystery of

259: Fa 23. [W 248]

Fa
iniquity", a matter for psychologic theologians to discuss. But what has a military court to do with it? Not to add that for us any possible investigation of it is cut off by xxx →<xxx→ the lasting tongue-tie of—him—in yonder," again designating the [*p* >mortuary] state-room. The prisoner's deed, [*p* >—] with that alone we have to do." [*add bracket for new paragraph*] To this, and particularly the closing reitteration, the [>marine] soldier knowing not how with good sense [*p* <with good sense ≯aptly] to reply, prudently said nothing. →<prudently said nothing→ sadly abstained from saying aught. The First Lieutenant who in the →<in the→ at the outset had not unnaturally assumed the →<the→ primacy in the court, now

260: Fa 24. [W 249]

Fa
overrulingly instructed by a glance from Captain Vere, a glance that →<that→ more expressive →<expressive→ effective than words, resumed that primacy. Turning to the prisoner, "Budd," he said, and scarse in equable tones, "Budd, if you have aught further to say for yourself, say it now."

Upon this the [>young] sailor turned another quick glance toward Captain Vere; then, as taking a hint from that aspect, one [<one ≯a hint] confirming his own instinct [*p* <instinct ≫instinct] [> (*below, circled, with guide-line to caret*) that silence was now best,] replyed [≯ (*below*) to his questi →<to his questi→ >to the Lieutenant] "I have said all, Sir."

The marine—the same who had been the sentinel without the cabin-door

[260a] 83†v:

[*Superseded pencil-draft fragment from Stage X, no foliation. Corresponds to matter now on Leaves 261–64.*]

X pencil
As he disappeared every →<every→ xx →<xx→ an alteration fell upon the faces of the four officers →<an alteration . . . officers→ every countenance altered. The four officers instinctively exchanged looks, but nobody spoke →<but nobody spoke→ and the four looks were as one, but nobody spoke. Then Captain Vere involuntarily [<Then Captain Vere *capitalize* involun-

tarily] dropping all sense of his rank but →<all . . . but→ the wonted manner
of his rank, but [<but ≯and] speaking as a man to fellow-men, said,

I fe →<fe→ Yes, to you as to me this is terrible. →<said . . . terrible →
(after fellow-men,) but thereby only the more signalizing the superiority
[<superiority ≯inherent supremacy (?)] of his nature, said, I think that
→<said . . . that→ turning upon →<turning upon→ addressing [≯ (before
addressing) rising and {<rising and}] the seated officers [<the seated officers
≯them in an unfaltering tone] said— [green crayon <The four officers . . .
nobody spoke. <only the more . . . tone] [blue crayon <Involuntarily . . . but
thereby] [p notation (underlined, in both margins) Restore (thus restoring The
four . . . nobody spoke.)]

[260b] 87†v:

[Superseded pencil-draft fragment from Stage X, folio 7. Matter has no
exact counterpart in final version, but cf. Leaves 262–66.]

X pencil

As the examination is closed, and the case →<the case→ [cut off here] [above
this line but circled for insertion lower on the leaf from which this clip was cut, is
the following I{ >respect it, I <respect it ≫respect it <respect it, I add (before
I) I respect it,} sympathize with it, but so far { >painfully} prevail with myself as not to let pity suspend resolution.]

[260c] 20v:

[Superseded pencil-draft leaf, Stage X, foliated 10 then 9². Matter was
subsequently expanded over F 20, 31, 36, 37. Leaf was originally foliated
B 71 but carried no B text (only clips); then it was turned other end up
and foliated 10 then 9² of this pencil draft of Vere's speech.]

X pencil

plain enough here. [<plain enough here >The blow without the death, would
→<would→ was mutiny. {<The blow . . . mutiny add (below, circled, with
guide-line to caret) The blow itself, setting aside its consequence, →<setting . . .
consequence→ was mutiny. And →<And alter period to semicolon→ but
→<but→}] That the man intended not homicide, however pregnant that fact
will prove to be before the bar of heaven, here it should avail nothing. For
the code martial which commands [<which commands >commanding] us,
looks not →<looks not→ goes [<goes >peers {<peers >ferrets}] not behind the deed. It is the reverse of the divine code inasmuch as takes no cog-
nizance of motives. [blue crayon <That the man . . . motives. {p add (to
follow mutiny;) the following:}] and hence [<and hence] a capital crime;
[>and] its consequence involved [alter to involves] another [<another >an
added] capital crime. B →<B→ And as to the last →<And as to the last→
But the man did not intend homicide— [add you feel it.] True. But however

[[391]]

pregnant that truth [<truth *add* verity] will prove to be before the bar of heaven, here it should avail nothing.
[*brown crayon cancel whole passage*]

261: Fa 25. [W 250]

Fa

at the time that the foretopman and →<and→ followed by the master-at- - arms, entered it—he, standing by the sailor throughout these [>judicial] proceedings, was now directed to take him back to the after compartment originally assigned to the prisoner and his custodian. As the twain disappeared from present sight →<present sight→ view, the three officers as partially liberated from some inward constraint associated with Billy's mere prescence, simultaniously stirred in their seats. They exchanged looks of troubled inde- cision, the more trying since they felt [*p* <the more . . . felt ⊁while { <while} yet feeling] that decide they must and without prolonged [*p* <prolonged ⊁long] delay. [*p begin then cancel addition at bottom of leaf* nor less →<nor less ⊁(*below*) and yet→ delay the →<the <and yet delay→]

262: Fb 26. [W 251]

* Fa[26]

For Captain Vere, he for the time stood— [*p* <stood ⊁(sitting)] unconciusly with his back toward them, in one →<in one→ apparently in one of his absent fits, gazing out from a sashed port-hole to windward upon the

Fb

monotonous dim [*p* <dim] blank of the [>twilight] sea. But the court's silence continuing, broken only at moments by low [<low ⊁brief] consulta- tions, this moved him to signs of impatience. [<this . . . impatience ⊁(*over erasure*) in low earnest tones, this served to arouse him and energize {energise?} him.] Wheeling round all at once, [*p* <Wheeling . . . once ⊁Turning,] he to- - and-fro paced the cabin athwart; in the returning ascent to windward, climbing the slant deck in the ship's lee roll; without knowing it symbolizing [symbolis- ing?] thus in his person [*p* <person ⊁action] a tenacious [*p* <tenacious] mind resolute to surmount difficulties. [*delete period and add* even if against primitive instincts strong as the wind and the sea.]

263: Fa 27. [W 252]

Fa

Presently he came to a stand before the three. After scanning their faces he stood [*p* >less] as one [<one] mustering his thoughts for expression, and tho' full of them [*p* <and tho' full of them] than as one inly deliberating how best to put them to well-meaning men not intellectually mature, men with

whom it was necessary to demonstrate certain principles [*mend*] that were axioms to himself. This [<This >Similar] impatience as to talking the primer [*p* <the primer] is perhaps one reason that deters some superior [*p* <superior] minds from taking part in [*p* <taking part in >addressing any] popular assemblies; under which class →<class ≯head→ is to be classed most legislatures in a Democracy. [*p* <under . . . Democracy *add period* (*after* assemblies)]

264: Fa 28. [W 253]

Fa

When speak he did, something both in the substance of what he said and his manner of saying it, showed the influence of unshared studies modifying and tempering the practical training of an active career. This, along with his phrasiology [*p correct to* phraseology] at times →<at times→ now and then was suggestive of the grounds whereon rested that imputation of a certain pedantry socially alleged against him by certain of his brother-captains, [<of his <brother-captains] [>naval] men of wholly practical cast, who ne →<who ne→ officers [<officers *add* men {<men ≫officers} {<officers ≯captains}] who nevertheless would frankly concede that his [*alter* his *to* His] Magesty's navy mustered no

265: Fa 29. [W 254]

Fa

more efficient officer of their grade than Starry Vere. [*underlined*]
What he said was as follows: [*p* <as follows >to this effect:] "Hitherto I have been but the witness, acting that part, [*p* <acting that part] little more; and I should hardly think [*p* >now] to take the [*p* <the ≯another] tone [*p add comma* ≯that] of your judicial [*p* <judicial] coadjutor; which now I propose to do, [*p* <which . . . do ≯for the time] did I not perceive in you, my friends, [*p* <my friends] —at the crisis too—a troubled hesitancy, proceeding, I doubt not, [<*comma*] from honest puzzlement of [*p* <honest . . . of ≯the clash of duty →<duty→ military duty and →<and ≯with→ moral] scruple—scruple vitalized by compassion. That compassion is natural. [*p* <That *add* For the <is natural] How can I otherwise than share it. But, mindful of [*p* >paramount] obligations I strive against

266: Fa 30. [W 255]

Fa

everything [*p* <everything ≯scruples] that may tend to enervate decision. Not, believe me, [*p* <believe me ≯gentlemen] that I hide from myself that the case to be decided [*p* <to be decided ≯before us {<before us ≯is}] is an exceptional one. Speculativly regarded, well might it [*p* <it ≯it (*before* well)]

be referred to a jury of casuists. But for us who are but military men here, [*p* <who ... here ≯ here acting as → <as→ not as private gentlemen → <private gentlemen→ casuists or moralists] and → <and→ it is a case practical, and under martial law practically [*p* >, not speculatively { ≮*comma* <not speculatively}] to be dealt with.

Your scruples: do they move as in a dusk? Challenge them. [*p* <Your ... them. {≫Your ... them. *add* But (*before* Your)}] Force them to [*p* <Force *add* Make <to] come out into the open → <come out into the open→ advance and declare themselves. Come now: do they import something like this. [*alter period to colon*] If, mindless of palliating circumstances,

267: Fa 31. [W 256]

Fa
we are bound to regard the death of the Master-at-arms as the prisoner's deed, then does that deed constitute a capital crime, and → <, and→ whereof the penalty is a mortal one. But in natural justice is nothing but the [*p* >prisoner's] overt act to be considered? How can we adjudge to summary and shameful death a man → <man→ fellow-creature innocent before God, and whom we feel to be so?—Does that state it aright? You sign sad assent. Well, I too feel that, the full force of it. [*p* <it ≯that] It is Nature. → <It is Nature.→ It is irresisable [*mend to* irresistable] [<It is {*p* <It is <irresistable}] It is Nature. But do these [*Fb add* buttons that we wear attest that]

268: Fb 32. [W 257]

Fb
our allegiance is to Nature? No, to the King. Though the ocean [*add comma*] which is inviolate Nature primeval, tho' this be the element where we move and have our being as sailors, yet as the King's officers lies our duty in a sphere correspondingly natural? So little is that true, that in receiving our commissions we in the most important regards ceased to be natural free-agents. When war is declared are we the commissioned fighters previously consulted? We fight at command. If our judgements approve the war, that is but coincidence. So in other particulars. So now. For suppose

269: Fa 33. [W 258]

Fa
buttons that we wear attest that we of the fleet → <of the fleet→ are actors in Nature's sphere are the commissioned officers of Nature? We are the commissioned officers of the King. And in recieving our [*p* >military] commissions we in certain regards ceased to be natural free-agents. Do you start? [*p* >But { <But >And} { ≮And}] Suppose [>now] our [*Fa⁺p* (*after tentative cancella-*

tions) <buttons ... our military commissions {*brown crayon* <buttons ...
Suppose now our *Fb expand matter as inserted leaf Fb 32*}] condemnation to
follow these [*p* >present] proceedings. Would it be so much we ourselves that
would condemn as it would be martial law taking effect [*p* <taking effect
≯operating] through us its sworn [<sworn >authorized] agents? [*p* <its
authorized agents *add question mark (after* us)] For that law and the rigour
of it, we are not responsible. Our vowed responsibility is in this: that however
pitilessly

270: Fa 34. [W 259]

Fa

that law may operate in certain instances, [*p* <certain instances ≯the present
case { <the present case *add* any} (*revision leaves incomplete phrase*)] we nevertheless adhere to it and administer it.

But the exceptional in the case [<case >matter] moves the hearts within
you. Even so too is mine moved. But let not warm hearts betray heads that
should be cool. Ashore in a criminal case will an upright judge allow himself
off the bench to be waylaid by some tender kinswoman of the accused seeking
to touch him with her pitious [<pitious >tearful] plea? Well the heart here
is as that pitious woman. The heart is the feminine in man, [*p* <The heart
is <the ≯sometimes the { <the ≫the} *transpose* sometimes the feminine in
man (*to follow* here)] and hard tho' it be she must here be ruled out."

271: Fa 35. [W 260]

Fa

He paused, earnestly studying them for a moment; then resumed.

"But something in your aspect seems to urge that it is not solely the heart
that moves in you, but also the conscience, the private conscience. But tell
[≯me] whether or not, occupying →<occupying ≫occupying→ the position
→<position→ factitious [*p* <factitious] position we do, private conscience
should not yeild to that pa →<pa→ imperial one formulated in that [<that
≯the] code under which alone we at all →<at all→ officially proceed?"

Here the three men moved in their seats, agitated by →<agitated by→ less
convinced than agitated by [*p* >the course of] an argument troubling but the
more the spontanious conflict within.

272: Fa 36. [W 261]

Fa

Percieving which, the speaker paused for a moment; then abruptly changing
his tone, went on.

"Do we waver? [*p* <Do we waver] To steady us a bit, let us recur to the
facts.—In war-time at sea a man-of-war's-man strikes his superior in grade,

and the blow kills. Apart from its effect the blow itself is, according to the Mutiny Act, [*p* <Mutiny Act >Articles of War] a capital crime. Furthermore—"

"Ay, Sir," emotionally broke in the marine →<marine→ officer of marines, "in one sense it was. But surely the man [<the man *add* Budd] purposed neither mutiny nor homocide."

273: Fa 37. [W 262]

Fa

"Surely not, my good f →<f→ man. And before a court less arbitrary and more merciful than a ma →<a ma→ from the →<from the→ a martial one, that plea would largety extenuate. [>At the Last Assizes it shall acquit.] But how here? We proceed under the law of the Mutiny Act. In feature no child can resemble his father more than that Act resembles in spirit the thing from which it derives—War. We know that in his [<We know that *alter* in his *to* In His] Magesty service—in this ship indeed—there are Englishmen forced to serve their [<serve >fight for *alter* their *to* the] King and fight the French [<and fight the French] against their will. Against their conscience, for aught we know.

274: Fa 38. [W 263]

Fa

What recks the enemy of that? [*p* <What . . . that *add* (*over erasures, at bottom of leaf, circled, with guide-line to caret*) As H→<H→ Navy officers what reck we of that, however much →<As . . . much >Tho'→ as their fellow-creatures {>of these men <of these men} some of us may feel about it →<about it→ for them →<feel . . . them→ appreciate their position, yet as navy officers what reck we of it? Still less recks the enemy.] Our impressed men he would fain cut down in the same swath with our volenteers [*p mend to* volunteers]. As regards the enemy's naval conscripts, some of whom may even share our own abhorrence of the regicial →<regicial→ regicidal French Directory, it is the same on our side. War looks but to the frontage, the appearance. And the Mutiny Act, War's child, takes after the father. Budd's intent or non-intent is nothing to the purpose.

275: Fa 39. [W 264]

Fa

But while, put to it by those anxieties in you which I can not but respect, I [>but {<but *add* only}] repeat myself—while thus strangely we prolong proceedings that should be summary—an →<an→ the enemy may be sighted and an engagement result. We must do; and one of two things must we do—condemn or let go."

[[*396*]]

"Can we not convict and yet x →<x→ mitigate the penalty [*add question mark*] ," asked the junior Lieutenant here speaking, and falteringly, for the first.

"Lieutenant, were that clearly lawful for us under the circumstances

276: Fa 40. [W 265]

Fa

consider the consequences of such clemency. The people" (meaning the ship's company) "have mother- [*ESM p* <mother- >native] sense; most of them are familiar with our naval usage and tradition; and how would they take it? Even could your →<your→ you explain to them—which our official position forbids—they, long moulded by arbitrary discipline have not that kind of intelligent responsivness that would ena →<would ena→ might qualify them to comprehend and discriminate. No, to the people the foretopman's deed however it be worded in the announcement will be plain homocide committed in a flagrant act of mutiny. What [*p* <What {≫What}]

277: Fa 41. [W 266]

Fa

[*p add* What {<What}] penalty for that should follow, they know. But it does not follow. Why? [*underlined*] they will ruminate. Will they →<Will they→ You know what sailors are. Will they not revert to the recent outbreak at the Nore? Yes →<Yes→ Ay. And they →<And they→ And they will recall [*p* <And ... recall ≯They know] the well-founded alarm—the panic it struck throughout England. A →<A→ The [*p* <The *add* Your] clement sentence they would account pusillanimous. They would think that we flinch, that we are afraid of them—afraid of practising a lawful rigor [*add* (*at foot of leaf, circled, with guide-line to caret*) singularly demanded at this juncture] lest it should provoke new troubles.

278: Fa 42. [W 267]

Fa

What shame to us such a conjecture on their part, and how deadly to discipline. You see then, whither, prompted by duty and [*p* ≯the] law I steadfastly drive. But I beeseech you, my friends, do not take me amiss. I feel even [<even >much {*p* <much}] as you do for this unfortunate boy. But did he know our hearts, I take him to be of that generous nature that he would feel even for us on whom in this military necessity so heavy a compulsion is laid.

279: Fa 43. [W 268]

Fa

With that, crossing the deck he resumed his place by the sashed port-hole, tacitly leaving the three to come to a decision. On the cabin's opposite side the troubled court sat silent. Loyal subjects, [<subjects >lieges] plain and practical, though at bottom they dissented from some things →<things→ points Captain Vere had put to them, they were without the faculty, hardly had the inclination to gainsay one whom they felt to be an earnest man, one too not less their superior in mind than in naval rank. But it is not improbable

280: Fa 44. [W 269]

Fa

that even such part of [<part of ≯of his] words as were not without influence over them, less affected [<affected >came home to] them than his closing appeal to their instinct as sea-officers in the forethought he threw out as to the practical consequences to discipline, considering the unconfirmed tone of the fleet at the time, should a man-of-war's-man violent killing [*p* >at sea] of a petty-officer [<petty-officer ≯a superior in grade] be allowed to pass for aught else than a capital crime. [*p add (at bottom of leaf, with guide-line to caret)* meriting →<meriting→ xx →<xx→ demanding prompt infliction of the {*ESM p* >penalty}]

Not unlikely they were brought to something more or less akin to that harassed frame of mind which in the year 1842

281: Fa 45. [W 270]

Fa

actuated the Commander of the U.S. brig-of-war Somers to resolve, under the so-called Articles of War, Articles moddled [*p alter to* modled] upon the English Mutiny Act, to resolve upon the execution at sea of a midshipman and two petty-officers as mutineers designing the seizure of the brig. Which resolution was carried out though in a time of peace and within not many days sail of home. An act vindicated by a naval court of inquiry subsequently convened ashore. History, and here cited without comment.

282: Fa 46. [W 271]

Fa

True, the circumstances on board the Somers [*underlined*] were different from those on board the Indomitable. [*underlined*] But the urgency felt, well- - warranted or otherwise, was much the same.

Says a writer whom nobody knows, and who being dead recks not of the oblivion, [<the oblivion >that, {p <nobody . . . that, ⊁few know}] "Forty years after a battle it is easy for a non-combatant to reason about how it ought to have been fought. It is another thing personally [>and under fire] to have to direct the fighting while at the same time [p <at the same time] involved in the obscuring smoke of it. Much so with respect to →<to→ to [p >other] emergencies involving both [<both]

283: Fa 47. [W 272]

Fa

considerations both practical and moral, and when it is imperative promptly to act. The greater the fog the more it imperils the ship, [<ship >steamer] and speed is put on tho' at the hazard of running somebody down. Little ween the snug card-players in the cabin of the responsibilities of the sleepless man on the bridge."

   In brief, the →<the→ Billy Budd was formally convicted and sentenced to be hung at the yard-arm in the early morning-watch, it being now night. Otherwise, as is customary in such cases, the sentence would forthwith have been carried →<carried→ out. In war-time on the field

284: Fa 48. [W 273]

Fa

or in the fleet, a mortal punishment decreed by a drum-head court—on the field sometimes decreed by but a nod from the General—follows without delay on the heel of conviction without appeals. [p alter to appeal] [p chapter-ending mark ——◇——] [p addition, erased (undeciphered)]

285: Fa 49. [W 274]

Fa

[p chapter-beginning mark ——◇——]

   It was Captain Vere himself who of his own motion communicated the finding of the court to the prisoner. For →<For alter period to semicolon→ for that purpose going to the compartment where he was in custody and bidding the marine there to withdraw for the time.

   Beyond the communicating [p alter to communication] of the sentence what took place at this interview was never known. But in view of the character of the twain briefly closeted in that state-room, each radically shareing in the rarer qualities of

286: **Fa 50. [W 275]**

Fa

our nature—so rare indeed as to be [*p* <be *add* be all but] incredable to commonplace [*p* <commonplace ≯average] minds however much cultivated —some conjectures may be ventured.

It would have been in consonance with the spirit of Captain Vere should he on this occasion havin →<havin→ have concealed nothing from the condemned one—should he indeed have frankly disclosed to him the part he himself had played in bringing about the decision, at the same time revealing his actuating motives. On Billy's side [<(*below, circled*) it is not improbable that] such a confession

287: **Fa 51. [W 276]**

Fa

would have been received in much the same spirit that prompted it. Not without a sort of joy indeed he may [*p* <may ≯might] have discerned →<discerned→ appreciated the brave opinion of him implyed in his Captain making such a confidant of him. Nor, as to the sentance itself could he have been insensble that it was imparted to him as to one not afraid to die. Even more may have been. Captain Vere in end may have developed the profound [*p* <profound >intense { <intense}] passion sometimes latent under a stoic exterior. [*p* <stoic > (*after* exterior) stoical or indifferent.] He was old enough to have been Billy's father. The monkish [*p* <monkish ≯austere] devotee of military duty letting himself melt

288: **Fa 52. [W 277]**

Fa

back into what is [<is ≯remains] primeval in our formalised [formalized?] humanity may in end have caught Billy to his arms →<arms→ heart as →<as→ even as Abraham may have caught young Isaac on the brink of resolutly offering him up in obedience to the exacting demand. [*p* <demand ≯behest] But there is no telling of [*p* <of] the sacrament, seldom if [>in] any case revealed to the gadding world wherever under circumstances at all akin to those here attempted to be set forth two of the [*p* <the ≯great Nature's] x →<x→ nobler order embrace. There is privacy at the time, not →<not→ inviolable to the survivor, and holy oblivion the desirable [*p* <desirable]

289: **Fa 53. [W 278]**

Fa

thing for [*p* <thing for ≯sequel to] each diviner magnanimity, naturally ensues. [*p* <naturally ensues ≯ (*below*) providentially covers all at last]

The first to enconter Captain Vere in act of leaving the compartment was the First [<First →senior] Lieutenant. The face he beheld, for the moment [p >one] expressive of the agony of the strong, was to him, [p <him ≯that officer] tho' a man of fifty, a startling revelation. That the condemned one suffered less than he who mainly had effected the condemnation was apparently indicated by the former's exclamation in the scene soon perforce to be touched upon.
[p chapter-ending mark ———◇———]

290: Fa 54. [W 279]

[*Verso of patch was inscribed earlier; see p. 431.*]

Fa
[*Fb+ blue crayon chapter-beginning mark* ———◇———]
  [*Fb+ blue crayon and brown crayon add bracket confirming paragraph opening*]
Of a sequence [p Fb <sequence >series] of incidents within a brief term rapidly following each other, the [>adequate] narrating of them [p Fb <narrating of them {p ≯narration}] apparently occupies a {p *alter a to an and transpose to read* occupies an apparently] disproportional [p <occupies . . . disproportional >(*below*) may occupy a te (*sic*) less brief] time, more especially if elucidation [p <elucidation >(*below*) explanation { <may occupy . . . more <explanation (*but not* especially *if*) >(*above, circled in blue crayon, with blue guide-line to caret following* narration) may occupy a term less brief, more especially if explanation *and also brown guide-line to end of cancellation*}] or comment [>here and there] seem indispensable → <indispensable→ required here and there → <required . . . there ≯ (*above* seem) here and there→ requisite to the right [p <right >(*circled*) better] understanding of such incidents. [p <to . . . incidents {≫(*by erasure*) to the right . . . incidents}] [p <narration <may occupy . . . explanation *and replace by revision-patch with ink guide-line indicating its insertion to follow* adequate *and precede* of such incidents]

† Fb
narration may take up a term less brief, especially if explanation or comment here and there seem requisite to the better understanding

Fa
Between the entrance into the cabin of him who never left it alive, and him who when he did leave it left it as one condemned to die; between

291: Fa 55. [W 280]

Fa
this and the closeted interview just given less than an hour and a half had elapsed. It was an interval long enough however to awaken speculations among no few of [p <no few of {≫no few of}] the ship's company as to what it was

that could be detaining [>in the cabin] the Master-at-arms and the sailor; for a rumor that both were there [*p* <were there >of them had been seen to enter it and →<and→ *add* (*at bottom of leaf, circled, with guide-line to caret*) and neither of them had been seen →<been seen→ emerged {*alter to* emerge ≫been seen >to (*before* emerge)} therefrom, {<therefrom ⤳thence} {<thence} this rumor] had got abroad upon the [*p* >gun-] decks and in the tops; the [>populous {<populous}] crew of x →<x→ a seven →<seven→ line-of-battle ship of the old order [*p* <crew . . . order (*except the word* ship) >people of a great war (*before* ship) being in one respect like villagers; they take [*p* <*semicolon* <they *alter* take *to* taking] [*p* >microscopic] note of every chance [*p* <chance ⤳outward] movement [*p* >or non-movement] going on. When therefore in weather

***292:* Fa 56. [W 281]**

―――――――――――

Fa

not at all tempestuous all hands were called in the second dog-watch, a summons [*p* >under such circumstances] unusual [*p* <un ⤳not] in those hours, the men [<men *add quotation mark* (*before* the) ⤳people" {*p* <people" ⤴*quotation mark* (*before* the) *add* crew}] were not wholly unprepared for some announcement extraordinary [*p add* , one] having connection [*p* >too] with the [*p* >continued] absence of the two men from their wonted haunts.

There was a moderate sea at the time; and the moon, newly risen and near to being a f →<a f→ at its full, silvered the white spar-deck whereon the clear-cut shadow of a →*alter* a *to* any→ moving man →<whereon . . . man→ wherever not blotted by the clear-cut shadows of →<of→ horizontally thrown of fixtures and moving men. On either side the quarter-deck the marine

***293:* Fa 57. [W 282]**

―――――――――――

Fa

guard under arms was drawn up; and Captain Vere standing in his place surrounded by all the ward-room officers, addressed his men. In so doing his manner showed neither more nor less than that of →<of→ properly pertaining to his supreme position aboard the " →<*quotation mark*→ Indomitable. [*underlined*] [*p* <aboard <Indomitable (*underlined*) ≫aboard >his own ship.] In clear terms and yet →<yet→ concise he told them what had taken place in his own [*p* <his own ⤳the] cabin; that the master-at-arms was dead; that he who had killed him had been immediatly [<immediatly >already] tried by a summary court and condemned to be hung; [*p* <be hung ⤳death] and that the execution would take place in the early morning watch.

294: Fa 58. [W 283]

Fa

The word mutiny [*underlined*] was not named in what he said. He refrained too from making the occasion an opportunity for any preachment as to the maintenance of discipline, thinking perhaps that under existing circumstanes in the navy xxxx →<xxxx→ the consequnce of violating discipline should be made to speak, in →<in→ and in no mincing tone, [*p* <and . . . tone] for itself.

Their captain's announcement was listened to by the throng of standing sailors in a dumbness like that of a seated congregation of believers in hell listening to the clergyman's announcment of his Calvinistic text. [*p add marginal notation* Jonathan Edwards]

295: Fa 59. [W 284]

Fa

At the close, however, a confused waxing [*p* <waxing] murmer went up. [*p* ≯It began to wax.] All but instantly, [*p* ≯then,] at a sign, it [*p* <it ≫it] was pierced and suppressed by [> (*below, circled*) shrill whistles of] the boatswain [*mend to* Boatswain] and his Mates piping down one watch. [*p notation* (*along left margin*) Another order to be given here in place of this one] [*p add revision* (*with fist, at top of leaf*) the word was given to about ship]

To be prepared for burial Claggart's body was delivered to certain petty- - officers of his mess. And here, not to clog the sequel with lateral matters, it may be added that at a suitable hour following the execution, [*p* <following the execution] the Master-at-Arms was committed to the sea with every funeral honor properly belonging to his naval grade.

296: Fa 60. [W 285]

Fa

In this proceeding as in every public one growing out of the trajedy [*p mend to* tragedy] strict adherence to usage was observed. Nor in any point could it have been at all deviated from [> (*below, circled, with guide-line to caret*) , either with respect to Claggart or Billy Budd] without begetting undesirable speculations in the ship's company, sailors, and more particularly men- - of-war's men, being of all men the greatest sticklers for usage. For similar cause, all communication between Captain Vere and the condemned one closed [*p* ≯ended (*without canceling* closed)] with the closeted interview already given, the latter being now surrendered to the

297: **Fa 61, F/G 61¹. [W 286]**

Fa

ordinary routine preliminary to the end. Put in irons, he was consigned to [*p* <Put . . . to ≯His transfer { >(*below, circled*) under guard} from the Captain's quarters to] the customary place set apart in [*p* >great] war-ships for the safe-keeping of prisoners previous to punishment. In →<In→ This [*p* <to the customary . . . This ≯tho' m →<tho' m→] was effected without any [*p* <any *add* unusual] precautions—at least no [<no ≯few {*p* <few ≫no}] visable ones—other than those usual in similar cases. [*p* <similar cases ≯every-day example ≯(*below*) of minor offenses. {*add period (after* ones) <other . . . offenses}] If possible not to let the men so much as surmise that their officers anticipate aught amiss from them is the tacit rule, →<*comma*→ in a military ship. And the more that some sort of trouble should really be apprehended the more do the officers keep that apprehension to themselves; tho' not the less unostentatious [>(*below*) vigilance] may be augmented. [*F⁺p chapter-ending mark* ────◇──── {*Ga* ≮*chapter-ending mark*}]

298: **F/G 61². [W 287]**

Ga

In the present instance the sentry placed over the prisoner had strict orders to let no one have communication with him but the Chaplain. And certain unobtrusive measures were taken absolutely to insure this point.
[*p chapter-ending mark* ────◇────]

299: **Fa 62. [W 288]**

Fa

[*p chapter-beginning mark* ────◇────]

In a seventy-four of the old order the deck known as the upper gun-deck was the one covered over by the spar-deck which last tho' [*ESM p mend to* though] not without its armament was for the most part exposed to the weather. In general it was at all hours free from hammocks; those of the crew swinging on the lower gun-deck, and berth-deck, underneath that and next above the orlop-deck →<underneath . . . orlop-deck→ the latter being not only a dormitory but also the place for the stowing of the sailors' bags, and as well →<and as well→ and on both sides lined with the [>large] chests or movable pantries of the many messes of the men.

300: **Fa 63. [W 290 {*skips* 289}]**

Fa

On the starboard side of the [>Indomitable's (*underlined*)] upper gun--deck, behold Billy Budd under sentry lying prone in irons in one of the bays formed by everty →<everty→ every two guns →<by . . . guns→ by the

regular spacing of the guns [<guns >pieces {*p* <pieces ≫guns}] comprising the batteries on either side. All these pieces, now obsolete were of →<now . . . of→ were of the heavier calibre of that period, →<*comma add period*→ Mounted on lumbering wooden carriges they were hampered with cumbersome harness of breechen and strong side-tackles for running them out. Guns and carriages, together with the long rammers and [>shorter] linstocks lodged in loops overhead—all these, as customary, were painted black; and the heavy hempen breechens tarred to the same tint, wore the same →<same ⋗like→

301: Fa 64. [W 291]

Fa

[>livery] of the undertakers. In contrast with the funereal hue of these surroundings the prone sailor's [⋗exterior] apparel, white jumper [*underlined*] and white duck trousers, each more or less soiled, dimly glimmered in the obscure light [>of the bay] like a patch of discolored snow in early April lingering at some upland cave's black mouth. In effect he is already in his shroud or the garments that shall serve him in lieu of one. Over him but not [*p* <not ⋗scarce] illuminating him, two battle-lanthorns [*ESM p alter to* lanterns] swing from two massive beams of the deck above. Fed with the oil supplied by the war-contracters, whose gains, honest or otherwise, are in every land an anticipated portion of the bloody [*p* <bloody] harvest of death, [*p replace commas by parentheses (around* whose . . . death)] with

302: Fa 65. [W 292]

Fa

flickering splashes of dirty yellow light they pollute the pale moonshine all but ineffectually struggling in obstructed flecks thro the open ports from which the tompioned cannon protrude. Other lanthorns [*p alter to* lanterns] at intervals serve but to bring out somewhat the obscurer bays which like small confessionals or side-chapels [>in a cathedral] branch from the long dim-vistaed [⋗broad-] -aisle between the two batteries of that [>covered] deck. [*p* <deck ⋗tier.]

Such was the deck where now lay the Handsome Sailor. Through [*add* the] rose-tan of his complexion, in part a weather-stain, [*p* <in part . . . stain] no palor [*p mend to* pallor] could have shown. It would have [>taken] days of sequestration from the winds and the sun to have brought about the effacement of that. [<that *add* that young sea-bloom. {*p add period (after* that) <young sea-bloom}]

303: Fa 66. [W 293]

Fa

But [>the skeleton in] the cheek-bone at the point of its angle was just beginning [>delicatly] to define itself [*p* <to define itself ⋗to be defined] under

the warm-tinted skin. Some [<Some > (*below, circled, with guide-line to caret*) In the {p <the > (*below*) fervid hearts} self-contained *add* some] brief experiences devour our human tissieu as secret fire in a ship's hold consumes cotton in the bale.

But now lying between the two guns, as nipped in the vice of fate, Billy's agony [p >, mainly] proceeding from a generous young heart's virgin experience of the diabolical [p ≯*revision* (*undeciphered*) hate (*?*) {≮*revision*}] incarnate [>and effective] in some men—the tension of that agony was over now. It survived not the something healing in the closeted interview with Captain Vere.

304: [left-corner number 7]; Fa 67. [W 294]

Fa

[*canceled lines at beginning are non-continuous with previous leaf*]
by most—of all that, crowded within so short a term, he had just gone through, abrupt experiences and emotions, some of them so →<so→ conflicting and intense. [<and intense >poignant.] The tension relaxed, and more. [F+*p and blue crayon* <by most . . . and more] Without movement, prone [<prone] he lay [p <he lay >the young mariner (*?*) lay {≮the young mariner lay ≫he lay}] as in [p >a] trance. That adolescent expression previously noted as his, took [p <took ≯taking] on now [p <now] something akin to the look of a slumbering child [p *transpose* slumbering *with* child {*cancel transposition*}] seen [p <seen] in the cradle when the warm hearth-light →<hearth-light→ hearth-glow of the still chamber at night plays on the dimples that at whiles mysteriously form in the cheek, silently coming and going there. For now and then in his [p <his >the gyved one's] trance a serene happy light born of some wandering reminiscence

305: [left-corner number 8]; Fa 68. [W 295]

Fa

or dream would diffuse itself over the [p <the ≯his] face, and then wane away only anew to return.

The Chaplain coming to see him and finding him thus, and percieving no sign that he was conscious of his prescence, after →<after→ quietly [p <quietly ≯not without emotion {<not without emotion ≯ (*below*) attentively}] gazed [p <gazed >regarded him] for a space, then slipping aside, withdrew for the time, peradventure feeling that even [p >he] the [p >war-ship's {<war- - ship's}] minister of Christ [p <Christ >peace {<peace ≫Christ}] [p >tho' receiving his stipend from Mars] had no consolation to proffer which could result in a peace transcending that which he →<he→ which not without natural reverence [p <which not . . . reverence] he beheld. But in the first of the [<first of the] small hours he came again. And the prisoner now awake to his surroundings noticed his approach

306: [left-corner number 9]; **Fa 69.** [W 296]

Fa

and civilly, all but cheerfully, welcomed him. But it was to little purpose that in the interview following the good Chaplain [*p* <Chaplain ≯man] sought to bring Billy Budd to some godly understanding that he must die, and at dawn. True, Billy himself freely named →<named→ referred to his death as a thing near [*p add* close (*without canceling near*)] at hand; but it was something in the way that children will refer to death in general, who yet among their other sports will with much gravity [<with much gravity] play a funeral, hearse and mourners. [<, hearse and mourners *add period* (*after* funeral) {≫hearse and mourners} {*ESM p* >with (*before* hearse)}]

307: **Fa 70.** [W 297]

Fa

Not that like children Billy was incapable of conciving what death really is. No, but he was wholly without irrational fear of it, a fear more prevalent among →<among→ in highly civilised [civilized?] communities than those so-called barberous [*p correct to* barbarous] ones which in all respects stand nearer to primitive [*p* <primitive ≯unadulterate] Nature. And, as elsewhere said, a barbarian Billy radically was; as much so, for all the costume, as his countrymen the British captives, who [*p* <who] living trophies, made to march thro' Rome [<thro' Rome] in the [*add* Roman] triumph of Germanicus. Quite as much so as those later barbarians, young men probably, [*p* >(*below*) and picked specimens] among the

308: **Fa 71.** [W 298]

Fa

earlier British converts to Christianity, [*p* >at least nominally such] and taken to Rome (as to day East Indian [*p* <East Indian] converts [*p*>from lesser isles of the sea] may be taken to London) of whom the Pope of that time, admiring the strangeness of their personal beauty so unlike the Italian stamp, their clear ruddy complexion and [>curled] flaxen hair, [<hair >locks] exclaimed, "Angles do you call them →<do you call them *add quotation mark* (*after* Angles)→ (meaning English [*underlined*] its →<its→ the [*p* >modern] derivative) "Angles do you call them? And is it because they look so like angels?" Had it been later in time one would think that the Pope had in mind Fra Angelico's seraphs some of whom, seen [<seen] plucking apples in some garden [*p* <some *alter* garden *to* gardens] of the Hesperides

309: Fa 72. [W 299]

Fa

have the faint rose-bud complexion of the [>more] beautiful English girls.

If in vain the good Chaplain sought to impress the young barbarian with ideas of death akin to those conveyed in the skull, dial, and cross-bones on old tombstones; equally futile to all appearance were his efforts to present to →<present to→ bring home to him the thought of religion [<religion ⳤsalvation] and a Saviour. Billy listened, but less out of awe or reverence [*p* >perhaps] than from a certain natural politeness; doubtless at bottom regarding all that in much the same way that most mariners of his class take any discourse abstract or out of the common tone of the work-a-day world.

310: Fa 73. [W 300]

Fa

And this sailor-way of taking it →<it→ clerical talk [<talk ⳤdiscourse] is not wholly unlike the way in which the primer [*ESM p* ⳤpioneer] of Christianity full of marvellous [*p* <marvellous ⳤtranscendent] miracles is →<is ⳤwas→ recieved long ago on tropic isles by any amiable →<amiable→ superior savage [*underlined*] so called—a Tahitian say of Captain Cook's time or shortly after that time. [*p* >Out { <Out >(*above, circled, with guide-line to caret*) Out of natural courtesy}] He recieved it, yes, but out of a sort of [*leave space for word* {*p add in this space* complaisance}] [<it . . . complaisance *add comma (after* recieved)] but did not apprropriate. It was like a gift placed in the [>palm of an] extended →<extended→ outreached hand upon →<hand upon→ hand upon which the fingers do not close.

But the Ch →<Ch→ "Indomitable"'s [*underlined*] Chaplain was a [>discreet] man possessing that sort of →<that sort of *add* the → good sense of a good heart. So he insisted not in his vocation he. [*p alter to* here.] At the instance of Captain Vere,

311: Fa 74. [W 301]

Fa

a lieutenant had apprised him of pretty much everything as to Billy; and since he felt that innocence was even a better thing than religion itself [<itself] wherewith to go to Judgement, he reluctantly withdrew; but in his emotion not without [>first] performing an act strange enough in an Englishman, and under the circumstances yet more so in any regular priest. Stooping over, he kissed on the fair cheek his fellow-man, a felon in martial law, one who though on the confines of death he felt he →>could→ never convert. [*p add* (*deleting period*) to a dogma; nor did he fear →<did he fear→ for all that did he fear for his future]

Marvel not that having been made acquainted with the young sailor's essential innocense
[*p notation (bracketed)* an irruption of heretic thought hard to suppress]

312: FG 75. [W 302]

* Fa 75
[*p notation* (circled) 76 omitted]
the worthy man lifted not a finger to avert the doom of such a martyr to martial discipline. So to do would

Fb
not only have been as idle as invoking the desert, but would also have been an audacious transgresson of the →<the→ the bounds of his function, one as exactly prescribed to him by military law as that of [*p* >the boatswain or] any other navy [*alter to* naval] officer. Bluntly put, a chaplain [*p* ⊁is an anomalous personage <is ... personage] is the minister of the Prince of Peace serving in the host of the God of War—Mars. As such, he is as incongruous as a musket would be on the altar at Christmas. [*p* <a ⊁that (*before* musket) ⊁(*after* musket) of Beecher &c <would be on the altar (*revision is incomplete*)] Why then is he there? Because he indirectly subserves the purpose attested by the cannon; because too he lends the sanction of the religion of the meek to that which practically is the abrogation of everything but sheer [<sheer ⊁(*below* brute)] Force [*no period*]
[*p chapter-ending mark* ——◇——]

313: Fa 77. [W 303]

Fa
[*p notation* (circled) 76 omitted]
[*p chapter-beginning mark* ——◇——]
The night so luminous on the waters and [*p* <waters and] spar-deck but otherwise on the cavernous ones below, levels so like the tiered galleries in a coal-mine—the luminous night passed away. But, like the prophet in the chariot disappearing in heaven and dropping his mantle to Elisha, the withdrawing night transferred its pale robe to the day-break. [*p* >breaking (*before* day) *add period* (*after* day) <-break] A meek shy light appeared in the East where stretched [<where stretched >veiled by {<veiled by ≫where stretched}] a diaphonous fleece of thin [<thin >white] furrowed vapor.

314: Fa 78. [W 304]

Fa
That light slowly waxed. Suddenly one bell [one bell *underlined*] [*p* ⊁eight (*above* one) *alter* bell *to* bells] was struck aft, responded to by a [<a >one]

[[*409*]]

louder [>metallic] stroke from forward. It was half past [p <half past] four o'clock in the morning. Instantly the [>silver] whistles were heard summoning all hands to witness punishment. Up through the great hatchways rimmed with racks of heavy shot, the watch below came pouring overspreading with the other [p <other] watch [p >already on deck] the space between the mainmast and foremast including that occupied by the capacious launch [*underlined*] and the black booms tiered on either side of it, boat and booms making a summit of observation for the [>powder-] boys and younger tars. [<younger tars {≫younger tars}]

315: Fa 79. [W 306 {*sic* for 305}]

Fa

A different group comprising one watch of topmen leaned over the rail of that sea-balcony, no small one in a seventy-four, looking down in [*alter to* on] the crowd below. Man or boy none spoke [*mend to* spake] but in whisper, and few spoke [*mend to* spake] at all. Captain Vere—as before, the central figure among the assembled commissioned officers—stood nigh the break of the poop- - deck facing forward. The marines → <The marines→ [*add* Just] Below him on the quarter-deck the marines in full equipment were drawn up much as at the scene of the promulgated sentence.

316: Fa 80. [W 306]

Fa

At sea in the old time, the execution by halter of a military sailor was generally from the fore-yard. In the present instance, [>(*below, circled, with guide-line to caret*) for per → <per→ stragetic {p <stragetic ≯special} reasons] the main-yard was assigned. Under the lee → <lee→ Indomitable's [*underlined*] lee yard → <Under . . . yard→ Under an [p ≯*notation* weather or lee] arm of that yard the prisoner was presently brought up, the Chaplain attending him. It was noted at the time and remarked upon afterwards, that in this final scene the good man evinced little or nothing of the perfunctory. Brief speech indeed he had with the condemned one,

317: Fa 81. [W 307]

Fa

but the genuine Gospel was more → <more→ less on his tongue than in his [>aspect and] manner towards him. The final preperations personal to the latter being speedily brought to an end by two of → <of→ boatswain's-mates, the consummation immediatly [p <immediatly] impended. [p >Billy stood facing aft.] At the penultimate moment, Billy's [p <Billy's ≯his] words, his only ones, words wholly unobstructed in the utterance were these—"God bless

Captain Vere!" Such a →<Such a→ [*p* >W →<W→ Syllables] So unanticipated a benediction [*p* <a benediction] coming from one with the ignominious
noose [*p* <ignominious <noose ⸜hemp {≫ignominious}] about his neck—a
[*p* >a felon's { ⸜a felon's >a conventional felon's}] benediction directed [*p*
>aft] towards the quarters of honor; [*p* >syllables too] delivered too [*p*
<too] in the clear melody of a singing-bird

318: Fa 82. [W 308]

Fa

warbling [*p* <warbling] on the point of starting →<starting→ launching
from the twig, had a phenominal [*p* *correct to* phenomenal] effect, not unenhanced by the [*p* ⸜rare] personal beauty of the speaker [*p* <speaker ⸜found-
ling-sailor { <foundling- *add* young (*before* sailor)}] spiritualised [spiritual-
ized?] now thro' late experiences so poignant as his. [*alter* poignant *to* poignantly <as his. *add* profound.]

Without volition as it were, as if indeed the ship's populace were but the
vehicles of some vocal current electric, from alow and aloft with one voice
[*transpose (circled, with guide-line to caret)* from alow and aloft *to follow* voice]
came a resonant [*p* ⸜(*below*) sympathetic] echo—"God bless Captain Vere!"
And yet Billy alone must [>at that instant {*p transpose (by circling and caret)*
at that instant *first after then before* Billy}] have been in their hearts, even as
he was [>alone {*transpose (circled, with guide-line to caret)* alone *to precede*
was} {*p* ⸜monopolized <alone was} { <monopolized (*leaving no verb*)}] in
their eyes.

At the pronounced words and the spontanious [*p correct to* spontaneous]
echo that voluminously rebounded them,

319: Fa 83. [W 309]

Fa

Captain Vere, either thro stoic self-control or a sort of temporary [*p* <tem-
porary ⸜momentary] paralysis induced by emotional shock, stood erectly
rigid as a musket in an armory's [*p* <an armory's ⸜the ship-armorer's] rack.

The cannoned [*p* <cannoned ⸜ponderous { <ponderous}] hull deliberatly
recovering from the periodic roll to leeward [*p notation (circled, with guide-line
to caret)* Insert from p. 84 { ⸜*notation*}] was just regaining an even keel, when
the preconcerted fatal sign [*p* <fatal sign ⸜signal { <signal >(*after* the *but
misplacing caret after* when) death-signal} { <death- *add* fatal} { <fatal *add*
last *add* (*after* signal) a >(*after* preconcerted) and →<and→ dumb one} (*passage finally reads* when the last signal a preconcerted dumb one)] was given.
At the same moment it chanced that the vapory fleece hanging low in the
East, suddenly dyed by the sun behind approaching nearer the horizon, took

on a [*p* <suddenly ... on a >was shot thro with a dyed →<dyed→ a soft] glory as of the [*p* ⫸fleece of the] Lamb of God seen in mystical vision. [*p* <*period*]

320: Fa 84. [W 310]

Fa

[*p* >and] Simultanious [*p* *alter to* Simultaniously] therewith, watched by the wedged mass of upturned faces, Billy ascended; and, ascending, took the full shekinah [*p* <shekinah ⫸rose] of that grand dawn. [*p* <that <grand <dawn. ⫸(*below*) the dawn]

In the piniomed figure, arrived at the yard-end, [*p* >(*above, circled, with guide-line to caret*) to the amazement { <amazement ⫸(*below*) wonder} of all] no motion was visable [*p* <visable ⫸apparent] but [*p* <but >save *add* none (*before* save)] that created but →<but→ by the slow roll of the hull, [*p* <hull >ship { <slow roll of the ⫷ship ⫸ship's motion.}] in moderate weather so solemn [*p* <solemn ⫸majestic] in a great ship heavy-cannoned. [*p* <heavy >heavily { <heavily >ponderously}] [*p* *enclose with brackets* in moderate ... cannoned. *add notation* (*circled, in left margin, with cross*) put on previous page { <*notation*}] When subsequently, in reference to this, the Purser, hardly →<hardly→ a worthy man but not the wisest, [*p* <a worthy ... wisest ⫸an honest { >impulsive} man and correct accountant but little more] said at mess to the Surgeon "What testimony to the force lodged in the human will," [*p* <the human will ⫸will-power *add* human (*before* will-power)] the man of the knife and saw replied [*p* <man ... replied *add* practical physicist, { ⫸(*below*) socially} a man of { >formal} { <formal >(*below, circled*) a sort of *add* severe (*circled*)} metallic politeness, said urbane in causticity { <a sort of severe metallic politeness >(*above, circled, with guide-line to caret before* urbane) formally}]

[*F⁺ green crayon cancel whole passage* When subsequently ... causticity]
[*blue then red crayon add chapter-ending mark* ———◇——— (*after* ponderously cannoned.)]
[*ESM? p notation* End of Chapter]

321: F/G 85. [W 311]

F/G

[*p add* A digression *followed by chapter-beginning mark* ———◇———]

When subsequently [*p* <subsequently ⫸some days afterwards] in reference to this, [*p* <this >the singularity just mentioned] the Purser [>a rotund man {*p* <a *add* a rather ruddy (*before* rotund) <man *add* person}] more accurate as an accountant than profound as a thinker, [*p* <thinker ⫸philosopher] said at mess to the Surgeon, "What testimony to the force lodged in will-power" the latter a man formally polite and [<man ⫸spare man { <formally polite and ⫸and tall} {*p* <a <man *add* (*before* spare) rather} {*p*

<rather ⊁ (*below, with line*) saturnine}]] whose [*p* <whose *add* (*after* tall) one in whom a] discreet causticity was →<was→ went along with a man [*p alter to* manner] cumbrously [*p* <cumbrously ⊁less genial than] polite, replied, "Your pardon, Mr. Purser. In a hanging scientiffically [*p correct to* scientifically] conducted—and under special orders I myself directed how Budd's was to be effected—any motion [<motion ⊁movement] following the completed suspension and originating in the body suspended, such motion →<motion→ movement but [<but] indicates

322: F/G 86¹. [W 312]

F/G
[*add* but {*p* <but}] mechanical spasm in the muscular system. Hence the abscence of that no more proceeds from [>is (*before* no more) <proceeds from >attributable to] will-power as you call it than from [<than <from >than to] horse-power—begging your pardon."

"But this muscular spasm you speak of, is not that in a degree more or less invariable in theses cases? [*no quotation mark*]

Cor →<Cor→ "Assuredly so, Mr. Purser."

"How then, my good sir, [>how then {<how then}] do you account for its absence in this instance?"

"Mr. Purser, it is clear that your sense of the singularity in this matter equals not mine. You account for it by what you call will-power a term not yet included in the lexicon of science. For me I do not,

323: F/G 86². [W 313]

F/G
with my present knowledge assume [<assume >pretend] to account for it [>at] all. Even should we assume the hypothosis that at the first touch of the halyards the action of Budd's heart, intensified by extraordinary emotion at its climax, abruptly stopt—much like a watch when in carelessly winding it up you strain at the finish, thus snapping the chain—even under that hypothosis how account for the phenomenon that followed."

"You admit then that the absence of spasmodic movement was phenominal [*correct to* phenomenal]."

[*no quotation mark*] It was phenomenal, Mr. Purser, in the sense that it was an appearance

324: F/G 86³. [W 314]

F/G
the cause of which is not immediatly to be assigned."

But tell me, my dear Sir, pertinaciously continued the other, "was but →<but→ the man's death effected by the halter, or was it a species of euthanasia? [*no opening or closing quotation mark*]

[[*413*]]

"Euthanasia, [*underlined*] Mr Purser, is something like your will-power: [will-power *underlined*] I doubt its authenticity as a scientific term—begging your pardon again. It is [*p* ⧸both {<both *add* at once}] immaginative, [*p* <*comma* ⧸and] metaphysical,—in short, Greek." →<*quotation mark*→ But" totally [<totally >(*below*) abruptly] changing his tone "there is a case in the sick-bay that I do not care to leave to my assistants. You will [<You will >(*below, circled, with guide-line to caret*) Beg your pardon, but] excuse me." And rising from the mess he formally withdrew [*no period*] [*p chapter-ending mark* ——◇——]

325: Fa 87. [W 315]

Fa

[*p chapter-beginning mark* ——◇——]

The silence accompanying the [*p* <accompanying the ⧸at the moment of] ascension [*p* <ascension >execution] and for a brief space [*p* <brief space >moment or two] continuing after it →<after it→ thereafter, a silence broken only [*p* <broken only ⧸but emphasised {emphasized?}] by the [*p* >regular] wash of the sea against the hull or the slatting [*p* <slatting ⧸flutter] of a sail doubtless caused by the slatting of a sail →<doubtless . . . sail,→ possibly [*p* <possibly] caused by the helmsman's eyes being tempted astray, [*p* >this emphased silence anon →<anon→ was gradually] was presently [*p* <presently] disturbed by a sound not easeily to be verbally rendered. Whoever standing by foot-hills, [<standing by foot-hills] has caught →<caught *add* heard→ the first audible murmer of the freshet-wave of a torrent suddenly [<the first . . . of the *add* the (*before* freshet-wave)]

326: Fa 88. [W 316]

Fa

swelled by pouring rains [*p* <rains ⧸showers] in tropical mountains, rains [<rains ⧸showers] not shared by the foot →<foot→ plain; whoever has heard the first audible [<audible >muffled] murmer of its advance descending [*p alter* advance *to* advanceing <descending ⧸descent {>(*after* its) sloping *alter* advanceing *to* advance <descent}] through forrests, [*p* <forrests >precipitous woods] may form some conception of the sound now heard not without concern by the officers assembled about Captain Vere. [*p add period* (*after* heard) <not without . . . Vere ⧸Its seem <Its seem >(*below, circled, with guide-line to caret*) Its seem →⧸Its seem→ The seeming remoteness of its source was because of its peculiar {<peculiar >(*below, circled*) murmerous} indistinctness] Yet [*p* <Yet >since] it came from close-by, even from the throng [*p* <throng *add* men ⧸massed] on the de →<de→ ship's spar- [*p* <spar- ⧸open] deck. That inarticulate murmer was [*p* <That *capitalize* inarticulate *add comma* (*after* Inarticulate) <murmer was *add* it was {*add*

⟦ *414* ⟧

Being *(before* Inarticulate)}] dubious in significance save that [*p* <save >further than <that] it seemed to indicate some capricious revulsion of thought or feeling such as shore- → <shore- → mobs

327: Fa 89. [W 317]

Fa

ashore ar → <ar >are→ subject [<subject ≯liable] to; →*alter semicolon to comma*→ in the present instance possibly implying the [*p* <the ≯a sullen] revocation on the men's part of their involunatary echoing of Billy's benedic-tion. But ere it [*p* <it >the murmer] had to →>time *(before* to)→ wax →<wax→ wax into aught of [*p* <aught of] clamor it was met by a stragetic command, the more telling that the →<the→ the men →<the men→ it came with abrupt unexpectedness:

"Pipe down the starboard watch Boatswain, and see that they promptly [*p* <promptly] go."

[>Shrill as the shriek of the sea-hawk] The shrill [<shrill >silver { <sil-ver} {≫silver}] whistles of that warrant-officer [*p* <that warrant-officer ≯the Boatswain] and his mates [*alter* mates *to* Mates] shrill →<shrill→ pierced that ominous low sound, like the →<like the→ dissipating it; and

328: Fa 90. [W 318]

Fa

yielding to the mechanism of disp →<disp→ displine the throng was thinned by one half. For the remainder most of them were set to those →<those→ temporary employments readily to be →<readily to be→ connected with trimming the yards & →<&→ and so forth, [*p* >business] readily to be got up [*p* >*(below, circled)* to serve occasion] by any officer-of-the-deck.

[*p add* Now] Each proceeding that follows a mortal sentence pronounced at sea by a drum-head court are →<are >is→ characterized [characterised?] by promptitude not perceptably attended by [*p* <attended by *add* merging ≯into] hurry. [*p alter period to comma* ≯tho bordering that.] The shotted [<shotted] hammock, [>the one which had been] Billy's bed when alive [*p add comma*] having already been prepared →<prepared→ ballasted with shot and otherwise prepared

329: Fa 91. [W 319]

Fa

to serve for his [*p* >canvas] coffin, the last office of the sea-undertakers, the Sail-Maker's Mates, were now speedily completed. When everything was in readiness the →<the→ a second call for all x →<x→ hands [*p* >*(below, circled, with guide-line to caret)* made necessary by the unusual { <unusual}

stragetic movement before mentioned] was sounded and now to witness burial.

[G ink begins]

The details of this closing formality it needs not to give. But when the tilted plank let slide its freight into the sea, a second strange inarticulate [<inarticulate] human murmer was heard, blended now with another in-articulate sound proceeding from certain gaunt [p <gaunt ⟩larger] sea-fowl whose attention having been

330: F/G 92. [W 320]

F/G

attracted by the [>peculiar] commotion in the water resulting from the plump [<plump >slant {<slant *add* heavy}] [p >sloped] dive of the pale [<pale] heavy [<heavy >shotted] hammock, [p *add* into the sea] flew scream-ing to the spot. So near the hull did they come, that the stridor or bony creak of their gaunt double-jointed pinions was audible. As the ship under light airs sa →<sa→ passed in, [*alter* in *to* on] leaving the burial-spot astern, they still kept circling it low down with the moving shadow of their outstretched wings and the croaked requiem of their cries.

Upon sailors as superstitious as those of the age preceeding ours, men-of- -war's men [p >too] who had just

331: F/G 93. [W 321]

F/G

beheld the prodigy of repose hanging from the yard-end; [p <hanging from the yard-end >in the {>form} suspended in air, the same →<the same→ and now foundering in the deeps;] to such mariners the action of the sea-fowl tho' dictated by an →<an→ mere animal appet →<appet→ greed for prey, was big with imaginative import of bale. [p <imaginative . . . bale ⟩no prosaic significance.] A dubious strange [p <A dubious strange ⟩An uncer-tain] movement began among them, in which some encroachment was made. It was tolerated but for a moment. For suddenly the drum beat to quarters, which familiar sound happening [⟩at least] twice every day, had upon the present occasion a p →<p→ sh →<sh→ ringing [p <ringing ⟩signal] peremptoriness in it. True martial discipline [p ⟩long continued,] breeds [<breeds >superinduces] in average man an instinct [p >of docility {<an instinct <of >(*before* docility) an impulse →⟨an *add* a sort of→} (*revision incomplete, reads* a sort of impulse docility)] whose p →<p→ instinct →<in-stinct→ operation [p >under →<under→ at the w →<w→ official word of command] much resembles [>(*below, circled*) in its promptitude] that [<that ⟩(*below*) the effect] of a natural one. [p <one ⟩cause.] [p *alter* a *to* an <nat-ural cause ⟩(*below*) instinct.]

[[416]]

332: F/G 94. [W 322]

F/G

Instantly the [p <Instantly *capitalize* the] drum-beat dissolved the multitude, distributing most of them along the batteris of [>the] two [*add* covered gun-] decks. There, as wont, the guns' crews stood by their respective cannon erect and silent. In due course the First Officer →<Officer→ Lieutenant →<Lieutenant→ Officer, sword under arm and standing in his place on the quarter-deck [>formally] recieved the successive reports of the sworded Lieutenants commanding the sections of batteries below; the last of which reports being made the summed report he delivered with the customary salute to the Commander. All this occupied time, which in the present case, was the object of [*write* in *over* of] beating to quarters at an

333: F/G 95. [W 323]

F/G

hour prior to the customary one. [p *add then erase* when the band plays & when →<when→ prayers are said] That such variance from usage was authorised [authorized?] by an officer like Captain Vere, a martinet as some deemed him, was evidence of the necessity for it [<for it *add* for >unusual action] implyed in what he deemed to be temporarily the mood of his men. "With mankind" he would say "forms [>, measured forms] are everything; and that is the moral →<moral→ import couched in the story of Orpheus taming the beasts." [p <taming the beasts >with his lyre spell-binding the wild denizens of the wood.] [> *(below, circled, with guide-line to caret)* And this he once applied to the disruption of forms going on across the Channel and the consequces thereof.]

At this unwonted call to [<call to ≯muster *add* at] quarters, all proceeded as at the regular hour. The band on the quarter-deck played a sacred air. After which the Chaplain went thro'

334: F/G 96. [W 324]

F/G

the customary morning service. That done, the drum beat the retreat; and toned by [>music and] religious rites subserving the discipline [p >& purposes] of war, the men in their wonted orderly manner, dispersed to their →<*alter to* the→ places alloted them when not at the guns.

And now it was full day. The fleece of low-hanging vapor had vanished, licked up by the sun that late had so glorified them. [<them >it.] And the circumambient air in the clearness of its serenity was [>like] smooth white marble in the polished block not yet removed from the marble-dealer's yard. [p *chapter-ending mark* ———◇———]

[334a] 361:

[Pencil-draft fragment of notations for chapters on (a) fight with French ship, (b) subsequent history of spar. From Stage X, no foliation. Verso of fragment was inscribed earlier; see p. 432.]

X pencil

They hoped it might prove to be the sail they had chaced the previous morning; but it turned out otherwise. It was the French   [French *written over erasure*] line of battle ship "The Directory"   [The *written over another word?*] [*single rule across leaf*]

For the Supplement. [*underlined*]

In the engagement the main yard from which Billy had been hung, fouling at close quarters with the rigging of the "Directory", was snapped off at the end

&c &c &c

[*single rule across leaf*]

& left at Gibraltar. [*underlined*]

[*remnant of caret-pointer where leaf is cut off here*]

[*Weaver? pencil notation, underlined, along left margin* Illegible {*notation erased*}]

335: F/G 97. [W 325]

F/G

[*p chapter-beginning mark* ———◇———]

The symetry [*correct to* symmetry] of form attainable in pure fiction can not so readily be achieved in a narration [>essentially] have [*alter to* having] less to do with fable than with fact. Truth uncompromisingly told will always have its ragged edges; hence the conclusion of such a narration is apt to be less finished that an architectural finial.

How it fared with the Handsome Sailor during the year of the Great Mutiny has been faithfully given to →*add period (after* given) <to→ But tho' properly the story ends with his life something in way of sequel

336: F/G 98. [W 326]

F/G

will not be amiss. Three brief chapters will suffice.

In the general re-christening under the Directory of the craft originally forming the navy of the French monarchy, the St. Louis [*underlined*] line-of- - battle ship was named [*leave space for name* {*p write name (above, with guideline)* Athéiste} {*ESM p add (in space left for name)* the Atheiste}] Such a name, like some other substituted ones in the F →<F→ Revolutionary fleet while proclaiming the infidel audacity of the ruling power was yet, tho' not so intended to be, the aptest name, if one consider it, ever given to a war-ship;

far more so indeed than the Devastation, [*underlined*] the Erebus (the Hell) [*both names underlined*] and seem →<seem→ similar names bestowed upon fighting-ships.

337: F/G 99. [W 327]

F/G

On the return-passage to the English fleet from the detached cruise during which occurred the events already recorded, the Bellipotent [*underlined*] fell in with the [*leave space for name* {*p write name (above, with guide-line to caret)* Athéiste} {*ESM p add (in space left for name) Atheiste (underlined)*}] An engagement ensued; during which Captain Vere in the act of putting his ship alongside the enemy with a view to [<to >of] throwing his boarders on her decks, [<on her decks >across her bulwarks] was hit by a musket-ball from a port-hole of the enemy's main cabin. More than disabled he dropt [*ESM p alter to* dropped] to the deck and was carried below to the same cock-pit where some of his men already lay. The senior Lieutenant took command. Under him the enemy was

338: F/G 100. [W 328]

F/G

finally captured and though much crippled was by rare good fortune successfully taken into Gibraltar, an English port luckily [<luckily] not [>very] distant from the scene of the fight. There, Captain Vere with the rest of the wounded was put ashore. He lingered for some days, but the end came. Unhappily he was cut off too early for the Nile and Trafalgar. The spirit that spite its philosophic austerity may yet secretly [<secretly ≯have] indulged in the most secret of all passions, ambition of broad →<broad→ fame, [<of fame] never attained to the fulness of fame.

Not long before death

339: F/G 101. [W 329]

F/G

while lying under the influence of that magical drug which soothing the physical frame mysteriously operates on the subtler element in man, he was heard to murmer words inexplicable to the →<the→ his attendant—"Billy Budd, Billy Budd." That these were not the accents of remorse, seems →<seems→ would seem clear from what the attendant said to the Bellipotent's [*underlined*] senior officer of marines who as the most reluctant to x →<x→ condemn of the membes of the drum-head court, too well knew tho' here he kept the knowledge to himself, who Billy Budd was.

340: Bc 75², p 75. [W 330]

Bc

[*X⁺p notation (with fist)* P 25 (pencil) follows →<follows→ precedes]

[*X⁺p notation (with fist)* (Speak of the fight & death of Captain Vere) {*p* <notation*}*]

[*p chapter-beginning mark* ——————— {*p second chapter-beginning mark* ————————}]

[*ESM p notation (at top)* follows 101 on side in pencil]

[≻To go back. { <To go back.}] In due time [*p* <In due time ≻Some few weeks] after the event, [*p* <event ≻execution, {*add* of the Foretopman} { <execution ≻end} { <end of the Foretopman *add* execution}]] among other matters under the head of News from the Mediterranean, [News . . . Mediterranean *underlined*] there appeared in an authorised [authorized?] naval Chronicle of the time, a [(*with circling and guide-line to caret*) *transpose* authorised *to this point, altering* an *to* a *and* a *to* an] weekly publication, an account of the affair. [*p* <affair ≻execution and alleged crime. { <execution and alleged crime ≫affair.}] It was doubtless [*p* >for the most part] written in good faith, tho' the medium, partly rumor, through which the facts must have reached the writer, served to deflect [*p* >and in part falsify] them. The account was as follows:—

[*p add quotation mark*] On the tenth of the last month a deplorable occurence took place [*p* <place]

341: Bb 76, 76ᵖ¹. [W 331]

Bb

place on board H.M.S. Indomitable. [Indomitable *underlined*] John Claggart, the ship's master-at-arms, discovering that some sort of plot was being hatched [*p Bc* <being hatched >incipient] among an inferior section of the ship's company, and that the plotter [*p Bc* <plotter ≻ringleader] was one William Budd a foretopman →<a foretopman *add semicolon (after* Budd)→ [*p* ≻he, Claggart] in the act of arraigning the man before the Captain [*p* <Captain ≻Comm →<Comm ≫Captain→] was [*p Bc* >vindictivly stabbed to the heart by the suddenly drawn sheath-knife of Budd.

The deed and the implement employed, sufficiently suggest that the [*Bc alter* the *to* tho']

† Bc

mustered into the service under an English name the assasin was no Englishman, but one of those aliens adopting English names [*p* <names ≻(*below*) cognomens] whom

342: Bb 77 [Bc 77 substitute top pasted on]. [W 332]

† **Bc**

the [>present extraordinary] necessities of the service have caused to be admitted into it. [*p* <*period by writing over it and add* in considerable numbers (*no period*)]

* **Bb 77**

The enormity of the crime and the extreme depravity of the criminal, appear the greater in view of the character of the victim, a man [*Bb*+*p* <a man ≯(*below*) a middle-aged man ≪a middle-aged man ≫a {*Bc* ≯middle-aged} ≫man] eminently [*Bc* <eminently] respectable, sober and [*Bc* <sober and ≯and] discreet, belonging to that minor [*p Bc* >official] grade in the →<the→ His Majesty [*p add* 's] navy [*Bb*+*p* <His . . . navy ≯serving in (?)] upon which [*Bb*+*p* <which ≯the petty officers *and several words* (*undeciphered*) upon whom as {*Bc* ≪the petty . . . whom as <His Majesty's Navy upon which, as >(*interlined*) , the petty-officers, upon whom, as}] none know better than the commissioned officers, [*Bc* <officers ≯gentlemen,] the efficiency of the service [*p Bc* <the service ≯His Majesty's navy] so considerably [*p* <considerably ≯largely] depends—the petty officers. [*Bc* <—the petty officers *add period* (*after* depends)] His function was a [*p Bc alter* a *to* an >onerous and] responsible one; [*p* <onerous and >at once onerous & thankless] and his fidelity in it the more marked [*p Bc* <more marked *add* greater] because of the [>peculiar] earnestness of [*Bb*+*p* <the peculiar earnestness of ≯(*below*) his →<his ≯a→ strong →<strong→ patriotic →<patriotic→ loyal impulse signalizing him →*alter to* that signalized him *then alter to* that signalizing trait in him,→ {*Bc green crayon* <greater because . . . in him}]

343: Bc 78¹. [W 333]

Bc

greater because of his strong patriotic impulse. In this instance as in so many other instances in these days, the example of this →<this→ the [*p* <example of the ≯character of this unfortunate] man signally refutes, if refutation were needed, that peevish saying attributed to the late Dr. Johnson, that patriotism is the last refuge of a scoundrel.

* **Bb**

The criminal paid the penalty of his crime. The promptitude of the example [*p* <example >punishment] has proved salutary. Nothing amiss is now apprehended aboard H.M.S. Indomitable." [*underlined*]

The above appearing in a publication now

344: Ba 78, Bc 78². [W 334]

Ba

long ago superannuated and forgotten is all that stands [*p* <stands ≯hitherto
has stood] in human [*p* <human >authorative { <authorative ≫human}]
record [*p* >up to the present time { <up to the present time}] to attest
what manner of men respectivly were John Claggart and Billy Budd [*no
period*]
[*B⁺p chapter-ending mark* ——◇——]
[*B⁺p notation* End {*B⁺p* <End}]
[*B⁺p add* Here ends a story not unwarranted by what sometimes happens in
this {*word undeciphered*} world of ours—Innocence and infamy, spiritual depravity and fair repute {*blue crayon* <Here ends . . . repute}]
[*B⁺p ending-mark* ——◇——]

345: B/X 79. [W 335]

B/X pencil

Everything is for a term venerated in navies. Sailors →<Sailors→ Any
tangible object associated with any x →<any x→ some striking incident
[≯of that →<that→ the service], is converted into a monument. The spar
from which the Foretopman was suspended, was for some years →<was for
some years→ was for some few followed →<followed→ years kept trace of
by the bluejackets. Their knowledges pursued [<pursued >followed] it from
ship to dock-yard and again from dock-yard to ship, following [<following
≯still pursuing] it even when [>at last] reduced to a meer dock-yard boom.
To them a chip of it was as a piece of the Cross. Ignorant tho' they were of the
secret facts of the tragedy, and not thinking but that the penalty was somehow
justly [<justly >necessarily { <necessarily >(*below*) unavoidably}] inflicted from the naval point of view,

346: B/X 80. [W 336]

B/X pencil

[>(*above*) view { <view}] instinctively they [<instinctively >for all that
they <(*original*) they {≫instinctively}] knew →<knew→ felt that Billy was
a bully boy, was a →<a bully boy, was a→ a true [<true >sort of] man
[>as] incapable of wilful murder, →<of wilful murder→ alike →<alike→ of
[>causeless { <causeless}] mutiny as →<as→ as of wilful murder. The
→<The→ They recalled his →<his→ the [>young {*add* fresh (*before*
young)}] image of the Handsome Sailor, its beauty and those features →<its
beauty . . . features→ that face upon which they had never seen a sc →<upon
. . . a sc→ never deformed by any →<any→ a vile [<vile >sneer or subtler
vile] freak within. →<within.→ of the heart within. Their →*alter to* This→

impression of him took →<took→ was doubtless deepened by his end →<his end→ the fact that he was gone, and [>in a measure] mysteriously gone. The general feeling on the gun decks of the Indomitable" [>(*after* feeling) at the time {<feeling at the time *capitalize* on *transpose* The general (*to follow* Indomitable") >(*after* general) estimate *continue down right margin* of his nature *add* and its bravery of simplicity (*circling, with caret* In general . . . simplicity)} {<bravery of >(*below, circled*) unsconscious}] found →<found→ eventually found rude utterance from one of the [<one of the *add* a {<a >(*with circling and caret*) another}] foretopmen [≫one of his mates, →<mates,→ own watch] gifted with →<with→ , as freq →<freq→ some sailors are, with the →*alter* the *to* a→ [<a ≫an artless] poetic [*G blue ink underline* poetic] temperament; written →<written→ but his →<his→ wholly →<but wholly *alter semicolon* (*after* temperament) *to period*→ He composed some [<some *add* these {<these ≫the}] lines that follow whereof the title is his own. →<the lines . . . his own→ a ballad →<a ballad <composed *add* (*after* He *and taking* He *as* The) tarry hands made some lines→ which after circulating

Leaf finally reads:
for all that they instinctively felt that Billy was a sort of man as incapable of mutiny as of wilful murder. They recalled the fresh young image of the Handsome Sailor, that face never deformed by a sneer or subtler vile freak of the heart within. This impression of him was doubtless deepened by the fact that he was gone, and in a measure mysteriously gone. On the gun decks of the [*no quotation mark*] Indomitable" The general estimate of his nature and its unsconscious simplicity eventually found rude utterance from another foretopmen one of his own watch gifted, as some sailors are, with an artless poetic [*underlined*] temperament. The tarry hand made some lines which after circulating

347: B/X 81. [W 337]

[*Verso of leaf was inscribed earlier; see p. 432.*]

B/X pencil
among the [>shipboard] crews for a while, finally got printed at Portsmouth as a [≫rude] ballad. [<rude *add* (*after* got) rudely <at Portsmouth *add* (*after* ballad) at Portsmouth {<(*after* ballad) at Portsmouth ≫(*after* printed) at Portsmouth}] The title given to it was his own. [<his own ≫the sailor's.]

Billy in the Darbies   [*title underlined*]

348: [p 1]; Bb 72, B/X 82. [W 338]

Bb

[*p ⪢ (at top right)* (Billy in the Darbies)]

Good of him, ay, [<him, ay, >the Chaplain] to enter Lone Bay

And down on his marrow-bones here and pray

For the likes [*p* >just] o' me, Billy Budd.—But, look:

Through the port comes the moon-shine astray: [*alter colon to exclamation mark*]

It tips the guard's cutlas and silvers this nook. [*p alter period to semicolon*]

But 'twill die in the dawning of Billy's last day! [*alter exclamation mark to period by scratching out*]

Ay, a [*p* <Ay *capitalize* a] jewel-block they'll make of me tomorrow,

Pendant [*p* <Pendant ⪢Yes a { <Yes a ≫Pendant}]] pearl from the yard--arm-end

Like the ear-drop I gave to Bristol Molly—

349: [p 2]; Bb 73, B/X 83. [W 339]

Bb

O, 'tis Billy, [*p* <Billy ⪢me] not the sentance they'll suspend.

Ay, Ay, all is up; and I must up too

Early in the morning, and never a cock will crow [<and . . . crow >aloft from alow.]

On an empty stomach, no, [*p* < , no, ⪢now] never it would do.

But they'll [*p* <But *capitalize* they'll] give me a nibble—bit o' buiscit ere I go.

Sure, a messmate will reach me the last parting cup, [*p alter comma to semicolon*]

†**Bc**

And, [*p Bcb* <And, >But,] turning heads away from the hoist and the belay,

Heaven knows who will have the running of me up. [*p alter period to exclamation mark*]

No song [*p Bcb* <song >pipe] to those halyards.—But aren't it all sham?

A blur's in my eyes; sure, its [*p Bcb* <sure, its ⪢it is] dreaming that I am.

A hatchet to my hauzer? all adrift to go?

350: [p 3]; Bb 74¹, B/X 84. [W 340]

Bb

The drum roll to grog, and Billy never know?

But a chum he [*p revise, by insertions, erasures, and restorations to* the Dansker *then to* a chum he *then to* the Dansker *finally to* Donald he] has promised to stand by the plank;

So I'll shake a friendly hand ere I sink.
But—no! T → ⧠T→ It is dead then I'll be, come to think.—
I remember Taff the Welshman when he sank.
And his cheek it was like the budded [*p alter to* budding] pink [*no period*]
Will they [*p* <Will they >But me they'll] lash me in my [<my] hammock,
   drop me deep? [*p alter question mark to period*]

351: [p 4]; Bb 75, 75², 74². [W 341]

Bb
Fathoms down [*p* >, fathoms down,] how I'll dream fast asleep.
I feel it stealing now. Sentry, are you there?
Just ease this iron [*p* <iron >shackles { <shackles >(*circled*) darbies}] at
   the wrist,
Ease it, [*p* <Ease it,] and roll me over fair. [*p alter period to comma*]
I am drowzy, [*p* <drowzy ⧣sleepy] and the oozy weeds about me twist.
[*p ending mark* ⸺◇⸺]
[*p notation* End of Book / April 19ᵗʰ / 1891]

Extra-Textual Leaves

1. *Leaves 365, 365B: A pair of conjunct leaves.*—Melville first used these during Stage *A* as a folder to hold early *Billy Budd* leaves. On the then front he noted its contents (in green crayon): "Beginning of / Billy Budd". Later he canceled this notation and noted above it (in pencil, underlined) "Ballad / of / Billy Budd". Still later, he erased that second notation.

Subsequently, Melville re-used these conjunct leaves as a folder to hold other matter unrelated to *Billy Budd*. To do so, he folded the leaves other side out—so that the side (*365*) with the above notations became the inside of the back. On the new (and now) front side, he noted (in pencil) its contents as "Travel Pieces" / (Various)", and later(?) below (canceling the above) as "Shakespere" (*sic*, underscored). Still later either he or Mrs. Melville crossed out the second notation. And finally she penciled, above, "Jack Gentian" in reference to the final contents.

Much later, when Raymond Weaver examined the manuscripts he penciled on the lower left corner of the now front side "4 sheets"—the number of leaves then in the folder: one leaf carries a brief passage about Shakespeare; the other three (foliated 17, 18, 19[1]) belonged to "Jack Gentian" at one stage. In her sorting of Melville's manuscripts Mrs. Melville penciled at the top of this folio 17 "These pages are probably from Billy Budd". Later she erased this notation, replacing it with two question marks. Still later, probably, she correctly labeled the cover "Jack Gentian".

2. *A pair of conjunct leaves of the darker (earlier) paper.*—As scissored from a larger sheet, these leaves have horizontal chain-lines. Melville used these conjunct leaves as a folder. First (in blue crayon) he noted on the then front the title "Asaph Blood"—an earlier title of "Daniel Orme"; this title he underlined in orange crayon. Later, by pencil, he canceled this title. Then he folded the conjunct leaves other side out so that the canceled title stood on what thus became the inside of the back cover. On the new (and now) front side, he made the following sequence of notations. First, he wrote in pencil "Daniel Orm / & / Omitted of / Billy Budd". Later, with green crayon, he canceled "& / Omitted of / Billy Budd" and underscored the title "Daniel Orm" with an ornamented rule. At some time, in pencil, he canceled the name "Orm" and wrote above it "Druid"; then he erased "Druid" and restored "Orm," altering it to "Orme". Later, probably in her sorting, Mrs. Melville penciled "Story of" above "Daniel Orme", with a guide-line, so that it now reads "Story of / Daniel Orme". At some time, notation numbers (10, 11, 16[?]) were written in column on the upper left corner, and later these were erased. In the lower left

corner, in pencil, Weaver noted the contents as "21 sheets"—the number of the "Daniel Orme" leaves in the folder.

Misinterpretation of these notations has led to some faulty conclusions by previous editors. Weaver first printed "Daniel Orme" (Standard Edition, XIII, 117) with the head notation "(Omitted from '*Billy Budd*')"—evidently his misinterpretation of the above cover notations. In this error Freeman followed Weaver, like him ignoring the large ampersand between the title "Daniel Orme" and the phrase "Omitted of Billy Budd". By thus ignoring the ampersand both Weaver and Freeman interpreted the phrase as a descriptive comment on "Daniel Orme", and so supposed it signified that "Daniel Orme" was at one time in the story of *Billy Budd*. Freeman included what he transcribed as "Version A" and "Version B" of "Daniel Orme" among the "related fragments" in his edition of *Billy Budd* (pp. 344–55; 52, 72). The unmistakable presence of the ampersand, however, removes the basis for this interpretation. The notations, actually, would seem to signify that Melville had placed two items in the folder: "Daniel Orm" and (later?) some leaves "Omitted of Billy Budd". What those leaves may have been we have no way of knowing. When he later removed them from the folder he canceled the notation.

3. *Leaves [57a, 67a]362, 362B.*—A pair of conjunct leaves, separated at the fold by wear. Melville first used them as a folder for *John Marr* matter, noting (in blue crayon) on its then front "John Marr / Sea-Weed". Below this (in pencil) he listed the numbers of various pages requiring corrections, with the notation "For Lizzie". (See Freeman's version, p. 368, #16.)

Later, Melville re-used these conjunct leaves as a folder for the Nelson chapter. He folded them other side out, so that the side (362B) with *John Marr* notations became the inside of the back. On the new front side (362) he noted the contents in green crayon, in a large hand: "Nelson / At / Trafalgar / &c". Presumably he did so at Stage *D* (late in 1888) when he decided to exclude altogether the Nelson chapter (as expanded in *Bb*). Although at Stage *E* he allowed folio-numbers for the possible re-insertion of the Nelson chapter, and at *G* revised and foliated it (1–10), he never put it physically back into the manuscript or foliated it in the final sequence of *E*, but instead left it in this folder. Later, Mrs. Melville labeled the folder (in pencil): "To be inserted / in Billy Budd", but did not put it in place in the manuscript. (See Freeman's report, p. 154, footnote 1.) Its contents have now been placed and foliated in proper order.

4. *Leaf [80a]363. [W 68].*—A disjunct leaf from a formerly conjunct pair now separated along the fold by wear. Melville used the conjunct leaves as a folder to hold the second Vere chapter. The back leaf is lost or unidentified. Melville noted the contents (in pencil) on this present leaf in a large hand: "About [*single rule*] / Captain Vere [*double rule*] / To be inserted after first account of him". (Mrs. Melville later copied this notation onto the first leaf of the chapter [Leaf 81] and placed the chapter in the manuscript, still in its

folder, since the leaves, including this folder-leaf, received *W* foliation.) See Plate VII.

Three further notations on the leaf, one by Melville and two by his wife, offer problems:

A penciled notation by Melville is on the upper right corner, with a large fist: "See P 177 / 2d Vol / Battle of B. N." Later, in blue crayon, this notation was circled and the fist was traced over. We have not satisfactorily identified the book referred to. Although the title corresponds to Joseph Allen's *Battles of the British Navy*, 2 vols. (London, 1852), nothing relevant to *Billy Budd* appears on the page cited. (A William Buddin is mentioned on the next page; and elsewhere occur references to the *Droits de l'Homme*—a French 74—and the *Indomptable;* see note to Leaf 64, *his sagacious dying injunctions.*)

Mrs. Melville penciled two notations. On the upper left corner she wrote "Van Tromp" and drew a fist. Across the leaf, below Melville's Vere notation, she wrote: "Texel—island in the Zuyder Zee owned by Holland—where prisoners of war were kept". "Van Tromp" seems clearly a reference to the famous Dutch admiral mentioned in the Nelson chapter. The "Texel" notation was apparently copied from a reference book. But we can suggest no connection between either notation and *Billy Budd*. It is possible that they relate rather to Melville's poem "At the Hostelry" (*Poems*, p. 324), in which both are mentioned.

5. *Leaf [87a]364. [W 76].*—Two library slips mounted on a leaf. The slips bear Melville's penciled notes from William James, *The Naval History of Great Britain*, II, 26, 73, 115–16; the occurrence on Leaf 53 of phrasing from one of the notes places their origin prior to composition of that leaf during Stage B. (Other matter possibly deriving from James appears on Leaves 50, 54, and 95–96: see notes to Reading Text.) There is no indication on the slips themselves about the library of their origin—presumably a departmentalized private institution, since the slips are headed "Reference Department" and carry instructions addressed to "Members."

In attempting, with the aid of present-day libraries and librarians in New York City, to identify the origin of the slips we have succeeded in definitely ruling out four institutions: the New York Society Library, in which Melville was a shareholder in 1848, 1850, and from November 20, 1889, until he died; the New York Mercantile Library; and the Astor and Lenox Libraries. But we have not been able either to confirm or to dismiss another interesting possibility: the Apprentices' Library of the General Society of Mechanics and Tradesmen, then located at 18 East Sixteenth Street within walking distance of Melville's residence at 104 East Twenty-sixth Street. This library maintained a reference department, made use of printed call slips, and employed a unique system of classifying its holdings, but apparently no slips from the 1880's survive for comparison with those on Leaf 364. One of the latter carries two penciled notations in Melville's hand—"2464" and "M146"—which might possibly be classification or folio numbers, but surviving records and holdings of the Society's library are insufficient to permit identifying the numbers or specifying the book possibly designated by some or all of them.

It is therefore impossible to report that the slips are from a particular institution, or even from the same library in which Melville read James. His statement in the text concerning details of the Nore Mutiny, "Nor are these readily to be found in the libraries" (Leaf 54), at least implies that he had sought information in other authors as well as in James, and in more than one locality.

Leaves with Inscribed Versos

Leaf	Verso (earlier) inscription	Recto (later) inscription
1	[238a] Xp Vere's difficult position	X+p dedication
4	pencil verse: "And thought and pl can so combine"	Ea 3 Liverpool sailor
20	[260c] Xp 10, 9² Vere speech	*Da on Ea leaf Red Whiskers
63	——— "Pebbles" (John Marr) [Freeman, p. 359, #1]	Bb 16⁸ Nelson 6
79†	——— "Timoleon" (Timoleon) [Freeman, p. 361, #4]	†late pencil Vere not brilliant
83†	[260a] Xp Vere speech	†late pencil on Eb Vere's reading
84†	[77a] Ea or Eb Vere gazing at sea	†late pencil Vere's politics
85 (darker paper)	——— "After the Pleasure Party" (Timoleon) [Freeman, p. 259, #2]	late pencil Vere's views
87†	[260b] Xp Vere speech	†late pencil Vere cites antiquity
88 (darker paper)	——— "After the Pleasure Party" (Timoleon) [Freeman, p. 360, #3]	†late pencil Claggart introduced
112† (darker paper)	——— Burgundy Club Inscription [Freeman, p. 365, #11]	†late pencil Dansker originated "Baby Budd"
133† (darker paper)	——— "Rip van Winkle's Lilac" [Freeman, p. 365, #12]	†late pencil Claggart's lunacy
134 (darker paper)	——— prose on Mediterranean [Freeman, p. 366, #13]	†late pencil Claggart's lunacy

Leaf	Verso (earlier) inscription	Recto (later) inscription
135 (darker paper)	———— "Madcaps" (*Weeds and Wildings*) [Freeman, p. 362, #7; *Poems*, p. 263]	*late pencil* Dark sayings
135† (darker paper)	———— "The Loiterer" (*Weeds and Wildings*) [*Poems*, p. 259]	†*late pencil* savor [of Holy Writ]
207†	[121c]*Eb 130 "What was the matter with the master-at-arms?"	†*late pencil* man-trap under the daisies
208†	[121b]*Ca 2 "why should *Jimmy Legs*"	†*late pencil* Vere congratulated Ratclif[f]e
222†	[191a] *Bb 53 Claggart appeared at . . . main-mast	†*late pencil* "The first mesmeristic glance . . ."
230	[135f] Eb 145 ". . . Spencer depicts envy . . ."	G⁺p 38 "The surgeon turned . . ."
231	[135d] Eb ⟨143⟩ ". . . an indirect inkling . . . antipathy . . ."	G⁺p 39 "Vere . . . judgment on Ananias . . ."
232	[131a] Eb 136 etc. "Hardly ever is he a wine-bibber."	G⁺p 40 "Struck dead by the angel of God . . ."
233	[58a] Bb 16⁵ "sea-encounters . . . gallantry . . ." (Nelson chapter)	G⁺p 41 surgeon and Vere move Claggart
234	[135c] Eb 142 "Claggart's figure . . ."	G⁺p 42 "Full of disquietude . . . the . . . Surgeon left . . ."
235	[135e] Eb 144 Claggart's envy	G⁺p 43 Surgeon mistrusts Vere's sanity
236	[131b] Eb 138 etc. ". . . assumed by the depraved one . . ."	G⁺p 44 "Who can draw the line . . ."
247†	[121a] Bb⁺ *pencil* "Some portraiture of Claggart . . ."	†*late pencil* the marine officer
290† (darker paper)	Verse fragment "After the Pleasure Party"? [Freeman, p. 362, #6]	Fb† on Fa 54 "narration may take up a term less brief . . "

Leaf	Verso (earlier) inscription	Recto (later) inscription
347	———	*B/X pencil 81*
	"Timoleon"	"... finally got printed ... as
	(*Timoleon*) [Freeman, p. 361, #5]	a ballad ..."
352†	[*1a*] *C?*	*C?*
	Sailors laugh at Claggart's quip	draft-title
361	———	[*334a*] *X*
	"Syra"	draft for chapter on fight with
	(*Timoleon*) [*Poems*, pp. 251–52]	French ship